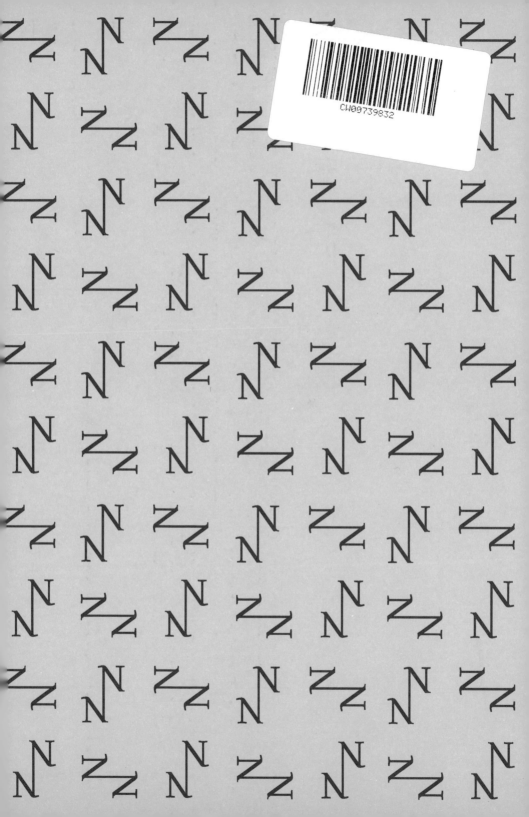

THE NEW NATURALIST LIBRARY

A SURVEY OF BRITISH NATURAL HISTORY

PARTRIDGES

THE NEW NATURALIST LIBRARY

PARTRIDGES

Countryside Barometer

G.R. (DICK) POTTS

Collins

This edition published in 2012 by Collins,
An imprint of HarperCollins Publishers

HarperCollins Publishers
77–85 Fulham Palace Road
London W6 8JB
www.collins.co.uk

First published 2012

A CIP catalogue record for this book is available
from the British Library.

Set in FF Nexus, designed and produced by
Tom Cabot/ketchup

All photos by the author unless otherwise credited.

Printed in Hong Kong by Printing Express

Hardback
ISBN 978-0-00-741870-1

Paperback
ISBN 978-0-00-741871-8

Contents

Editors' Preface   vii
Author's Foreword and Acknowledgements   ix

1   Introduction   1

2   On the Origin of Partridges   35

3   Going with the Grain   65

4   Nesting and Predation   106

5   Chick Food and Survival: From the Steppes to
    Conservation Headlands   152

6   The Cereal Ecosystem and the Abundance of Chick Food
    in the Sussex Study Area (1968–2011)   195

7   Parasites Lost?   237

8   Living with Raptors   272

9   Hunting   313

10 Norfolk Estate: Restoration of Biodiversity   327

11 Resetting the Barometer   375

Appendices: Research Data   385
List of Species   394
References   398
Index   455

Grey partridge. (Chris Knights)

Editors' Preface

NEW NATURALIST NO.2, *British Game*, by Brian Vesey-Fitzgerald – then editor of *The Field* – was published in 1946, it's striking Ellis dust jacket and quality photographic colour plates reinforcing the high publishing standards set, in the immediate post-war years, by the first New Naturalist, *Butterflies*, by E. B. Ford, published a year earlier. More important, in the context of this volume, *Partridges*, early access to his father's copy of *British Game* fired in Dick Potts an intense and life-long enthusiasm for partridges. Inevitably it would seem, this led to a career in game bird research, for decades as the lynchpin (and for most of those as Director of Research) of the Game and Wildlife Conservancy Trust, and ultimately to his emergence as the world authority on the grey partridge.

Both Vesey-Fitzgerald and Dick Potts, as a Yorkshire lad, considered grey partridges as both widespread and common. For the grey partridge, the primary focus of this text, how things have changed! Vesey-Fitzgerald (who wrote of it as the common partridge) noted with some relish in *British Game* the record shooting bag of 1,671 partridges killed by eight guns in one day at Holkham in Norfolk in 1905 and considered that bags of 'over 1,000 partridges in one day have been obtained on many occasions'. But he was prescient enough to write also: 'Modern farming practice has, of course, affected the partridge grievously'. Today the British and Irish population in total is probably less than one hundred times the 1905 record one-day bag, and the total European population, estimated pre-World War II as over 75 million, is now considered to be less than 3 million. Across Britain, few would be able to call the grey partridge 'common', and for many it has become a red-letter-day bird if not locally extinct!

Partridges covers every conceivable aspect of partridge life, including challenging areas such as hunting and predation, which are dealt with (as are all other aspects) with well-reasoned and well-presented factual clarity. There is also a lot of new material about red-legged partridges. Many may find some of the conclusions unexpected and intriguing, particularly the detailed analysis revealing the complex interactions between predators (including man) in the past compared to today. Through this book, Dick Potts outlines his diagnoses of the root causes of the catastrophic grey partridge decline, but also outlines his prescriptions for halting it and engendering a recovery – prescriptions that have been successfully field tested, resulting in some flourishing populations of grey partridge and far more species of plants, insects, mammals and birds besides.

Dick Potts has been publishing scientific papers regularly since 1960, in an unusually wide range of journals – agricultural, ornithological, game and environmental, and as he says: 'this book is about far more than partridges' – it is 'a heady mix of hunting; farming; predation; parasites; disease and climate change.' This volume is an account with extraordinary depth and erudition, written with deep feeling rather than emotion, and with an elegance that does not detract from, but rather enhances its erudition. It is a very worthy and enjoyable addition to the New Naturalist series.

Author's Foreword and Acknowledgements

I N 1946 MY FATHER BOUGHT *British Game*, the second volume in the New Naturalist Series, and I spent many happy winter nights drawing copies of the colour plates in the light of a paraffin lamp. Grey partridges were familiar to me from an early age and abundant on the family farm in North Yorkshire. As a schoolboy I found several nests, and the seed was sown.

Globally, there are at least 45 species of game bird that can have the word partridge in their name, but this book is devoted to the grey, red-legged and chukar partridges. There is a large emphasis on the grey because of its well-known decline. Until World War II the September numbers in Europe alone were at least 75 million. This number has now fallen to less than 3 million. Many readers in Britain may be surprised that this book includes so much material from overseas but one simple fact provides the explanation: we have only 2–3 per cent of the global population of 'English' partridges.

This book is about far more than partridges. Mankind and partridges have evolved together, both ultimately dependent on grasslands rather than forests. For thousands of years, both ate grass seeds and this continued until cereals largely replaced them. Hundreds of species of plant and insect that partridges and other birds eat thrived on farms for thousands of years until the dawn of the pesticides era. Since then the long decline in partridge abundance has been a barometer for biodiversity over vast swathes of the Northern Hemisphere.

In a separate development, more and more ecologists are finding that prey species suffer from an excess of middle-sized predators, in large part because the natural top predators are missing, such as the wolf, lynx and brown bear. Nobody noticed the effects on partridges because a large army of gamekeepers replaced the top predators, but now they have gone as well.

This is a complex story with a heady mix of hunting, farming, predation, parasites, disease and climate change. The way these factors have interacted tells us a lot about how lesser known species have fared and how they can be conserved for the future. This needs to be taken on board quickly as farmers respond to the needs of an extra 3 billion people worldwide, not just for food but for bio-fuels and other resources. Make no mistake, the pressures on farmland wildlife will intensify further in the coming years.

The grey partridge has overcome the effects of several ice ages and thrived in World Wars but it is now expected to disappear completely from huge areas of farmland. We know how to avoid this and there is a happy ending with the example of the Norfolk Estate in the Sussex Study area. Both grey and red-legged partridge numbers are now higher than recorded before. Not in some kind of museum but in a highly productive and profitable system of farming and an oasis in what has often looked and sounded like a desert. In a small corner of England we can now see farmland wildlife much as it was before pesticides came on the scene.

ACKNOWLEDGEMENTS

The Sussex Study set up in 1968 has many times hung by a thread. Its aim was to restore grey partridge numbers. Funds to set it up were organised by the founder of the Game and Wildlife Conservation Trust (GWCT) Chris Hunt and after he died in 1970 the focus was on securing the GWCT itself. The research bodies ARC, NERC and MAFF funded short-term projects but were not prepared to contemplate long-term funding. In February 1973 with the future of the GWCT secured, Charles Coles organised a seminar at Kings College London inimitably chaired by HRH the Duke of Edinburgh, who has maintained a strong interest in the Sussex study ever since, and things got a lot better.

Obviously, over 44 years many colleagues have come and gone at the GWCT and I am grateful to them all, especially of course those involved in the Sussex Study. Steve Moreby joined in 1981 and he still patiently sorts through the D-vac (Dietrick vacuum insect net) samples, identifying, so far as practicable, 3 million insects just for the Sussex Study alone. At Durham, John Coulson launched my career as his research assistant working on shags on the Farne Islands. Nicholas Aebischer, trained in mathematics and from Switzerland later developed my studies further north, on the Isle of May. In 1986 I appointed him to computerise the Sussex Study and his contribution borne of a rare combination of skills has been outstanding ever since. I owe most to having been brought up on a North

Yorkshire farm; equally blessed in Nebraska, Julie Ewald joined the team in 1995, and the Sussex Study database at Fordingbridge is now processed in her capable hands. Very many colleagues and students in the GWCT have helped as well, especially Malcolm Brockless and the stubble counting teams. In Sussex two generations of farmers, landowners, gamekeepers and farm staff have all given an amazing amount of support throughout; that of the Goring and Passmore families has been extraordinary, especially Chris Passmore at Applesham. Another friendship begun in Sussex and enduring more than forty years has been with David Clark, now Head of the Game Department at Sandringham. As will become apparent later Edward Duke of Norfolk and his staff, especially estate manager Peter Knight, and gamekeepers Charlie Mellor, Andrew Stringer and Beau Whitney, have made the most important contributions of all. Eddie Norfolk's enthusiasm and personal commitment have been the key ingredients.

I was brought up knowing that hedgerows were important to partridges, but then I visited some of the high-density areas in France and found no hedges. It was a shock and ever since I have taken the opportunity to study partridges overseas, including some very remote areas. I have been made very welcome and driven many thousands of miles, by far too many to mention. I must have exasperated others by seeking translations here and there, but they didn't show it. Mike Wilson at the Edward Grey Institute's Alexander Library continued to help, as he has done for 30 years, and Gillian Gooderham at the GWCT obtained obscure publications. In Picardie, Jacques and Isabelle Hicter were the first to reassure me that lots of partridges and modern farming can co-exist; over five years I learned an enormous amount comparing their farms with Sussex. Tom Gullick introduced me to red-legged partridges in La Mancha as nobody else could, and the experience gained on Patricia Maldonado Vidal's Las Ensanchas can never be equalled. In Portugal the de Mello family, especially Pedro and Gonçalo, taught me much about red-legged partridges thriving in a completely different habitat, as did João Bugalho. Guy Cheney enabled me to study grey partridges in Russia, Zhang Zhengwang to study Daurian partridges and Wang Nan to see Tibetan partridges. For help with various technical details I thank Frances Abraham, Chris Davis, John Holland, Tuija Liukkonen, Ettore Randi, Antonio Sánchez-Marco, John Stewart and Nikita Zelenkov.

I especially thank those who so generously contributed their photographs, particularly Chris Knights, a friend since the filming of *Vanishing Hedgerows* and *The Partridge Puzzle* in the early 1970s. My son Gareth, and most of all my wife Olga, gave huge support at every stage.

CHAPTER 1

Introduction

T HIS BOOK IS NOT JUST about partridges. It is not just about species
struggling to cope with modern agriculture. It is about the
fundamental relationship between the cereal crop ecosystem and
food production that lies at the heart of the current biodiversity crisis. A full
understanding of the ways in which partridges are being impacted by modern
agriculture requires a global approach and this is taken throughout. The story
reaches deep into pre-history and it is told against a background of frustration
with too few resources and with nearly all partridge populations declining. There
is however the happy ending.

The story centres on the grey, red-legged and chukar partridges, the only
three to have bred in the wild in Britain, with some comparative information on
the closely related Daurian, Tibetan and rock partridges.

The grey partridge, *Perdix perdix*, was originally known in Britain as the
'pertridge', 'partryche' or 'pertriche', onomatopoeic interpretations of its 'rusty-
gate' call (which can be heard on www.xeno-canto.org). The species was once very
numerous and well known to country dwellers across the vast area of farmland
stretching from the west coast of Ireland to Mongolia. Always a popular bird it
was introduced very successfully to North America so that it now occupies a total
area of more than 12 million sq. km worldwide, considerably greater than the area
of Europe and one of the largest ranges of terrestrial birds. Some ornithologists
have classified the bird as one of twelve 'specialist' farmland bird species, whereas
in fact it is equally at home in mountain and lowland meadows, arable farms
(hilly or flat), steppe grassland, raised bogs, moorland edge, sand dunes and
young plantations. The numbers prior to 1953 were estimated at about 110 million
globally (Potts, 1986) but they are now very seriously depleted almost everywhere.
The grey partridge has a sister species, the Daurian or bearded partridge

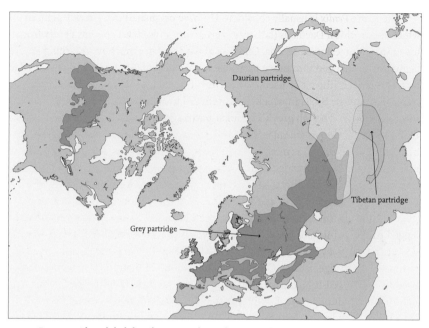

FIG 1. Grey partridge global distribution in the early 1980s. The natural Eurasian distribution of the grey partridge has a range of 8.5 million sq. km in 47 countries and the Daurian partridge has a range of 7.5 million sq. km in 9 countries; note the overlap. The grey partridge has also been introduced successfully to the US and Canada where it occupies a range of 3.5 million sq. km (from Potts, 1986).

Perdix dauurica, that was equally well known from Kazakhstan to Korea but it too is in serious decline, and in Russia the sub-species *P. P. suschkini* has been red-listed. These two sister species have been studied across 15 time-zones in 54 countries, as far north as Oulu in Finland at 65° and as far south as 37° in Turkey and Iran and, including fossils, 31° in Israel. The global range is shown in Figure 1.

The grey partridge was assigned to the genus *Perdix* by the French zoologist M. J. Brisson in 1758 and contains not just its sister Daurian partridge, but also the more distantly related Tibetan partridge *Perdix hodgsoniae*. This third species was named after Brian Hodgson the famous Cheshire-born pioneer of Indian ornithology. Excluding the Italian sub-species recently shown to be indistinguishable on DNA evidence, there are 14 currently recognised sub-species of *Perdix*, 2 or possibly 3 known extinct species and 3 variants one of which is extinct and 2 extremely rare.

The name *Perdix* is usually considered to have originated in a Greek legend in which the mythical Daedalus (father of Icarus) threw his clever student Perdix from a tower in a fit of jealousy. Athena, Goddess of wisdom (and much more) seeing Perdix begin to fall, changed him into a partridge to save his life. But what kind of partridge was it? *Perdix* was the name used for the chukar partridge (*Alectoris chukar*) in early translations of the Bible, in which it was referred to about a dozen times (Parmelee, 1959; Yapp, 1983). Though grey and chukar partridges are to be found in Greece, the rock partridge (*Alectoris graeca*) is more widespread there, and the account of *Perdix* by Aristotle (384–322 BC) as interpreted by Turner in 1544 (Evans, 1903) seems to be referring to the rock partridge. Either way, it is inescapable that the name *Perdix* was first used for an *Alectoris*. Both *Alectoris* and grey partridges were named as *Perdix* by the Holy Roman Emperor and falconer Frederick II in the thirteenth century (Blüchel, 2005, p.103). In another twist, in 1758 Linnaeus classified both grey and red-legged partridge (*Alectoris rufa*) as grouse: *Tetrao perdix* and *Tetrao rufa* (literally the red grouse!) respectively. The grey partridge then became *Perdix cinerea* in 1790 and the red-legged partridge became *Caccabis rufa* but a number of other Latin names have been used. The red-legged partridge was first named *Alectoris rufa* by the German naturalist J. J. Kaup, in 1829. Lest it be thought that all this re-naming caused confusion, consider that in the early nineteenth century J. A. Naumann listed ten different common names for the grey partridge in German alone.

FIG 2. Bellicourt, in Picardie, France, has the highest average recorded density of grey partridges in the world. (Jacques Hicter)

PERDIX

The *Perdix* partridges originated at least 3 million years ago on grasslands in the area that has since been raised to form the Tibetan plateau, as described in the next chapter. These birds feed and roost on the ground, spending the autumn and winter in groups of a dozen or more known as coveys. Pairing takes place in spring and nests are also made on the ground, usually in dead grasses from the previous season ('residual grasses'). After the laying of the second and subsequent eggs, the hen covers them carefully with dead grasses and other dead vegetation, keeping them safe until incubation can start. The clutch size of the grey partridge is large, around 15 but rising to 18 in areas where the onset of spring is later and more rapid, to 16–17 in the Daurian partridge (Zhang & Wu, 1992; Zhao *et al.*, 1992), but with only 8 in the Tibetan partridge (Lu *et al.*, 2003). On average the chicks hatch in 25 days, after which they are dependent on insects for the first two to three weeks. Chicks are able to flee ground predators by the tenth day and they can fly properly for short distances at 15 days. After fledging, the family stays together often joined by neighbours without chicks, especially bereaved males, to form the covey. Outside the breeding season, coveys feed at dawn, and then especially at dusk, preferably gleaning grain and larger weed seeds from cereal

FIG 3. Native grass-shrub steppe near Eyebrow lake, south Saskatchewan. Grey partridges occur here in good numbers but mainly where this habitat is contiguous with spring-sown cereals.

FIG 4. Pair of Tibetan partridges, Sichuan. Although the adults look very different from grey partridges the juveniles are virtually identical. (Wang Nan)

FIG 5. Daurian partridge north of Xining Qinghai at 2,500 m in May. (Christian Jensen)

stubbles, spending the rest of the day in cover. In fine weather, the night is spent in a tight group in open areas preferably 25–80 m from the nearest tree; this is known as 'jugging'. Coveys break up with pair formation, when the young males, but not the young females, disperse from their natal area. In Britain this dispersal usually takes place in early February, after which the pairs begin to search for nest sites, preferably in tall dead grass tussocks under thorny shrubs. This is the time when the risk of predation by raptors is greatest. The entire behaviour of the grey partridge is finely tuned to reducing the risk of predation but it remains the most important source of mortality.

ALECTORIS

The *Alectoris* partridges probably originated in Africa in areas with warm wet winters and hot dry summers, at least six million years ago, with the evidence reviewed in the next chapater. The red-legged partridge *Alectoris rufa* was originally confined to Spain, Portugal, southern France and northwest Italy but with successful introductions to the UK in the seventeenth century. Even with the addition of Britain, its current range is less than 10 per cent that of the grey partridge (the ranges here were taken from the maps in del Hoyo & Sargatal (1994) by the World Pheasant Association). The worldwide range of the chukar *Alectoris chukar* is enormous, even greater than that of the grey partridge. This range includes a remarkably successful introduction to the mountain states in the US from Pakistan in 1893 (Christensen, 1970) and the species was also introduced successfully to Hawaii, New Zealand, South Africa (Robben Island), and St Helena, with a recent attempt to introduce the species to Argentina. Largely unsuccessful and unwanted introductions to southern Europe and in 1970 to Britain bring the species into this book. In 1934, in his list of birds of the world, Peters listed the chukar as a subspecies of the rock partridge *Alectoris graeca* and for many authorities it remained so, until after the investigations of Watson (1962), when it was restored as a full species. For a few years some

FIG 6. Red-legged Partridge, La Mancha. (Patricia Maldonado Vidal)

FIG 7. (Top) Habitat with a high density of red-legged partridges: Las Ensanchas, La Mancha, Spain (Patricia Maldonado Vidal). (Middle and bottom) Habitat with a high density of red-legged partridges: Vale de Perditos, Portugal. Production is higher in years with good winter rains. However, in Mediterranean climates the herbaceous vegetation dies back and dries out in early summer, with a large adverse effect on the availability of chick food, even after good winter rains.

continued to refer to the chukar as *Alectoris graeca*, and *Alectoris kakelik* was also used. *Alectoris* comprises seven species with the ranges of the red-legged partridge and the chukar shown as Figure 8.

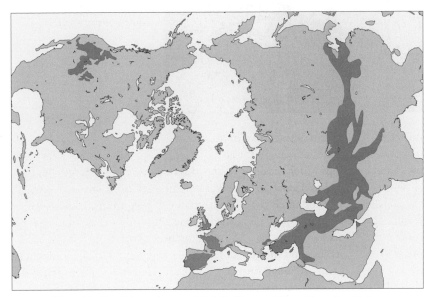

FIG 8. Red-legged (red) and chukar (green) global distributions. The red-legged partridge was introduced to Britain in 1673 from France and the chukar was introduced to North America from Pakistan in 1893. Other successful introductions of the chukar include New Zealand. Unsuccessful or unwanted introductions have been made to Britain, Spain, France, Italy and other countries. The rock partridge distribution, not shown, is centred on Italy and the Balkans, with natural hybridisation with the red-legged partridge in France/Italy and with the chukar partridge in Greece/Bulgaria. Sources for red-legged partridge: Otero (1999), Atlas Equipa (2008), Vallance *et al.* (2008), GWCT and Hagemeijer & Blair (1997). Chukar: Kirwan *et al.* (2008), Dement'ev & Gladkov (1967), Adamran & Klem (1999), Cheng (1976), Christensen (1970 updated), Yahya (2000) and Shrestha (2001).

DIFFERENCES AND SIMILARITIES

The grey/Daurian partridge and the red-legged/rock and chukar partridges occupy a vast part of the Northern Hemisphere with highly varied habitats that overlap to a significant extent. In many ways therefore the *Perdix* and *Alectoris* partridges are similar, but there are important differences. *Alectoris* partridges have a higher wing-loading so they fly less, downhill if possible, and they run

FIG 9. Red-legged partridges often roost on roofs, or similar high structures, something never recorded in the grey partridge. (Jesus Nadal)

more. Red-legged partridges thrive in thinly wooded areas, less so on open plains and they are often seen in the shade of trees or perched on branches or on rocks and buildings which they use for roosting. In their natural range chukar partridges are generally more numerous in rocky mountainous areas, roosting on cliffs if available and rarely perching on trees, but they are also found in the feather grass (Kuz'mina, 1992) and sagebrush steppes (Christensen, 1970). By contrast the *Perdix* partridges have only very rarely been recorded roosting off the ground, or perching off the ground. *Perdix* partridges very rarely drink water when not in captivity, although they do so in really arid environments, whereas all *Alectoris* partridges regularly do so and this and some other adaptations enable them to survive when the vegetation has become desiccated in hot dry summers. Having stronger beaks the *Alectoris* partridges frequently dig for roots, tubers and bulbs, whereas *Perdix* partridges rarely do this, except in the same dry mountainous regions where they use water. Whereas the grey partridge is mainly active at dawn and dusk the *Alectoris* partridges are often active during the day, unless it is too hot, and in winter peak activity is often around midday. Other differences include a smaller clutch size in the red-legged partridge, usually eleven or twelve but with many females laying two clutches: the male incubating one and the female the other in what is known as double brooding. *Alectoris* eggs are camouflaged to some extent but the eggs are not covered during the laying period and this is one reason why their nest predation rate is high. *Alectoris* chicks have been thought to depend much less on insect food than *Perdix* chicks but this appears not to be the case, as is explained in Chapter 5. Covey formation is the same as in *Perdix* but instead of the young males moving away from the winter home range when the coveys break up, it is the young females that move.

These differences are important but the bulk of the evidence in this book points to a high level of adaptability to local conditions in both types of

FIG 10. (Left) Chukar returning to nest in thorns at 2,000 m near the border between Kazakhstan and Xinjiang, 1987 (Vladimir Litun); (right) first chukar recorded in the Sussex Study area, 1971. (David Duncalf)

FIG 11. Good chukar habitat: high-altitude montane grasslands with patches of juniper near Lake Alakol, Kazakhstan. (Vladimir Litun)

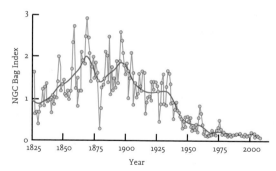

FIG 12. Grey partridge: the GWCT's UK bag index from 1826 to 2008, as numbers shot per 100 ha with 1826 set to 1.0. The overall trend is attributable to game management but the sustained low numbers from the 1950s are due to changes in farming.

partridge. The species composition of the diet of both *Perdix* and *Alectoris* varies greatly from country to country but with considerable overlap, likewise for predators and parasites. The clearest differences are often found in behaviour, such as the double brooding, rather than in ecology. Most important, the conservation requirements of the *Perdix* and *Alectoris* are fundamentally the same; indeed where they occur together they share many foods, predators and parasites.

Much of the general interest in the grey partridge story stems from the fact that it remains the only proven case where the use of herbicides has resulted in a decline in populations of a farmland bird (Fig. 12). This is not to say that other species are not affected; many are, but the formal proof that comes from experimental evidence is lacking for them. As a result of changes in farming and increases in nest predation due to fewer gamekeepers, four of the five species of partridges in the EU have been classified as having 'unfavourable conservation status'. The exception is the Barbary partridge confined to Sardinia and Gibraltar. Four widespread species in trouble demands attention but there is far

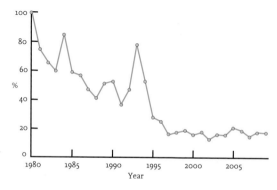

FIG 13. Grey partridge trend in breeding population in Europe since 1980: from the European Bird Census Council.

more at stake. The mix of factors responsible for declines in the *Alectoris* species differ from place to place but agriculture is usually involved. In Spain red-legged partridges have been forced to nest in cereals through lack of permanent nesting cover, with nests destroyed by the earlier harvesting of recent years (Casas & Viñuela 2010).

I estimated the worldwide decline in grey partridge numbers as 80 per cent by 1984 (Potts 1986). This continued, with a decline of 82 per cent from 1980 to 2011, the most of any farmland bird (Fig. 13). The decline in Europe is near 96 per cent since 1914 (98 per cent in Britain), yet BirdLife International classified the bird as one of 'least concern'.

A SHORT HISTORY OF RESEARCH ON PARTRIDGES AT THE GWCT

The GWCT, as it is known throughout this book, has been successively: the Imperial Chemical Industries (ICI) Game Research Station; the Eley Game Advisory Service and the Game Research Association (a period when research and advice were unfortunately separated); the Game Conservancy; the Game Conservancy Trust and the Game & Wildlife Conservation Trust (GWCT). This book is centred on the long-term study on the Sussex Downs, a study directly evolving from GWCT work at Damerham. In turn the Damerham study was born out of experience at Great Witchingham in Norfolk, at Knebworth in Hertfordshire and at the University of Oxford as described in Potts (1986).

THE DAMERHAM STUDY: 1948–60

This benchmark research was carried out on the former 1,477 ha (with 79 ha of woodland) West Park Estate, on chalk hills near Damerham just west of Fordingbridge, Hampshire. The research program began in 1946 funded by ICI's Game Department and it was a major investigation of the demographic factors influencing the density of partridges on farmland, and of the role of recruitment and mortality in a population managed for shooting. Preliminary work was undertaken by Doug Middleton from 1946, joined by Terence Blank in 1948 and John Ash in 1951. Phyllis Clapham was pathologist until 1958. The research ended in 1960.

The area was farmed by 11 tenants and there was no control over cropping or habitats. In 1955 the average field size was 6.44 ha; it had been a little smaller in

FIG 14. Part of the Damerham study area in December 2010. In the 1950s the area shown held more than 100 pairs of grey partridges, in 2011 2–5 pairs. Today there are more trees than in the 1950s but the landscape would easily be recognised by a Rip van Winkle who had slept for 60 years.

1948 but it did not change significantly through the 1950s. The average number of partridges shot annually between 1914–45 was 1,025 but this dropped to 600 during the 1950s with a maximum of 1,143 in 1957. The percentage of red-legged partridges varied annually from 3–15 per cent of the bag and the average annual bag of common pheasant (hereafter simply pheasant) ranged only from 100–300. There were no gamekeepers employed during World War II but five gamekeepers were taken on full-time in 1948 and this was the situation until the end of 1960: one gamekeeper per 280 ha.

Meticulous records were kept of nests found and predators seen and killed. A small number of clutches were rescued from mowing and incubated by domestic fowl for rearing and release. Grain was provided but only in winter. This unique study, which included more than one thousand individually marked birds, has not been properly written-up. A vast amount of work was done but after ICI cut the funds in 1959 there was little enthusiasm to write up the results and significant data were lost. Spring and stubble counts continued until 1969 when attention switched to the Sussex Study. Tables of 'essential data' from Damerham are given here as Appendix 1. Other data have been used as the basis for a key factor analysis (Blank *et al.*, 1967) or in analysis of chick survival rates from brood sizes (Aebischer

& Reitz, 2000). The main cause of the dramatic decline in partridges at Damerham in the early 1960s was undoubtedly the loss of the full-time gamekeepers dedicated to partridge conservation. Nevertheless there were strong and justified concerns about the decreasing trend in chick survival from 1954.

THE SUSSEX STUDY

There had been considerable interest in the grey partridge on the Sussex Study area for some time before the Sussex Study itself began in 1968. As we see in Chapter 5, two chicks were sent to the University of Oxford in 1934 and as related in Chapter 7, birds were sent to Fordingbridge for postmortem from 1952. Spring pair counts, stubble counts and detailed bag records began at North Farm,

FIG 15. The Sussex Study area has traditionally been farmed with a rotation of grasses, cereals and fodder crops for sheep, as here at Applesham. Through the 1970s and 1980s this system was replaced by cereals (bottom) – but in the past decade there has been a marked reversion to mixed farming.

FIG 16. Sussex Study area; Norfolk Estate in winter showing kale strips.

Washington, in 1957 to replicate those at Damerham. It was the small size of the broods in the mid- to late 1960s stubble counts on North Farm that led directly to what has become known as the Sussex study. North Farm itself was 800 ha but three smaller farms to the southeast were added in to comprise the North Farm shoot of 1,316 ha. Other farms including those on the Norfolk Estate were added to bring the area to 6,200 ha. The Sussex Study began in March 1968 and still continues at the time of writing – of course, it is difficult to write up research while it is ongoing!

The Sussex Study has throughout been based on what I called the '3M system'. The first stage is **Monitoring** to define problems, followed by **Modelling** to test solutions to the problems on paper, leading to **Management**, at first experimental, and then for real. If at any point a stage fails, the work goes back a step. A paper in 1980 in *Advances in Ecological Research* and my 1986 book focused on modelling. This book focuses on natural history and the results of long-term monitoring. It also documents, the only case – the Norfolk Estate – where all management recommendations have been adopted.

The chosen area for the Sussex Study is on the West Sussex Downs, a range of low hills that was designated successively as an AONB in 1966, an ESA in 1986 and a National Park in April 2011. The soils are chalk rendzinas with some clay caps. The study area covers 4 per cent of the National Park. During World War II all the higher parts of the area were used for military training. After the war, with government grant aid, the area was gradually cleared of unexploded ammunition and thorn scrub, fenced and supplied with drinking water. The famous seabird biologist Bill Bourne lived nearby and reflected on this period.

I have been to a lot of good places for birds all around the world, but none have been better than the Sussex Downs at dusk on a fine night in June before the bull-dozers came, with butterflies giving way to moths over the flowers on the lynchets, Hobbies overhead, Nightingales, Nightjars and Woodlarks tuning up all round and Stone Curlews calling in the distance. It is sad that more was not done to save them, but nobody said a word about it at the time and their fate appears to have been forgotten. (Bourne, 1996)

The tenant of North Farm was Chris Hunt (the founder of the Game Conservancy) who had learned his farming on Applesham Farm in the eastern part of the Sussex Study area. In 1947 Chris Hunt, Fred Allen the gamekeeper, and local farmers organised a series of shoots over the whole 1,316 ha. Most of the area was devoid of game and the total bag for the season was 5 partridges and 17 male pheasants. Rabbits were however abundant, with around 10,000 removed annually in the

FIG 17. The Norfolk estate – sheep grazing stubble turnips.

early 1950s to make crop growing possible. After myxomatosis struck in 1954 Fred Allen began to control predators, later with the help of two gamekeepers each with beats of 440 ha. Predator control was thorough, with a high number of Fenn traps (mapped in Tapper *et al.*, 1982), and the numbers of partridges rose rapidly (Fig. 249). Grain was fed through the winter but not in spring. Crucially, the farming was thoroughly commercial using new pesticides as they became available.

In the late 1960s a number of theories for the poor survival of chicks were being proposed including some effects of DDT, but the frontrunner was probably the effect of herbicides on insect food based on the work in Hampshire at Lord Rank's Micheldever estate and at Highclere, by Dick (later Sir Richard) Southwood. There was however a strong body of opinion that grey partridges were not declining but simply suffering from an unusual run of cold weather. The crucial evidence that this was not the case came from the finding that chick survival was reduced more by a given degree of cold after 1962 than it had been prior to 1952 (Potts, 1970a). After warm springs there were enough insects for chicks but with the adverse effect on insects caused by herbicides this was no longer the case after cold springs. Springs have become warmer and the herbicide effect via cold springs is no longer so evident.

From the start the Sussex Study focused on insects, not just insects that chicks ate but on the role of insects in the whole cereal ecosystem. My major fear was that the use of insecticides on cereals would become much more frequent due to rising numbers of cereal aphids, in turn due to an absence of their predators. There was rising concern about pesticide treadmills in cotton and other crops (reviewed by Van den Bosch, 1978) and it was feared they might be operating in British crops. Consequently entomologists at Rothamsted Experimental Husbandry Station near Harpenden and at the Glasshouse Crops Research Association in Rustington joined the Sussex Study to form the Joint Cereal Ecosystem Study funded by what was then the Agricultural Research Council. The University of Southampton joined in, with the first student being Nick Sotherton, who investigated the knotgrass beetle, then various predatory beetles, which led to his invention of the beetle bank, of which more later (p. 329). Some of the first beetle banks were created on the John Lewis partnership's Leckford Estate in Hampshire. It was a retired couple walking their dog through the estate that first used the name with its double meaning. Many other studies on invertebrates evolved out of the early work in the Sussex Study including the work at the UK government's Boxworth Experimental Husbandry Farm during 1982–90 (Greig-Smith *et al.*, 1992). It has been estimated that this spin-off work amounts to the equivalent of one hundred PhDs (Wratten, 2004), a huge body of information that can only be touched on very briefly in this book. As it turned out

FIG 18. (Left) Juvenile grey partridges aged 8 weeks (Chris Knights); and (below left) 11 weeks (Malcolm Brockless).

the cereal aphid problem receded and we turn to this in Chapter 6. The reasons are not understood, especially given the strong body of evidence that cereal aphid numbers are higher when invertebrate predators are lower (Wratten & Powell, 1991), which sits uncomfortably with the finding that few aphid predators have increased and many have decreased (Chapter 6).

STUBBLE COUNTS: ESTIMATING CHICK SURVIVAL AND NESTING SUCCESS

It was essential to the Sussex Study that chick survival rates could be determined over large areas and a range of farm types. On this scale it was impossible to find an unbiased, reasonably large sample of nests or to attach enough radios. Instead I developed a method of estimating chick survival rates from the average brood size whereby the percentage chick survival = (geometric mean brood size) $^{1.293}$ × 3.665. If, however, the mean brood size is 10 or more the percentage chick survival

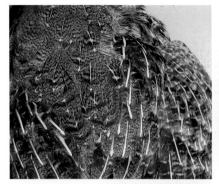

FIG 19. (Top left) Shoulder coverts of adult female grey partridge; (top right) male coverts – note absence of cross-bars. This is the most reliable indicator of sex, short of dissection; (bottom left) the mysterious shoulder spot, described for first time as recently as 1988, by John Carroll.

rate = mean brood size/13.84 × 100/1 (Potts, 1980). This method has been validated against the Damerham data and verified by four radio-tracking studies: (Green, 1984a; Rands, 1986b; Aebischer & Reitz, 2000; Browne *et al.*, 2006). Throughout this book the symbol ± means plus or minus one standard error. In Stephen Browne's study in East Anglia the chick survival was 32±4 per cent. The estimate using my 1980 method was 29 per cent; no significant difference.

The next step is to calculate the Brood Production Rate. The number of chicks hatching per clutch did not vary significantly in Britain between 1907 and 1978, remaining at 13.84±0.10 (Potts, 1980), and given that chick survival can be calculated (as we have just seen), then the number of broods produced is obtained from the number of juveniles surviving, divided by the proportion of chicks surviving to the juvenile stage, divided by 13.84. Hatching success does not vary with clutch size (Lack, 1947) but at Damerham first clutches averaged 15.26±0.05 with replacement clutches 11.23±0.20 (Blank & Ash, 1960). It follows that the number of chicks hatching per nest will be lower where many first clutches are lost. For this reason the 13.84 chicks hatching is not appropriate where nest predation is high; in this case the brood size at hatching is 12.1±0.23 (Potts, 1980). In other countries further corrections are also needed for the number of chicks hatched per clutch which shows considerable variation (Lack, 1947; Pulliainen, 1971). The number of chicks hatching per successful clutch size is 13.8±0.38 in Poland (Olech, 1988b), the same as Britain, but it is lower at 11.8 in France (Aebischer & Reitz, 2000), 12.1 in Italy (Montagna & Meriggi, 1991), 12.6±0.20 in Croatia (Romić, 1975) and 13.2 in Hungary (Peterfay, 1935, 1938; Szederjei et al., 1959). Areas with higher numbers hatching than in the UK include 15 in Wisconsin (McCabe & Hawkins, 1946), to 16 in North Dakota (Schulz, 1977; Carroll, 1992), northern Finland (Putaala & Hissa, 1998) and northern Kazakhstan (Ul'yanin, 1949).

The method of calculating the chick survival has some limitations and it cannot be used as a basis to calculate the loss of females during incubation separately from those that occur after hatching. During Rhys Green's Norfolk radio-tracking, a fox killed a female with chicks. In Finland several females died after they had successfully hatched chicks (Putaala & Hissa, 1998). So the Brood Production Rate (BPR) does not always measure the number of broods actually hatched per pair per year. Another problem apparent from research in France is that the calculations from stubble counts cannot measure the loss of adult males caused by raptor predation (Aebischer & Reitz, 2000). In Sussex this loss was considered to be indicated by the number of lone females with chicks.

It is important to compare the BPR estimates with those from the traditional method where nesting success equals the number of nests hatched divided by the number of nests found. This method gives substantial under-estimates of losses, with a main reason being that few nests are followed from day one i.e at risk for the whole period (21 days to lay eggs and 25 to hatch them (Potts, 1980). A correction for this is often made by using the Mayfield method, which calculates the daily rate and then extrapolates it to the full period of risk. Hötker (2010) gave an equation for correcting the traditional method which increases the average nest losses by 16 percentage points. Replacement nesting 'corrects' in the other direction giving net nest losses 18 per cent lower than with the traditional method (from the re-nesting data given in Potts, 1980). In the grey partridge at least the Mayfield correction increasing losses and re-nesting reducing net losses cancel out leaving BPR and the traditional method interchangeable.

The indirect method of calculating chick survival and BPRs derived from the Sussex study has greatly extended the information obtained from counts on stubbles after the breeding season. It effectively separated the nesting and chick survival components of breeding success, which was necessary for the experimental approaches described in this work.

For the red-legged partridge, chick survival rates take into account the lower number of chicks at hatching, which from several studies was estimated at 11.0±0.4

(Potts, 1980). The comparable figure for the chukar would be higher, ranging from 13.2 in Kazakhstan (Grachev, 1983) to 14.3 in the US (Mackie & Buechner, 1963). The calculation of BPRs is too difficult with *Alectoris* due to the highly variable system known of double brooding whereby the females can lay two clutches one incubated by the male, one by the female (see p. 127).

The deduction from the Sussex Study that herbicides had halved chick survival rates was contentious and it clearly needed a farm-scale experiment to settle the issue one way or another. Predation was also a highly controversial topic, and a major drawback of the work at Damerham had been that there was no information from areas without gamekeepers. The conclusion that density-dependent nest predation was very important in the regulation of partridge numbers and that it was preventable by gamekeepers (Potts, 1986) derived from the simulation modeling of field data obtained in the Sussex Study. It needed to be rejected or supported by experimental evidence before it could carry much weight with the outside world. Two separate farm-scale experiments were therefore set up: at Manydown on chick survival and on Salisbury Plain to investigate nest predation, as outlined below.

Many things have changed on the Sussex Study area one of which has been the substantial increase in the number of the red fox (henceforth fox), badger and raptors. Particularly noticeable has been the dramatic increase of the common buzzard (henceforth buzzard) which was at first correlated to increased losses of grey partridges (Aebischer, 1999). This finding necessitated Mark Watson's investigation which found predation in spring by female sparrowhawks to be the main impact of raptors and we explore this and related issues in Chapter 8. The peregrine, raven, red kite, marsh and hen harriers, have increased as also has the kestrel. Recently the polecat has also spread into the area.

MANYDOWN 1982–7

Small-scale trials with unsprayed cereal crop headlands began at North Farm in the Sussex Study in 1970 but were highly unpopular and abandoned after the death of Chris Hunt. Farmers elsewhere were unwilling to host a formal experiment until the generous offer from Hugh Oliver-Bellasis and his family who farmed the Manydown Estate just west of Basingstoke in north Hampshire. The first trial took place in 1982 followed rapidly by the GWCT's Cereals and Gamebirds Project headed by Nick Sotherton, later Director of Research at the GWCT. Field work was carried out on game-birds by Mike Rands, later Director of BirdLife International (we look at his work in Chapter 4 and especially Chapter 5), on agronomy by Nigel Boatman (later of Loddington), butterflies by

FIG 20. Sussex Study area: conservation headland on the Norfolk Estate, with poppies and cornflowers. Away from the headland the field is treated with herbicides.

John Dover, rare arable weeds by Phil Wilson and small mammals by Tom Tew (later Chief Scientist at Natural England). From 1984, back-up and extension work was increasingly set up on many farms throughout Britain (Sotherton, 1991).

The basic approach at Manydown was the setting up of six blocks, each with 90 ha of cereals. Half the blocks were 'controls' with conventional use of pesticides, with the other half 'treatments' that were sprayed conventionally excepting for the outer 6 m – the headlands – which were sprayed selectively. Few insecticides were used and none on the conservation headlands, and herbicides were restricted to those that were specific to black-grass, wild oats and couch-grass but did not kill broadleaved weeds. The main phase of the experiment was during the years 1984–7. The trials were a great success and the resulting management technique, conservation headlands, eventually became a key option in the UK government's Higher Level Stewardship Scheme described in detail in Chapter 10.

SALISBURY PLAIN EXPERIMENT 1984–91

It had taken a long time to persuade anyone to host an experiment testing the effects of herbicides, but experimenting with predator control was even more unpopular and indeed impossible until the Ministry of Defence Land Agents

FIG 21. Hedgerow on the Salisbury Plain study area; suitable for partridges but hardly stock-proof!

offered their training area on the gently undulating chalk upland of Salisbury Plain. Two experimental areas were selected, one 564 ha, the other 496 ha. Most military training with tanks took place on the grassland not in the cereals and caused little trouble, as was the case with the public access to many tracks that crisscrossed the area. The gamekeeper, Malcolm Brockless, controlled predators on one of the areas (chosen on the toss of a coin) for three years, switching areas after three years. With a one year study prior to the experiment and one after, the whole study lasted eight years; full details are given in Tapper *et al.* (1996) and we turn to the results later in this introduction and in Chapter 4.

LODDINGTON 1992–

As the Salisbury Plain project was closing down, the GWCT were keen to secure a farm or estate where it could combine predator control (as on Salisbury Plain) and habitat improvement (as at Manydown). Eventually, thanks to a generous bequest from Lord & Lady Allerton, a 217 ha farm at Loddington, Leicestershire was purchased with 36 ha added later. The area was fundamentally different from all the others mentioned above because the soil was not over chalk but consisted of heavy Hanslope series clay requiring an intensive lattice of under-drains.

FIG 22. Loddington Farm, Leicestershire, area showing some of many field trials aimed at improving the management of set-aside.

Predator control was carried out by Malcolm Brockless, as on Salisbury Plain, but this time the farming could be controlled, though within a financial framework that typical farmers and farm managers would find realistic. In the first year 1991/2, the field size was 7 ha. Six fields were then divided by beetle banks but with the added large fields (two in the 36 ha) the size was 6 ha in 1994/5. The aim was to fund the costs of partridge conservation out of the farm profits. The work at Loddington led by Nigel Boatman provided the cost basis for the government's support of field margin management. The numbers of grey partridge did not increase however, due to a low chick survival rate (27 per cent) but the numbers of red-legged partridges strongly increased, as did numbers of most other bird species, especially those that had recently declined on farmland elsewhere (Stoate & Leake, 2003).

ROYSTON 2002–10

From 2002 the GWCT managed a grey partridge recovery project on the chalk hills southwest of Royston, north Hertfordshire. Six contiguous farms totaling 996 ha were managed through predator control, hopper feeding from October to March and the creation of cover for wintering, nesting and brood-rearing. Malcolm Brockless moved from Loddington to control predation and had a difficult job covering an area twice the size of those he had worked on in the Salisbury Plain project. In addition, field size averaged 17 ha, more than twice the optimum size, and there was a reliance on strips of set-aside to provide extra brood-rearing cover rather than conservation headlands. A surrounding area of 1,311 ha, also consisting of six farms, was monitored but not managed.

Grey partridges increased six-fold from 3 to 18 pairs per 100 ha on the managed area in only five years but only two-fold on the surrounding area. On the area with predator control, nesting success remained constant despite the increase in nest density, consistent with the predictions of the Sussex computer model (Potts, 1980, 1986). Red-legged partridges increased three-fold overall despite 60 per cent being shot per annum, sustained in part by the immigration of pen-reared birds. Great care was taken to avoid shooting grey partridges, as is covered in Chapter 9. The phasing out of set-aside halved the amount of nesting cover and after the project ended, the farmers were unwilling to reduce field size with beetle banks or improve brood rearing cover with conservation headlands despite the availability of generous grants through Higher Level Stewardship, and we look at this issue in Chapter 11 in relation to incentives. The details are to be found in Aebischer & Ewald (2010).

LARGE NUMBER OF OTHER STUDIES

The first modern studies on grey partridges were inspired by two giants in early ecology: Charles Elton at the University of Oxford, which led through Doug Middleton to the Damerham study, and Aldo Leopold at the University of Wisconsin that led to the work of Yeatter and of many others in the US. In the 1940s there were several major studies in eastern and northern Europe that largely fizzled out in the 1950s but with major work instigated in France from the 1960s and in Italy from the late 1980s. Work on the red-legged partridge received a huge stimulus with the teams of workers, including pathologists, set up at the University of Cuidad Real in Spain in the 1990s and in the south of France by the Office National de la Chasse.

As already mentioned the scope of this book had to be limited. The vast amount of research on what are here called pen-reared partridges, including those on game farms and released from any game-rearing facility, is excluded so far as is reasonable to do so. There was temptation throughout to compare results with work on other Galliformes, particularly that on the pheasant and on the bobwhite

FIG 23. Typical view of the Lajta study area in Hungary where grey partridges have been studied for more than 20 years. (Sandor Faragó)

and California quails, but the tome would have been unwieldy to say the least. The same goes for the rock and Barbary partridges, although some work on these is mentioned where necessary. Dealing with three species of partridges means the term partridge can only be used when the species does not matter. Importantly the term hunting is used throughout in preference to shooting, as is normal outside Britain, or harvesting, which confuses with farming.

The useful scientific literature on partridges is scattered over a wide spectrum from high-level science to the more serious hunting magazines. The literature is also large: Trego and Upgren compiled their *Hungarian (Grey) Partridge Bibliography* in 1975, which included 1,024 items published up to May 1974. That number would now be about 2,750. *The Zoological Record* shows the relative importance in the scientific literature of the three species that feature in this book. From 1978 to 2011 it abstracted 869 papers on the grey partridge, 388 on the red-legged partridge and 262 on the chukar partridge. The number of scientific papers grows at about 5 per cent per year while the numbers of wild partridges declines by about the same amount.

The red-legged partridge hybridises naturally with the rock partridge in the western Alps; the rock partridge hybridises naturally with the chukar in Thrace and unnaturally on game farms, and these hybrids produce fertile offspring.

Consequently some authorities combine all three as a super-species (which also includes the Przevalski's partridge of China). I have adopted this approach because there is so much less information about the *Alectoris* species and have given most attention to the red-legged partridge, long established in Britain and the chukar present in Britain at times from 1920–40 (Lever, 2009) and from 1970 to 1993, with some hybrids still present. This is justified only for considering basic *Alectoris* ecology for comparison with *Perdix*. I have always shared the concerns of Barilani *et al.* (2007) that native *Alectoris* gene pools are threatened by the introductions of chukars and regard the banning of the chukar from Britain in 1992 as an example others can follow.

I have taken care to consult as many of the older works as possible, with a variety of abstracting services used, but it is inevitable that significant papers on partridges remain hidden, especially those in the Slavic, Cyrillic and Arabic languages. Some of the literature quoted in this book was very difficult to locate. With the 'Proceedings of *Perdix*' and earlier specialist conferences on the grey partridge now available at http://gamebird.forestry.uga.edu/quailvi, this is now easier. Trego & Upgren's *Bibliography* is also available here.

THE SCIENCE: SOME FUNDAMENTALS OF PARTRIDGE ECOLOGY

Much has been made of the 'balance of nature' but more and more evidence is accumulating to support Elton's contention that, 'despite its many attractions, such a self-correcting balance does not exist and perhaps never has existed' (Elton, 1930). In this book however, an ecosystem approach is taken and it is clear that at this level nature fluctuates within boundaries by following fundamental rules with vital checks and balances. That was one reason why the Convention on Biological Diversity signed in Rio de Janeiro in 1992 advocated an ecosystem approach. As we shall see, the balance between the abundance of mega-herbivores (those that are so large that the adults are not affected by predation, such as elephants and many extinct species) and the grasses to trees ratio is of crucial importance; partridges are basically shrub grassland birds and grasses rather than trees generally benefit from grazing. The partridges in this book have no place in climax forests. We explore these issues in Chapter 3. There are also the balancing processes between top-predators such as the wolf, lynx and eagle owl and middle-sized predators such as the fox and some raptors, with profound implications for their prey species. There are also the important interactions between predators and prey and between parasites and hosts.

At one time there was a stimulating debate about whether the abundance of species such as the partridge was determined by the weather or by such factors as competition, predation and parasites. Accepting that insects are important to chick survival and are affected by the weather, then the population dynamics of partridges shows the reality to be a simple mixture of the two, albeit producing complicated outcomes. To understand this we need to separate the **long-term** average level of partridge abundance from the **short-term** essentially annual fluctuations.

The six earliest studies of grey partridges where September numbers per 100 ha were assessed for ten years or more before modern farming began are shown in Figure 24. Only in the case of Damerham could partridges have been impacted by herbicides, probably in 1954 and in 1958 as discussed in Chapter 5, but with little long-term effect on numbers because of compensation from less shooting (Chapter 9). Later there is the Sussex Study and of course there are many others, mostly of low-density populations affected at least in part by modern agriculture.

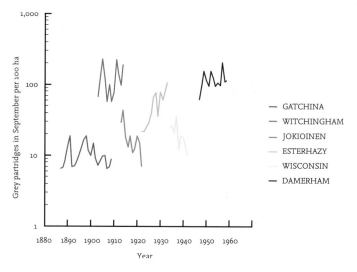

FIG 24. Six early studies of grey partridge September population densities. Each shows similar annual fluctuations but there are large differences in the average levels and in some cases trends in these levels. From left to right these studies are: (1) Gatchina, near St Petersburg, Russia, where Tsar Nicholas II took a close interest (Dits, 1917); (2) Great Witchingham to 1914 (Middleton, 1936b); (3) Jokioinen in southwest Finland (Fazer, 1925); (4) The Duke of Esterházy's estate near Fertőd, Hungary (Potts & Faragó, 2000); (5) Faville Grove, Wisconsin (McCabe & Hawkins, 1946); (6) Damerham Hampshire. Note the logarithmic scale.

The factors that change the long-term level of partridge numbers before modern agriculture have to be separated from those that cause the annual fluctuations, because doing so is very important in conservation planning. The six earliest studies illustrate the difference well. In these the long-term levels of partridge numbers in September ranged 12-fold from 10 per 100 ha in Russia to 124 per 100 ha in Norfolk. We clearly need to understand the factors that determine such large between-estate variations. In contrast, the annual fluctuations show very little difference between estates. These fluctuations can be measured by the coefficient of variation which is the standard deviation (a measure of the spread of the numbers per 100 ha) divided by the average numbers per 100 ha converted to a percentage. Across the six studies this percentage ranged from 31 per cent at Damerham to 56 per cent in Finland. This 1.8-fold difference is tiny compared to that between estates. Any manager of partridge populations should therefore first concentrate on how to raise the long-term levels rather than on how to achieve good years. Unfortunately this has usually not been the case, hence the undue weight put on the weather in Ascot week. Many waited for years for the weather to improve whilst numbers declined.

It is true that one way or another the short-term, essentially annual, variations are due to the indirect and direct effects of the weather but quantifying this has eluded generations of partridge biologists. Hard winters certainly cause problems in North America, Scandinavia and Russia. In Poland where winters can be just as harsh, Bogumila ('Buki') Olech found the only statistically significant effect was from the depth of snow during January to 31 March but that this only explained 6–17 per cent of the annual variation because densities were partly controlled in the long term by density-dependent factors (Olech, 1987). The hard winters had a greater impact in more recent years because 'greater nest predation pressure' delayed the recovery (Olech, 1988a).

So now we turn to the crucial long-term factors that control the average density levels over a period of many years. By far the most important of these factors is predation at the nest. In the Sussex Study, during the years 1968–84 nesting success was 62.6± 2.5 per cent where there was a full-time gamekeeper dedicated to wild partridges. Where there was no gamekeeper the nesting success was 36.7± 1.7 per cent. This may seem convincing but it needed the Salisbury Plain experiment to clinch the matter, through the main results given in Figure 25. As explained earlier this project used six areas with predator control and ten without it. Unfortunately one of the ten areas with no predator control could not be counted in 1991, which explains only nine and not ten red points on the graph. Although not counted, numbers were known to be very low and a shoot produced a total bag of only one old male.

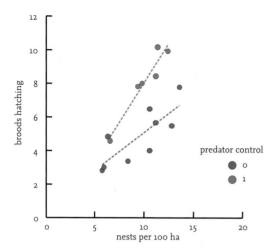

FIG 25. The Salisbury Plain experiment showing in blue that the number of broods hatching increases in line with the number of pairs if there is a gamekeeper controlling nest predators. When this was not the case (the red line) the number of broods responded more slowly to the increase in pairs.

Note that the lines in Figure 25 diverge; the difference becomes greater as the density of nests increases. This divergence is statistically significant (P<0.05) even though nest densities on Salisbury Plain never exceeded 15 per 100 ha and the density effect intensifies from about 15 nests per 100 ha (see Fig. 93). The same divergence was found through the Sussex Study during 1968–85 (Potts, 1986) and again during 2003–10 when predator control was restored (see Table 32). With 15 pairs per 100 ha the area with predator control would be expected to produce 12.7 broods but the same 15 pairs without predator control would produce only 7.3 broods, 43 per cent fewer. The prediction from the Sussex Study was that BPRs would be on average 1.6 times higher with nest predator control. On Salisbury Plain the average BPR was raised from 49.8±5.0 per cent to 79.7±2.8 per cent, exactly 1.6 times higher. The benefit of predation control is very substantial.

Whilst reassuring in the sense that they verified the computer model, the differences demand explanation. Something is dragging down the number of broods hatching and doing so with more effect as the nest density increases. In Chapter 4 a large amount of evidence is reviewed showing that the force dragging down the brood production rate is predation at the nest. This downward force is the expression of density dependence and it is essential to visualise how it works, otherwise it is difficult to see how nesting success can be very high without predator control. Basically, as nests become grouped closer together predators find them more easily. The evidence from studies of red-legged and chukar partridge shows predation is even higher on these species than it is on the grey partridge, partly because their eggs are not hidden.

Seventy years ago the story could have ended at this point. Today this is where the story of the impact of modern farming begins, especially the adverse effects on vital insect food supplies for chicks; there is no point saving nests from predators if the chicks are left to starve to death.

THE DECREASE IN CHICK SURVIVAL RATE

Prior to modern farming cereal fields appear to have been a near perfect place for foraging broods and a suitable substitute for the natural steppe grasslands of their origins. Chicks need to feed secure from aerial predators beneath a protective canopy offered by tall grasses such as feather-grass, wheatgrass or cereals, but they also need to be able to move freely over the ground, not with a risk of becoming trapped by thick, often wet vegetation. Most importantly insects and other suitable invertebrates need to be abundant.

Three studies mentioned above together illustrate the way in which the survival of grey partridge chicks has been impacted by modern herbicides, first introduced in 1946 and used on virtually all cereal crops in Britain by 1962 (Potts, 1970a). The first of the three was the study at Great Witchingham in Norfolk maintained from 1903 to 1938. Chick survival was usually good (Figure 26), near 50 per cent

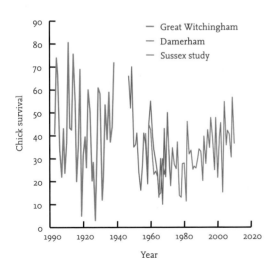

FIG 26. Grey partridge chick survival to age six weeks from 1903 to 2010 on Great Witchingham, Norfolk (blue), Damerham in Hampshire (green) and the Sussex Study (red). Note the general agreement where estimates overlap, the decline in the number of good years since the early 1950s and the partial recovery in the 1990s. Areas with conservation headlands are excluded.

in 10 of 36 years despite the presence of the disease strongylosis (Chapter 7). The results at Damerham from 1948 to 1957 were similar to what was expected from Great Witchingham. From 1957 chick survival rates at Damerham and Sussex were similar, with chick survival higher than 50 per cent in only two years.

WORDS INTO BIRDS

It is now more than 30 years since the causes of the grey partridge decline were formally quantified. Assuming an open landscape with half the fields in cereals, three factors were shown to be involved for Britain. Each had a similar impact; (1) an increase in field size with the removal of hedgerows and other nesting cover, (2) reduced control of nest predators and (3) reductions in the insect food supplies for chicks caused by the use of pesticides. All three factors interacted to cause the population decline (Fig. 27) and attention to all three was essential to reverse the situation (Potts, 1980). Particularly important was the decline in

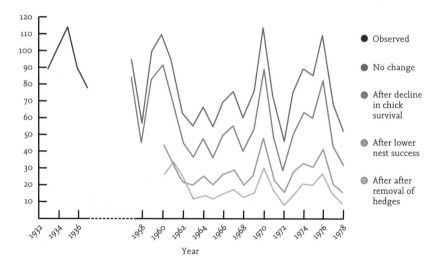

FIG 27. Observed (GWCT National Game Census) and computer-simulated September numbers of grey partridges per 100 ha and computer simulations illustrating how the three main factors – loss of insect food for the chick, loss of hedgerow nesting cover and increased nest predation combined to bring the population to a low level by 1978. The simulation was a close fit to the levels observed in the 1930s and to the bottom line 'after removal of hedges' (Potts, 1980).

FIG 28. Sussex Study area: the Norfolk Estate.

predator control that was a consequence of poor chick survival. It was a common perception that saving nests from predators simply meant more chicks dying. Nesting cover was also removed for the same reason; with poor chick survival it was no longer worth retaining.

There was very little response to this diagnosis of the causes of the grey partridge decline, with instead a great increase in pen-rearing and releasing, especially of red-legged and chukar partridges. Ten years later ornithologists began to realise that other species were declining on farmland as well (Marchant *et al.* 1990), but progress was very slow. Farmers didn't like the story and, to be fair, it is difficult to agree to the planting of cover such as hedges only a few years after it has been removed. Farmers have been especially unwilling to reduce field size and they certainly did not want to let up in their continual war against weeds. Not surprisingly, as we have seen, the numbers of partridges and other affected birds have continued to decline.

At the beginning of the present century many thought it was too late and too difficult to restore partridge numbers and eventual extinction was widely predicted and accepted as inevitable, including on the Sussex Study area. Fortunately in Britain we now have the excellent government-supported agri-environment scheme known as Higher Level Stewardship, available for essential habitat improvement. The aim of this book is to persuade others, especially recalcitrant governments in the European Community, that this is the way forward, not on its own but in combination with predation control and in a practical partnership between large-scale landowners and governments that benefits taxpayers and biodiversity alike.

There is one test of all this science, as Charles Coles, Director of the GWCT for many years, asked of us – 'Can we turn the words into birds?' We know conservation management needs to be concentrated on aspects determining the long-term levels, particularly nest predation. We know too that instead of blaming the weather in Ascot week we need to focus on the management that can mitigate the effects of the weather, such as ensuring a high availability of insect food.

It would however be a very serious mistake to view partridge conservation as an exercise in managing a species for shooting. Partridges are countryside barometers; their abundance measures biodiversity and the proper stewardship of rural resources. Something must be done or we could lose the threatened species from farmland. Partridge conservation could provide the motivation and it would bring with it a significant slice of farmland biodiversity and rural heritage within a framework of profitable farming. This book emphasises that now is the time for action.

THE BASIC APPROACH IN SUBSEQUENT CHAPTERS

The many studies on partridges covered in this book combine to give us a uniquely comprehensive picture of the major long-term changes in farmland ecosystems, especially those based on cereals. When the Sussex study started, the use of computers in ecological research was in its infancy. The dramatic developments since then have resulted in a rapid expansion of monitoring, mapping and modeling. The development of radio-tracking has greatly improved our understanding of movements, and studies of DNA have transformed our understanding of the fossil record and species relationships. Particularly important have been the field experiments. What has often been missing is a basic understanding of natural history to join up the dots. This book aims to fill this gap.

What can we do to restore partridge numbers? That is the question.

CHAPTER 2

On the Origin of Partridges

Nothing in biology makes sense except in the light of evolution.
Theodosius Dobzhansky (1973)

MANY THEMES THROUGH THIS book depend on comparing and contrasting the responses of the *Perdix* and *Alectoris* partridges to agriculture. If we could understand the reasons for the differences it would greatly help us to understand the birds. What extinct species most closely resembled the present day species? Where did they live? What was their most recent common ancestor and where did it live?

Analyses of fossils and of DNA show that the *Perdix* and *Alectoris* partridges have been in separate lines of evolution, well separated geographically, for 20 million years or more. In many ways they may be more similar now than in the past due to convergent evolution. The *Perdix* partridges originated in the area now occupied by the Tibetan plateau and the *Alectoris* partridges came from Africa. This could explain most of the differences between the two types of partridge.

The grey partridge occurred in the Sussex Study area 475,000 years ago, though with several absences from Britain later as advancing ice forced the species as far south as the Dead Sea. Red-legged partridges never occurred in Britain in the past, not even in the warmest inter-glacial when *Hippopotamus* splashed in the Thames. The natural range of *Perdix* and *Alectoris* partridges is vast, but it has also been greatly expanded by other human intervention, for example with grey partridges from central Europe and chukar partridges from Pakistan introduced into North America.

FIG 29. Boxgrove, 10 km west of the Sussex Study area, *c.* 475,000 years ago. Grey partridges were present. Whether they were caught and eaten by *Homo heidelbergensis*, seen here butchering a Hundsheim rhinoceros, is not known but very likely – however, horses were the main source of meat for these people. (Painting by Richard Jones from *Fairweather Eden*, Arrow Books, 1998)

FOSSILS AND CALIBRATING THE DNA CLOCK

The basic principle that underpins the study of bones to work out the evolutionary relationships of species is that the individuals that share the most features (in the surface structures, for example) are those that are most closely related. Smaller differences can be expected to represent shorter time scales than larger differences. The time scale itself can be calibrated by analysis. Bones younger than about 40,000 years before present (BP) can have their age determined from the ratio of their isotopes of Carbon 13 (a stable isotope) and Carbon 14 that has a half-life of about 5,600 years. In this account dates obtained from the ratio of these isotopes are given as ^{14}C BP. For older material uranium/ thorium ratios or other techniques are used. The fossil record is however notoriously incomplete, with skeletons often highly fragmented and dispersed, although this is less of a problem with partridges because many of their bones were left in caves by early humans and other predators.

Analysis of DNA is a more powerful way of determining relationships than bone morphology but it is not without its problems, particularly in relation to determining the timing of important evolutionary steps. Any sample of tissue will contain one nuclear genome (the chromosomal DNA) per cell consisting, in our own case, of about 25,000 genes. Every cell also contains many copies of molecules of the mitochondrial genome (henceforth mtDNA), each containing 37 genes in partridges and humans alike. Just after fertilisation an egg will contain one nuclear genome, half inherited from the father and half from the mother and several mitochondrial genomes, all inherited from the mother. After amplification of nuclear or mtDNA using a procedure known as the polymerase chain reaction (PCR), which has been so useful in solving crime, the two kinds of DNA can be selected. The distinction is important when trying to calculate where and when species originated.

Every time any DNA replicates itself, with every cell division, there is a possibility of an error or an externally caused change (such as can result from some kinds of radiation). This results in what are known as mutations, the term used here to include nucleotide substitutions, insertions or deletions or other changes in the DNA sequences. It has often been assumed that the rate of mutation is constant, with a greater number of mutations indicating a greater length of time. This assumes that the mutations are neutral with respect to natural selection. In reality many mutations will often be harmful and effectively discarded, or beneficial and 'fixed' through natural selection. The problem here is that the number of mutations per unit of time in what is usually referred to as the molecular clock is not constant; it varies with species and circumstances, with the genes involved and the evolutionary pressures. An example of the latter is the very rapid spread amongst insects of resistance to insecticides. The molecular clock has therefore to be set and adjusted by reference to fossils and rocks of known age, or to ancient DNA. Enough ancient nuclear DNA has been extracted from the hair of 20,000 year old woolly mammoths preserved in the permafrost to assemble a virtually complete genome. MtDNA has also been recovered from the bones of some even older large extinct mammals and from the bodies of penguins buried in permanent Antarctic ice 44,000 years ago. But no ancient DNA has yet been recovered from partridges.

It has recently become clear that some characteristics of species can change extremely rapidly on an evolutionary time-scale. Peter and Rosemary Grant's studies of Galapagos finch beak size on the island Daphne Major found that significant changes in beak size (e.g. +3.7 per cent inherited after only one severe drought) evolved and were reversed within a period of less than 30 years. In only 30 generations a population of blackcaps has divided, with different migration routes and significant changes in wing length and beak size and shape (Rolshausen, et al., 2009), and equally rapid changes have occurred in three-spined sticklebacks in Alaska and a range of other species (Le Page, 2011).

As we shall see, a diet rich in insects is very important to partridge chicks and the question has often been asked why partridges have not evolved to overcome the shortages due to the use of pesticides. We now know that evolution may occur so fast that the obvious answer, not enough time with serious insect shortages dating only from the mid-1950s, may be wrong. Astonishingly, lizards off the coast of Croatia were found to have evolved to cope with a diet largely of plants instead of largely of insects in 37 years (Herrel *et al.*, 2008). If we recognise that evolution can be speeded up like this, then partridge evolution can be considerably clarified, as we shall see.

THE FIRST PERDIX IN THE FOSSIL RECORD

Anyone interested in Palearctic Pleistocene fossil birds is indebted to Dr Tommy Tyrberg of Linköping University, Sweden. He has diligently compiled the hitherto highly dispersed records of sub-fossils (henceforth fossils) for many years and made the results available in a book regularly updated on the internet. Surprisingly the grey partridge is the most numerous species in this fossil record. Beginning about three million years ago there has been a more or less steady escalation in the numbers; perhaps with a temporary fall-off during the Anglian glaciation, the most severe glaciation in those western countries where the most fossils have been found, especially France. The Saalian was the most severe glaciation in Eastern Europe but far fewer *Perdix* fossils have been found there. *Perdix* has been identified from more than 700 layers at 246 European

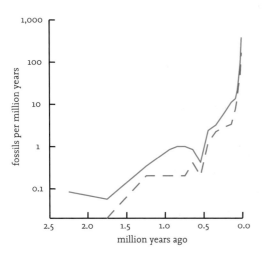

FIG 30. Frequency of fossil *Perdix perdix* (713, blue line) and *Alectoris* spp. (461 red broken line) per million years in the Palearctic through the Pleistocene, from Tyrberg (1996, *et seq.*). The dip in numbers around half a million years ago coincides with the severe Anglian glaciation (*see main text*). Note the vertical scale is logarithmic.

sites, mostly caves but also including open sites such as at Boxgrove near the Sussex Study area. The fossil record for the *Alectoris* partridges is essentially similar, but with a lower relative frequency of *Alectoris* during the early to middle Pleistocene. It is obvious however that the fossil record of both species is at best very incomplete beyond two million years ago (Fig. 30).

In 1963 Dr Margarita Erbajeva, a world authority on pikas (small relatives of the hare), uncovered the earliest evidence of any species of *Perdix*. Working at the Russian Academy of Sciences, Ulan-Ude, just southeast of Lake Baikal, she found fossil remains of the bird described and named *Perdix margaritae* in her honour by Evgeny Kurochkin (1985). Further fossils of this species were found very near the border between Russia and Mongolia (Zelenkov & Kurochkin, 2009). From other species found at these sites the area was then, 2.5 million years ago, an open landscape and forest-steppe inhabited by ancestors of the modern horse and other open landscape grassland animals such as ground squirrels and voles with rooted molars that do not re-grow once worn down (Erbajeva & Alexeeva, 2000).

The four bones of the type specimen of *Perdix margaritae* (only part of a humerus is shown in Fig. 31) appear slightly different from those of a modern grey partridge, although many fragments from Shaamar, just 25 km inside Mongolia, were 'similar in size and morphology to living *Perdix*' (Zelenkov & Kurochkin, 2009). The differences led Antonio Sánchez Marco at the Catalan Institute of Paleontology, Barcelona, to argue that the humerus was sufficiently different to exclude its classification as *Perdix* because: (1) the *fossa pneumotricipitalis dorsalis* (arrowed yellow) is too deep; (2) the foramen in the *fossa pneumotricipitalis ventralis* is too large and elongated (red); and (3) the *crista bicipitalis* protrudes too much

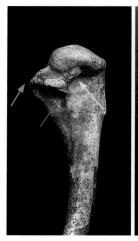 

FIG 31. Humerus: (left) *Perdix margaritae*, Trans-Baikal, Russia, about 2.5 million years ago (from Zelenkov & Kurochkin, 2009); and (right) modern *Perdix perdix* from Sussex Study. The coloured arrows indicate features important in species determination (*see main text*).

and is triangular rather than round (blue) (Sánchez-Marco, 2010). Working at the Paleontological Institute, Moscow, Nikita Zelenkov (*in press*) strongly defends *Perdix margaritae*, point by point: (1) this would exclude the Daurian partridge *Perdix dauurica*, which has a deep fossa; (2) this character varies and at least two specimens of *Perdix perdix* in the Moscow collection are similar to *Perdix margaritae;* and (3) in fact the match is good with the *Perdix perdix* in the Moscow collection. In addition the carpometacarpus, a wing bone, was similar to *Perdix*.

THE SPECIES OF *PERDIX*

A number of other fossil sub-species or species have also been claimed. The first was *Perdix jurcsáki* described from Romania (Kretzoi, 1957, 1962), later relegated to *Perdix perdix jurcsáki* by Jánossy (1976). The most interesting of the claimed species is *Perdix palaeoperdix* described by the indefatigable Dr Cécile Mourer-Chauviré (1975; 1993) from 240–300,000-year-old fossils found in caves in the Massif Central of France. Working at the University of Lyon she showed that the mean length of 108 main wing bones (humeri) was 3.6 per cent shorter and the mean length of 56 femurs 4.0 per cent shorter than in modern *P. perdix*; both differences were statistically significant. This is however unsound evidence of a different species for two reasons. First the measurements are within the ranges found amongst the present day sub-species of *Perdix*: for example, *P. p. robusta* has wings that are 6–7 per cent longer with a 5 per cent longer tail, also shorter metatarsi (legs), mid toes and a larger bill. Second there are 217 records of fossil *Perdix* identified

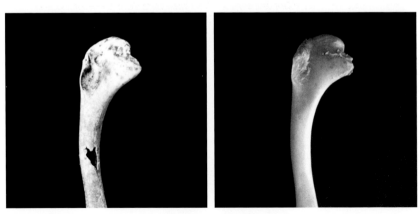

FIG 32. *Perdix* wing bones (proximal humerus cranial view): (left) from Boxgrove, Sussex, about 475,000 years ago (John Stewart); and (right) from the Sussex Study area in 2010.

FIG 33. The three extant species of *Perdix* (left to right): grey (male left); Daurian (male right); and Tibetan (female right) – illustrated by specimens in the Berlin Museum. (Jörg Tillmann)

in France after 1975, the year when *P. palaeoperdix* was first described. Despite the overlap of measurements mentioned above, the identifications since 1975 show no *P. palaeoperdix* more recently than 125,000 years ago and only one *P. perdix* older than this. The two 'species' did not occur at the same time in France and so the separation essentially depends on a comparison of ancient fossils and modern *Perdix*. Finally, John Stewart, now at the the University of Bournemouth, found that the *Perdix* from Boxgrove, 475,000 years ago, is indistinguishable from modern *Perdix* (Fig. 32).

The astonishing claim by Boev (2001) that *P. perdix* and *P. palaeoperdix* co-existed in western Bulgaria almost to the Holocene (the last 10,000 years) could be explained by the presence of some small individuals of modern *Perdix*. In any case the basis for the most recent record was insufficient, merely the diametre of the end of one tibiotarsus. About similar material from the northern Caucasus Nikita Zelenkov writes: 'I would agree with you that *P. palaeoperdix* might not be a separate species, bones of this form were described by Potapova & Baryshnikov in 1993 and when examining them, I could not find a difference from the living *P. perdix*'.

Mlíkovský (2002) has combined *Perdix palaeoperdix* with *Perdix perdix*, and although some of his combinations appear unjustified (e.g. merging *Palaeortyx* and *Coturnix* quails), in the case of *Perdix* they appear justified. In a further simplification *Alectoris sutcliffei* from Devon has been re-assigned to *Perdix perdix* (Stewart, 1996). The newest fossil species of *Perdix* currently being described lived in the Caucasus; it had very strong legs more suitable for climbing somewhat similar to *Alectoris* but of course without spurs (Zelenkov, *in litt.*).

In conclusion we have one species *Perdix perdix* that has existed for 2 million years and the earlier *Perdix margaritae*. There are however also two other living species of *Perdix* and to see how they fit in we have to look at their DNA.

THE DNA EVIDENCE WITHIN *PERDIX*

As part of a recent dramatic expansion of work on DNA of gamebirds in China, a team of seven researchers led by Xinkang Bao of the University of Lanzhou, Gansu, have helped to explain the evolution of the three living species of *Perdix* (Bao *et al.*, 2010). Analysis of a nuclear gene shown to be a useful marker for evolutionary relationships and of some mtDNA has confirmed that the ancestral *Perdix* evolved on the steppes of Asia. The ancestor would have been adapted to treeless areas, nesting and roosting on the ground, feeding on seeds of grasses

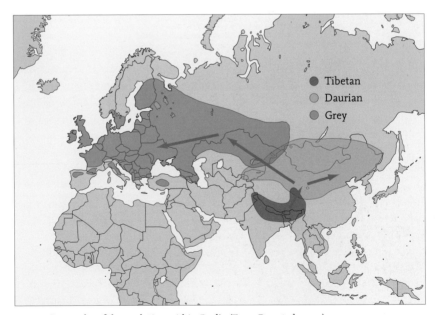

FIG 34. Geography of the evolution within *Perdix*. (From Bao *et al.*, 2010)

(with a high silica content these are tough, necessitating a strong gizzard) and the fruits of steppe bushes and plants, and being able to thrive in dry (but not arid) conditions and survive very cold winters. From the DNA of the living species, Bao and his co-workers suggest that an ancestor of *Perdix* spread to the Tibetan plateau about 3.6 million years ago, a time of great advance of the Pliocene steppe. (Geological time scales are here those of the UNESCO International Stratigraphical Chart.) Then in stages beginning 3.4 million years ago, the plateau rose in altitude changing the area from a savanna into a cold arid zone unsuitable for *Perdix*. Some of the partridge populations survived in low altitude places in the south where steppe grasslands remained; these were the ancestors of the Tibetan partridge. Other partridges avoided the adverse conditions by moving off the plateau to the north, later becoming separated into two groups: grey partridge to the west and Daurian partridge to the east (Fig. 34).

FIG 35. (Above left) New hedge planted in winter habitat of Tibetan partridge in Sichuan; (left) feather grass. (Dominik Thiel)

What separated the grey and Daurian partridges is not known but the ongoing Lake Baikal drilling program is documenting the initiation of much northern hemisphere glaciation, at about 2.7 million years ago. The lake area itself was not glaciated, but the climate was very cold and arid. Already by two million years ago, after the species were separated, the known combined distribution of the grey and Daurian partridges included Italy, Romania, the Ukraine, Turkey, Mongolia and northeast China. The oldest known fossil *Perdix perdix* is two million years old from the Ukraine (Mlíkovský, 2002).

When more favourable conditions returned, the Tibetan partridge spread back onto the plateau so that it now occupies a range extending to 2.3 million km². The Daurian partridge also expanded its range westwards until it now overlaps slightly with that of the grey partridge, occupying an area of 7.6 million km². This overlap presumably occurred after the Pleistocene because during that ice age the Daurian partridge refuge was in the Qaidam Basin to the west of Lake Qinghai (Cao *et al.*, 2010).

This new hypothesis of *Perdix* evolution based on the Lanzhou research would explain why the Tibetan partridge adults, but not young, are so different in appearance from the other two species (Fig. 33). Because the Tibetan partridge is the most ancient of the three species its bones could be really important in finally settling a dispute about the relationship between *Perdix margaritae* and the living species, but Tibetan partridge bones have not yet been described. Bones have not hitherto been taken from museum specimens for such a purpose but in this case it would surely be justified.

OVERLAP BETWEEN GREY AND DAURIAN PARTRIDGES

Where the distributions of the grey and Daurian partridges overlap there are notable differences in habitat. One area of overlap just to the south of Lake Alakol in Dzhungaria, on the border between Kazakhstan and Xinjiang, has been studied by Annenkov & Litun (1989). Here the Daurian partridge distribution showed a preference for higher altitudes, overlapping with the chukar and even the Altai snowcock. The grey partridge on the other hand overlapped with the quail and pheasant and only a little with the chukar. This locality, with both *Perdix* partridges, the chukar, quail, snowcock and black grouse all close together, begs further study. In Jilin Province in northeast China the Daurian partridge is also most common in hilly areas, especially in the 'grassland-forest' and often near trees but not in the forest itself (Zhao *et al.*, 1992). Hybridisation has been recorded between Daurian partridge and grey partridge in Kazakhstan but it is rare (Karpov & Belyalov, 2005).

SUB-SPECIES OF *PERDIX*: THE EASTERN AND WESTERN CLADES

Today the natural range of the grey partridge is amongst the largest of any species in Eurasia. Not surprisingly, with such a vast distribution, many sub-species have been claimed, but 15 seemed excessive especially considering there are only 3 sub-species of the Daurian partridge. Aiming to reduce the number of sub-species of the grey partridge, Pavlova (1987) used morphological data such as wing, beak and tail lengths. In the event she described two additional sub-species. One was based on only 14 birds from the Naurzumskii reserve, northern Kazakhstan, where Ul'yanin did his work in the 1930s (later), the other was obtained through splitting *lucida* into its sedentary and migratory forms. Pavlova thought that two sub-species, *buturlini* and *furvescens*, were not valid and so settled on a final total of seven for the former USSR; the same number that she started with. Further analysis of her data shows that the grey partridge subspecies fall into two groups, or clades: (1) grey – the migratory *robusta* and *lucida*; and (2) brown – the nominate *perdix*, *arenicola* and *canescens*. DNA bar-coding analysis also places the migratory grey clade ancestral to the brown clade (Kerr, 2010). This is further evidence supporting the hypothesis of Xinkang Bao and his colleagues that the grey partridge evolved westwards from the Tibetan plateau.

PARTRIDGE MIGRATIONS

The nominate sub-species *perdix*, the one present in Britain, is well known as sedentary, often spending its life within the confines of two or three adjacent fields. In 1667 it was the first species of wild bird to be ringed in Britain, although many of the birds ringed in private schemes were pen-reared, and such birds disperse more widely than wild birds. None of the thousands of wild birds ringed at Damerham were known to travel further than 8.3 km. In Denmark and elsewhere about 2 per cent of recoveries of pen-reared birds travelled beyond 20 km (Paludan, 1963; and separate, more recent studies). In the Sussex Study area in the 1960s two pen-reared birds (0.4 per cent of recoveries) were shot at 40 km. By far the greatest distance recorded for the *Perdix perdix* was a bird released in Italy that travelled 140 km.

The eastern sub-species *lucida* is well known to migrate south in response to deep snow, but only up to about 535 km (Kuz'mina, 1992). In autumn large numbers flew south along the Volga lowlands so regularly that shooting butts were permanently placed in their line of flight. Unfortunately not much is known about the return movements, nor is it known how far the migrating individuals travelled or how far they could fly in one day. It was well known however that the flights continued after dark. From 1925 to 1977 a total of 4,597 grey partridges were ringed in the former USSR but there were only 37 recoveries; 0.8 per cent compared to the 5 per cent obtained in Britain. The furthest movement was by an individual of the *lucida* sub species that was caught in April 1963 in the Vladimir Oblast, about 120 km east of Moscow, and re-caught in the autumn of the same year 430 km to the east of Vladimir (Litun, 1982a). One *Perdix perdix robusta* in the St Petersburg Zoological Museum, presumably from east of the Urals was found in central Poland (Roald Potapov and pers. obs.). These movements had some of the characteristics of Pallas' Sandgrouse irruptions and like them, they are no longer evident.

During 16–18 February 1972 a large batch of Daurian partridges was trapped and ringed in the Russian republic of Tuva, just to the west of the World Heritage Mongolian lake Uvs Nuur. In subsequent years some of these partridges were recovered up to 470 km to the northwest, in Khakasskaya on the upper Yenesey. The preceding movement south to Tuva was considered a response to deep snow. Astonishingly, to avoid the snow the partridge had to cross two mountain ranges with many peaks in excess of 2,000 m and the wintering area was just as cold, though without the deep snow (Litun, 1982a).

DIVERGENCE OF THE *PERDIX* SUB-SPECIES: THE GLACIATIONS

The reason for the separation of the eastern (grey) and western (brown) clades of grey partridges was tackled by Tuija Liukkonen and her colleagues working at the University of Oulu in Finland. Their mtDNA analyses showed that the eastern and western partridges differ by 2.2 per cent mutations in the control region of the mitochondria and 3.6 per cent in domain one of this control region (Liukkonen-Antilla *et al.*, 2002) – see map, Figure 36. For comparison the average difference is 4.3 per cent between species in the same genus (Kerr *et al.*, 2010) and the difference between red grouse and willow grouse has been put at 3.1 per cent (Lucchini *et al.*, 2001). Contrary to popular perception these percentage differences do not equate to real differences between species. Humans are sometimes said to have DNA sequences that are only ~1 per cent different from chimpanzees but this ignores the overriding importance of other parts of DNA not measured such as the switching mechanisms that turn genes on or off. It is the structure of the genome that counts, not only the genes.

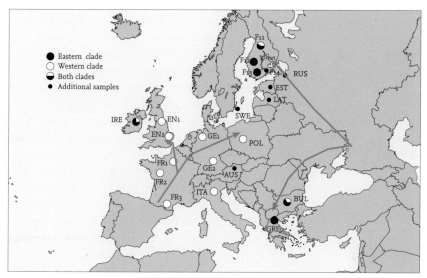

FIG 36. The distribution of genetic variation in the grey partridge: mitochondrial DNA (D loop), showing the eastern (grey) and western (brown) haplotypes, from Liukkonen-Antilla *et al.* (2002).

At one time a rate of 1 per cent mutation (substitution) per million years (Myr) per lineage (or a 2 per cent divergence) was used for birds and this led the Oulu team to estimate that the separation of the two groups of partridges took place 1.1 million years ago. Domain one of the control region differed more, by 3.6 per cent, but it evolves faster (Baba *et al.*, 2001), indicating a divergence about 173,000 years ago. A different approach to the data based on the genes that tend to be inherited together (haplotypes) led to an estimate of 385,000 years ago. We therefore have three different estimates from two parts of the mtDNA!

As indicated earlier, evolution is now known to proceed more rapidly than formerly assumed and the inadequacies of the 1 per cent mutation rule per lineage (the 2 per cent divergence rule) are becoming apparent.

A much higher rate of 7 per cent mitochondrial mutations per lineage per Myr was long ago advocated for grouse by Drovetski *et al.* (2003) and a unique study of the Adélie penguin entire mtDNA genome supports this faster rate. MtDNA extracted from ^{14}C dated specimens preserved in the Antarctic ice enabled direct comparison of birds as old as 44,000 years with living birds (Subramanian *et al.*, 2009). It turns out mutation rates in the control region within species (not between species) are likely to be in the range 5–7 per cent per Myr per lineage. A 6 per cent per Myr rate for the grey partridge would date the separation of western and eastern grey partridges at 183,000 years ago, very close to the University of Oulu's estimate based on domain one but far less than the 1.1 million years estimated using the 2 per cent divergence rule. Importantly the more recent date fits the Saalian glaciation; the most extensive glaciation ever recorded in Europe. This was not the most severe glaciation in the UK (where the Saalian is known as the Wolstonian) but in Eastern Europe a wide deep tongue of glacial ice reached Kiev in the Ukraine. It is clear this would have been sufficient to effectively separate the eastern and western clades. The western clade can be presumed to have survived mainly in the Iberian Peninsula, with the eastern clade doing so south of the Caucasus Mountains.

RESPONSE OF THE GREY PARTRIDGE TO THE MOST RECENT GLACIATION

The most recent Pleistocene glaciation (known as the Devensian in the UK) may not have separated the western and eastern clades but there can be no doubt that the species was driven out of Britain for about 10,000 years. During that time the fossil record shows the species concentrated in northern Spain, southern France and Italy (Fig. 37).

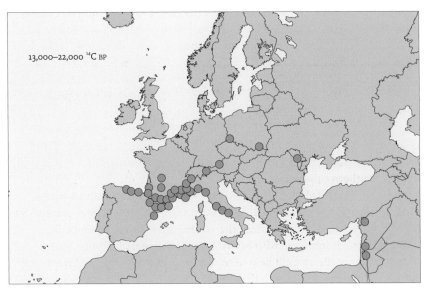

13,000–22,000 ^{14}C BP

FIG 37. The distribution of radiocarbon-dated grey partridge during the most recent glaciation; well to the south of the current range (see Fig. 1) (from Tyrberg, 1998 *et seq.*).

FIG 38. Spring census of grey partridge in the Pyrenees by students from the University of Lleida, Catalonia. (Jesus Nadal)

The most northern record during the Devensian is from Silesia 17,450 years ago, where the partridges were found co-existing with capercaillie, willow grouse and black grouse. There are other similar records to the east (southeast Poland, Moldova, see Fig. 37) yet at the time these areas were on the edge of the zone known as the steppe-like steppe-tundra during a period of intense cold when permafrost extended to the latitude of central France (Adams & Faure, 1997) and mammoths were found as far south as Granada in Spain (Álvarez-Lao & Garcia, 2011).

Turning to the southern range margin, the fact that the grey partridges were distributed so far south suggests the northern sub-species that moved south must have had contact with the southern sub-species *P. p. hispaniensis* in Spain, *P. p. italica* in Italy and *P. p.canescens* in Turkey. If the northern and southern sub-species had a continuous distribution they would have interbred and the southern sub-species will have been geographically separated for only about 13,000 years. Differences in their amino acids indicate a divergence of *hispaniensis* ~150,000 years ago (Blanc *et al.*, 1986). How the southern sub-species could have remained separate from the northern for such a long period when polar bears interbred with brown bears is a mystery but once again a faster-track evolution would help to resolve the issue. The extent of the mystery has recently been reduced with the validity of the Italian sub-species not supported by recent investigations of mtDNA in museum skins (Randi *et al.*, 2003, and *in litt.*).

The fossil record is so poor outside Western Europe that we do not know how far the eastern races of the grey partridge and the Daurian partridge moved south; it would be fascinating, say, if they reached India.

By about 14,000 ^{14}C BP, conditions had improved sufficiently to enable modern humans to thrive in Britain (Yalden & Albarella, 2009). The grey partridge followed but rather later. By 12,630 ^{14}C BP, it had reached the Ardennes in Belgium, with the first known return to Britain in the Mendip Hills of Somerset 12,370 ^{14}C BP. The species thus crossed the land bridge to England about 1,600 years after modern humans, missing the woolly mammoth by only ~400 years. Importantly, the move to Britain occurred more than 5,000 years before cereals began to be cultivated. The oft quoted scenario that the grey partridge came here with agriculture is therefore incorrect. As we have seen, it was here 475,000 years ago. In contrast the SW England–SE Ireland land bridge was severed before the arrival of grey partridges in England and unlike the Irish mountain hare or Irish red grouse, which are distinct sub-species, there is no clear evidence that the partridge reached Ireland naturally.

THE ENGLISH PARTRIDGE

Supporting evidence that the grey partridge has been present continually in Britain for 12–13,000 years came in 2011. Samples of DNA taken from partridges on three widely separated localities: Raby in County Durham, northwest Norfolk and the Norfolk Estate in the Sussex Study area, analysed at the University of Oulu, revealed no detectable difference in mt DNA. Their DNA was however markedly different from that in all samples from France, the Ukraine, Finland (wild and captive), Greece and Bulgaria. Moreover the analyses point to numbers being low at some point prior to the separation of England and France; the heterozygosity index is low as measured by the Garza-Williamson index (the number of alleles [one of two copies of genes] divided by the allelic range) indicating what is known as a 'bottlenecked population' (Tuija Liukkonen, *in litt.*).

For generations many people in England have referred to the grey partridges in Britain as 'English' and the red-legged partridge as 'French', without realising there were more English partridges in France than in England. Now it doesn't matter how many are overseas and we can use 'English' with some justification!

The variety of partridge known as *Perdix perdix* var. *montana* is another indicator of geographical variation being found only in the range of the western (brown) clade. It seems to have been the result of a recessive gene mutation arising in the mountains of Lorraine in the very early Holocene, with birds

FIG 39. *Perdix perdix* var. *montana*. Hand-coloured lithograph by J. G. Keulemans from Ogilvie-Grant (1895).

FIG 40. *Perdix perdix* var. *montana*, somewhat like red grouse, Tring, London Natural History Museum.

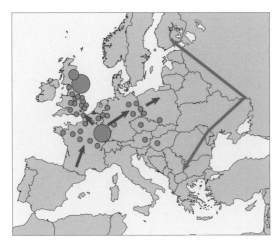

FIG 41. The distribution of *Perdix perdix* var. *montana* showing that all records are within the western clade (sources include Orts-Anspach & Dalimer, 1954, and see Potts 1986).

containing the mutation spreading to Britain before the land bridge was severed, with an astonishing concentration in Northumberland near Morpeth (see map, Fig. 41). The two last known examples were shot near Morpeth in 1979 and in Cleveland in 1984; the variety is apparently extinct.

THE GENUS *ALECTORIS*: SPECIES AND SUPER-SPECIES

There are seven species in this genus: Arabian partridge (*A. melanocephala*); Barbary partridge (*A. barbara*); Philby's partridge (*A. philbyi*); chukar partridge (*A. chukar*); rock partridge (*A. graeca*); Przevalski's partridge (*A. magna*) and red-legged partridge (*A. rufa*). The last four produce natural fertile hybrids where their ranges overlap (Bernard-Laurent & Boev, 1997; Petrov *et al.*, 1969) and thus may form a super-species. None of these species has occurred naturally in Britain. The only extinct species is *A. peii* from the middle Pleistocene of China.

Red-legged partridge

It is surprising that the red-legged partridge never occurred naturally in mainland Britain during the warmer inter-glacials and there is even doubt about its provenance in the Channel Islands; it used to be known as the Guernsey partridge. As we have seen, the grey partridge range was shifted as far south as the Dead Sea in the Devensian glaciation, so one might expect that the red-legged partridge would have occurred further north than it does now when the climate was warmer than now. There are a few fossil *Alectoris* from the Holocene as far north as the present Czech Republic, Hungary, the Crimea and Lake Balkash in Kazakhstan but the vast majority are well within the present distribution (Jánossy, 1994). It is possible some of these were due to early introductions; Odoric of Pordenone reports 4,000 partridges being taken from Venice to Trebizond (northeast Turkey) in 1316. Probable rock partridges were introduced to the Mosel region of Germany (just east of Luxembourg) where they apparently were well established until the later nineteenth century, at which time they also disappeared from most of Austria. Red-legged partridges from France were introduced to Britain in 1673, in the reign of Charles II.

The molecular phylogeny of the seven species of *Alectoris* has been investigated for two decades principally by Professor Ettore Randi, now Director of Research at the Istituto Superiore per la Protezione e la Ricerca Ambientale (ISPRA), Bologna, and his colleagues. They announced the early exciting results at Fordingbridge in September 1991 during Perdix VI, the First International Symposium on partridges, quails and francolins (Randi *et al.*, 1992). At that time genetic relationships were estimated using variations in amino-acid structures (Gutierrez *et al.*, 1983; Blanc *et al.*, 1986). Ettore's analyses suggested that the Barbary partridge and chukar were sister species with an African ancestor. The next step was to examine mtDNA; first Cytochrome *B* (Randi *et al.*, 1996) and then D-loop (displacement loop or control region) (Randi *et al.*, 1998a). This time the evolutionary picture changed with the rock partridge and chukar as sister species and the red-legged partridge earlier than either (see discussion in Randi *et al.*, 1996; and Fig. 7 of Randi & Lucchini, 1998). Later investigations by Filippo Barbanera and colleagues at the University of Pisa that involved nuclear DNA finally showed the Rock partridge as the ancestor of both the chukar and the red-leg (Barbanera *et al.*, 2009). One event that needs to be fitted in to this phylogeny is the event known as the Zanclean flood which occurred about 5.3 million years ago filling the Mediterranean and separating partridge ancestors in North Africa from those in Europe. It has been calculated that the filling of the Mediterranean took place rapidly with the sea rising 10 m per day at the peak (Garcia-Castellanos *et al.*, 2009). This flood is a probable cause of the separation of the ancestors of the rock partridge in southern Europe from the Barbary–Arabian partridge ancestors that emerged in north Africa 5.9–6.4 million years ago (Randi & Lucchini, 1998). There are alternative views. First that *Alectoris* moved from Africa to Europe through the Straits of Gibraltar after the Zanclean flood. This does not place the rock partridge as ancestral; neither does an alternative 'journey' through Israel–Turkey. Whatever the solution, it has to account for the fact that the most ancient *Alectoris* in Europe is the rock partridge on Sicily (Randi *et al.*, 2003). It seems unlikely that geographical changes such as a much lowered sea-level at a time of maximum glaciation could have been sufficient for ancestral rock partridges to fly across a gap between Tunisia and Sicily, but it remains a possibility.

FIG 42. Red-legged partridge at the edge of a grouse moor in Scotland. Cold does not seem to bother them; note the hoar frost on this bird's mantle. (Harry Scott)

If the above picture (rock partridge ancestral) is accepted there are serious issues with the fossil record. For example, 54 fossil Barbary partridge have been recorded in mainland Europe (Tommy Tyrberg, updated website). The range included: southeast Spain (it still exists in, or was introduced to Gibraltar); Italy (it still exists on Sardinia or was introduced there) and France as far north as the Dordogne. This raises the question of why it became extinct in mainland Europe so late: sometime during the past 10,000 years (Tyrberg, 1996) just as the red-legged partridge was spreading from its glacial refugia (Ferrero *et al.*, 2011). There is no easy answer here, unless Antonio Sánchez Marco is right. From the Catalan Institute of Paleontology, Barcelona, he writes: 'Concerning *Alectoris rufa, barbara* and *graeca*: in some of my papers I "identified" *A. rufa*. With time, I've gained more experience and self-confidence. Now I'm sure that these species (or whatever they are) can't be distinguished on osteological features. So, in my opinion, all the fossil remains attributed to *Alectoris* should be referred as *Alectoris sp.* (in Morocco, Portugal, Spain, France, Italy, etc.)'. This is surely the correct approach and Tyrberg had doubted whether the closely related species *rufa, graeca* and *chukar* could be separated from bones (Tyrberg, 1996). Rock partridges (*Alectoris graeca*), accounting for 46 per cent of the *Alectoris* fossils, are far more numerous in the fossil record than one would expect from their small current range and given, for example, records from Kazakhstan and Uzbekistan. As we have seen in the introduction this is attributable to a now superseded use of the name *Alectoris graeca*.

The introductions of red-legged partridges into England involved the French sub-species; *Alectoris rufa rufa*, not *A. r. hispaniensis* which is more colorful with a darker necklace and stronger bill. The first birds were imported from Chambord in the Loire valley and released in Windsor Great Park, but they soon died out. By around 1790 the species was established on the Suffolk coast but despite this early date red-legged partridges remained uncommon in England until the late 1950s, probably kept so by shooting pressure. This species was shot heavily, along with the much more numerous grey partridges, and as these shooting pressures declined, red-legged partridges increased (Potts, 1980). Beginning in 1964, and becoming widespread in the 1980s, rearing for shoots developed on such a scale as to obscure the bird's more natural status as well as its origins.

Chukar partridge

Today the chukar has a much greater world range than the red-legged partridge: almost 12 million km^2 extending from Greece virtually to Korea, including 11 sub-species. Barbanera *et al.* (2009) have described two clades, A and B (Fig. 43). It is astonishing that some of the introductions to Western Europe were from the eastern 'Clade B', from China. Chukars from Pakistan were also very successfully introduced to the western mountain states of the US, Hawaii and New Zealand (Christensen, 1970).

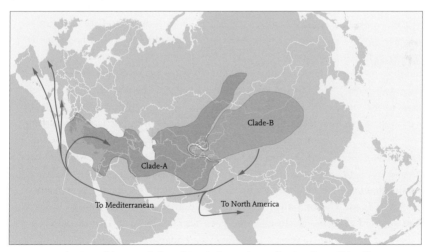

FIG 43. Distribution of the two clades of the chukar and introduction from China (from Barbanera *et al.*, 2009).

The
chukar
problem

Distinguishing features of the chukar (left) and pure redleg (right). Hybrid features are intermediate between the two.

FIG 44. Educating hunters about difference between chukar and red-legged partridges: illustration from *Shooting Times* magazine, December 1988.

In 1970 and for a number of years thereafter hundreds of chukars originally from a source in Italy were released from a game farm on the Sussex Downs. Some ornithologists at first reported these birds as rock partridges (see *British Birds*, 65, 404–5), but this species has never been released into the British countryside. Also increasingly, many of these released birds were chukar hybrids, in particular an F1 hybrid chukar x red-leg known as the OGridge (after Ormesby Game farm in Lincolnshire). From 1970 to 1985 the number of *Alectoris rufa*, *A. chukar* and *A. chukar x rufa* hybrids released in the UK increased 12-fold with the percentage of estates releasing these birds annually increasing from 4 per cent to 24 per cent. It is important however that the hybrid mating mainly took place on game farms. From a game-farm standpoint the chukar has several advantages over the red-legged partridge, particularly a much higher egg production.

As part of the Sussex study I recorded 992 pairs of *Alectoris* during 1971–75, and judged from their general appearance that both birds in 249 pairs appeared to be *A. rufa*; both birds in 692 pairs were *A. chukar*, with only 51 mixed pairs. The overall proportions of the two species gave an expected 398 mixed pairs with random pairing, a highly significant difference (Potts, 1980).

TABLE 1. Breeding success of red-legged and chukar compared; Coveys on stubbles Sussex Downs in 1971 and 1972 and on ten estates across southern England in 1988

coveys on stubbles	composition of pairs	old	young	young per old
(a) Sussex Downs	red-legged	316	239	0.76
	with 1 or 2 chukar	398	54	0.14
(b) Southern England	red-legged	483	552	1.14
	with 1 or 2 chukar	767	253	0.33

Many surveys were carried out by the GWCT and these showed that 'native' red-legs bred three to five times better than the introduced chukar hybrids and mixed pairs (Table 1). Since the vast majority of both groups were reared and released the disparity was attributed to differences in their origin and a ban on the releasing of chukar and hybrids eventually became effective in 1992. Given that pen-reared chukars, hybrids and red-legged partridges tended to mate strongly with their own kind, have a poor breeding success and lack of survival 'fitness' (Casas *et al.*, 2011), it is not surprising that the present day red-legged partridges in Sussex show no external sign of long-term adverse effects of the chukar releases (Fig. 45). There has been no sign of chukars or hybrids in Sussex for more than a decade and on the Norfolk Estate wild red-legged partridges are breeding extremely well with a high rate of double-brooding (see Fig. 91).

Chukars and hybrids have been released throughout the range of the red-legged partridge with 21 per cent of samples from the native range indicating chukar introgression (Barbanera, 2009, 2010).

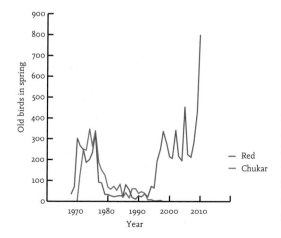

FIG 45. Numbers of red-legged and chukar partridge (including hybrids) older than one year in the Sussex Study area during 1968–2010. The releasing of chukar and hybrids was banned from 1992.

THE ANCESTORS OF *PERDIX* AND *ALECTORIS*

It is only seventeen years (1995) since the discovery of the feathered tree-dwelling dinosaurs in China and in that time there has been an enormous surge in interest in the evolution of birds. Studies based on the DNA molecule have transformed our understanding of the evolution of gamebirds, whereas studying evolution from fossils is a bit like trying to complete a jigsaw puzzle with most of the pieces missing and no picture on the box. However, a group led by Professor Tim Crowe based at the Percy Fitzpatrick Institute of African Ornithology, University of Cape Town, rose to the challenge of reconciling the DNA and fossil records. The results published in a landmark paper in the Journal *Cladistics* in 2006 by Tim and co-authors including Ettore Randi, mentioned earlier, clearly resolved the ancestry of *Alectoris* but the origins of *Perdix* were as obscure as ever. Using the mixture of DNA data, morphology, behaviour and geography, Crowe *et al.* put the *Alectoris* partridges firmly in the Coturnicinae, an essentially Afro-Asian group that includes the present day common, Japanese and Chinese quails, snow cocks and spur fowls.

In 2009 Nikita Zelenkov, at the Paleontological Institute, Moscow, quantified 11 characteristics from the important bones of 17 Phasianid genera, 6 of which are extinct (Zelenkov, 2009). My own correlation analysis of the data given by Zelenkov

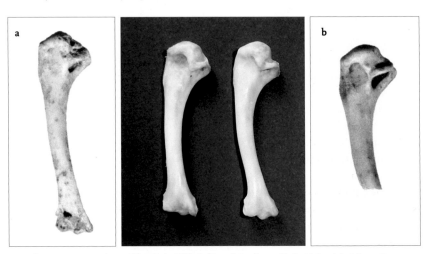

FIG 46. Humerus: modern *Alectoris* (middle left) and *Perdix perdix* (middle right) from Sussex Study compared to those of two *Palaeocryptonyx donnezani* from Spain older than one million years (a and b from Sánchez Marco, 2009, Fig. 2.). On twelve bone characters the fossils are close to both *Alectoris* and *Perdix*.

FIG 47. Blood pheasants, Daocheng, Sichuan; DNA suggests a common ancestor with *Perdix*. (Wang Nan)

suggests that the best fit of modern *Perdix* partridge to an extinct bird is found with the ancient partridge *Palaeocryptonyx* (Fig. 46) a fascinating bird we return to later. The bones of *Alectoris* are however also very similar.

The evolutionary position of *Perdix* was unresolved in the work of Crowe *et al.* partly because there were at the time no data for the Tibetan partridge. With the DNA of the Tibetan partridge analyzed, as mentioned earlier, Bao *et al.* (2010) were able to show that *Perdix* belonged not to the *Coturnicinae* quails but to the true pheasants with a possible sister relationship to the blood pheasant. This last species has a short tail with an upright stance and some very *Perdix*-like behaviour, although it uses trees some of the time and is far more likely to scratch for food. This closeness to the pheasants is strongly supported by Zelenkov's study of bones. However, given that the best fit of *Perdix* to an extinct species is with *Palaeocryptonyx*, could this be the ancestor of *Perdix*?

Palaeocryptonyx was first described by Depéret (1887, 1892) on the basis of Pliocene fossil 'quails' found in the Pyrenees near Perpignan, with *P. donnezani* the dominant species (see Fig. 33). The closeness to *Perdix* has caused confusion; for example, a right metacarpus that was first listed as from *Palaeocryptonyx donnezani* was in fact from *Perdix perdix* (Mlíkovský, 1995). The nomenclature of extinct *Alectoris* is also a vexed issue. There is for example a 13 million year gap between the first fossil *Alectoris, A. bavarica*, described from Germany on the basis of the end of a single metatarsus (lower leg) (Ballman, 1969) and the origin of the genus about 6 million years ago based on the DNA evidence (Randi & Lucchini, 1998). Furthermore Mlíkovský (2002) bundled four fossil genera from the Pliocene to early Pleistocene – *Chauvireria, Plioperdix, Paleocryptonyx* and *Alectoris* – into one new species: *Alectoris donnezani*. A wholesale revision is clearly necessary based on a modern re-examination of all the material. In the meantime it is important to recognise that at least from the early Pliocene, several genera of partridges appear to have been numerous with a very wide distribution including Germany, Poland, the Czech and Slovak Republics, Hungary, Romania, Moldova and the Ukraine in addition to the present range.

The genus *Palaeocryptonyx* with six recognised species occurred from Spain to Eastern Europe through an extraordinarily long 11 million years from the mid-Miocene (Pavia *et al.*, 2012). Although the name *Palaeocryptonyx* is derived from *Cryptonyx*, an old name for the black wood-partridge currently found deep in the tropical forests of Malaysia, no relationship between the two is known. In France *Palaeocryptonyx donnezani* survived until the early Pleistocene, and in Spain *P. novaki* was present even later (Sánchez Marco, 2009). These species would therefore have co-existed with *Perdix* and so could not qualify as an ancestor. Several million years earlier, *Palaeocryptonyx hungaricus*, from its bones with a size and ground-living lifestyle like that of the Daurian partridge had inhabited the dry grasslands of Hungary (Jánossy, 1991).

Prior to the DNA work, Birkan and Jacob (1988) had portrayed *Palaeoperdix* as the ancestor of *Perdix*, as its name suggests should be the case. This genus was first described by Milne-Edwards (1869–71) from Sansan in the Massif Central of France, where it lived around 13–15 million years ago. The known range extended to Spain and Kazakhstan but the genus became extinct by about 5 million years ago. The presence in the male *Palaeoperdix* of a spur (Zelenkov, 2009), one of the characters not found in *Perdix*, and several other skeletal structures point to the ruffed pheasants as being the nearest living relatives (Cheneval, 2000) not *Perdix*.

At about the same period – the mid-Miocene – a partridge named *Palaeoalectoris songlinensis* was found in Jiangsu, Sihong, China (Hou, 1987), but described only from two fragments of bone: the ends of a left ulna and a left metatarsus. If the bird really was an ancestor of *Alectoris* it quashes the 'out of Africa' hypothesis. It would however take more than a couple of bone fragments to do that. Another misfit *Palaeoalectoris* in Nebraska is now accepted to have been an extinct prairie grouse.

The partridge, *Plioperdix ponticus* was widespread from the early Pliocene of the southern Ukraine to the late Pliocene of Trans-baikalia and northern Mongolia (Zelenkov & Kurochkin, 2009). Somewhat like a sand partridge this bird would probably have co-existed with *Perdix margaritae* and with the *Perdix* ancestor that moved onto the steppes of the Tibetan plateau before it was raised. A sister species, *Plioperdix africana*, occurred in Morocco when it was steppe grassland (Mourer-Chauviré & Geraards, 2010b). *Plioperdix* occurred too late to be an ancestor of *Perdix*.

Finally we should mention *Palaeortyx*. This was an important genus of forest quails that first appeared in the late Oligocene. These birds were widespread in the Miocene with fossils reported from France (many), Spain, Italy, Germany, Czechoslovakia and southwest Africa. Some later species may have been migratory. Fully articulated skeletons are very rare in the fossil record but a virtually complete *Palaeortyx gallica* from central Germany has been dated to 25 million years ago (Mayr *et al.*, 2006). Almost certainly ground feeding but roosting in trees, this bird was about halfway between a modern *Coturnix* quail and a modern *Perdix* in size, perhaps with a life-style like the present day Hill partridges of southeast Asia (Ballman, 1969). Like hill partridges, *Palaeortyx* had no spurs, the gizzard contained grit typical of a modern partridge and the skull was very partridge-like (Mayr *et al.*, 2006). Grit is well known from dinosaurs but this record of grit is the earliest in any phasianid. An early *Palaeortyx* was probably near to an ancestor of *Palaeocryptonyx*.

A MYSTERY?

We began this review by asking two questions: what are the most likely nearest extinct relatives to *Perdix* and *Alectoris*? And what is their most recent common ancestor? We have seen that the grey partridge and Daurian partridge ancestor diverged from the Tibetan partridge about 3.6 million years ago so it is obvious that the *Perdix* ancestor must be older than this, and a lot older than the oldest known fossil, *Perdix margaritae*, dated at about 2.5 million years ago.

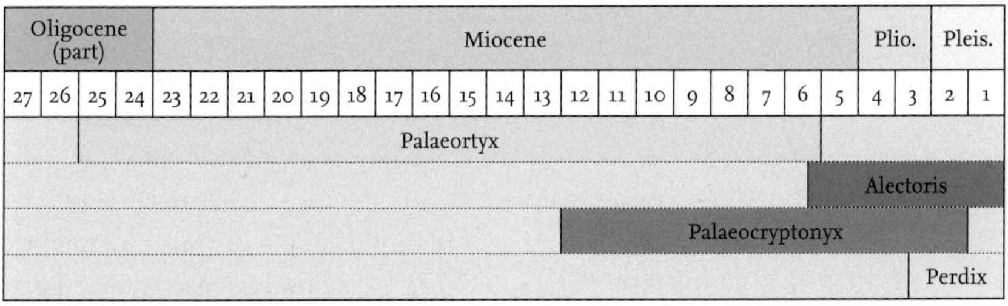

Oligocene (part)				Miocene																		Plio.	Pleis.
27	26	25	24	23	22	21	20	19	18	17	16	15	14	13	12	11	10	9	8	7	6	5	4	3	2	1

Palaeortyx

Alectoris

Palaeocryptonyx

Perdix

(Plio. = Pliocene; Pleis. = Pleistocene)

FIG 48. A hypothetical time-line (millions of year BP) of the evolution of *Alectoris* and *Perdix* and related genera based on fossils and current DNA-based estimates of divergences.

Conversely the oldest fossil *Alectoris* is the *A. bavarica* already mentioned and dated at 19 million years ago in southern Germany (Ballman, 1969). This cannot be reconciled with the well-supported DNA evidence of an origin of *Alectoris* in Africa 5.9–6.4 million years ago from a francolin-like stock (Randi & Lucchini, 1998; Crowe *et al.*, 2006). These dates are compared in the time-line diagram (Fig. 48). It is clear that *Alectoris* has a more ancient origin than *Perdix*. Is it therefore possible that *Perdix* is an offshoot from *Alectoris*? This is not likely because the *Perdix* ancestors lived in the area now occupied by the Tibetan plateau, and it is difficult to see how *Alectoris* would get there about four million years ago from Africa. The chukar that eventually did so only originated 1.8–2.0 million years ago in the eastern Mediterranean countries (Randi & Lucchini, 1998), i.e. long after *Perdix*.

We can speculate that the ancestors of the *Perdix* that spread to the Tibetan plateau about four million years ago (before it was raised) may have diverged about 5–7 million years ago from a stock of birds near *Palaeocryptonyx hungaricus*.

At the present time we cannot answer the second question; all we can do is suggest that the nearest common ancestor is earlier than *Palaeocryptonyx* and probably a contemporary of *Palaeortyx* (Fig. 48) or possibly an African ancestor of the huge group of African francolins. Despite the speculation it is certain the *Perdix* and *Alectoris* lines have been separate for about 20 million years. Later we see there is further evidence for this from their different parasites. Although separate for so long the two lines have evolved largely in parallel, at times converging. For example, where they now occur together they feed on the same food species. The main message here is one of extraordinary resilience and adaptability.

CLIMATE CHANGE

The two genera of partridges have been separate for perhaps 20 million years and although they are superficially similar there are many differences, as we saw in Chapter 1, that determine their different geographical distributions. It is clear grey partridges live in areas that are further north than the *Alectoris* species but the relationships with climate are complex. For example, in captivity chukars prefer ambient temperatures in the range 25–31°C (Laudenslager & Hammel, 1977), whereas grey partridges are as stressed by 30°C as they are by -30°C (Branković *et al.*, 1967). Yet the food consumption in both species increases the same two-fold between +15°C and -15°C, so despite the different preferences they are adapting in the same way to temperature (11 investigations in Potts, 1986, for the grey partridge and the study of Warren & Clark, 1986, for the chukar). Chukars are in fact highly adaptable regarding temperature, found on the Tibetan plateau at altitudes from 1,200 to 5,000 m (Cheng *et al.*, 1983), though like the Daurian partridge not able to deal with much snow (Kuz'mina, 1992). Climate limits partridges in many subtle ways, as will become apparent in subsequent chapters, and we will see that the links between climate and suitability of the habitat is not as straightforward in partridges as some of the global warming predictions have suggested.

Huntley *et al.* (2007) made a series of predictions of the late twenty-first-century distribution of partridges in Europe based on assumptions about climate change. Most of Spain would, they say, become unsuitable for the red-legged partridge but it was considered that the Barbary partridge (of North Africa) would have 'no potential future in Europe' even though it is already in Sardinia and Gibraltar. Instead the chukar would predominate in Spain, although how it would travel from Turkey to Spain is not explained, especially when it did not do so in the warmest interglacials. In fact at the present time the grey partridge is expanding its range in southeast Turkey (Kirwan *et al.*, 2008) and in Nebraska, both places at the southernmost edge of its global distribution. Meanwhile it is predicted that the species will not extend as far north as the Arctic Circle, yet it has been virtually there since the nineteenth century (Dementiev & Gladkov,

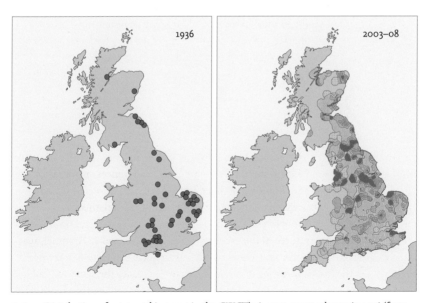

FIG 49. Distribution of estates taking part in the GWCT's August count scheme in 1936 (from Potts, 1977) and spring pair densities during 2003–08 (from Aebischer & Ewald, 2010).

1952). Turning to the situation in Britain there has been a remarkable shift, with the least severe declines of the grey partridge in the northern half of England. Maps prepared at the beginning of the GWCT's august count scheme show the best areas to be along an axis from Dorset to Norfolk, whereas recent analyses (2003–8) show they are now much further north (Fig. 49). There is however no suspicion that these changes have anything to do with climate change. In Sussex, where the decline has been as severe as anywhere, grey partridge are now virtually confined to the Sussex Study area and within that hugely concentrated on the Norfolk estate. The best grey partridge areas are in France way to the south.

It appears that predictions of range changes in partridges have put far too much emphasis on climate and far too little on other factors such as the developments in modern farming, to which we now turn.

CHAPTER 3

Going with the Grain

If the open landscapes are anthropogenic then where did all the species of open habitats live before man came along?

Sir Edward Salisbury, *Weeds and Aliens*, 1961

TODAY MOST *PERDIX* PARTRIDGES live on arable farmland, and *Alectoris* partridges benefit from arable crops, grazing of mountain pastures and water supplies for crop irrigation.

Both species therefore largely depend on so called artificial habitats that have existed for less than 15,000 years, less than 0.5 per cent of the time these partridges have been on Earth. Where did they and the other species that today share their habitats with them live before agriculture? If not dependent on farmers, what governed their abundance? What did they eat and how much did they have to change to thrive on farmland? Finally, how did they cope when agriculture became more intensive and threatened to sweep the rug from under their feet?

It's a story that begins with the evidence that adult partridge diets consisted mainly of large seeded grasses (equivalent to grain, for example the foxtail millets) and weed seeds that did not originally owe their existence to agriculture; they were dependent on the mega-herbivores. After a long run with food supplies augmented by agriculture, weed seeds became much less abundant with the use of herbicides, and with modern combine harvesters waste grain became more difficult to find. The number of plant species found in the diet of partridges dropped by ~ 65 per cent during the twentieth century. Since the 1990s hopper feeding with grain has been adopted with great success. The *Alectoris* partridges also benefit from hopper feeding and, in hot dry areas, the provision of water. Against this background however, we will see that partridges use a wide variety of habitats.

FIG 50. Habitat created by extensive grazing by cattle and by the cultivation of cereals with a high density of Daurian partridges: Luliang Mountains, near Ningwu, China. What created partridge habitats before agriculture?

This chapter begins the search for an understanding of the needs of partridges that will enable us to overcome the difficulties presented by modern agriculture.

GREY PARTRIDGE HABITATS PRIOR TO AGRICULTURE

The former abundance of a steppe species now found almost entirely on farmland raises fundamental questions about the nature of the Pliocene–Pleistocene countryside and of habitats existing prior to agriculture. We can estimate the type of habitat partridges encountered in Britain after the last glaciation by considering some other species known to be present and when we do so, we find evidence of many open-country species. After excluding some dubious archaeological layers (with admixtures of domestic fowl, pheasant or turkey), there are 17 reliable records of partridges in England between 12,370 BP and 10,000 BP (Tyrberg, 1998 *et seq.*; Yalden & Albarella, 2009). Eleven of the finds are associated with grassland species such as the skylark and meadow pipit but all are associated with the red grouse that today is dependent on heath and peat-bog communities. Is it possible that the red grouse was then not confined to heather, occupying steppe grasslands somewhat like the willow grouse in Kazakhstan found nesting in cereal fields (Uly'anen, 1949; Kuz'mina, 1992)?

Eleven of the 17 fossil *Perdix* records from England were in layers where fossil ptarmigan were also found. The ptarmigan is currently a high-altitude or tundra bird but it once had a much wider distribution through lowland Europe (Tyrberg, 1995). Since the most recent glaciation the species has retreated from all but the highest mountains of Europe, as discussed by Yalden & Albarella (2009). At one time the willow grouse and ptarmigan had rather similar distributions with willow grouse ranging as far south as southern Italy and the Crimea. We do not know what its requirements were at this time; maybe it too was then a steppe species, filling a niche something like that of the sharp-tailed grouse in North America?

Today ptarmigan and the grey partridge are still found together in a few places in the Pyrenees but with the partridge mainly on south-facing slopes in the altitudinal range 1,400–2,500 m and the ptarmigan on cooler eastern slopes in the range 1,900–2,800 m. In one survey partridges were found at 22 sites and ptarmigan at 44 sites with both species at only 10 sites (Novoa & Gonzalez, 1988). The fact that the two species can occur so closely together reminds us once again that the grey partridge must have endured some very cold conditions in the past, for example during the Younger Dryas that started 11,000 years ago (*Dryas octopetala*, the mountain aven, was abundant in the lowlands). This period was undoubtedly very cold (Blois *et al.*, 2010) with a small ice cap over the Scottish mountains (Yalden & Albarella, 2009). Reindeer, mountain hares and lemmings were found right across England, yet it appears that the grey partridge also managed to survive. The Russian biologist Professor Formozov (1946) was curious about how species of tundra and steppe had apparently co-existed in the later Pleistocene. Explaining how grazing woolly mammoths were vulnerable to snow, he concluded that the explanation was the extreme dryness that kept the landscapes relatively free of snow. Provided there is some snow for snow-hole roosting, if food is plentiful partridges can certainly withstand extreme cold and by breaking ice crusts mammoths made food more available to grouse and probably grey partridges. Grey partridges have survived remarkable changes in climate. The Younger Dryas ended suddenly with an 8°C rise in mean July temperature in Britain in 50 years (Dansgaard *et al.*, 1989). The studies of the reaction of grey partridges to temperature change mentioned earlier (p. 62) should be repeated for *Alectoris* partridges. In the meantime it appears they are less tolerant of cold and certainly more tolerant of heat.

More detail about the pre-agriculture habitats occupied by the grey partridge in Europe can be obtained by examining their 'fossil' distribution with that of willow/red grouse and quail. The total of fossil layer records for all three species is 1,536, with red/willow grouse accounting for 37 per cent, grey partridge 40 per cent and quail 23 per cent. The probability of grey partridge and willow/red grouse randomly occurring in the same layer is 14.8 per cent (175 of 1,182), almost the same as the observed 166 (Table 2). In Britain at the time, all the grey partridges were found in layers with fossil red grouse, so why should grey partridges be found near red grouse habitats in Britain but not near willow grouse habitats in Europe as a whole? We do not know, but comparison with the quail is revealing. The probability of grey partridge and quail randomly occurring together is 9.2 per cent (of the 961 specimens see table); 88 compared to the observed 220. This indicates that in Europe as a whole the grey partridge tended to be found in quail habitats (relatively tree-less grasslands) where only 6 per cent of red/willow grouse were located ($P<0.001$).

The Mesolithic period, at the beginning of the Holocene, lasted more than 4,000 years, during which there are only three records of grey partridges in Britain but this is probably sufficient to show that the species persisted naturally. Supporting this hypothesis it is estimated from pollen records that a third of the Mesolithic countryside was open country (Yalden & Albarella, 2009) probably suitable for grey partridges. These natural open ecosystems supported not just

TABLE 2. Overlap in Pleistocene habitats of red/willow grouse, grey partridge and European quail, compiled from Tyrberg listings.

	red/willow grouse	grey partridge	European quail
grouse alone	388 (67.5%)	0	0
partridge alone	0	292 (48.1%)	0
quail alone	0	0	113 (31.9%)
grouse and partridge	95	95	0
grouse partridge and quail	71	71	71
partridge and quail	0	149	149
grouse and quail	21	0	21
Totals	575	607	354

the partridge but the great bustard, lapwing, larks, pipits and buntings. The fossil record certainly shows they were all present before agriculture. As we have seen, convincing DNA evidence suggests the grey partridge was in Britain long before it was separated from France. All this evidence leads to the conclusion that grey partridges did not immigrate to Europe from the Near East with farming as is sometimes argued (e.g. Glänzer, 1984; Toso & Cattadori, 1993). In any case as we saw earlier, the grey partridge was in England during several interglacial periods.

From this we can conclude that the grey partridge tended to occupy drier, warmer steppe grasslands of the kind that are today occupied in summer by quail, although with a notable presence on the edge at least of cooler, damper grazed heaths, blanket bogs and raised peat-bogs that have been or still are occupied by willow/red grouse and to a lesser extent ptarmigan and black grouse. One sub species of grey *Perdix p. sphagnetorum* was adapted to living on the raised *Sphagnum* bogs and heaths of Belgium and the Netherlands (Peus, 1929). There are current examples of grey partridge and willow/red grouse breeding more or less together along the edge of grouse moors in Britain, in western Finland, in Northern Belarus, in Russia and in parts of Kazakhstan. In the Pyrenees *Perdix p. hispaniensis* is found in mountain and subalpine shrub-lands with broom, box, juniper and bearberry, whereas in the northern Iberian and Cantabrian mountains heathers (*Calluna* and *Erica*), various brooms and bilberry predominate (Lucio *et al.*, 1992). All these habitats can be described as 'open' with grasses, but with huge variations.

MAINTENANCE OF OPEN HABITATS

The open or shrubby habitats used by partridges were at one time widely presumed to be early successional ecosystems created by the felling of trees, or by burning or browsing and grazing of farm livestock; goats in the case of the Shrub Steppe. However, in an earlier volume in this series Sir Edward Salisbury pointed out that weeds do not owe their existence to the 'conditions created by man'. His examples included several species such as the *Polygonums* that are favoured by partridges. For the obvious reason of cultivation, as we shall see, most arable weeds are annuals and the same goes for the species eaten by partridges. Where did partridges find this kind of food for the first few million years, or did they live on other food?

These are pertinent questions because there is a poor understanding of the factors that determined ancient vegetation cover below the natural tree-line. Even today simulations of the past global cover of forests based on soil characteristics, precipitation and other climate statistics are woefully inadequate, frequently predicting vastly more forest cover than is the case. The reason for this is that these models have not yet factored in the mega-herbivores (Terborgh & Estes, 2010). Many open areas have always existed so that farmland today is in effect partially replacing many habitats created by the extinct mega-herbivores that effectively disappeared soon after the most recent ice age, in or around the Younger Dryas already mentioned.

As the mega-herbivores gradually disappeared hunting will have become much more difficult and the possibility that this was the trigger for agriculture has been the cause of heated debate. Either way it is clear that by around 10,000 years ago, cattle and goats and wheat and barley were beginning to be domesticated; with rice perhaps much earlier (Smith, 1995). The grey partridge exploited these changes in agriculture, at least until pesticides came along, so much so that in the nineteenth century Sir Alfred Newton found it to be the most common bird on farmland (Newton, 1861). As we have seen, the fossil evidence shows partridges to have been widespread and probably numerous in Europe for at least two million years.

Studies on the diet of *Alectoris* partridges have detailed the importance of grasses and grasshoppers, and all-year studies in the Alps (Bernard-Laurent 1986; Didillon, 1988) emphasised the importance of maintaining cattle grazing to ensure an adequate supply of food, otherwise the partridge habitats would eventually close up with dense shrubs and too many trees. This process is considered to be a main cause of the decline of the rock partridge in Italy (Rippa *et al.*, 2011). In the Cantabrian and Pyrenean mountains of Spain the widespread abandonment of cattle and sheep grazing has adversely affected both grey and red-legged partridges (Lucio *et al.*, 1996). Claude Novoa and colleagues made a particularly detailed study of the autumn diet of grey partridges in the eastern Pyrenees from 1980 to 1996 (Novoa *et al.*, 1999). A total of 75 plant taxa (species or genera) were identified from 94 birds shot, including many grasshoppers, various beetles (especially jewel beetles Chrysomelidae) and ants. The majority of the plant taxons were found to be characteristic of pastures grazed by cattle, for example meadow grasses, buttercups, dandelions, plantains, sorrel and *Polygonums*.

The feeding habits of partridges, on the ground, in the open, with a strong gizzard to break open plant cells and a large caecum (blind gut) to digest them, evolved to deal with a diet of grass and weed seeds. But, what maintained such open areas in the absence of farming? What could have restricted the thickets and woodlands and even tall grasses, and maintained open areas?

Francis Vera (2000), mainly in the Netherlands and Germany, and Oliver Rackham (2006) in Britain, examined these questions and the traditional view

FIG 51. Traditional grazing is important in maintaining open habitats in the absence of mega-herbivores: here by grey cattle in Hungary (left) and by yaks in China (right).

of closed-canopy forest as the climax vegetation through much of Europe. Vera reviewed a great deal of evidence and concluded that large areas of open grassland could arise from the grazing and browsing of large or very large (mega) herbivores in a way that actually sustained trees and savannahs. Vera considers that thorny shrubs protect tree seedlings from grazing during their early stages. It is a crucial part of his hypothesis that heavy grazing results in patches of herbivore-resistant thorny shrubs, precisely the nesting cover that the partridges need (Chapter 4). Examples are blackthorn, buckthorn, hawthorn, the thorny acacia-like pea-shrub and the brambles. The *Alectoris* species utilise various thorns including Christ's thorn, thorny acacias, the prickly kermes oak, and grazing resistant brooms.

Rackham looked at the pollen deposits, finding many species that do not tolerate shade, concluding that the original forest cover included many areas of open grassland. The pollen record from peat bogs in the vicinity of the Sussex Study area illustrates this with species such as *Chenopodium* and *Artemisia* that are normally found on disturbed soils in open landscapes (Tittensor, 1991). Similarly many species of beetle that were present would have depended on herbaceous flowers in sunny situations (Anderson *et al.*, 1993).

After examining Vera's evidence Rackham intriguingly concluded: 'Whatever may be said about the last ten thousand years, Vera's model works better for the previous interglacial.' This is exactly what one would expect, because few of the mega-herbivores were present after about 12,000 BP. The elephants, rhinoceroses, bison, wild horses, Irish elk, aurochs and many others had gone, or were going (e.g. Yalden & Albarella, 2009), so the forests would be more extensive than would otherwise be the case.

Allan Savory (1999), a legend in bush farming circles on several continents, has pointed out that the larger herbivores of open country naturally cause little damage to plants or soil while they are feeding. Once feeding is over however, the same herbivores herd together for safety from predators. He showed time and again how the disturbance to the soil created by the trampling of hooves was just as important as grazing and browsing and was vital to the breaking up of the soil surface to 'provide a good seed-bed for new plants'. The wolves, lions, cheetahs, wild dogs and hyenas were crucial in maintaining the tight herds and keeping their prey on the move. Allan Savory concludes: 'There was no other influence that could realistically have both created the necessary soil disturbance to provide a good seed bed for new plants and protect bare soil by trampling down old material.' In pristine environments natural fire would be less important in encouraging such species as the wild relative of the wild wheat, *Aegilops geniculata* known in Portugal as partridge grass, than it is today because grazing animals would limit the accumulation of tinder.

For most of their history partridges thus appear to have been dependent on now extinct herbivores and top predators: the mega fauna. These are the very animals that have suffered massive declines: in Africa (partial, beginning slowly around 400,000 years ago); Australia (40,000 years ago); North America (12,000 years ago); Madagascar and New Zealand (1,000 years ago). In each case the declines and extinctions occurred when these large slow-breeding animals first encountered modern humans. Less well known is the same phenomenon in Europe and Asia. The main colonising thrust of hominids, *Homo heidelbergensis*, reached central Europe and Britain about 500,000 ago. Spears were used as early as 400,000 years ago to kill horses (Thieme, 1997). There were, however, very few people and a severe decline of the mega fauna did not take place until the arrival of modern humans *Homo sapiens* in larger numbers. In Britain the early demise of large hyenas, followed by browsing rhinoceros, elephant and hippopotamus, may have had little to do with the arrival of humans. It is clear that northern cold-adapted species such as the musk ox, woolly rhinoceros and woolly mammoth retreated or became extinct mainly as a result of climate warming (Lorenzen *et al.*, 2011). On the other hand the catastrophic loss of giant deer, bison, wisent, wild horses, wild cattle and (further south) many elephant and other species certainly involved hunters (in Levy, 2011). This entire fauna that promoted savannah rather than closed-canopy forest was gone from Western Europe within a few thousand years.

Until recently many ecologists have failed to recognise man as a keystone predator with indirect impacts on the vegetation (Kay, 1998, 2009). This is important because very large animals are not much affected by predation, except by man. The maximum size of prey that can be killed by most predators in the Serengeti ecosystem is high relative to their own weight, especially when they hunt in packs. The larger predators appear most efficient when preying on animals about 1.5 times their own weight. Because the lion is the heaviest predator at 150 kg, such species as buffalo (500 kg) and giraffe are scarcely affected by predators and rhinoceros spp., hippopotamus and elephant (3,000 kg) rarely suffer predation as adults and only occasionally as juveniles (Sinclair, Mduma and Brashares, 2003). Thus the five top herbivores are not predator limited. They are food limited and can have a major impact on the flora.

The effects can be catastrophic when herbivore numbers are unnaturally high. For example, elephant populations lived in equilibrium with Baobab trees for centuries, though now in some areas they are destroying them and no natural regeneration can take place, a case being the Tarangire Reserve, Tanzania (pers. obs.). In the example of the Sussex savannahs of 475,000 BP the numerous elephantines, rhinoceros, bison, horse and giant deer would not have been controlled by the lion or wolf. The large herbivores would thus be the main factor determining the flora, creating habitats for the partridges.

Amongst predators man is of course the exception, for he alone can reduce the number of large herbivores and thus reduce browsing and grazing effects. As Charles Kay showed, the early Native Americans were not conservationists; they had a dramatic impact that limited the effects of herbivores more than the wolves and other carnivores had previously (Kay, 1998). One result was an increase in the number of man-caused fires. Large numbers of ungulates and large prairie fires are mutually exclusive because heavy grazing reduces standing plant biomass, prevents the accumulation of plant litter and creates discontinuous fuel patterns, all of which prevent the growth and spread of large fires. It was largely the irrepressible Ed Komarek of Tall Timbers Research Station at Tallahasse, Florida, who countered the Smokey Bear (no fires) campaign in the 1950s by showing the advantages of rotational controlled burning in preventing a build-up of tinder. It is a lesson not yet fully learned; in 2003 80 per cent of the disastrous fires in Portugal were said to be due to too little grazing and browsing and an absence of the alternative controlled burning. So what about the huge areas of Australia where rich fire-adapted floras benefit from fire, some of it natural. Could today's preponderance of fires be due to the loss of mega-herbivores? There were no elephants or bison but we know particularly from the Riversleigh Station excavations (Archer et al., 2000) that there was a very significant assemblage of cow-sized marsupials, particularly the diprotodontoids that died out around 35,000 BP. Some of these marsupials were the size of a hippopotamus (Johnson, 2006). As in other continents the cause of their demise was almost certainly hunting by man, maybe in combination with a natural disappearance of rain forest.

In summary by domesticating grazing animals and by clearing habitats for arable land, agriculture has maintained habitats partly created by the mega-herbivores.

THE NATURAL FOOD OF THE ADULT GREY PARTRIDGE

Today we cannot study the original natural habitat of the grey partridge, for there is nowhere on earth that has a full complement of mega-herbivores and top predators in its range and in consequence displays a truly natural flora. The area that comes nearest is probably the 88,000 ha Naurzumskii National Nature Reserve in northern Kazakhstan. Here the top-predator community is nearly intact, with both wolf and lynx present. Four species of eagle breed in the area, with the imperial eagle numerous and few harriers (Katzner *et al.*, 2005) – a subject we return to in Chapter 8. There are many small mammals and colonies of marmots, ground squirrels and pikas. The vegetation is a mosaic of grasses (feather grass, crested wheat grass and bunch grass), *Artemisia*, rose bushes and areas of pine woodland. Most of the grey partridges are found where the soil is sandy and the steppe grasses short. Although there are no mega-herbivores and few cattle, moose and wild boar are present and there had been some cattle and horses in the past. The reserve is now well known for research on the many eagles found there but one of the first studies was undertaken by Ul'yanin, who investigated the ecology of the black grouse, willow grouse and grey partridges in the 1930s. Ul'yanin died in World War II; fortunately his pioneering work was discovered and published (Ul'yanin, 1949).

FIG 52. Of all species of seeds eaten by the grey partridge the most important were those of the black bindweed.

FIG 53. (clockwise from top left) Three species of grasses important as grey partridge foods: green pigeon-grass (a wild millet); green pigeon-grass seeds (Strand Memorial Herbarium); cockspur grass; and annual meadow-grass in a wheat crop. The pigeon grasses and cockspur grasses have been used for making flour when cereals were unavailable. (Nigel Cattlin/FLPA)

The diet of 34 adult grey partridge collected between March and August of 1935 and 1936 by Ul'yanin was dominated by seeds of species of *Polygonum* and by white millet grain. Together these foods comprised more than half the diet (by volume). Some partridges had eaten only the white millet. Fifteen other species of plants were eaten but infrequently, including hawkweeds, vetches, crested wheat grass and bulbous-meadow/blue-grass, fescues, greater knapweed and the now endangered golden-yellow tulip. The main insect foods were short-horned grasshoppers and various ants. Only a tiny part of the area had been cultivated and the millet was growing wild. The pre-agricultural large grain grasses such as the wild millets and the other ancestors of the present day cereals are the key here. Humans fed partly on such grass seeds until agriculture started and presumably partridges did the same. As for other natural habitats, not very much is known about the food of grey partridges that occupied the raised bogs in Ireland but Kieran Buckley has seen coveys eating the seeds of the marsh arrow grass that is very common in damper parts of the cutaway (harvested) peat bogs.

The larger grain grasses were eaten commonly by people in Israel as early as 23,000 years ago (Weiss *et al.*, 2008). As we have seen (Chapter 2), grey partridges were there at the time and they surely must have fed on seeds of the same wild species: barley, emmer wheat and grasses such as the bromes with soft seed coats (caryopses). Wild millet gruel was a staple food for many people in Eastern Europe until the arrival of the potato, as was crabgrass (Behrendt & Hanf, 1979). Elsewhere many wild grass seeds are eaten by humans and partridges alike. For example, the main seed eaten by the chukar in Kashmir is a grass, *Eragrostis* (Oakleaf & Robertson, 1971), that is made into bread, as were the seeds of cockspur grass (Freedman, 2011). In fact so many wild seeds were utilised that the distinction between cereals and grasses becomes semantic.

Investigations of the remains of ancient seeds from Abu Hureyra, Syria, showed development of wild varieties of wheat and rye 13,000 years ago, with a gradual selection of cereals with larger seeds that did not shatter and so could be harvested (Hillman *et al.*, 2001). In Eurasia, 4 wild grasses out of a possible 33 (Blumler, 1992) were domesticated: wild barley, einkorn, emmer and the primitive wheat *Aegilops* (Evans, 1998). Some of these domesticated varieties, having originated east of the Mediterranean, were introduced into the UK by 6,000 BP, with the first known bread made in England about 5,500 years ago (Robinson, 1999). Grey partridges therefore selected many species that people have used as food, and palatability must be important; the *Polygonums*, fat hen and corn spurrey have all been made into gruels of one kind or another.

As far as the partridges are concerned all this evidence points to a gradual change in emphasis in the diet from species living in natural disturbed plant communities to species living in cereal fields.

Already by 6,000–9,500 years ago the floras of the earliest cereal fields in Iraq, Syria and Turkey somewhat resembled those found in Western Europe in the days before herbicides (Green, 1999; Wilcox, 1999). About 70 per cent of the species of weed in these earliest cereals have been found in the Sussex Study area and about half of them were frequently eaten by partridges prior to the use of herbicides. For their first few thousand years, over 99 per cent of their history, cereal fields appear to have represented ideal feeding grounds.

DAURIAN PARTRIDGE FOOD

In the Trans-Baikal region, in an area where herbicides had not been used, Vladimir Litun found that the Daurian partridges spent much of the spring and summer on the steppe but after the cereal harvest they switched to cereal stubble

TABLE 3. Daurian partridge: use of habitats in daytime in the Trans-Baikal; adapted from Litun & Flint (1993).

habitat	Daurian partridges per 100 ha in spring in daytime	Daurian partridges per 100 ha in autumn in daytime
steppe slopes with some birch	<20	20
steppe slopes with fescue-tansy, meadowsweet and some *Prunus*	8	53
steppe meadows with shrubs	7	14
unploughed stubbles	1	27

(Table 3), especially when feeding. Although these cereal stubbles amounted to only 10 per cent of the area, they supplied almost all of the bird's food through autumn and winter, which was predominantly the seeds of arable weeds (Prokoviev, 1975). The importance of the species was in order (by dry weight): field penny-cress, black bindweed, green pigeon-grass, pigweed and hemp nettle (Litun and Flint, 1993).

Daurian partridges are widely distributed in the north and northwest of China. A study has been made just to the west of Dongzhuang village, in Ningwu County, Shanxi, where there is a mosaic of steppe and oat fields at an altitude of 2,000 m (Zhang & Wu 1992) (Fig. 50). At the end of September 2005, 270 birds were counted on two evenings in an area of 500 ha. Towards sunset I found that they all gathered to feed on oat stubbles rather than on the surrounding steppe.

FIG 54. Field penny-cress (centre) in conservation headland on Norfolk Estate, Sussex Study area. Eaten by Daurian partridge but rarely by grey partridge.

The same appears to be the case in the natural grasslands of the Tibetan plateau, Mongolia and Russia, and indeed for partridges everywhere where cereals are grown. Even amongst the bogs of central Ireland, the *Perdix* partridges currently feed to a large extent on cereal stubbles. As we have seen, the decline of both *Alectoris* and *Perdix* partridges in many mountainous areas such as the Apennines, Alps and Pyrenees is often put down to the retreat of arable farming from the higher valleys and the consequent loss of cereals. As the habitats of the larger grain grasses and weeds of disturbed soils were adopted for agriculture, cereal crops became crucially important to partridges. Several studies were combined by Kuz'mina (1992) to produce a list of the food of 200 adult Daurian partridges indicating a diet similar to that reported by Litun & Flint (1993). However, in some dry remote areas, diets may yet be unaffected by agriculture and she writes about Daurian partridges in the dry Tian Shan mountains east of Almaty where 95 per cent of the diet (by volume) of 15 of 16 birds shot in September–October was, just like the *Alectoris* partridges, tubers.

Clearly the diet of partridges can depend on what is available; so how well have they coped with recent changes in farming? In the late 19th century the diet of grey partridges in Bavaria was described as cereal grains, grass and weed seeds and leaves, supplemented in summer with beetles, ants, ant 'eggs' (pupae), crane flies and sawfly caterpillars (Jäckel, 1891). In Britain the insects were listed as grasshoppers, beetles, ants, ant eggs, crane flies and caterpillars, with the plant diet given as cereal grains, grass seeds and weed seeds including those of plantains, hemp nettle and the leaves of winter cereals, grasses, clover and 'buttercups' (Archibald, 1892). Such diets will have changed with modern agriculture, but how, and by how much? We look at the evidence for plants next, with insects covered in Chapter 5.

SEASONAL CHANGES IN THE FOOD OF GREY PARTRIDGE ON FARMLAND

Typically at the start of the open season for hunting, prior to the use of herbicides, grain and weed seeds comprised up to 80 per cent of the volume of food in the diet. This percentage declined through autumn, reaching negligible amounts by March (Fig. 55), by which time the diet had switched to the leaves of cereals, grasses and clovers. From June, weed seeds again feature increasingly in the diet until the start of the cereal harvest in July, with weed seeds and grain dominating. Even where the climate and habitat are utterly different, the picture is roughly similar and this applies to *Alectoris* partridges. To take but

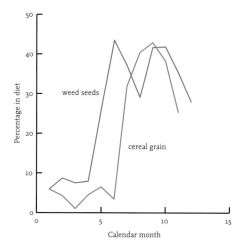

FIG 55. Adult grey partridge diet by percentage volume through the year showing high frequency of weed and grass seeds in summer and autumn and a high frequency of cereal grains from July (harvest) to December. Data from Britain, Hungary, Czechoslovakia, Germany and Poland combined. These studies were made during 1890–1961 and were therefore virtually unaffected by herbicide use.

one example, in the Negev desert of Israel the intake of seeds was 64 per cent in summer and autumn but only 4 per cent in late winter (Alkon *et al.*, 1985). This picture changes only slightly from country to country, although where it does not germinate because of the cold, for example in parts of Canada, grain can feature in the diet throughout the winter. In this section we explore how the seed and grain diet has changed with the advent of modern farming.

MAJOR STUDIES

The most comprehensive picture of the seed and grain diet of adult grey partridges originated with research funded by the Hungarian Government's Game Department (Vertse *et al.*, 1955). Starting in the 1880s the diet of 1,007 grey partridges had been quantified by 1953, importantly before modern herbicides had been used in Hungary. The partridge crops were obtained throughout the year, though mostly in August to October when the birds were shot for sport. A total of 111,172 seeds were identified, so on average each partridge had eaten 110 seeds. Of these, 53 per cent were from broadleaved weeds, 39 per cent were from grasses and only 8 per cent from cereals. The most frequent of 131 species of broadleaved weed were in order: fat hen, black bindweed, knotgrass, pigweed and cornflower. Two of these species, fat hen and pigweed, have tiny seeds and all seeds frequent in the diet are generally much smaller than cereal grains. The most frequent grasses eaten were the millet grasses, green pigeon-grass, pale pigeon-grass, cockspur grass and crabgrass.

In Britain during 1933–37 the crops of 429 grey partridges were examined as in Hungary, throughout the year but mostly in September and October. A total of 153,480 seeds were identified, an average of 358 seeds eaten per bird (Middleton & Chitty, 1937). This is more than three times higher intake than in Hungary and we do not know why this is the case; it might have something to do with the way the birds were chosen for examination. A total of 70 species were recorded, with 67 per cent of the seeds coming from broadleaved weeds, 24 per cent from grasses and 9 per cent from cereals. The most frequent broadleaved species were knotgrass, orache, black bindweed and *Persicaria*. The most frequent grasses in the diet were meadow grass and meadow fescue.

In Czechoslovakia from 1949 to 1951, diets were investigated using a large sample of 2,038 birds, mostly shot specifically for the purpose. Typically only the percentage of grey partridge crops that contained the species was given, not the number, weight or volume of seeds. The result was a total of 3,958 occurrences of 78 species, with the most frequent broadleaved weeds, in order, black bindweed, hemp nettle, chickweed and *Persicaria*. The most frequent grass was, as in Hungary, green pigeon-grass (Janda, 1957). A similar study near Poznan, Poland, of 420 adult birds in 1960 and 1961 recorded 40 species (Oko, 1963). Cereals dominated, especially wheat, and with weed seeds accounted for 43 per cent of

FIG 56. The winter hardy pigweed, an important grey and Daurian partridge food increasing throughout Europe; here in the Sussex Study area where it was first found in 2007.

FIG 57. Male on alert for other males or raptors whilst the female feeds on sugar-beet: a food recorded in red-legged partridges in England and France, in grey partridges in France, Austria and Hungary, and in chukar partridges in Israel. (Chris Knights)

the diet. The most frequent broadleaved weeds were, in order, black bindweed, cornflower, fat hen and pigweed. The most frequent grass seeds eaten were cockspur grass, followed by green pigeon-grass.

In Alberta a detailed study was made of the August to April diets based on 304 grey partridges collected during 1948–62 (Westerskov, 1966). The main food was oats, barley and wheat, with the main weed seeds hemp nettle, black bindweed and fat hen. From August to April only 27 species of seeds were found in the diet. Several studies in Russia involving altogether 600 grey partridges showed 109 species of plant in the diet (Kuz'mina, 1992), with the most abundant species being, once again, black bindweed.

A particularly detailed study of adult grey partridge diet was made in Bulgaria throughout 1950–3 (Georgiev, 1955). His sample of 176 adults had eaten 100 species of seeds dominated by pale pigeon grass, green pigeon-grass, pigweed and *Polygonums*. Also in the early 1950s Dr Heinz Brüll, famous for his work on the goshawk, examined the contents of 295 grey partridge crops in Schleswig Holstein and Niedersachsen (Brüll & Lindeman, 1954; Brüll, 1960). Three-quarters of the sample was from September and October but some birds were examined every month. Green foliage of clover grasses and cereals were the main food by volume but seeds of 38 species were recorded. Grain was present in one-third of crops with barley and wheat eaten more often than rye and oats. The main grass seed eaten was annual meadow-grass. The main broadleaved weed seeds were, in order, black bindweed, chickweed, hemp nettle and fat hen.

Two all-year studies in Austria should be mentioned (Vetiska, 1979; Huss, 1983) because they are directly comparable with the early studies in Hungary and Czechoslovakia. In both studies the food in winter was mostly leaves of autumn-sown cereals. In the first study maize and sugar beet were eaten in quantity, with seeds of 41 other species recorded. The use of grain was in the order barley > maize > oats > rye > wheat; with broadleaved weeds black bindweed > chickweed > dandelions. In the second study the use of grain was in the order barley > wheat > maize > millet > rye > sorghum (also known as milo or dari), with many seeds of cultivated grasses especially rye grass. *Polygonums* were the main broadleaved weed seeds eaten, especially black bindweed, with fat hen next most important. In all, 40 species were identified, less than in the older studies.

Finally there are two remarkable studies based on analysis of droppings (faeces). The first was in eastern Denmark where droppings were collected throughout the years 1985 and 1986, with 21 species of weed seed and many insects identified (Steenfeldt *et al.*, 1991). Of all the studies on partridge food, perhaps the most remarkable is that by Orłowski *et al.* (2011) in Poland. They identified more than half a million plant items from droppings, with the most important weeds being pigweed, the memorably named three-lobed beggarsticks and fat hen.

The above studies show that although many species of plant seeds are eaten by partridges, a few appear to be particularly important: the *Polygonums*, especially black bindweed, hemp nettle, the pigweeds and the pigeon grasses.

THE FOOD OF ADULT *ALECTORIS* PARTRIDGES

The red-legged partridge was uncommon in England at the time of Middleton & Chitty's (1937) work and they were able to examine the contents of only 29 crops (7 per cent as many as *Perdix*, so about in the same proportion of birds available). As with the grey partridge the grain in the diet was dominated by wheat, barley and oats. The important broadleaved weed seeds were black bindweed and knotgrass. This is very much the situation with the grey partridge.

One of the first detailed studies of red-legged partridge diet within its natural range was that of Maria Vizeu-Pinheiro in the Contenda reserve near Beja in southeast Portugal. She identified the food items in 141 crops of birds shot

FIG 58. Excellent red-legged partridge habitat: Las Ensanchas, Spain. Many isolated Mediterranean oaks with the double lines indicating beetle banks and new olives at bottom right.

through the years 1968–9. Although wheat and oats were eaten, various bulbous and tuberous roots dominated the diet from the beginning of August until the end of October: jersey buttercup, tuberous hawkbit, bulbous meadow grass and false oat. This is during the driest part of the year and as well as gaining food the birds would be gaining moisture (see later). Feeding on grasshoppers was another way of gaining moisture and valuable nutrients but with a risk of infection with parasites (Chapter 7). In the winter the diet consisted of a variety of seeds and leaves of legumes and land quillwort sporangia (Vizeu-Pinheiro, 1977). A more restricted diet was found in 74 red-legged partridges shot near Santarem, northeast of Lisbon in November and December 1993. The main cereals were oats and maize and the main seeds of broadleaves were, in order, vervain, vetches and pigweed (Tavares *et al.*, 1996).

In southern Spain, between November and January 1987–89 the crop and gizzard contents of 98 red-legged partridges showed the most important food to be wheat and barley grains followed by olives. Also eaten were vetches, pigweed and fat hen, and minor amounts of further species, bringing the total to 26 (Jiménez *et al.*, 1991).

To investigate diets, a direct comparison of the diet of wild grey partridges and red-legged partridges was made in the Sussex Study area in October 1969.

TABLE 4. A comparison of the diets of wild grey and wild red-legged partridges in fields where both species were shot on the same day – Sussex Study area, October 1969.

	frequency grey	frequency red-leg	sig. difference?
sample sizes	58	72	
grain	79	85	no
leaves and shoots	47	22	no
clover leaves	24	4	<0.01
Polygonum seeds	31	18	no
chickweed seed heads	41	25	no
field beans	3	15	<0.05
others	10	10	no
categories per bird	2.35	1.79	no

The birds were shot over the same area on the same day. The details given above show that the grey partridges were eating more clover and the red-legged partridges were eating field beans that were perhaps too large for the greys, but the diets were similar (Table 4).

This similarity was confirmed by a study in Hell's Canyon, a spectacular place in Idaho and Oregon gouged out by the Snake river that is in places more than 1,600 m below the surrounding plateau. In this remarkable place chukar partridges and grey partridges live side by side in roughly equal numbers, with an 80 per cent overlap in their diets (Churchwell *et al.*, 2004) Their study of 143 chukar crops in Hell's Canyon showed the main food to be the root nodules of the beautiful prairie-star followed by bulbous meadow/blue-grass stem bases, sunflower, knotgrass and fiddleneck (*Amsinckia*). The crops of 105 chukar partridges from Nevada showed a concentration in autumn on downy brome (cheatgrass), the roots and bulbils of prairie star, fiddleneck and sunflower seeds (Weaver & Haskell, 1967). Downy brome provides the bulk of the food of chukars through autumn and winter in the sagebrush steppe of the western US but it is not a good enough diet to maintain body weight and the deficiencies are made up largely by the consumption, even in autumn, of grasshoppers and ants (Weaver & Haskell, 1967; Savage *et al.*, 1969).

FIG 59. Hell's Canyon by the Snake river in the northwest US in 2004: note the scarcity of trees except on steeper parts; grey partridge and chukar live side by side in more or less equal numbers feeding on the same foods. (John Ratti)

A large number of investigations have been carried out on the food of the chukar in its native range. Several studies in the former USSR were collated by Kuz'mina (1992). The diet of 1,300 birds mostly shot in autumn showed a preponderance of tubers, bulbs and roots. In southeast Kazakhstan 42 per cent of the winter diet of the chukar consists of bulbs, tubers and corms (Kuz'mina, 1992) including those of the purple tartary lily, still sometimes found as a weed in wheat fields in central southern Asia, and the tuberous cranesbill. An intensive study of the chukar in Bulgaria was carried out throughout 1955–9, with the diet of 382 birds determined (Georgiev, 1961). An astonishing 262 species of plants, 102 species of insects and 12 species of other invertebrates (mostly snails) were recorded. The most important broadleaved species were, in order, various vetches (*Vicia* and *Lathyrus*) and knotgrass. The most important grasses and cereals were wheat, crabgrass and green pigeon-grass. In Iran a sample of 46 chukar had eaten more than 40 species of plant, mainly bulbous bluegrass, various saltworts, lesser celandine and milk vetch, in addition to cereal grains and ants (Khaleghizadeh & Sehhatisabet, 2006). A sample of 29 chukar partridges shot near Srinagar in Kashmir in 1961 had a diet completely dominated by grass seeds (*Eragrostis* > *Brahiani* (a meadow-grass) > *Elymus* > *Setaria* > *Stipa*) but also wheat after harvest and in all 22 species of weed seed (Oakleaf & Robertson, 1971). Similarly in China

Przelwalski's rock partridge living in very arid areas in the Qinghai plateau includes many bulbs and roots in its diet (Naifa & Yang, 1992).

The diet of rock x red-legged natural hybrid partridges in the Maritime Alps has been studied from microscopic analyses of droppings (Didillon, 1988). In winter the diet was dominated (68 per cent) by the leaves of grasses found in meadows. In spring the diet switched to buds, flowers and later seeds and insects, then back towards the winter diet of grasses in the autumn. The study clearly showed that the selected species were of higher nutritional value and that the grazing of cattle was important to maintain an adequate diet. The seemingly rather poor autumn diets obtainable at high altitudes were confirmed by a study of 111 rock partridges shot in the central Apennines where 37 plant species were dominated by moss-campion, hawkweeds and the seeds of grasses (e.g. *Poa alpina*) and rushes, with no grain and few arable weed seeds (Danova *et al.*, 2012).

SIMILARITY OF DIETS

In summary, a clear pattern emerges from all these studies: the diet relates more to the climate and the locality than to the species of partridge. The *Alectoris* partridges have obviously stronger beaks (especially the rock partridge) and feet with more effective claws, and in very dry, hot areas away from arable farmland the natural diet of the *Alectoris* species in the dry season is dominated by tubers, bulbs, bulbils, roots and rhizomes obtained by digging. Where grey and chukar partridges occur together, as in Hell's Canyon, they eat virtually the same foods. In Kazakhstan both grey and Daurian partridges dug up bulbs and roots. In hot, dry areas insects appear to be important even for adults, providing protein and moisture. Interestingly the dry season diets of *Alectoris* are very like that of many francolins and spurfowls in Africa. For example, in the Drakensburg Mountains, the grey-winged francolin adult diet consists mainly of the corms and bulbs of sedges obtained through digging with the bill not scratching with the feet (Little *et al.*, 2000 and pers. obs.).

SELECTION OF FOOD

How much of these diets of weeds is a deliberate choice by the birds and how much is it the result of feeding on anything suitable they could find? The food selection of the chukar has been said to be 'indiscriminate' (Kuz'mina, 1992) but it is clear that this is not generally the case in partridges. An early study of preference for different foods was a series of choice experiments that showed clear preferences, in the order maize (kibbled or cracked) > wheat > buckwheat > oats > sorghum > barley (Hawkins, 1937b; Fisher, 1943). Similar winter conditions can occur in Finland, where Erkki Pulliainen measured the preference of different grains in a series of ingenious trials during 1964/5. With maize not tested, the preference was wheat > rye > barley > oats with other seeds in the order hemp, hemp nettle > grass seeds > fat hen (Pulliaianen, 1965). Of necessity these studies were of captive birds. Sunflower seeds appear to be selected preferentially (e.g. Weigand, 1980; Hupp et al., 1980; Carroll, 1990) but this is a relatively new crop in many areas and there appear to have been no trials to quantify this.

TABLE 5. Grey partridge: comparison of the frequency of weed species on stubbles and in diet in the Sussex Study area in 1968, shading indicates most important species in the diet

	% frequency on stubble	% frequency in diet	ratio x 100
sample size	200 quadrats	222	
chickweed seed capsules	78	53	68
speedwells	65	1	2
forget me not	27	12	44
scarlet pimpernel	27	3	11
knotgrass	26	18	69
black bindweed	25	25	100
field pansy	23	4	17
groundsel	18	0	0
mayweeds	13	0	0
mouse-ear	12	1	8
sow thistles	9	0	0
hemp nettle	4	4	100
white campion	3	0	0
dwarf spurge	1	1	(100)

In the Sussex study a survey of food species frequencies on stubbles was carried out immediately after shooting for comparison with the diets of the shot birds (Table 5). It was abundantly clear that the black bindweed was far more frequent in the diet than expected from its frequency on stubbles. It was clear that plant species can dominate the diet through preference, palatability, and also ease of handling, size and accessibility as well as frequency. Teasing out which of these factors would be most important would be difficult and preference is not at all the same as importance.

This study in Sussex supports the results from other studies that black bindweed and the other *Polygonums* really are important to grey partridges. This is almost certainly partly due to the suitable size of their seeds, as is also the case for the similar-sized hemp nettle, corn spurrey and cornflower, but it also may be due to palatability (see p. 62).

The alternative to selecting large seeds is to select species where many seeds can be taken in one bite. Examples here are fat hen, pigweed, many-seeded goosefoot and chickweed. In these cases many tiny seeds are eaten on the raceme-bunches of seeds at a single bite or in seed capsules as for example chickweed. The small black seeds of pigweed can be eaten in large quantities: 23 droppings in Poland contained the remains of over 7,000 seeds with only a few (<0.3 per cent) passing through the gut unharmed (Orlowski & Czarnecka, 2009). One partridge shot in February 1996 near St Petersburg had eaten 4,167 fat hen seeds (Potapov, 2003). In the most spectacular example, seven chukar in Bulgaria were found to have eaten more than a quarter million seeds of tobacco, equivalent to about 80 pods with 3,000 tiny seeds in each (Georgiev, 1961).

THE EFFECT OF HERBICIDES ON THE FLORA OF CEREAL FIELDS: THE SUSSEX STUDY

A total of 214 species have been identified in the cereal weed flora of the Sussex Study area (Potts *et al.*, 2010). Of these, 116 were annuals (53 per cent), including 63 (54 per cent) ancient weeds (archaeophytes), 40 (34 per cent) native species and 13 (11 per cent) more recently introduced species (neophytes). The combined biennials and perennials numbered 101, including 8 (8 per cent) archaeophytes, 79 (79 per cent) native species and 14 (14 per cent) neophytes. This is a pretty impressive list but in the average cereal field the species frequency was calculated to have declined by 52 per cent during the period 1948–67. Since then, annual surveys have been made. The use of herbicides in

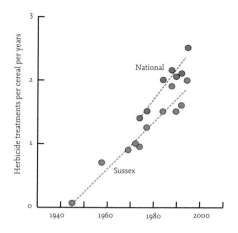

FIG 60. Use of herbicides in cereal crops in the Sussex Study area from 1946 and comparison with use in England and Wales showing slightly lower use in Sussex.

the Sussex Study area closely paralleled that in England and Wales (Fig. 60). The slightly higher use nationally is due to the presence of proportionally fewer traditional leys.

Each year all cereal fields were sampled on or as soon after 16 June as weather permitted; this required a minimum of two days. Sample sites were consistently in the same locations within fields, with the number of fields sampled varying according to the availability of cereal crops across the 12 farms in the area. The frequency of occurrence of each weed species and the overall weed abundance of broadleaved weeds and grass weeds were ranked separately on a scale of 0–5.

During the 36-year study there was no significant trend in overall weed abundance, although grass-weed abundance was slightly greater in the early 1980s than at other times (Fig. 61). Surprisingly, in view of the growing intensity of herbicide use, there was no sign of an overall collapse of the flora. No trend was

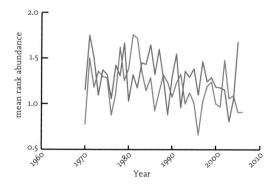

FIG 61. Sussex Study area: the average abundance of broadleaved weeds (red) and grass weeds (blue) in mid-June conventional cereal crops from 1970 to 2005. In conservation headlands the mean rank abundance of broadleaved weeds averages 3.0 (Chapter 10).

detected for 15 per cent of the species, 27 per cent showed increases and 58 per cent showed complex changes. Essentially the flora was adapting to the farming, with weeds keeping pace. There was also an important sustained increase in the occurrence of perennial dicot species, tall species having considerable ecological importance such as hogweed, *Artemisia* and burdock. Analysis of herbicide usage and cropping showed that these increases were most probably due to the loss of traditional leys that interrupted life cycles.

Although the flora of cereal crops crashed when herbicides were first introduced, since 1967 it has remained relatively stable; the depletion has not worsened because the soil seed-bank shows remarkable resilience. Incorporating early records of the Sussex Botanical Recording Society, particularly those in the early years of the twentieth century kept by the vicar of Burpham Church and those provided by the late Frank Penfold, another Burpham resident, in the 1950s and 60s, including the *Sussex Plant Atlas* (Hall, 1980), a balance sheet of gains and losses was drawn up. Fifteen species and one subspecies (7 per cent of a total of 217) have been lost, eleven before the study (seven before widespread herbicide use and four following it) and five during the course of the study. Offsetting these losses there were fifteen gains, six before widespread herbicide use and none during 1948–67. Nine species were gained after 1968 (Potts *et al.*, 2010).

On the basis of the response of weeds in herbicide-free plots, it was estimated that between 1948 (the first time herbicides were used in the Sussex Study area) and 1967 there had been a 64 per cent decline in the abundance index of broadleaved weeds. Very little is known quantitatively about the community of weeds that existed in cereals prior to the use of herbicides but a community had been identified in the Netherlands in 1935–40 known as the 'corn poppy–night-flowering catchfly association' (Wasscher, 1941). Incredibly this community was found virtually intact where herbicides were not used in recent years on the Norfolk Estate, and this after 65 years of herbicide use. We look at this in detail in Chapter 10.

This all indicates that the soil seed bank can still regenerate the distinctive components of the pre-herbicide community; we have not achieved the entirely weed-free cereal crops that were predicted in the 1960s. Part of the explanation seems to be the buffering effect of seed longevity in the soil seed bank. Our loss of weed abundance and of weed species per sampled site was close to what we expected from what is known about seed longevity and about the same as the loss of seeds from soils in 'arable landscapes' in Britain between 1945 and 1985–2000 (Robinson & Sutherland, 2002). However, with up to 7,000 seeds per m^2 for corn poppy and 2,845 per m^2 for charlock (Thompson *et al.*, 1997), with a pre-herbicide

FIG 62. The hemp nettle, once abundant is now scarce due to herbicide use. Its seeds have a high fat content and were a favoured food of grey partridges, especially in Finland.

abundance of all dicotyledons species in the soil seed bank approaching 70,000 per m^2 (Brenchley & Warington, 1930) and with annual replenishment (albeit at a much lower rate than in the pre-herbicides era), the soil seed-bank is not yet empty. If continually suppressed by herbicides this resilience matters not one jot. But with conservation headlands there is a sustainable biodiversity benefit and we return to this later when dealing with the biodiversity value of conservation headlands (Chapter 10).

In Finland, Erkki Pulliainen found no change in October diet from 1962–4 to 1968–70 but by 1979–81 the amount of hemp nettle seed, a valuable high-fat food, had dropped by 20 per cent and the amount of grain had increased by 20 per cent (Pulliainen, 1983). Erkki showed the importance of variety in the diet using captive birds; after being fed wheat alone for 20 days, their weight declined seriously, with abnormal behaviour due to a lack of vitamin A. Green food was crucial in preventing this (Pulliainen, 1965). Normally in the wild this would not present a problem. The frequency of hemp nettle monitored in the Sussex Study is given in Figure 63; the species, abundant until about 1960, is now rare in herbicide-treated cereals.

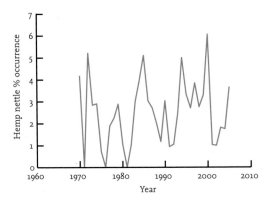

FIG 63. Sussex Study area: the sustained low frequency of occurrence of hemp nettle in herbicide-treated cereal crops from 1970 to 2005.

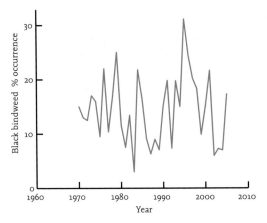

FIG 64. Sussex Study area: the frequency of occurrence of black bindweed in herbicide-treated cereal crops, with no overall trend from 1970 to 2005.

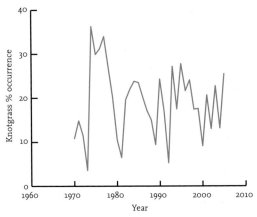

FIG 65. Sussex Study area: showing frequency of occurrence of Knotgrass in herbicide-treated cereal crops, with no overall trend from 1970 to 2005.

FIG 66. Partridge-eye view of stubble showing knotgrass (right) and black bindweed and, not eaten, field pansy (top).

The number of black bindweed seeds eaten by grey partridges in all studies had dropped by 75 per cent between 1968 and 1977 (in Potts, 1986) and the story of black bindweed in the Sussex Study area illustrates the complex interaction between agriculture, partridges and their plant food. In autumn stubble surveys in 1968, the species was found at 26 per cent of sampling points. In 1970 it was even more abundant, being found at 63 per cent of points. However by 1973 most stubble fields were burnt soon after harvest to an extent that made sampling pointless. Although stubble burning was banned in 1992 the cultivation and straw incorporation that replaced it resulted in fields with very few weeds in autumn. This all began to change in 2004 with stubbles left due to the DEFRA-funded over winter-stubbles option. Black bindweed, the most favoured weed of all, as we have seen, occurred on 10 per cent of stubbles in 2004 and 16 per cent in 2005. Meanwhile the frequency of black bindweed in cereals in June has been measured every year since 1969, showing no statistically significant trend (Fig. 64), as also was the case with the other main *Polygonum*, knotgrass (Fig. 65). So the scarcity in the diets after 1972 was due to stubble management not herbicides.

LONG-TERM CHANGES IN THE DIET

Declines in weed abundance have been reported in many studies. For example, at sites north of Prague the number of species found in cereal crops decreased from 95 in 1975 to 45 in 2005 (Tyšer *et al.*, 2009). So, what can the diet studies tell us about the long-term changes in weed abundance? The number of species eaten has been reported in 32 studies of grey partridge involving 9,442 birds and in 17 studies of *Alectoris* partridges involving 3,333 birds. Deliberate feeding with grain (next section) was not evident in any of the studies. Obviously with more species of seeds were found with larger number of birds in the sample but the number increasing linearly with the square root of the sample size. This enabled a correction for sample size to be made for all 49 studies such that zero is an exact agreement between observed and expected. After the correction for differences in sample size, numbers were higher in the partridge's native range and in all-year-round studies but these

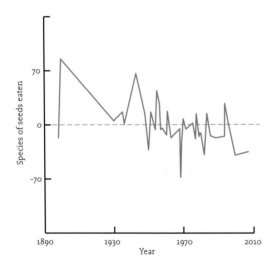

FIG 67. Trend in the number of species of seed species eaten by adult partridges from 1890 to 2010, corrected for sample size.

Data from 49 studies in: Brüll & Lindeman (1954); Campbell (1936); Churchwell *et al.* (2004); Dayani (1986) Georgiev (1955, 1961); Hammer *et al.* (1958); Hunt (1974); Hupp (1980); Huss (1983); Janda (1956); Jimenez *et al.* (1991); Kelso (1932); Khaleghizadeh & Sehhatisabet (2006); Khanmamedov (1955, 1962); Kobriger (1980); Kuz'mina (1992); Lebeurier (1958); Litun & Flint (1993); Lósy (1903); Melinchuk (1981); Middleton & Chitty (1937); Oko (1963); Orłowski *et al.* (2011); Potts (1970b); Pulliainen (1984, 1985); Rörig (1900); Steenfeldt *et al.* (1991); Sussex study; Thaisz (1899); Ul'yanin (1949); Vertse (1955); Vetiska (1979); Weaver & Haskell (1967); Westerskov (1966); Yeatter (1934, 1939); Yocom (1943).

differences were not statistically significant, as was the case amongst the different species or genera of partridges. When all studies are combined a downward trend is evident that coincides with the introduction of herbicides and with modern farming systems generally from the late 1940s (P=0.010). In 1900 the number of species of seeds recorded in the diet (corrected for sample size) was 80, which reduced to 28 (65 per cent) by the year 2000.

Detailed comparisons provide further evidence of an effect of herbicides on adult partridge diets. In Middleton & Chitty's 1936–7 study the dry weight ratio of weed seeds to grain in the diet was 1:1.2. By 1968–9, when 280 partridge crops were examined on the Sussex Study area, this ratio had dropped to 1:15.7. Not only were fewer weed seeds eaten but species that were rarely eaten in the past came to dominate the diet. Chickweed accounted for only 0.15 per cent of seeds and grain in Middleton & Chitty's study but for 37 per cent in Sussex in 1968–9. By 1977, and again on a dry weight basis, the ratio of weed seeds to grain had dropped further, to 1:23. When chickweed began to decline, in about 1987, the ratio would have dropped still further (Fig. 68). The change in diet had another main cause – stubble-straw burning – but by the time this was banned chickweed was largely unavailable. Straw burning was universally practised in the Sussex Study area from 1973–92 with a major change to earlier autumn cultivation for oilseed rape and autumn-drilled cereals. For this reason the switch to grain, evident through the studies of diet until the mid-1980s was stopped in its tracks by improved combine harvesters leaving less grain on stubbles that were very short-lived. It has been estimated that in 1970 there would have been 250 cereal grains per square metre and 20–60 by 1995 (Robinson & Sutherland, 2002).

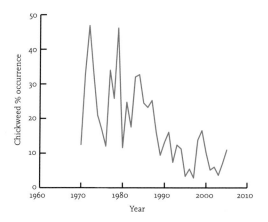

FIG 68. Sussex Study area: the decline in frequency of occurrence of chickweed in herbicide-treated cereal crops from 1970 to 2005.

FIG 69. Burning, sometimes carried out at night, was the usual way of dealing with surplus straw in the Sussex Study area from 1967–92. As intended, this greatly reduced the abundance of stubble weeds in autumn.

FIG 70. Two favoured foods of grey partridge: chickweed left and black bindweed.

THE FINAL ACT: GRAIN IN HOPPERS FOR WINTER AND BEYOND

It is clear from the above sections that adult partridges have a harder time obtaining weed seeds on modern farms than in former times. In winter and spring they have to depend on leaves of cereals and oilseed rape or on grass weeds. Wheat leaves are abundant but require about 24 times as much time and feeding energy as grain (Potts, 1986) and this forces the birds to feed outside the normal periods of sunrise and sunset. Oilseed rape leaves present similar problems. The presence of chickweed and autumn-germinating species clearly depends on herbicide use. This deterioration is compounded by a huge reduction in good-quality green foods in the form of the forage legumes such as clover, lucerne, vetches and sainfoin (Potts & Vickerman, 1974) due to the loss of traditional leys. As if all this was not enough, the grain put out for pheasants is mostly in the wrong places for partridges, as Westerskov (1977) showed in France. Whereas the value of feeding grain in hard weather is widely appreciated, although not often practised, there has been no tradition of feeding grain at other times of year.

Against this background there has been the major development of providing grain in hoppers, although it has a long history. In 1275 Marco Polo travelled through Inner Mongolia and described:

FIG 71. Grey partridges (six can be seen) are well adapted to find food under snow provided there is no icy crust. The difficulty of seeing raptors becomes more serious when there are fewer eyes. (Chris Knights)

FIG 72. Kublai Khan: his gamekeepers fed grain to wild partridges in the thirteenth century.

.... *a plain, where is found in great numbers, cranes, pheasants, partridges and other birds. Nearby is a valley frequented by great numbers of partridges and quails, for whose food the Great Khan (Kublai) causes millet, and other grains suitable to such birds, to be sown along the sides of it every season, and gives strict command that no person shall dare to reap the seed; in order that the birds may not be in want of nourishment. Many keepers, likewise, are stationed there for the preservation of the game, that it may not be taken or destroyed, as well as for the purpose of throwing the millet to the birds during the winter.*

When this kind of feeding began is unknown but there is a tradition of hand feeding rice and other grains to Tibetan partridge, white-eared pheasant and blood pheasant, for example in the sacred groves adjacent to the Buddhist monasteries of Daocheng, western Sichuan, where the practice goes way back into the mists of time (Fig. 73).

In Britain in the 1920s a survey showed 56 per cent of estates practised winter feeding, although some did this only in the severest weather (Parker, 1927). Chalmers (1928) referred to the hungry days between 1 March and 15 March when some keepers put little heaps of grain along hedgerows with, if possible, the inclusion of hemp and pearl barley. A lot of the value of this would depend on the weather. Deep snow and ice is a notable problem in the eastern North American part of the grey partridge range: for example, in the winter of 1936/7 a blanket of ice covered fields in Wisconsin from 6 January for two months. Partridges died in large numbers but few birds were lost on areas where grain was provided (Hawkins, 1937b).

Before the benefits of winter feeding could be measured virtual year-round hopper feeding began in France (Viart, 1978). The first scientific work appears to have begun near Soissons in 1973 (Aubineau *et al.*, 1975). A system of 'cafeterias' was set up on half of Vauberon Farm, consisting of a dusting shelter, shrubs, a trap for stone martens, a box or tube for rat poison (rats like grain too!), a shallow water trough and a drum with slit feeders dispensing

FIG 73. An ancient practice: monk feeding wild white-eared pheasants, Xiongdeng monastery, Sichuan. Note domestic fowl. (Wang Nan)

waste grain and weed seeds. The system worked, with far more pairs settling near to the cafeterias, but the part or parts of the six-part system that attracted pairs most could not be quantified. In Seine et Marne, a five-year study from 1982 by Aufradet highlighted a high consumption of grain in winter and spring but with little eaten in summer. Consumption peaked in March and April at 35 g per partridge per day (Aufradet, 1996). After harvest the stubble counts showed that the percentage of females with chicks was increased by 43 per cent (from 30 per cent to 43 per cent) where coveys were located within 150 m of a hopper. This was a big difference but one reason for this could have been better predation control near feeders.

In about 1987, Jean Grala, a farmer near Lille in northeast France, began using small hoppers filled with wheat, dispersed around the farm. A survey of 29 areas was carried out in 1996 that showed that overwinter survival was not improved with more feeders but that breeding success was higher with more than ten hoppers per 100 ha. A follow-up trial in Flanders in 1997–9 in which a third of the food in the hoppers was made up of guinea fowl chick crumbs with a sheep's head buried by each hopper to provide a supply of maggots, failed to show a statistically significant effect. In the meantime others had begun to experiment, especially Jacques Hicter in Picardie. Soon the system of feeding virtually throughout the year was the most widely used method of partridge management (Mayot, 1999).

FIG 74. Jacques Hicter of Savy, Picardie, the first to popularise virtual year-round feeding of grey partridges. The sign says (in translation): 'We also think'.

Mark Watson studied the food intake rate (pecks per minute) of 72 radio-tagged birds, which averaged about 30 pecks per minute. In pairs the peck rate was lowest near permanent cover and most birds fed about 40 m from permanent cover. In general the food intake rate was reduced by the need for vigilance against predators and in males by the need to look out for opportunistic single males. Using Mark's estimates of grey partridge food intake rates we can calculate the amount of time needed for feeding per day. At a benign 15°C, grey partridges require only 72 calories per day, with each grain of wheat containing 0.155 calories and each peck of wheat leaf 0.007 calories (Potts, 1986). So the required daily food intake can be estimated as 464 wheat grains, which could be eaten at 30 per minute in 15 minutes. Erkki Pulliainen's birds kept at room temperature in Finland ate 478 wheat grains per day.

At the other extreme, in the absence of grain or equivalent seeds, 10,000 pecks of wheat leaf would require more than 5 hours of feeding. In the coveys in Ostrobothnia, Finland, Erkki recorded behaviour for 2 minutes every 15 minutes and feeding was often the dominant activity for periods of more than 5 hours at a time. The provision

FIG 75. Feeder for red-legged partridges at Las Ensanchas: perhaps this feeder was a little too high! (Patricia Maldonado Vidal)

FIG 76. Typical feeders on the Norfolk Estate, in kale (left) and chicory (right). (Olga Potts, left)

of wheat, millet (i.e. white millet) or other grains, or availability of good-quality weed seeds like black bindweed and hemp nettle or hemp, would greatly reduce the time required for feeding. No feeder currently available can cope with seeds of greatly differing sizes but grown wild bird seed mixtures do help. The basic aim here is to provide feeding conditions that reduce the exposure of partridges to predation; it not simply a question of nutrition. We return to this in Chapter 10.

WATER

Grey partridges are only very infrequently seen drinking water (once in my experience) and in summer it is not available in many of their habitats except in the form of dew. They clearly need to drink much less water than many birds; however, in the arid mountain steppe in southern Armenia grey partridge coveys made regular flights to a river to drink (Dal', 1944). In northern Kazakhstan they were able to breed more than 10 km from the nearest permanent water only where they had access to green vegetation and many insects (Ul'yanin, 1949).

Where they live in hot, dry areas the *Alectoris* partridges must have access to water. Studies in Israel have shown that chukar partridges feeding on ripe seeds only obtain 30 per cent of their water requirement from food (Thomas *et al.*, 1984; Degan *et al.*, 1984). In Uzbekistan 78 per cent of chukar partridges observed during laying and brood rearing were within 100 m of water (Lynov, 1978). In Utah chukars visit water sources in the middle of the day and prefer sources near shrubs. Both preferences are to reduce the risk of predation (Larsen *et al.*, 2009). In Spain and Portugal it is normal, especially in hot weather, for red-legged partridges to be seen drinking in the afternoon at water holes or using drinkers especially put out for them. A four-year study near Valladolid in northwest Spain showed red-legged partridges drank most water in the driest and hottest parts of each summer, especially when the temperature was above 30°C (Gaudiosa Lacasa *et al.*, 2010). Their results supported Borralho *et al.* (1998) on the importance of water but did not support Larsen *et al.* on the value of shrub cover. In Britain and France, with access to green food, soft-bodied insects and such foods as sugar beet, drinkers do not appear to be necessary.

In La Mancha, on stubble counts with Tom Gullick and Tom Cook, it was obvious that in hot, dry seasons most of the good broods had access either to water or succulent vegetation and this appeared to show that water was most critical to chicks, not adults. This has not been investigated properly. However, in the case of the California quail where 'greenery' also vanishes in mid-summer, there is good evidence that water is required by growing chicks unless succulent insects are available (Leopold, 1977). We return to this in Chapter 5.

RISING DEMAND FOR CEREALS

The human population on earth is increasing more slowly than at one time feared but it is still set to reach 9.3 billion, on a mid-projection by 2050, a third higher than at present within a generation (UN Population Division). Coupled with this is the demand for bio-fuels (currently 30 per cent of US maize is used for this purpose) and more varied diets, especially more meat, milk and other resources. If the intensification of production was to be kept at its present level, the extra land needed for agriculture would grow by far more than a third, with catastrophic effects on natural habitats. The only way of stopping this is to intensify production. For many years a series of technological developments, especially the use of dwarf varieties led by Norman Borlaug in the Green Revolution, did indeed lessen the need to encroach on natural habitats but they were still being lost at 0.4 per cent a year. In the past decade this rate has increased to 0.6 per cent per year (Clay, 2011), with spectacular adverse effects in Brazil (Soy beans for China) and southeast Asia (Palm oil). In Malaysia and Indonesia 55–59 per cent of the expansion of palm oil production during 1990–2005 was at the expense of natural forest (Koh & Wilcove, 2008). It is difficult to see how biodiversity can be saved by market forces; although there are valiant efforts in this direction, governments will have to intervene.

Though not in relation to biodiversity, government regulation of agriculture has a long history, with Acts of Parliament in the UK regulating the trade in cereal grain as early as 1360; duties on imports date from at least 1670 and subsidies on exports from 1689 (Prothero, 1917). When the price of wheat increased dramatically during the Napoleonic Wars, large areas of the Sussex Study area were ploughed for the first time in centuries and by 1808 the area of wheat in England and Wales exceeded that at the present time. This was due to the naval blockade and other effects of the conflict; nothing to with farming as such. After the wars prices were steadied by the 'Corn Laws' and they held up well after their effective repeal in 1849 (finally in 1869) due to increased demand but crashed when imports started to flow in from North America in the 1890s. This had an indirect adverse effect on grey partridges at the wetter, cooler fringe of cereal cropping, in Ireland and western Britain, whilst creating new habitats in the Great Plains of North America. In eastern Britain partridge numbers remained high until World War I, increasing with the number of gamekeepers. After World War I the proportion of farmland in grass was further extended in the west and partridge numbers fell again. There was some respite when the area given over to cereals increased in World War II but the decline in the number of gamekeepers (see Fig. 97) and the increasing use of pesticides then became dominant factors.

From 1947, when deficiency payments started and when pesticides came onto the scene, the growing of cereals became easier and more profitable, with subsidies linked to yield per unit area; so much so that by 1984 the 'mountains' of surplus grain became embarrassing. Eventually, in the 1992 'Reforms of the Common Agricultural Policy', the EU introduced the requirement for compulsory set-aside based essentially on the same model that had existed in the US on and off since the 1930s (Fig. 77).

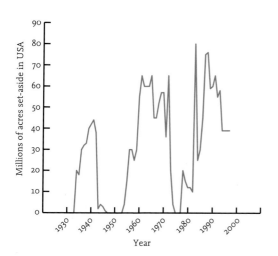

FIG 77. The area given over to set-aside in the US from 1933–2000; no benefits to grey partridges were documented.

FIG 78. Set-aside was usually not managed properly to help farmland wildlife and it was often harmful to it. Unmanaged (left) it grew tall and very dense, whilst at the other extreme to help arable farming, it was sprayed (below left) with glyphosate and thus at a crucial time of year virtually devoid of plant-dependent wildlife.

By 1993/4, 21 per cent of land in the EU that would normally have been given over to cereals was diverted to set-aside. At the same time an area ten times larger than the area of cereals in Britain was abandoned in Russia following the collapse of the Soviet Union (www.faostat.fao.org). The aim of set-aside in the EU was simply to reduce the stocks of grain and in this it was successful aided by increasing demand. In Sussex it was very difficult or impossible to manage set-aside in a way that would benefit partridges. Where it was not sprayed, it quickly became an impenetrable jungle of thistles; where it was sprayed, cover and insect supplies were poor. Fortunately the EU recognised the harm being done to the environment by the drive for higher yields and set-aside was accompanied by the agri-environment measures dealt with in the next chapter.

For the first time subsidies were paid on the area cropped not on the tonnage of grain produced. This was a good idea but by itself i did not go far enough and partridge numbers continued to plummet throughout Europe. Nevertheless, enouraged by the Convention on Biological Diversity (CBD) signed in Rio de Janeiro in 1992, there were hints of further progress. By 2001 the EU had embraced the idea of halting the loss of biodiversity and in 2004 the environment was put at the centre of EU agricultural policy with the aim that by 2010 31 per cent of the €5 billion per annum European Agriculture Fund for Rural Development (EAFRD) would be made available to 'protect and support' biodiversity.

With the increasing demand for cereals there are also signs that even the existing level of agriculture is coming under increasing pressure from new pests. Wheat yields are increasing but much more slowly than in the past and another 132 million tonnes per annum will be needed by 2030 for food alone (www.faostat. fao.org). With a considerable restructuring of its agriculture the former USSR might produce much of this wheat, but if so it will be with an enormous cost to biodiversity unless mitigating measures are taken. Meanwhile world wheat production is currently threatened by a new strain of the wheat-stem black rust found in Uganda in 1999 (hence known as Ug99), which has quickly spread south to South Africa and north as far as Iran. Many now consider that in a short time it will reach the most important wheat-growing area in the world: the Punjab.

Maize, the second most important cereal in the world, is threatened by the western corn rootworm, the larvae of the Chrysomelid beetle *Diabrotica virgifera*. This pest originated, like maize itself, in Central America, spreading to the US. Then during the Balkan wars in the early 1990s it arrived in Europe speculatively in a cargo plane belonging to the US military. It was identified in Hungary and then spread rapidly, becoming established in England near Heathrow airport between 2003 and 2007, before apparently dying out in Britain.

Soybean, one of the world's most important crops, is currently threatened by a rust from eastern Asia, that spread first to Brazil and then to the US. Perhaps even more serious is the new mad soy disease that infects GM glyphosate-tolerant varieties. It is clear agriculture will struggle to keep everyone fed. It follows that environmental considerations will take a back seat. With these kinds of pressures it is simply not realistic, in the longer term, to advocate whole farm-scale relaxations of agricultural production to help farmland wildlife.

It is clear that, if partridges are to be saved, this will have to be done against a background of tough competition for resources: farming led by an increasing demand for food. To save farmland wildlife we have to develop measures that maximise wildlife abundance on small areas whilst producing as much food as possible on large areas. We approach Chapter 4 with this in mind.

CHAPTER 4

Nesting and Predation

Partridges, when anyone comes near their nest, cast themselves down before his feet that looks for it, running and flying as if they were lame, by that means drawing him away from their nests, and enticing him to follow them; which when they have done, themselves fly away.

Aristotle (384–322 BC) quoted in John Ray,
The Ornithology of Francis Willughby, 1678.

IT HAS BEEN WELL ESTABLISHED for several decades that the three main causes of nest losses in the grey partridge are predation, mowing, and occasional flooding by heavy rain. Mowing losses have declined in predominantly cereal growing areas as ley farming has been outmoded and flooding is unusual, especially so where the nests are on free-draining earth banks along traditional hedgerows. Predation has therefore come to be recognised as the most important cause of nest loss. One reason is the convincing experimental

FIG 79. Pair (right) with 23 young and bereaved male (arrowed), perhaps the largest brood ever photographed. Strange though it may seem, when brood sizes can be as big as this, the production of young is mainly a function of nest predation. (Jacques Hicter)

evidence from an area where the mowing was not changed, namely the Salisbury Plain Experiment already mentioned. Another is the accumulating evidence from further experiments and computer simulations that nest predation increases with nest density to an extent where it can effectively put a cap on the density of pairs in an area. Predation at the nest has been sufficient to have contributed importantly to the overall decline in partridge abundance and it has to be reduced if partridge conservation is to be sustainable. The picture for the red-legged partridge is similar but with nest predation even more important, although with compensation arising from the double-brooding habit.

NESTING ON THE GROUND

A virtual absence of trees is part of the definition of the steppes, where grey partridges evolved, so at first it seems obvious this must be the reason why they nest on the ground. On reflection, however, it is not at all obvious. One EU Commissioner for the Environment on a visit to a partridge estate in northwest Norfolk asked: 'If losses to ground predators are so important why do partridges not nest in trees?' David Lack long ago had struggled to find the answer. Many

FIG 80. Szechenyi's monal-partridge can either nest in trees or on the ground, as in the vicinity of Pamuling Monastery, Sichuan. What stops grey partridges from doing this? (Wang Nan)

species, he argued, did not nest in holes in trees or even in trees because there was 'more room on the ground' (Lack, 1954) and he may have been right. In Szechenyi's monal-partridge (Fig. 80), which can nest on the ground or in trees, nests on the ground are more successful (Zhang et al., 2011). Most species of the pheasant family, including many species of partridge, live in forests or amongst trees and roost in them yet nest on the ground. Only the Tragopan pheasants of Asia and the curassows, guans and chachalacas of Central and South America nest in trees. All things considered it is most likely that the ancestors of partridges nested on the ground long before the evolution of grasslands, much like the forest quails of the Americas and the francolins today in Asia and Africa.

The red-legged partridge is frequently found in open woodland with many trees and is often seen perching, calling from or even roosting in trees, yet nearly all nests are on the ground. One at Loddington was on top of a tall stump in a hawthorn bush and others have been found on buildings, but nests in trees appear not to have been recorded.

There may be 'more room on the ground' in natural conditions but on farmland the ground is a dangerous place, with nest sites exposed to predation, flooding, irrigation, trampling, grazing, mowing, cultivations, harvesting, and farm traffic. So where do partridges choose to nest? Another difficult question because the nests are really hard to find, perhaps not for foxes with their scent detection far better than any dog (Budgett, 1933), but certainly for us.

FINDING NESTS

In his pioneering studies on the Palouse Prairie, Washington State, Chuck Yocom at first tried dragging a rope across likely nesting areas, a technique that by disturbing incubating birds readily revealed the nests of hen harriers and short-eared owls (Yocom, 1943). This method was however hopeless for partridges because the females sat too tightly to be flushed. In a later study 21 grey partridge nests were found and 112 nests of the hen harrier (Kantrud & Higgins, 1992), yet the partridges were more numerous than the harriers. So far as nest finding is concerned, cold searching with a stick has usually been found to be the most effective method, but it is only feasible at high densities or when the hen has been watched back to the nest. Prior to incubation the eggs are carefully buried under many fragments of dead grass and leaves, so it is no use looking for eggs. The key with searching is to spot the 'hole' in the hedgerow ground vegetation that is the entry to the nest-tunnel, but this requires a trained eye because the track is usually indirect, leading left or right, and there are always many

FIG 81. Incubating grey partridges can be exceedingly tame.

'holes' in the vegetation made by rabbits. Pointing dogs are not used because sitting birds give off so little scent, especially in dry conditions, and through fear of disturbing the birds and causing them to desert. Many nests were formerly found by following the mowers around field edges to save the eggs for hatching in incubators or under domestic fowls, but this method biases any estimates of nesting success. Given the difficulty of locating nests and the biases involved, radio-tracking of birds caught before nesting starts is the best way of locating them. Today the success or otherwise of almost 30,000 nests found has been recorded and a clear picture emerges, supported by the recent radio-tracking evidence and stubble counts.

CHOICE OF NESTING COVER: GREY PARTRIDGE

In the 1930s the natural nest sites of the grey partridge were studied by Ul'yanin (1949) in the Naurzumskii Reserve of northern Kazakhstan, already mentioned. He described the preferred nest sites as having a general colouration that allows

FIG 82. Near natural nesting cover with juniper, Amberley Mount, Sussex Study area.

the sitting hen to use her camouflage, especially grass foliage from the previous year ('residual grass'). Most nests were under rose bushes or in clumps of meadowsweet or on the top of small sand dunes covered in crested wheatgrass, but some were in the open feather-grass steppe and yet others were in grassy clearings in loosely wooded pine groves. Ul'yanin argued that there was no shortage of nest sites because the partridges had such a wide choice of them. The nest sites chosen by the Daurian partridge in the Trans-Baikal are described as situated in shelter of the prevailing wind, on the slopes of valleys, under low shrubs such as the thorny pea but also under dwarf birches (Litun & Flint, 1993). Again it was considered that nesting cover was plentiful. Both of these observations of nesting in semi-natural habitats were however made in areas and at a time with no harmful grazing or browsing by domestic animals. With heavy grazing, nest sites could be in shorter supply, although we can safely conclude that nest sites would be plentiful in the natural shrub-steppe habitat.

In *British Game* Vesey-Fitzgerald wrote: 'Very occasionally you may find a nest in an odd or foolish situation, in a haystack or between the sleepers on a railway siding, and as these nests are invariably recorded in the press the partridge has acquired something of a reputation as a careless nester. This is very far from the truth.' He was right. On the traditional well-hedged partridge manors, especially in Norfolk, the proportion of nests in hedgerow banks was always high. At Great Witchingham, the number of nests found along hedgerows was about 50 per

cent of the number of pairs present in spring and many in hedges were not
found; at least 75 per cent of the total pairs were nesting in hedgerows (Potts,
1986). Even on poorly hedged downland in Hampshire 76 per cent of nests were
in hedgerows or overgrown fencerows (Huband, 1969). In areas with still fewer
hedgerows many pairs have no alternative but to nest in crops. After allowing for
the biases in searching mentioned above, Yocom (1943) concluded that 25 per cent
of all the nests in his area were in hayfields, mostly sown to lucerne (alfalfa), with
72 per cent of these nests lost due to mowing. The high percentage of losses in
the hayfields was offset by the small proportion of the farmland that was in hay.
Three early studies of radio-tracked females found a relatively high proportion
of nests in hedgerows even in poorly hedged areas. In Wisconsin Kevin Church
found 10 of 24 (42 per cent) in hedgerows and fencerows (Church, 1980), in North
Dakota John Carroll found 10 of 13 (77 per cent) (Carroll, 1990) and on Salisbury
Plain Jonathan Reynolds found 13 of 32 (41 per cent) (Reynolds *et al.*, 1992). There
are even fewer hedges and fences in the North-Central France study areas of
Elizabeth Bro and colleagues, leaving many partridges there with no alternative
but to nest in crops. An astonishing 548 nests were located by radio-tracking
females, with 64 per cent of first clutches laid in cereals and only the remainder
in linear features such as banks and hedgerows. Replacement clutches were more
evenly dispersed, with only 37 per cent in cereals (Bro *et al.*, 2000). In Greece 10
of 13 nests were found in cereal crops in an area with tiny fields but very few

FIG 83. Grey Partridges nest in cereals if more permanent nesting cover is poor or absent.

FIG 84. Ideal dispersion of nesting cover on the Norfolk Estate Sussex Study area with no need for the partridges to nest in cereals.

hedges (Thomaides & Papageorgiou, 1992). In Bavaria Wolfgang Kaiser showed with radio-tracking that hedgerows were the preferred nesting habitat in spring although subsequently almost 50 per cent of nests were in cereals (Kaiser & Storch, 1996).

Even where nesting is in cereals or other crops, field size, crop edges and hedgerow cover are still crucially important. In Hungary during 1946–55, 46 per cent of nests in cereals were within 3 m of the field margin (Szederjei and Szederjei, 1960). Using the same methods in Czechoslovakia in the 1950s, 54 per cent of nests in crops were within 3 m of the border (Škultéty, 1965). In France 60 per cent of the nests in cereals were within 10 m of the edge of the crop, with many near tramlines (Bro *et al.*, 2000). In some circumstances high partridge densities can be achieved without any hedges at all, but this is only possible if the fields are very small. For example, in an entirely hedge-less area of 62 ha in Poland, 14 of 15 pairs nested in cereal crops, mostly early growing rye, where fields averaged only 0.65 ha (Wübbenhorst & Leuschner, 2006). It was not clear what the birds used as cover before the rye grew in spring.

Almost everywhere field size has increased. In Britain prior to the nineteenth-century enclosures, arable cropping was in narrow strips and these strips were

FIG 85. Huge fields, averaging 148 ha, with shelter belts near Yankel on the Caucasian plain, Russia: the grey partridge density is very low.

found all over Europe until the 1950s. They still persist in parts of southeast Poland but elsewhere most strips have been amalgamated or consolidated into larger fields. In Austria, for example, Reichholf (1973) describes the removal of 800 km of field boundary from an area of only 750 ha in the late 1960s, with 'the network of unsprayed, little-contaminated banks and field borders destroyed'. Despite the fact that hunting (shooting) ceased and there were no goshawks, the pair density dropped by 65 per cent.

The lengths of hedge and or field edges (henceforth hedge) per 100 ha were estimated from maps in the original papers and with reference to the authorities listed in Appendix 2. Where only field size was available the length was calculated by the equation log_{10} length= $1.53-0.60 log_{10}$ field size. Measured and calculated information together show a loss of 40 per cent of hedge across the grey partridge range from 1940 to the end of the century (Appendix 2).

Because field size is so important, even when partridges nest in crops, the process known in France as farm consolidation has had a serious impact on densities (Reitz et al., 1999). As Bro et al. (2000) put it: 'An increase in cereal farming in France might have favored the grey partridge if field size had remained small and permanent cover strips had not been destroyed.' The

importance of permanent boundaries is why grey partridge numbers were so
affected in Britain by hedge removal in the 1960s and 1970s, even though many
birds could have nested in crops. Nests in crops are less exposed to predation in
France (Bro *et al.*, 2000) but they are more susceptible to flooding by very heavy
rain. Probably for this reason intense rainfall has such a significant adverse effect
on the number of young partridges produced per female in France (Birkan &
Pépin, 1984; Reitz, 1988; Pépin *et al.*, 2008). This was not evident in Sussex except
on 2 June 1981 when 76 mm of rain fell in a few hours causing some flooding and
the loss of an estimated 28 per cent of nests.

There are many other reports of nest desertion due to heavy rain, but these
effects of rain are not straightforward. In June 1903 the incubating females on 65
(61 per cent) of 107 nests deserted due to 76 hours of 'incessant' rain (Alington,
1910), but the fact that some birds died on the nest, with others in very poor
condition, suggests strongylosis was also involved. Wet weather can increase fox
predation on incubating females, as shown best by a study of 54 hen pheasants
where most of 17 incubating females lost to foxes were lost in wet weather (Hill
& Robertson, 1988, extended *in litt.*). As shown by studies on red grouse by Peter
Hudson and colleagues, weather, disease and predation may all interact to
increase nest losses. So far as partridges are concerned, it is hoped that future
studies with simultaneous automatic activity recording and automatic cameras at
nests will help to disentangle the factors. In the meantime the 1981 event, itself
rare (once in 43 years), is I believe a worst possible case because there was virtually
no control of foxes, nesting cover was scarce and the sitting females had no grain
or other seed resource to rapidly replace the natural depletion of body reserves
that takes place during incubation

RESIDUAL GRASS

Kevin Church drew attention to what he called 'residual grass' (Church, 1984)
and its value has been recognised by many authors (e.g. Döring & Helfrich, 1986,
Kantrud & Higgins, 1992; Zhang & Liang, 1997). Mike Rands compared nest
sites with randomly chosen sites in north Norfolk, Hampshire and Wiltshire.
He found that grey partridges chose to nest in hedgerows with 'residual grasses'
on a bank (Rands, 1986b, 1988). In France, in areas with far fewer hedges and
banks, it was similarly concluded that four factors were important, namely: 1) a
good availability of dead cover to provide materials to build the nest; 2) a good
cover height and density to hide clutches and sitting females from predators; 3)
a presence of boundaries and/or particular features such as stakes or stones to

provide landmarks indicating roughly the nest location; and 4) a presence of linear features to offer corridors for daily movements and to escape from predators (Bro *et al.*, 2000). Drainage was not mentioned. Taller residual grass reduced predation rates at grey partridge nests (Rands, 1986b, 1988), but elsewhere thorns are probably more important in protecting nests from ground predators, especially those that hunt by scent and not sight. In Kazakhstan grey partridge nests have been found under the camel thorn (Dementiev & Gladkov, 1952; Annenkov & Litun, 1989). Grey partridges in Saskatchewan favor the thorny Siberian pea shrub (Hunt, 1974). This bush is a native of the Tibetan plateau and Tibetan partridges frequently nest under it or dwarf junipers (Kuz'mina, 1977; Lu, 2003).

Linear features such as hedgerows and fencerows would not have been important prior to agriculture but they are vital today. In Britain, where relatively many hedges, fences and walls remain around fields, grey partridge nest densities increase with the length of linear cover per unit area. This is mainly due to reduced dispersion and increased efficiency of recruitment of young females where the nesting cover is better (Potts, 1980, 1986; Rands, 1986b). In Britain the maximum length useful to partridges is considered to be 10 km per 100 ha (Potts, 1986). Where fields are in strips, the length of linear cover can be much higher. In the Elbe lowlands of Czechoslovakia there were 22 km per 100 ha in 1949, mostly grass baulks, of which only 4 km remained by 1996 (Figala *et al.*, 2001). Not surprisingly the 40 pairs of grey partridge per 100 ha in the 1940s (Kokeš & Knobloch, 1947) suffered a decline of 93 per cent by 1996. In Huesca, Spain, 85 per cent of bushes and hedges were removed between 1975 and 1985, with many fields of more than 50 ha created and contributing to a large decline in breeding numbers of red-legged partridges (Nadal *et al.*, 1996).

Scarce crop edge and linear cover can be overwhelmingly important in determining low grey partridge numbers even where cereal crops are untreated with pesticides, weedy (full of ragweed, larkspur and *Polygonum* spp.) offering good brood-rearing habitats. In 2004 on a 44,000 ha farm at Yankel on the Sal'skie steppe, Caucasian plain, field size averaged an astonishing 148 ha (range 49–400 ha), with only 1.8 km of edge per 100 ha (Fig. 85). The pair density was 0.3 pairs per 100 ha overall, rising to 1 pair in the best places. This low density occurred despite a very high chick survival rate of ~70 per cent (Potts, unpublished). The arable fields here were created after farm mechanisation but reduced (to 148 ha!) later when many shelter belts were planted throughout the region to prevent soil-blow, as directed by Nikita Khrushchev, later Premier of the USSR.

This brief overview has shown that the variation in field size is enormous. The largest fields are in the wheat belt of Eastern Europe, at an average of about 150 ha, followed by North America, central Europe, Britain and Western Europe, with some very small fields in Italy, the former Yugoslavia, Greece and southeast Poland. In all parts of grey partridge range the field size has increased and the amounts of hedgerows, other cover and edge have decreased (Potts, 1986). As was mentioned in the introductory chapter, this had a large adverse effect on grey partridge numbers in Britain, which we will explore further after considering the other partridge species.

CHOICE OF NESTING COVER: RED-LEGGED AND CHUKAR PARTRIDGES

In Mike Rands' study of nest site selection mentioned above, red-legged partridges preferred hedgerows with nettles and generally more cover; and taller vegetation was found to give red-legged partridges protection from crow predation (Rands, 1988). Overhead vegetation was very important, especially if thorny (Fig. 86). A study of the vegetation at 63 nests in southern France showed that red-legged partridges selected uncultivated habitats, especially hedgerows. Cultivated cereals and vineyards were avoided unless weedy and 95 per cent of nests were within the outer 16 m of 'vegetation patches' (Ricci *et al.*, 1990b). The most favored shrub in this study was the prickly leaved shrub known as the

FIG 86. Red-legged partridge nest in Portugal with eggs uncovered but protected by brambles.

Kermes Oak, also favoured by nesting rock partridges (Thomaides *et al.*, 1992). In contrast the gum rock rose in Spain and Portugal offers poor nesting cover because it suppresses other ground cover using 'natural herbicides'. In the hills of the northern Apennines grey and red-legged partridges both nest in the 7,700 ha study area of Alberto Meriggi of the University of Pavia. The habitats of the pairs in spring were similar for both species, with both avoiding woodland; however, red-legged partridges chose shrubs and rocky areas and grey partridges chose hedgerows and rows of trees (Meriggi *et al.*, 1992). In western France 31 per cent of 362 red-legged partridge nests were in hedgerows, with 33 per cent in meadows, compared to grey partridge nests where 13 per cent of 93 nests were in hedgerows with 67 per cent in meadows (Brun, 1991). In the Cantabrian mountains of northern Spain grey and red-legged partridges have overlapping distributions which enabled a comparative study of habitat selection by 61 grey partridge coveys and 95 red-legged partridge coveys during 1994–7 (Junco, 2002). The vegetation characteristics of the chosen habitats were much the same, with both preferring species of broom, except that grey partridges occurred at higher altitudes with Provence broom as cover and red-legged partridges preferred steeper slopes with common broom and *Genista florida* as cover (see also Lucio *et al.*, 1992).

Aristotle mentioned that rock partridges chose nest sites where the sitting hen was protected from raptors by thorns and in Bulgaria, Georgiev (1958) found that chukar partridges prefer to nest under bushes of Christ's thorn (relative of buckthorn). Grachev (1983) gives details for 175 nests in Kazakhstan, with a clear preference for sites under rocks giving shelter to the north. Litun & Annenkov (1989) described nests under 'prickly cover'. In Israel thistles were selected, including the very prickly globe thistle (Alkon, 1983). I have also found a Barbary partridge nest under a prickly pear. The cacti had been introduced from the Americas, so this is a relatively new development. In Texas bobwhite quail frequently choose to nest under prickly pear and tests showed that raccoon predation on bobwhite quail was greatly reduced if nests were protected in this way (Hernández *et al.*, 2006).

These observations show that the *Alectoris* partridges in particular are clearly selecting the kind of thorny or spiny vegetation that would be most likely to protect their clutches from predators. Otherwise the nest sites of the two species are quite similar but with shrubby cover more important in the red-legged partridge. This is what we would expect from its habit of not covering its eggs. Meadows and tussock grasses are preferred by grey partridges, especially along low hedgerows and again this is what we would expect given that it is a shrub-steppe species. Where the preferred nest sites are absent, both species nest in crops and this can have a big impact on nest success.

PREDATION AT THE NEST, AND THE ROLE OF GAMEKEEPERS

A characteristic of grassland birds is that they have low nesting success, with the primary cause being predation (Vickery *et al.*, 1992); partridges, as we shall see, are no exception. Evidence to examine nest losses is available directly, from nests found, and indirectly from the Brood Production Rates obtained from stubble counts, as explained on page 18. The high rate of nest predation surprised many who assumed that they had unwittingly increased the loss rate and gave up looking. In partridges this is not the case and in former times gamekeepers were encouraged to find nests and check them regularly.

There are however difficulties in diagnosing the causes of the loss of nests where predation is involved. Lots of nests are described in the literature as being 'abandoned' or 'deserted' but without knowing whether the male or female was predated away from the nest. This means that almost all estimates of losses due to predation are underestimates; sometimes the number of nests probably abandoned through predation on adults can be as high as the number of predated nests (Khanmamedov, 1969; Grachev, 1983). In Poland 48 per cent of radio-tracked females were predated during the nesting season (mostly by foxes and other carnivores), with half of them killed away from the nest (Panek, 2002).

Excluding cases where fewer than ten nests were found, there are 43 'studies' of the grey partridge reporting the success for more than 28,000 nests where nest losses have been quantified, and one each for Daurian and Tibetan partridges (Table 6). There are only thirteen similar studies for the red-legged partridge, seven for the chukar partridge and two for the rock partridge, with one for a hybrid population. These have been combined to give an *Alectoris* sample of 23, with 1,918 nests found in total (Table 7).

Even though nest predation is underestimated – the problem of abandoned nests and losses biased towards mowing – these studies show the importance of nest predation. In the grey partridge total nest losses increased by 0.623±0.193 per cent for every 1 per cent increase in nest predation (P=0.003). In the *Alectoris* partridges total nests losses increased by 0.715±0.180 per cent for every 1 per cent increase in nest predation (P=0.002). The contribution of predation to total nest losses is therefore not just very important, it was strikingly similar in the two species. Not only that, predator control reduced total losses by 48 per cent in the grey partridge and by 46 per cent in *Alectoris*, but remembering that the relationship with nest density is even more important than these percentages imply, due to the effects of nest density on predation.

There are far more data about total losses than is available from nests found; in the grey partridge an additional 29 sets of stubble counts can be brought into the picture (29 after Sussex Study counts were grouped into two periods; up to 1985 and since 1985, adding in other GWCT counts where I have been involved (see Appendix 3). There were no statistically significant differences between the stubble count estimates and those from nests found. All 74 'studies' were therefore taken together and classified according to whether they had a full-time gamekeeper dedicated to partridge conservation or not. This was defined as the presence of a full network of tunnel traps for the smaller ground predators and at least one gamekeeper per 600 ha. Some studies will have had nest predation effectively controlled by hunters themselves and almost everywhere sheep and poultry farmers and others will have removed some predators, so the distinction is not as clear as it was in the Salisbury Plain experiment (p. 30). Further classification used the middle year of the study and the length of hedge per 100 ha.

The effects of a gamekeeper (P=<0.001) and length of hedge (P=0.005) were statistically significant. Overall these two variables explained 52 per cent of the variation through all 'studies'. Nest losses were, on average, 29 per cent per cent with a gamekeeper and 52 per cent without, so that the losses were reduced 44 per cent by gamekeepers (P<0.001). The comparable figures from the Salisbury Plain experiment were 20 per cent and 50 per cent, with losses reduced by 60 per cent. The influence of gamekeepers and hedges can be compared as follows. With a poor 5 km of 'hedge' or edge per 100 ha the losses are estimated to be 36 per cent with a gamekeeper and 60 per cent without. With a very high 15 km of 'hedge' the losses are 26 per cent and 50 per cent respectively. Without a gamekeeper the nests losses increased 1.7 times with 5 km of hedge, and 1.9 times with 15 km of hedge. The loss of 10 km of hedge increased losses by 0.2 times without a gamekeeper and 0.28 times with a gamekeeper. So far as nest losses are concerned, the presence of a gamekeeper had 2.4 times as much impact as the length of hedges. There was very little trend through time after the gamekeeper effect had been accounted for (Fig. 88).

It is important to bear in mind (from the introduction) that hedges are very important in regulating the recruitment to nesting stocks. In Sussex the length of hedgerow was found to be crucially important in determining the nesting density by regulating the recruitment of young females to the breeding stock (Potts, 1986). This was confirmed by Mike Rands in a study of 17 estates across Britain (Rands, 1986b). The main importance of field size is in regulating nesting numbers not nesting success.

The effects of the absence of linear cover can be reversed if nesting cover is reinstated in combination with predation control. On the Walbeck estate in

TABLE 6. Grey partridge: studies of nests found, reporting overall losses and losses to predation at the nest. Losses on areas with dedicated partridge keepers are indicated by shading. Data from reared and released birds have been excluded so far as possible. Daurian* and Tibetan** partridges are indicated.

site	period of study inclusive	nests found	% clutches lost	% nests predated	authority
East Anglia	1902–3	211	42	16	Alington (1904)
Berwickshire	1907–14	2,831	18	10	Douglas-Home (1938)
Hampshire	1911–24	4,181	23	14	Middleton (1967)
Berwickshire	1919–37	4,756	22	12	Douglas-Home (1938)
Michigan	1929–32	143	68	18	Yeatter (1934)
Britain	1933–4	1,041	26	15	Middleton (1967)
Iowa	1933–5	26	69	38 (?)	Errington & Hamerstrom (1938)
Kazakhstan	1935–6	16	40	?	Ul'yanin (1949)
Britain	1935–7	5,633	24	11	Middleton (1967)
Wisconsin	1936–42	435	68	7	McCabe & Hawkins (1946)
Washington	1940–2	113	63	3	Knott *et al.* (1943)
Denmark	1946–55	1,073	31	11	Westerskov (1949b)
Finland	1946–52	55	31	21	Siivonen (1953)
Damerham	1948–59	3,133	39	15	Middleton (1967)
Micheldever	1953–5	200	30	18	Jenkins (1961b)
Czechoslovakia	1955	389	?	13	Sekera (1959)
Russia	1952–66	17	?	25	Loshkarev (1975)
Czechoslovakia	1959–60	270	50	4	Škultéty (1965)
Azerbaijan	1955–69	40	60	17	Khanmammedov (1969)
Wisconsin	1960–5	69	84	28	Gates (1973)
Czechoslovakia	1961–3	1,358	>41	5	Hell (1965)

North Prairies	1963–91	21	52	>14	Kantrud & Higgins (1992)
Czechoslovakia	1965	76	88	46	Bouchner & Fiser (1967)
Iowa	1967–73	58	76	>50	Bishop *et al.* (1977)
Sussex Study	1968–71	111	37	17	Potts (1980)
Montana	1969–73	10	60	20	Weigand (1980)
France	1980	768	60	17	Birkan (1986)
Saskatchewan	1971–2	17	53	36	Hunt (1974)
Iowa	1972–7	23	74	39	McCrow (1982)
Poland	1974–84	62	40	15	Olech (1988b)
West France	1977–85	93	<80	36	Brun (1991)
Wisconsin	1978–9	24	71	33	Church (1984)
Norfolk	1980–1	22	68	~68	Green (1982; 1984)
		–	38	~38	
New York St.	1982–3	11	27	20	(Church (1993)
Hampshire	1984–7	42	43	33	Rands (1988)
South Dakota	1978–9	44	55	34	Hupp *et al.* (1980)
North Dakota	1985–7	32	69	26	Carroll (1989)
France	1986–7	28	64	50?	Birkan *et al.* (1990)
Finland	1991–6	33	23–30	>20	Putaala & Hissa (1998)
Poland	1991–2004	45	63	51	Panek (2002)
France	1995–7	588	57	36	Bro *et al.* (2000)
Shanxi*	1991–3	60	39	28	Zhang & Liang (1997)
Czech Republic	1997–9	11	~64	~36	Šálek *et al.* (2002)
Lhasa Mts.**	1991–2001	26	56	45	Lu *et al.* (2003)
Switzerland	1999–2003	19	67	58	Buner (2006)
totals (averaged)		**28,214**	**51**	**26**	

FIG 87. As shown by Ahti Putaala and colleagues in Finland, these birds will cover 4 m in the first second after take off, leaving predators to rely on surprise.

FIG 88. Nests losses of grey partridge through the twentieth century based on 74 studies comparing areas with predator control (blue) and without (red).

North Rhine–Westphalia, Germany, pair densities increased from 15 per 100 ha with 8 km of crop edge per 100 ha to 45 pairs with 20 km per 100 ha (Pethig, 1994). In La Mancha, Spain, red-legged partridge densities are higher in areas with smaller fields (Fortuna, 2002), and at Las Ensanchas an additional 6 km of linear cover per 100 ha doubled the density of breeding pairs. The restoration of numbers on the Norfolk Estate could not have happened without new, reinstated and improved hedges (Chapter 10). All three successes were characterised by intensive predator control. When this was absent, particularly the trapping of the smaller mustelids (especially stone marten), the provision of extra linear cover did not help grey partridges in Switzerland (Jenny *et al.*, 2002), France (Bro *et al.*, 2004) or Hungary (Báldi & Faragó, 2007; Faragó *et al.*, 2012).

ALECTORIS

As yet there is nothing equivalent to the Salisbury Plain experiment for the *Alectoris* partridges. Nevertheless comparisons of areas with and without predator control in the south of France show nest losses and nest predation both 1.9 times higher (Ricci *et al.*, 1990). In Spain an interesting attempt to prevent nest predation (Coll in Puga, 2002) surrounded 33 nests with 12 x 12 cm mesh netting to keep out crows and foxes. Almost half the nests were still lost to other predators including the garden dormouse. More important, with 97 nests located, mostly in the outer 5 m margin of cereal crops in an area with

TABLE 7. Red-legged and chukar partridge: studies of nest losses from nests found and estimates from the Sussex study. Data from reared and released birds have been excluded so far as possible, as have studies with ten or fewer nests found. Losses on areas with dedicated partridge keepers are indicated by shading.

site and species	period of study inclusive	nests found	% clutches lost	% clutches predated	authority
England (red)	1933–5	86	8%	8%	Middleton (1936)
Hampshire (red)	1953–4	18	22%	?	Jenkins (1957)
Bulgaria (chukar)	1953–6	35	54%	?	Georgiev (1958)
California (chukar)	1954–5	17	75%	45%	Harper *et al.* (1958)
Washington (chukar)	1958–60	24	75%	75%	Mackie & Buechner (1963)
Sussex (red)	1969	49	41%	29%	Sussex study
Israel (chukar)	1970–1	37	68%	?	Alkon (1983)
Kazakhstan (chukar)	1974–8	76	45%	25%	Grachev (1983)
western France (red)	1977–85	362	68%	24%	Brun (1991)
Portugal (red)	1978	17	59%	18%	Bugalho & Lopes (1979)
Spain (red)	1978	21	29%	?	Stenheil *in litt.*
Norfolk (red)	1980–1	78	38%	38%	Green (1982, 1984b)
	1980–1		85%	85%	
Spain (red)	1982–3	33		48.5%	Coll in Puga *et al.* (2002)
Spain, Guedea (red)	1982–4	606	15%	15%	Llandres & Otero (1985)
Hampshire (red)	1984–7	65	62%	41%	Rands (1988)
southern France (red)	1986–9	32	41%	41%	Ricci *et al.* (1990a)
		29	79%	79%	

France (red x rock natural hybrid)	1986–8	14	57%	43%	Bernard-Laurent (1990)
Western Greece (rock)	1998–2001	32	72%	69%	Manios et al. (2007)
Greece (rock)	<1991	33	40%	?	Thomaides et al. (1992)
Idaho (chukar)	1995–6	23	59%	45%	Lindbloom et al. (2003)
Spain, Malaga (red)	1996–7	111	?	21%	in Puga et al. (2002)
Oregon (chukar)	1997–8	23	49%	?	Walter (2002)
La Mancha, Spain (red)	2003–5	97	64%	27%	Casas & Viñuela (2010)
totals		1,918	52%	40%	

gamekeepers, Casas & Viñuela (2010) found losses to agricultural activities (particularly early harvesting) were much higher than losses to predation. Ultimately these losses to harvesting are due to the removal of nesting cover. With or without predator control it seems the first priority is to reinstate the cover.

Over all *Alectoris*, combined nest losses were 34 per cent with a gamekeeper and 63 per cent (1.9 times higher) without a gamekeeper (P<0.001), virtually the same increase as in the grey partridge. Nest losses can be expected to be somewhat higher in *Alectoris* partly because the eggs are not covered. They are spotted brown however, whereas the eggs of the grey partridge are a uniform olive, and this camouflage appears to reduce predation rates (Castilla *et al.*, 2007). In *Alectoris* the main adaptation to higher nest predation is for each female to lay in two nests: double brooding, sometimes called double nesting, though this can be confused with repeat nesting.

DOUBLE BROODING IN THE RED-LEGGED PARTRIDGE

The number of chicks hatched by red-legged partridges in Britain is on average 17 per cent less per successful nest than in the grey partridge (Potts, 1980). But this does not mean fewer chicks hatching per pair and this is because of double brooding.

FIG 89. In good production years in Spain the majority of broods are seen with only one parent. (Patricia Maldonado Vidal)

More than 2,000 years ago Aristotle found that rock partridge males incubated the first of two clutches laid by the hen (Capponi, 1979) and through the early twentieth century there was a succession of reports of incubation by both male and female red-legged, chukar and Barbary partridges, with two clutches laid by the same female in separate nests (e.g. Heinroth & Heinroth, 1928; Sprake, 1934; in Spano & Csermely, 1985). But this double booding behaviour was only properly quantified using birds individually marked with numbered back tags (Jenkins, 1956) or followed by radio-tracking (Green, 1984b). Rhys Green carried out detailed studies at 78 nests in north Norfolk; with double brooding, two clutches with a total of 28 eggs were laid in 34 days. The nests were of two types: 54 per cent were 'delayed' where at most only one egg was laid in the 10 days before incubation started, whereas in the remaining 'undelayed' nests at least two eggs were laid in this period. Clutch sizes at the two types of nest were not statistically different and incubation started simultaneously at delayed and undelayed nests. Females incubated all undelayed nests and 17 per cent of delayed nests with males incubating the remainder, with the basic plan set out in Figure 90. Rhys found that ~70 per cent of females older than one year laid two clutches for separate incubation, with each pair incubating an average of 1.33 clutches per pair per year. Older red-legged partridges lay earlier (Mourão *et al.*, 2010), thus giving them more time to lay two clutches. A four-year study in the native range of the species, in central Spain, has found 1.38 clutches incubated per pair per year (Casas *et al.*, 2009).

One indication of double booding is in the high percentage of red-legged partridge broods that are accompanied by only one adult, which can be of either sex. This percentage fluctuates from zero in the worst production years to 70 per cent in the best. Data from Sussex, Spain and Portugal all appear to fit the same

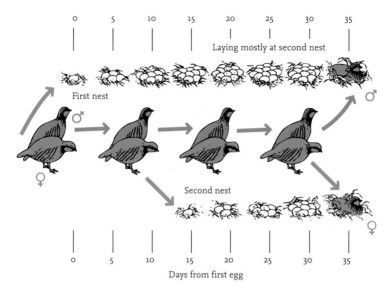

Laying mostly at second nest

First nest

Second nest

Days from first egg

FIG 90. Scheme of double brooding in the red-legged partridge. (after Rhys Green; GWCT archive)

relationship (Fig. 91) and it is an important one. At Las Ensanchas, La Mancha, with a total of 1,288 broods, 622 (48 per cent) were accompanied by only one adult, with the remainder accompanied by two or more adults. On this estate it therefore appears that double booding almost doubled the production of young. The reasons for the low percentage of broods that are accompanied by only one adult in poor years are however not clear. Pointing out that Mediterranean

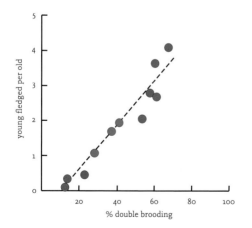

FIG 91. Double brooding, measured as percentage of broods with only one adult, is very important as it greatly improves the overall production of young (red – Las Ensanchas, Spain; blue – Sussex Study; green – Vale de Perditos, Portugal).

climates are characterised by a high annual variability in temperature and rainfall, Casas *et al.* (2009) suggested that because females can lay more eggs in wet springs when the vegetation is more nutritious, the best breeding strategy would be to split them into two clutches, to increase the probability that at least one will not be predated. It seems however more complicated than this because very different conditions can be responsible for low percentages of single adults accompanying broods; massive hail storms in 1999 and little vegetation growth in 2005 each gave the same outcome at Las Ensanchas. Either way it is clear from Figure 91 that double brooding is absent in the very poor years when breeding fails.

The reason that double brooding occurs in red-legged and *Alectoris* partridges but not grey partridges demands explanation. The laying of 28 eggs that together weigh 30 per cent more than the female's body weight does not appear to be a problem except perhaps in droughts, but one obvious cost in the system arises from egg predation during the extra days that the delayed clutches are at risk prior to incubation (Green, 1984b). There are also other costs, one being the lack of shared surveillance against predators, as when the male guards the female grey partridge when she is incubating, but this may not matter so much in areas with more cover where there is little chance of seeing ambush predators in time to take avoiding action, against a dark background of rocks or trees. Perhaps the most serious cost of double brooding is that chicks must be brooded by only one parent. So much for the costs – what about the advantages? One advantage arises in maximising the availability of insects to chicks in a situation where the hatching of replacement clutches would be too late. The abundance of preferred insect food species falls rapidly as the vegetation ripens and dries out in Mediterranean summers. The only important insect foods which do not rapidly decline in abundance in early summer are ants, but these may carry parasites (Chapter 7). If this is the case, double brooding is driven by the seasonal abundance of insects. It would be interesting to follow this up by investigating the situation in another *Alectoris*, Przevalski's rock partridge which, does not double-nest (Naifa & Yang, 1992).

PREDATION ON NESTS IN RELATION TO NEST DENSITY

In the Potts model brood production rates (BPRs) decrease with increasing nest density if there is no predator control. This was based largely on the evidence from the Sussex study up to 1985, contrasting areas with gamekeepers and those without. The experiment to verify this finding was the one on Salisbury Plain described earlier. This found that the BPR with no predator control was 50 per

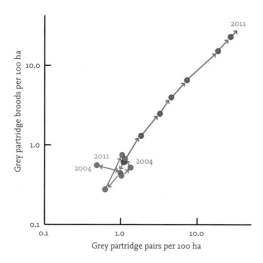

FIG 92. Sussex Study area 2004–10, showing the relationship between the numbers of broods hatching and the density of pairs contrasting the area without predator control (blue) and with (red); the trajectories since 2004 are plotted showing what happens when there is no density-dependent predation.

cent; with predation control it was raised to an average 80 per cent. With 12.1 chicks hatching without predation control and 13.8 with it (due to fewer repeat nests with lower clutch sizes, see p. 19) – the number of chicks hatching per pair rose from 6.0 to 11.0, or an 83 per cent increase in production.

Predator control in the Salisbury Plain experiment was completed in 1990. Would the relationships hold in the twenty-first century? The results on the Norfolk Estate, with systematic predator control, are compared with those on the rest of the Sussex Study area in Figure 92. The differences were greater than on Salisbury Plain, with the BPR increasing from 39.0 per cent to 85.3 per cent, giving 4.7 and 11.8 chicks hatching per pair respectively, or a 151 per cent increase. More importantly, there was no density-dependent nest predation, so the population could grow without that constraint.

These crucial relationships are not special to Sussex and Salisbury Plain. In Poland Marek Panek found an increase in nest predation with increasing nest density in all three of his study areas (consolidated in Fig. 93). Moreover, as earlier in Sussex, his simulation models showed nest predation was the most important factor determining population size (Panek, 1992).

The rise in nest predation rate with increasing nest density is extremely important but, paradoxically, in the absence of experiments, it is very difficult to detect. There is another twist too. Because nest losses in relation to density are so important in determining the size of the partridge population in a particular locality, when one compares different localities we get the opposite of a density-dependent relationship; nesting survival is higher, where populations

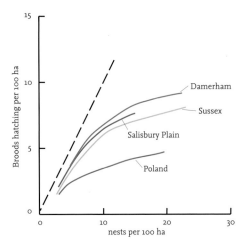

FIG 93. Number of broods hatching per 100 ha in studies with no predator control showing declining success with increasing nest density: Salisbury Plain (Tapper *et al.*, 1996); Sussex and Damerham (Potts, 1980); and Poland (Panek, 1997). The broken line indicates the expected slope with 100 per cent nesting success.

are higher. Nevertheless, in France Bro *et al.* (2000) measured survival at various stages of the life cycle in ten localities. The only measure that was statistically significantly density-dependent was female survival in summer, which as explained above decreased with density. In a later study of 85 sets of population data for grey partridges in France, 82 per cent of those with more than seven years data showed a linear decrease of breeding success with increasing pair density (Bro *et al.*, 2003). At Micheldever in Hampshire, David Jenkins was the first to observe that ground cover is crucially important, finding that the success of nests and chicks were both low at densities over 40 pairs per 100 ha due to a combination of poor cover and a high amount of social interactions (Jenkins, 1961a, 1961b). In Italy the same reduction in breeding success with density was found at 10 per cent of the Micheldever density (Montagna & Meriggi, 1991). Since chick survival has not been convincingly shown to be related to density, the underlying cause in France and Italy is most probably the same combination of poor nesting cover and high nest predation that was observed in Sussex and Poland. The French data would repay further analysis.

There is clear evidence from Jacques and Isabelle Hicter's farms in Picardie, where pair densities have been the highest recently recorded anywhere, that nest losses do not increase with an increased density of nests (Table 8). Nest predators are controlled here, so the result is what we would expect: although the nest losses are 10 percentage points higher than the global average, they do not increase with nest density. Similar evidence for the red-legged partridge is given in Table 9.

There is some evidence from the US that predation increases with nest density. Yocom's early study on the Palouse Prairie, Washington State, has been

TABLE 8. Highest recorded grey partridge pair densities and brood production rate; Hicter Farms, Picardie, France. With predation control the losses are not higher at these very high nesting densities.

year	pairs per 100 ha	calculated nest losses
2000	82	43%
2001	91	36%
2002	74	42%
2003	80	44%
2004	82	39%
2005	84	43%
average	82	41%

TABLE 9. Counts of red-legged partridges at Las Ensanchas showing effects of hailstorms of 4–5 June 1999 and of the severe drought of 2005. Note very high density of pairs and no decline of young per old with higher pair (nesting) densities. The high percentage of single-parent families in the good years is also striking.

year	pairs per 100 ha	young per old in July	single parent families
1996	37	2.6	–
1997	52	1.1	–
1998	74	0.6	–
1999	85	0.1	13%
2000	54	3.8	68%
2001	70	3.7	60%
2002	102	2.8	59%
2003	103	2.1	53%
2004	82	2.4	?
2005	102	0.1	19%
2006	90	4.1	67%
2007	111	2.4	?

FIG 94. Some 55 km of new beetle banks and nesting cover like this have been provided for red-legged partridge, Las Ensanchas, Spain. (Patricia Maldonado Vidal)

mentioned earlier. After the main study in the early 1940s, numbers continued to be monitored, with a marked decline from the early 1950s. Extremely low population levels were reached in the 1960s, less than 1 pair per 100 ha, and monitoring became impracticable. Then after a gap of two decades the area was revisited, with numbers found to be higher even than in 1940 (Rotella *et al.*, 1996). Because the counts were not continuous over the 53-year study, there were data on breeding success for only 15 years. These data showed that nest predation rate was high, and 'strongly density-dependent'. Jay and colleagues speculated that the small amount of nesting cover allowed predators to find nests easily except when nest densities were low.

The key point here is that by increasing disproportionately with nest density, nest predation is capable of very strongly limiting grey partridge population density. The evidence suggests the same may be true of the *Alectoris* partridges. Predation is the most important cause of nest loss because it is density-dependent, increasing losses disproportionately as nests become more crowded.

David Lack generalised in *The Natural Regulation of Animal Numbers* (1954): 'The large edible eggs of nidifugous species provide palatable food for various mammals and birds, and nearly all the egg losses in such species are from predation.' Partridges illustrate his point well.

DENSITY-DEPENDENT NEST PREDATION AND NEST DISPERSION

Earlier we saw that partridges must nest on the ground but given this – why do they not nest in colonies? The most plausible reason appears to be the need to avoid high nest predation. It is true there is no need to disperse where predation is controlled, but the dispersal has been 'hard-wired' into partridge evolution for millions of years whereas gamekeepers have not. At relatively high densities, 5–25 pairs per 100 ha, it has been well established that partridge pairs disperse to a greater extent when linear nesting cover, such as hedgerows, is scarce (Rands, 1986). The dispersion of nests along hedgerows is far from random; in fact it is close to what is known as an 'ideal free distribution' where the dispersion has evolved as an adaptation to the predation pressure (Potts, 1986).

The prairie chicken is also noted for spacing nests far and wide, and a benchmark paper, *Increasing the Numbers of Grouse*, addressed the issues head on (Bergerud & Gratson, 1988; also Bergerud, 1992). Tom Bergerud found that forest, tundra and steppe grouse space their nests to be inconspicuous so as to minimise the risk of predation. A 26-year study of prairie chicken had shown higher predation at higher nest densities and that pre-nesting dispersal increased nesting success overall. Tom had mainly worked on moose and woodland caribou, finding that the calving sites are spaced out to reduce the encounter rate with wolves but, he maintained, the principles are the same.

Rabbits and nest predation in partridges

Rabbit hemorrhagic disease caused very high mortality among rabbits in Spain during 1988–94, reducing numbers hunted by 90 per cent. During the same years the numbers of red-legged partridges were reduced by 80 per cent and it has been suggested that this was due to the disease triggering 'hyper-predation' (Moleón et al., 2008). It was shown that the proportion of red-legged partridges in the diet of the golden eagle and goshawk (in areas with poor forest cover) increased, but there was no supporting evidence from detailed monitoring (Blanco-Aguiar et al., 2012).

A similar event occurred in the Sussex Study area when the numbers of rabbits killed by trappers and gamekeepers was reduced by 98 per cent in 1954 by myxomatosis. Over the following four years the number of stoats dropped by 90 per cent (Potts & Vickerman, 1974) and grey partridge numbers increased markedly. Meanwhile at Damerham the rabbits were similarly affected but with no discernible effect on the closely monitored grey partridge numbers. There was no general decline in grey partridges in Britain of the kind that occurred in red-legged partridges in Spain until the mid-1960s and that had nothing to do with a scarcity of rabbits.

The rabbit reduction in 1954 led to higher numbers of voles and hares, and the abundance of these may have an effect on chick survival rates, with more partridge chicks in the diet of the stoat when vole numbers were at a low point in their quasi-cycles of abundance (Tapper, 1976).

SOME OTHER IMPORTANT CAUSES OF NEST LOSS

Mowing

One of the best-known causes of nest loss has been mowing, not just by modern machines but in the past by scythes, or even sickles (Naumann, 1805, 1833; Von Thüngen, 1876). Within about eight days of hatching-hen partridges with nests in crops sit tight just like leverets and roe deer fawns, giving off as little scent as possible to avoid predation. With a little care, eggs can even be removed for inspection with the female continuing to sit. This is suicidal behaviour and it is the reason why the various modifications made to mowers such as hanging lengths of chain or tin cans in front of the cutter bar (Sekera, 1959) were so ineffective.

Until the 1960s, favoured nesting crops such as lucerne and other fodder legumes were planted typically in a quarter of fields and mowing caused the loss of 60 per cent of nests found in the less well hedged areas of North America and Central Europe. In the dairy state, Wisconsin, Bob McCabe and Arthur Hawkins found 50 per cent of their 435 nests in lucerne, of which 85 per cent were subsequently lost due to mowing, 42 per cent of the total (McCabe & Hawkins, 1946). There can be no doubt this was the reason for the decline in this partridge population.

More generally the proportion of nests reported in hay or lucerne was usually 40–50 per cent and where there was deliberate searching over large areas these figures dropped to 12–17 per cent (Olech, 1988a). In many countries large numbers of clutches were rescued from mowing and transferred to game farms for rearing, for example in Denmark more than 1,000 clutches per year in the late 1930s (Paludan, 1954). As already mentioned, a major problem with mowing is the number of sitting females that are killed. In one study in Czechoslovakia 78 nests were destroyed by mowing, with 68 females killed (Škultéty, 1965), in another 419 nests were destroyed, with 206 females killed (Hell et al., 1965). These studies were carried out long before radio-tracking became possible and it is difficult to judge how important mowing was in reducing grey partridge numbers because the proportion of the overall total of nests that were destroyed or where females were killed is not known. However, using the figures above, an estimate of 10 per cent would be appropriate. This was the actual outcome in the uniquely well-manned study at Damerham where 10 per cent of the 2,354 nests found were lost through mowing. Three decades later on Salisbury Plain, where traditional hedgerows were much less frequent than at Damerham, losses were somewhat higher, with 10 per cent of radio-tagged females killed (Reynolds *et al.*, 1992). Importantly however, this same study showed foxes killed twice as many females as did mowing.

With tractors today going so much faster than they did in the 1950s, typically 15 km per hour or more, with wider mowers and with earlier and more frequent mowing due to the switch from hay to silage in the 1960s and 1970s, nest losses could now be expected to be much greater than in the 1950s. But this is not so; modern farming uses far less fodder legumes, which were the main mowed crops used for nesting, and farm systems have polarised into grass and non-grass ley systems. In Britain this resulted in large numbers of farms without partridges in the west and large numbers of farms in the east without grass, as first shown by Southwood (1972). In Germany nest losses remain high and there is the related problem of 90,000 roe deer killed by mowing annually (Jörg Tillmann, CIC advisory leaflet, 2011). How many partridges are involved is not known and with less than one pair per 100 ha it would be very difficult to quantify. Infra-red sensors are marketed for fawn detection, but further research is needed to explore the benefits for partridges and such species as the curlew and black-tailed godwit. In the meantime through the CIC, Jörg Tillmann has issued an excellent brochure in three languages to increase awareness of the problem.

Studies on an organic farm, Pollybell, near the northern boundary of Lincolnshire, have surprisingly revealed high nest losses to mowing during organic 'conversion'. This period before entry into organic production can be very dangerous to partridges and presumably other ground-nesting species, especially skylarks. Clutches, with or without incubating females and broods of flightless chicks can all be destroyed during the frequent cutting to form an organic mulch. The conversions were carried out on a block basis, many contiguous fields together, so partridges could not avoid the dangers. The overall effect of conversion was to reduce local grey partridge breeding stocks by 68 per cent in two years (Table 10). This phase lasts for two years, until the farm can be classified 'organic', free of agrochemicals. By 2012 numbers at Pollybell had recovered to 24 pairs per 100 ha.

On some organic farms much of the mowing can be avoided by grazing, providing that there is brood-rearing habitat available. So far as partridges are

TABLE 10. Pollybell organic farm, Lincolnshire: grey partridge counts for four years 2004–07 showing increased losses of clutches and incubating females during the organic conversion compared with conventional cropping (female loss P< 0.001). Broods hatching based on stubble counts by the author.

	conventional	organic conversion
pairs counted	373	79
females surviving	301	52
female loss	19%	34%
broods hatching	200	16
broods per pair	54%	20%
young	1296	60
young per pair	3.47	0.76
chick survival	33%	17%
potential females for year 2	949	82
above per pair	2.54	1.04

concerned there have been a number of disappointments from switching to organic farming (Wookey, 1987) and part of the problem may be the mowing in the conversion period. The Lincolnshire case is a temporary worst case example of the mowing pressures that led to the virtual extinction of the Corncrake in much of Western Europe, where mowing destroyed nests and broods even though adults were rarely killed (Green *et al.*, 1997).

There has been a large amount of controversy about the value of organic farming to biodiversity but this should not be surprising; there are many types of organic farming, particularly whether livestock are present or not, and properly controlled and replicated experiments are impracticable. An alternative approach is computer simulation modeling. Chris Topping at the University of Århus, Denmark, has simulated the response of six species (*Erigone atra*, a money spider; *Bembidion lampros*, a small ground beetle; field vole; brown hare, skylark and grey partridge) to a range of organic and conventional scenarios for three landscapes (Topping, 2011). Partridge abundance was predicted higher in two of these three landscapes but his overall conclusion was that targeted management would produce more predictable results.

Crop irrigation

Poyakov (1955) showed that the nest had to be kept not just dry but at a constant 34°C, which must be impossible if water is seeping in. Yet, despite the widespread use of centre-pivot and 'walking' irrigation for cereals, there has only been one study of the effects on partridges. In the southern part of the Beauce, 38 grey partridges were radio-tracked in wheat crops that were irrigated up to six times per season. The great extent of the irrigation is shown in the map below (Fig. 95). Being so extensive it was difficult for the partridges to avoid irrigation, and the successive wettings caused females to desert clutches and to re-nest up to five times. Predation by foxes and stone martens was also very high and chicks from late replacement clutches that could not fly were frequently destroyed during the cereal harvest. The 206 pairs that suffered irrigation fledged 2.5 young each, whereas the 27 'pairs' that did not suffer irrigation produced 6.1 young each; breeding success was therefore reduced 59 per cent by the irrigation (Serre *et al.*, 1989; Birkan *et al.*, 1990). These authors describe one pair that moved 350 m due to centre pivot irrigation, where it again ran into irrigation. After failure it moved 200 m back towards the centre-pivot system that first caused it to move, before failing again and moving another 400 m to where the female was found dead. Such issues were solved for the bobwhite quail by providing excellent nesting cover.

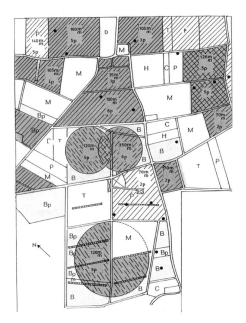

FIG 95. The study area of Serre *et al.*, 1989 in the southern part of the Beauce showing in blue the extent of irrigation and the number of passes '1p ... 6p' (from Serre *et al.*, 1989).

RELATIVE IMPORTANCE OF DIFFERENT NEST PREDATORS

In a survey of 16 estates in Britain in 1909–10 grey partridge hen predators were ranked: stoat > fox > cat, with egg predators, rat > stoat > hedgehog, but foxes ranked low because they were absent from several estates (Maxwell, 1911). For estates in Britain where there were professional partridge keepers, Doug Middleton reviewed the causes of the losses at 10,855 nests (Middleton, 1967). All the areas involved carried out predation control, yet predation accounted for 60 per cent of losses. The main egg predators were ranked: rook > rat > badger > hedgehog and the main hen predators: fox > dog > cat > stoat. Additionally the Damerham study provides the classic example where losses to predators are known from an area with intensive predator control and highly professional game management staff; the results are summarised in Table 11. It does not have the power of an experiment because there was no 'control', but it is the best data we have prior to radio-tracking.

The partridge keepers concerned will have found many nests and trapped many predators at nests, and they had a pretty good idea of what predators were involved in nest losses, but in other circumstances major difficulties in identifying the predators can be apparent. For example, in North America, where

31.33 inHg ↑   🌡 8°C   ◯   03/01/08 07:29 PM   0000000031

FIG 96. Fox, the most important predator of grey partridges: one of the images obtained by Jörg Tillmann during his unique night time studies of partridges in Germany. (Jörg Tillmann)

TABLE 11. Species of predator responsible for loss of 448 grey partridge nests at Damerham, Hampshire, during 1948–59; species that are shaded usually kill the incubating bird.

predator	%
corvids	30
fox	22
badger	8
stoat	8
rat	8
cat	7
hedgehog	7
others	5
unidentified	4

partridges had only recently been introduced and were not well known, 24 nests were destroyed by predators during 1929–32 in Michigan (Yeatter, 1934). Seven females were killed during incubation, one by a Cooper's hawk and most of the others by feral cats. The hairs of striped skunk, opossum, feral cat and long-tailed weasel (similar to a stoat) were also found at 16 nests, and skunk faeces contained partridge egg shell fragments. The egg punctures made by the carnassials of the long-tailed weasel are distinctive, similar to those made by a stoat, but even so the causes of some of the losses could not be confirmed.

In 1969 I ranked the predators at nests, in a part of the Sussex Study area where there were full-time gamekeepers as: fox > rat > dog > stoat > badger > grass-snake and jackdaw. The most comprehensive study of nest predation took place in France where 488 nests were found by radio-tracking (Bro *et al.*, 2000); the results are set out in Table 12. Predation on eggs by mustelids (the weasel family) was higher in France than at Damerham due to the presence of the stone marten and polecat.

The observation that the 'nest predation literature is largely a series of unfinished Whodunits' (Lahti, 2009) will surely soon change with the more extensive studies using automatic cameras and geo-activity recorders. At bobwhite quail nests these have confirmed that several predators can be involved in the same case of nest predation. For example, snakes could kill and remove the hen but not eat the eggs, leaving them for raccoons (Staller *et al.*, 2005). Without

TABLE 12. Species of predator responsible for losses of eggs and females from grey partridge nests in France (Bro *et al.*, 2000).

	% of lost nests attributed to	
	egg predators	hen predators
mustelids	33.0%	28%
fox	1.5%	34%
raptors (mainly hen harrier)	0%	13%
cat	1.5%	4%
crows	11.6%	0%
hedgehog	7.2%	0%
unidentified	4.3%	0%

the video evidence it might have been assumed that the raccoon was the cause of nest loss; a wrong identification of the culprit. At Damerham, where the visits to nests were almost daily, the researchers explicitly took great care not to be misled. Despite a bias against the fox as the first predator (because, like the snake in the case above, they often kill the hen but leave the eggs), the Damerham data clearly showed the fox to be by far the most important predator.

Nest predators in Finland were in order of importance fox > goshawk (of which more later) > hooded crow > feral cats and dogs > badger (Siivonen, 1953). Crows, magpies, hedgehogs and feral dogs were most important in one study in Czechoslovakia (Bouchner & Fišer, 1966, 1967). Another study in the same area had given the ranking as 'black crow' and magpie > hedgehog > others (Skultéty, 1965). In both areas the fox was very uncommon. In France the stone marten is important, with fox, polecat, feral cat, hen harrier and badger cited (Birkan *et al.*, 1990; Birkan & Jacob, 1988). More recently in France the importance of the mustelids, mainly stoat, stone marten and polecat, was emphasised by radio-tracking that showed they accounted for 67 per cent of nests predated (Bro *et al.*, 1999). In France the predation on females increased with the abundance of hen harriers, a subject we return to later. In the Trans-Baikal region the only confirmed mammalian predator of the Daurian partridge was the steppe polecat (Litun & Flint, 1993), a species that occurs through a vast part of the Eurasian range of *Perdix*, as do the marbled polecat and Pallas's cat, both likely nest predators. The most commonly cited predators of partridge nests in North America are striped skunk, raccoon, fox, the American crow (equivalent of carrion crow) and domestic and feral cats and dogs (Carroll, 1989). The large-billed crow was the main cause of loss of Daurian partridge clutches (Zhang & Liang, 1997).

BADGER

The role of the badger (also a mustelid) in nest predation is very difficult to quantify and poorly researched; science is on the back foot here. As has been well established by Hans Kruuk, badgers mainly eat earthworms, but they also eat many small mammals, cereals, beetles and other plants and invertebrates (Andersen, 1993; Madsen *et al.*, 2002). They are opportunists (Melis *et al.*, 2002). There is a good deal of evidence that about 2 per cent of eggs were eaten by badgers pre World War II (Middleton, 1967) and that this figure rose to 8 per cent in the 1950s at Damerham (Table 11). Badgers were frequently controlled until the early 1970s and were scarce, yet there are two cases where individual badgers destroyed many clutches: 18 in Shropshire in about a week in 1934 (Middleton, 1936) and 14 at Damerham in 1954. According to Doug Middleton badgers allegedly attack mainly during incubation, in which case the hen may be killed but not eaten; however, all the eggs are eaten, mostly whole. Since these findings reported by Doug Middleton (1936, 1967), badgers have much increased but their current impact on partridges and other ground-nesting birds has not been quantified. Common sense indicates that badgers must find clutches while foraging, and eat the eggs. Badgers were however numerous on the area used for the Salisbury Plain predation control experiment and not controlled. In 1991 badgers destroyed two nests of fifteen found by radio-tracking but in these cases the females survived (Reynolds *et al.*, 1992). In Hungary badgers can be controlled but nest losses are very high (Faragó, 2012), which shows other species are more important. In Sweden, Notini examined the diet of 1,889 badgers at a time when grey partridges were much more numerous in the country than today. He also carried out experiments on semi-domestic badgers but found no evidence they represented a problem to game-birds (Notini, 1948). We do not know whether this is still the case.

Hedgehogs were often much more numerous in the past than now and they were a serious cause of egg loss. Even at Damerham they caused as much damage as the badgers. In France hedgehog numbers rose in line with grey partridge numbers, both presumably responses to the control of ground predators (Birkan & Pépin, 1984). Middleton records a case where a badger had eaten four adult hedgehogs in one feeding session (Middleton, 1935).

PREDATORS AT *ALECTORIS* PARTRIDGE NESTS

The nest predators of the red-legged partridge in Spain include fox, feral dog, brown rat, hedgehog, badger, 'crows', magpie, Montpellier snake and (a major prey of the snake) the eyed lizard (Coles, 1979; Otero, 1999). In northeast Spain night lamping counts during 1992–2006 gave relative abundances of possible mammalian predators of red-legged partridges as fox > feral dog > wild cat > feral cat > polecat > badger > stone marten > weasel and genet (Sobrino *et al.*, 2009). In southeast Portugal the main predators were fox, stone marten, mongoose and polecat, with the mongoose probably most important at Vale de Perditos. In Kazakhstan the main predator at chukar nests is the fox, followed by the stone marten (Grachev, 1983). The same was true in Greece with the rock partridge (Thomaides *et al.*, 1992).

THE HISTORY OF PREDATOR CONTROL TO INCREASE GAME-BIRD NUMBERS

We have no way of knowing when hunters first realised that predator control increased small game species. This is because of the overriding importance of the protection of poultry from early times. Nevertheless, from 1457 when James II of Scotland instigated new legislation for the purpose, the control of enemies of farm crops and game became increasingly systematic, for example with the bounty payments that became well established by the middle of the sixteenth century (Lovegrove, 2007).

From 1718, probably beginning in northern Germany, the purpose of removing predators changed from protecting poultry to explicitly protecting hares, partridges and grouse. This was carried out on a large scale but it was not yet universal. Thus, between 1705 and 1800 more than 600,000 birds of prey were killed in the region centred on Hannover but with no discernible decrease in numbers (Kumerloeve in Bijleveld, 1974). This indicates a geographically limited campaign. It was the nineteenth century that saw the great spread of predator control throughout Europe, with drastic consequences for predatory mammals and birds but with a dramatic upsurge of small game and no doubt some other species. After allowing for the gamekeeper effect there was no important trend in nest predation through the twentieth century (Fig. 88). Over the whole countryside nest predation has increased because there are fewer gamekeepers, but even with higher predator numbers it is still possible to control nest predation (Chapter 10).

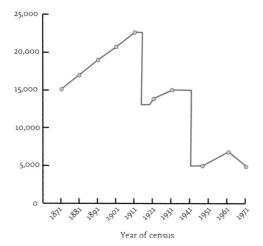

FIG 97. Number of gamekeepers in Britain from 1871 to 1971 (from the National Census; Potts, 1980).

Year of census

The number of full-time gamekeepers has declined from a maximum of 23,000 in 1914 to less than 5,000 in the 1970s (Fig. 97), with most of them involved with reared pheasants. At one time gamekeepers were responsible for predation control over huge areas of the countryside in Britain and the position was similar in much of Europe. Predator control was the norm (see Rudd, 1964, for North America; Yalden, 1999, for mammals in Britain; and Biljeveld, 1971, for raptors in Europe), but this is no longer the case.

Early figures are difficult to obtain; for a variety of legal and ethical reasons very few useful records have been kept of the numbers of predators killed to protect partridges. Even where lists are available absences do not mean absence of the predator. Between 1807 and 1816 the predators killed on the Burley Estate near Oakham, Leicestershire, include polecats and pine martens but there was no mention of foxes (Carter, 2001). From 1947–60 the list of predators killed at Damerham include many little owls (to 1954) and sparrowhawks, which were not protected at the time, but there is no mention of the foxes killed for fear of exacerbating relations with fox-hunting interests. The most complete records are from Hungary. One of the few complete records for an individual estate where partridges were the main consideration is that for the Tótmegyar Estate, in what is now the Slovak Republic. The main house is now known as Palarikovo, home of the CIC Museum, but today most of the land is no longer managed for game and grey partridges are rare. Yet during the eight years 1930–37 an astonishing 80,482 wild grey partridges were harvested (67 per 100 ha per year). In the predator record the virtual absence of the fox and stone marten is striking (Table 13), yet these had been numerous in the country as a whole (Faragó, 2007).

TABLE 13. Mammalian predators killed on Tótmegyar, an estate in the (present day) Slovak Republic during 1930–37 at a time of very high abundance of grey partridge. (Faragó, 2007)

species	killed per year per 100 ha
fox	0.02
stone marten	<0.01
polecat	1.37
stoat and weasel	6.23
hedgehog	3.77
feral dog	3.61
feral cat	6.17

Today in Britain thorough nest predator control involving a network of tunnel traps is confined to relatively few estates. Until 1954, when myxomatosis struck, the gin trap, a less humane equivalent of the tunnel trap, was almost ubiquitous. In the 74 studies analysed earlier the percentage of study areas with gamekeepers dropped from 54 per cent prior to World War II to 33 per cent from then to 1990 and was 14 per cent after 1990. Because studies are easier to make in areas with gamekeepers, these figures are biased towards areas with gamekeepers. Nevertheless it is obvious that today gamekeepers are either absent (or, in Britain, preoccupied with rearing) over most of the huge geographical range of partridges.

INCREASE OF THE FOX

Because foxes were controlled to protect poultry and game, foxes declined in Eastern Europe from the eighteenth century until World War I (e.g. Nováková, 1966, for Czechoslovakia). During and after World War II a recovery of fox numbers began in Britain, Netherlands, France, Germany, Austria, Hungary and Poland. In Britain the return and recovery in numbers was very slow at first, for example in East Anglia (e.g. Elvedon, Turner, 1954), but then with a massive increase. In most countries numbers remained relatively low; Harry Frank effectively controlled predators on an experimental area in North Rhine–Westphalia Germany by removing only 0.7 fox, 2.4 stoat, 2.4 house cat and 3.2 crows and magpies per 100 ha per year from 1959 to 1969 (Frank, 1970, 1971). Fox densities were very low at 0.08 per 100 ha in North Rhine–Westphalia

(Spittler, 1973) partly due to periodic rabies outbreaks, although later with a large increase. Work in Hungary as part of Sándor Faragó's Lajta project showed fox numbers increased following vaccination against rabies (Faragó & Buday, 1998; Szemethy & Heltai, 2001). Fox numbers were also increasing rapidly in countries without significant rabies. In France, lamping surveys show a widespread four-fold increase from 1989 to 2000 (Vallance *et al.*, 2008). There were also checks in the increase in fox numbers in Europe. In the 1960s they were controlled to prevent rabies reaching Denmark (Jensen, 1970; Strandgaard & Asferg, 1980). The spread of the scabies-like sarcoptic mange through Sweden is another example (Lindstrom & Mörner, 1994). Nevertheless in recent decades the overall increase has been dramatic. During 1930–37 eight years of intensive predator control on the 15,000 ha Tótmegyar Estate, only 19 foxes were killed (0.02 per 100 ha per year) (Károlyi, 1953). The number of foxes killed on a similar area (Moson) in Hungary in the past decade has been 57 times higher (Faragó, 2006). A fox rabies vaccination programme in Poland resulted in a three-fold increase in fox numbers from 1990–2004 and a marked decline in grey partridge numbers, as shown in Figure 98, caused by increased nest predation (Panek, 2000, 2005). Long before this three-fold increase the fox was calculated to have been killing 228,000 grey partridges per year in Poland (Pielowski, 1982). Marek Panek followed 44 pairs during 1991–2000, during a period when breeding pair densities declined by 92 per cent in his study area. Twenty females (45 per cent) were lost during nesting, mainly to foxes. Such predation is also likely to have been the explanation for the lower numbers of

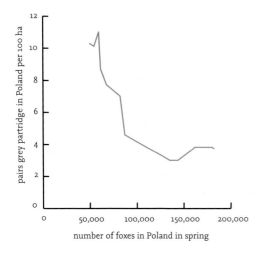

FIG 98. Decrease in grey partridge in Poland with increase of the fox. (from Marek Panek)

grey partridges, with higher numbers of foxes observed extensively in Germany in 1982–4 (Pegel, 1987). An analysis of bag records from 1958–98 concluded that habitat improvement would better help the grey partridge than fox control (Knauer *et al.*, 2010), but the analysis did not allow for density dependence in nest predation. Had it done so, the conclusions would have been different.

There is similar evidence of an increase of foxes in the US (Gosselink *et al.*, 2007) and of jackals in South Africa due to a decrease in Leopards, bringing us to the next issue.

ELIMINATION OF THE LARGE CARNIVORES AND IMPLICATIONS FOR PARTRIDGES

In the late-Pleistocene plains of middle Europe and in Britain, six species of large carnivore were present in the areas occupied by the grey partridge: the cave bear, brown bear, lion, wolf, spotted hyena and lynx. Similarly in North America in the areas with prairie grouse, there were five large carnivore species (Prugh *et al.*, 2009).

The cave bear, much bigger even than the polar bear, was the first to become extinct in Europe about 19,000 years ago, in the coldest part of the Devensian ice age, followed by the spotted hyena after most of the ice had retreated. In Britain the brown bear was gone by about AD 750 and the lynx by medieval times (Hetherington *et al.*, 2006). The wolf remained until completely eradicated from Britain and Ireland at the end of the eighteenth century. Our interest in the demise of these top-predators is in the indirect impact they may have had on the lower predators known as meso-predators that are the main natural cause of nest loss in partridges.

Only in the last decade has it been widely realised that large carnivores often suppress the populations of lower predators and thus increase the abundance of many herbivores including game-birds. The earliest clear recognition of the management value of top predators to partridges was when Heinz Brüll wrote in relation to predation control: 'Basically, in the countryside of today, the hunter must replace the controls of the past – the wolf, lynx, eagle owl … to bring home a bag, however modest' (Brüll, 1964). More recently, Korpimäki and Nordström (2004) concluded: '… the return of the golden eagle and wolves in central and southern Finland could have beneficial effects on small game …. This might reduce the recent need for gamekeepers to control medium-sized carnivore populations.' Here we consider the extent to which the high predation on grey partridges and probably red-legged partridges, necessitating predation control, is at least partly caused by a lack of top-predators. And we explore whether the conservation of small game could be helped by encouraging top-predators and by basing protective legislation more on ecological science than is the case today.

Nobody can now know the ecological repercussions of the removal of the top-predators from Europe or North America; it all happened too long ago. What we do know about the extent to which top predators reduce the numbers of meso-predators suggests a hugely important part of ecology waiting to be revealed (Terborgh & Estes, 2010).The sequence of events is indicated by the recent rapid removals of large carnivores from parts of Africa. A unique study in Ghana started monitoring predators and prey in the late 1960s (Brashares et al., 2010). At the start there were eight species of large carnivores, more than in North America or Europe, in pristine conditions, but this position didn't last long. The detection rate of the four largest – lion, leopard, spotted hyena and wild dog – had declined by 91 per cent by 2004. During the same period olive baboons increased by 365 per cent, with the changes in time and space consistently showing that this increase was due to the absence of the largest top-predators. An associated study of the nesting success of birds showed fledging success of 19 per cent in areas with high abundance of the baboons, compared to 52 per cent in areas with low abundance.

Nearer home, statistics covering the whole of Sweden show a large increase in the fox as the wolf and lynx were extirpated. This study by Elmhagen & Rushton (2007) is important because it also factored in changes in landscape and

FIG 99. Grey partridges apparently thrived in the area of the Chauvet cave, Ardeche, France, 36,000 years ago in a balanced ecosystem, co-existing with lions (16 shown), bison and rhinoceros. No such ecosystem supports grey partridges today. (Jean Clottes with permission)

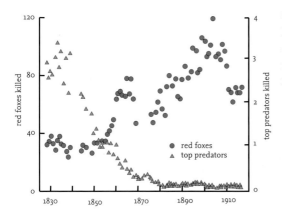

FIG 100. Numbers of wolves, lynx and foxes killed per 1,000 km² in Sweden from 1828–1917. (from Elmhagen & Rushton, 2007)

agriculture. The spectacular rise of fox abundance in Sweden as wolves and lynx declined is shown in Figure 100.

One of the few studies showing how foxes might be impacted by a larger species of dog describes the competition between the coyote and the fox (Table 14). Sargeant & Allen (1989) summarised 42 accounts of interaction between the two predators. In 79 per cent (33) of the cases, the coyote was dominant, whereas no case of the reverse was reported. They concluded that 'avoidance of coyotes by foxes is believed to be the principal cause of spatial separation of the two species'. It follows that the increase in coyote numbers that resulted from the control of deliberate poisoning might benefit nesting birds and this has been shown by Marsha Sovada's work at the Northern Prairie Wildlife Research station, Jamestown, North Dakota. There, largely by displacing foxes, the coyote reduced fox predation on duck nests by 85 per cent. Other predators have increased, however, and the high rates of nesting success of the 1930s has not returned (see Bergerud & Gratson, 1988).

TABLE 14. The differential effects of the coyote and fox on duck nests in the Dakotas, US. (from Sovada *et al.*, 1995).

Canid	Study areas	% Nesting success (95% confidence limits)	Losses due to fox
fox	13	17 (11–25)	27%
coyote	17	32 (25–40)	4%
both	6	25 (13–47)	?

This study was followed up in California where increasing numbers of coyotes were shown to depress the abundance of meso-predators by 56 per cent including the grey fox and domestic cat, with the result that the California quail and seven other bird species increased in abundance (Crooks & Soulé, 1999). Further north, the control of the coyote appears to have resulted in an increase in foxes and American badgers, with consequential increased mortality in sage grouse (Mezquida *et al.*, 2006). Dingoes, another species of large dog, have been protected in parts of Australia to conserve the endangered malleefowl where its numbers have been reduced by high fox predation, the fox having been introduced from Europe to help control rabbits (Johnson & Van der Wal, 2010).

There is also growing evidence that some populations of several grouse species increase when top predators are re-introduced. Reviewing the data from the Kluane Project, Yukon (in Krebs *et al.*, 2001), and his own work in Finland, Erkki Korpimäki considered that forest grouse usually benefit when fox numbers declined following an increase in numbers of lynx (www.cic/IUGB Workshop, Uppsala, 2007), and similar conclusions arose from work in Sweden (Helldin *et al.*, 2006). Analyses from a major recent study in Finland over 17 years has concluded that fox numbers were depressed by lynx, and hare numbers were depressed by the fox (Elmhagen *et al.*, 2010). In general there is a lot of evidence that the larger dog species (mainly wolf, coyote, golden jackal and dingo) suppress the abundance of smaller dog species (mainly various species of fox) (Terborgh & Estes, 2010). This reduction is similar in extent to the reduction in fox abundance achieved with predator removal experiments, where overseas it ranges from 30 per cent (Trautman *et al.*, 1974) to 50 per cent (Henke & Bryant, 1999) with ~76 per cent in Britain (Tapper *et al.*, 1999).

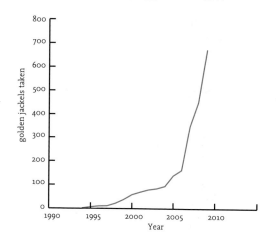

FIG 101. Increase of golden jackal in Hungary as shown by bag statistics; so rapid, that current hunting pressure is unable to restrain it. (Sandor Csányi, Hungarian Game Management Database, Szent István University, Gödöllő)

The adverse effect of large dog species on smaller dog species are well substantiated, but the fox probably did not increase much in Britain as a consequence of the extirpation of the lynx and wolf because it was increasingly harvested for fur and controlled to protect poultry and lambs and later game. Man has for millennia been the top predator; our ancestors extensively harvested foxes (even for food, Yeshurun *et al.*, 2009), beaver, martens and other species; Lovegrove (2007) went so far as to suggest that fur trading and not prostitution was the oldest of all trades!

The golden jackal fills a niche similar to that of the coyote and it is much feared by the fox (Scheinen *et al.*, 2006). It is possible that instead of trying to control the spread of the golden jackal into Eastern Europe as at present, we should encourage them and thereby obtain an augmented control of fox numbers in prime grey partridge range (Fig. 101). Maybe like the coyote this jackal will take some partridges but with this predation outweighed by its suppression of the meso-predator(s), as was concluded from work with coyote and bobwhite quail in Texas by Henke & Bryant (1999). New predators such as the raccoon and raccoon-dog may be less welcome (Heltai *et al.*, 2011; for bag statistics in Hungary see Csányi *et al.*, 2010).

In Spain, the Iberian lynx is an important controller of the abundance of the fox and Egyptian mongoose, both predators of red-legged partridge and of rabbits (Palomares *et al.*, 1995). Iberian lynx reintroduction programmes are under

FIG 102. What it has all been about: chicks successfully hatched. (Chris Knights)

way and the species is expected to spread soon to estates conserving red-legged partridges, where it will benefit from an abundance of rabbits and could help to conserve red-legged partridges. It is hoped that research and monitoring will rise to include the implications for game management. It follows from these cases that an ecosystem approach to predation control is the best way forward. Where there is high predation on rare species due to the absence of top predators, then a re-balancing of the predator community by the top predator, man, is justified where it is impractical to reintroduce top predators.

CONCLUSIONS

Since the late 1970s, 63 per cent of grey partridge pairs in Sussex have not hatched any young, with at least half of the losses preventable by predation control. Gamekeepers are hugely important in reducing such nests losses. To plan the conservation of this red-listed species without factoring-in the necessity of dealing with nest predation (as is usually the case) is to defy science as much as common sense. The potential increase in nest predation rates at higher densities of nests appears to be a crucial factor capable of determining the long-term average level of partridge abundance not just in Sussex or on Salisbury Plain, but generally. There is evidence pointing to nest predation being high, not just because of farmland as a habitat but because the top predators are missing.

CHAPTER 5

Chick Food and Survival: From the Steppes to Conservation Headlands

*... and the same rule was found to apply to caterpillars, all the brown and green
(or protectively colored species) being greedily eaten by birds, while showy kinds
which never hide themselves – like those of the magpie-, mullein- and burnet-
moths – were utterly refused by insectivorous birds, lizards, frogs, and spiders.*

Alfred Russel Wallace,
Contributions to the Theory of Natural Selection, 1870

T HE RELATIONSHIP BETWEEN INSECT foods and partridges has been
researched from several different angles for many years. These have
included quantifying the diet from crop and gizzard contents of many
hundreds of partridges; assessing the nutritional benefits of insects compared
to plants; comparing the *Perdix* and *Alectoris* partridges, which have different
adaptations, and quantifying the relationship between chick survival rates and
insect abundance on a farm scale with and without conservation headlands. This
chapter is based on the identification of about 120,000 invertebrates in the diet of

FIG 103. Male leads twelve
chicks searching for insects, with
the female bringing up the rear.
Normally such a scene is hidden
from view under a canopy of
vegetation such as feather grass
or cereals that protects the
parents and chicks from aerial
predators. (Chris Knights)

partridge chicks. Diets change from study to study but a clear picture emerges of a bird which discriminates carefully in its choice of food, including in its response to shortages of favourite prey.

Chicks are often said to forage for themselves, but this is hardly fair on their parents. Contrary to some old accounts, the chicks are not actually fed by their parents, although they do hugely influence the chick's choice of food. It is this that makes interpretation of the results of imprinted or fostered chicks so difficult. Very soon after hatching, it is not unusual for parents to lead the chicks for considerable distances to a richer source of food. One radio-tracked brood at Manydown travelled a straight line distance of 800 m through sprayed fields in the first two days, stopping when it reached a better supply of food. The parents also help chicks by pulling down grasses and weeds, knocking down insects, eating the right kind of foods and training by example. This is why, as we shall see later, adult partridges only eat a significant amount of insects when with chicks and why the chick diet so closely resembles that of their parents. Partridges do not normally scratch the ground like domestic fowl or pheasants but they do so in the fine soil at ant hills, to create dusting areas and to clear snow.

Overhead cover is very important to partridge chicks and this is why cereal crops are so beneficial to brood rearing, providing they are not too thick with weeds that impede progress when damp or wet. This cover is particularly important at night when, as a further safeguard, sites are chosen that are far from the perching sites of owls (Enck, 1990).

The background to this chapter for the grey partridge is a chick survival rate (to six weeks) of just over 50 per cent prior to 1952 that is now 30 per cent across all studies and lower still in areas of modern agriculture, where there is no mitigation of its effects, such as conservation headlands. Here we explore the extent to which the diet that sustained grey partridges on the steppes, heaths and bogs for millions of years prior to arable farming has been altered by agriculture. This is not obviously the case in the red-legged partridge or chukar and in many mountainous areas their diet may not have altered much, provided there is still a reasonable amount of semi-natural grazing and browsing.

SOME INITIAL COMMENTS ON METHODS

Some researchers have investigated only crop contents; others include food from the proventriculus (pre-stomach) and gizzard or resurrect diets from fragments in the faeces. In Sweden Jens Dahlgren even invented a suction device to extract food from the crops of living chicks. Georgiev's study of chukar chick diets in

Bulgaria incorporated the results from 27 chicks fostered by domestic fowls
in a total of 112 (Georgiev, 1963). Chicks imprinted on researchers were used
in a Minnesota study (Erpelding *et al.*, 1987). The results from these different
methods are not readily comparable and they have to be interpreted with care.
For example, a few insects, most notably the lucerne flea, leave no trace in the
chick faeces; soft- and hard-bodied insects fragment at different rates.

A different problem has been that several authors have grouped the insects
in the diet into inappropriate taxonomic groupings: for example, the term 'flies'.
Thus hundreds of species of flies that are never or hardly ever eaten have not
been distinguished from favourite food species such as crane flies; an adult grey
partridge killed in March had eaten 261 crane-fly larvae (Vesey-Fitzgerald, 1946).
In 8 studies (of 28) where they have been separated, adult crane flies account for
35 per cent of the total of flies eaten. The larvae of hover flies are also sought after,
as are occasionally those of the Bibionidae, a family that includes St Mark's fly.

FIG 104. The age of chicks is determined from the progression of their wing moult, in this
case from the excellent key of Marcel Birkan (Birkan & Jacob, 1988) developing the work of
Bureau (1911). The age of this chick is put at 36 days.

FIG 105. 1982: Vehicle used by Kevin Church to radio-track grey partridges in Wisconsin using solar-powered radios.

FIG 106. 1984: Radio attached to hen at Manydown so as to find roosting sites of chicks and collect droppings for diet analysis.

Two adult grey partridges shot in October 1911 had eaten several thousand of the closely related *Bibio lepidus* (Evans, 1912). Although abundant, most flies are totally ignored or in some way unavailable to partridge chicks and so do not appear in the diet. As with the flies, harvestmen have been lumped with spiders in arachnids, yet in the 16 studies where they were separated, harvestmen accounted for 26 per cent of the arachnids in the diet. In the Sussex Study harvestmen accounted for up to 50 per cent of the arachnids eaten but for only 1 per cent of arachnids in cereal crops.

Several authors have combined leaf beetles with weevils, seed weevils with leaf weevils and plant bugs with leaf hoppers. Stinking bugs (eaten rarely) and the other plant bugs have also usually been lumped together. Finally, although the distinction would be important in relation to the risk of ingesting parasites, some authors do not distinguish mainly vegetarian species of ground beetles (e.g. *Amara aenea*, *Harpalus rufipes*, *Zabrus tenebriodes*) from predatory or scavenging ground beetles. Large or small, nocturnal or diurnal ground beetles have been combined, sometimes even with rove beetles. Both adults and chicks are opportunists. We have seen that with the relative of St Mark's fly, but there are other examples: there are several reports of grey partridges eating heather beetles during the outbreaks of 1935 and 1936 (in the *Scottish Naturalist* of the time).

In what follows, chicks are strictly speaking young partridges up to the age of 28 days when the juvenal feathers begin to be replaced by the post-juvenal feathers, after which the birds become juveniles, but given an age range of many weeks it is easier to mention chicks in a generic sense. Likewise on many occasions the term insects is often expanded to include harvestmen, spiders, centipedes, other arthropods and snails. In addition to the Sussex Study there have been 25 separate studies reporting insect items for the grey partridge chick diet and 18 for the adult diet. The quality of these studies varies greatly, but with ~100,000 insects identified from 1,500 grey partridge chicks a clear picture emerges. The comparable figures for *Alectoris* combined are ~18,000 insects identified from 300 chicks.

GREY PARTRIDGE CHICK FOOD

The steppes

The first major study of the virgin steppe insect fauna was carried out near Orsk in Orenburg Province in 1936 by Professor Bey-Biyenko of the then Leningrad Agricultural Institute. This study is astonishing in several ways: it involved steppe ploughed for the first time ever and the professor was also the first to sample and count non-pest as well as pest insects living in wheat crops anywhere in the world.

In all, 330 species of insects and other arthropods were identified in the virgin steppe, of which 40 were found in the majority of samples (Table 15). Many of these 40 species were also found in other parts of the steppe zone. By contrast the samples from wheat fields were impoverished, with only thrips, aphids and in some areas plant bugs more abundant than on the steppe. The only ant present in wheat fields was *Tetramorium caespitosum* but its numbers were reduced by 83 per cent compared to the steppe. In a more recent Russian study, the insect biomass in wheat fields within an area of steppe was measured using a sweep net and found to be only one-fifth of that on the virgin feather-grass steppes (Kubantsev & Vasil'ev, 1983). Recently the Great Bustard Group based on Salisbury Plain used sweep nets to estimate the insect communities on the feather grass steppe east of Saratov, on the Volga. The dominance of grasshoppers and leaf hoppers was very clear (Litzbarski & Watzke, 2007). The same is true on the short grass prairies of the Great Plains of North America where densities of grasshoppers often reach 15 per m^2 with 60 recorded (US Department of Agriculture). Unfortunately none of

TABLE 15. Number and density of species counted on the feather grass (*Stipa*) steppe in the spring and early summer of 1936 (from Bey-Biyenko, 1961). The main partridge chick foods, indicated by shading, include 43 per cent of all individuals.

group	number species	density per square metre
woodlice	1	1
mites	1	2
lucerne flea	1	8
other springtails	1	5
steppe cockroach	1	3
grasshopper	1	3
plant bug	7	9
plant hopper	8	12
aphids	1	0
'booklice'	2	6
thrips	4	9
beetles	5	3
Lepidoptera	2	1
ants	6	50
other species	289	87
Total	**330**	**199**

this work has been related to partridges. Although the evidence is fragmentary, what there is indicates a rich source of food for chicks.

During 1978–1987 Vladimir Litun collected nine Daurian partridge chicks from the steppes of the Trans-Baikal, one aged 2 weeks, one aged 4 weeks and seven aged 8 weeks (Litun & Flint, 1993). At the time only 10 per cent of the area was in arable farming with no pesticides used, so we are surely as near a natural situation as it is possible to get? Adults and pupae of ants accounted for 75–84 per cent of the two youngest chick's diet. Six older chicks had eaten bush crickets, five had eaten plant bugs, weevils, caterpillars and ants and two had eaten grasshoppers. The main plant food was the seeds of the spreading pigweed.

FIG 107. A pen-reared chukar in Iran, ready for release to help control the number of plant bugs known as sunn pests. (FAO, Rome)

The dominance of ants on the virgin (feather-grass) steppe is remarkable and it surely helps to explain the preponderance of ants in the grey partridge chick diet, although ants are abundant in most places, comprising more than half the biomass of all insects (Hölldobler & Wilson, 1990). Where, however, the steppe is converted to arable crops, ants usually remain abundant only at the field edges.

In the former Soviet Union a series of studies were made on the ecology of shelter belts in the 1930s and some included data about grey partridge diets. In 1936–8 near Voronezh seven young had mainly eaten tortoise beetles, the striking red and black firebug (a plant bug) and ants, whereas five older partridges had mainly eaten tortoise beetles, the Russian ground beetle, sunn pests and black bindweed. In all the 12 birds had eaten 328 insects, including 137 tortoise beetles (Bud'nichenko, 1965). Further east in the Volga steppe in 1938, 16 grey partridges (adults and young) had eaten 152 insects, including 48 tortoise beetles but no ants (Mel'nichenko, 1949). We return to tortoise beetles later. Further down the Volga, broods were found to concentrate in shelterbelts where birch sawflies and grasshoppers, ants, beetles and plant bugs were found in the crops of chicks as well as the sawflies (Osmolovskaya, 1961). In the Kuberle area of the steppes near Rostov-on-Don, one 8–9-day-old chick had eaten 250 ants (pupae and adults), 1 knotgrass beetle, 1 comb-clawed beetle and a weevil, but no plant food. Two 20–25-day-old chicks contained 97 ants, 2 ground beetles and 75 weed seeds. A sample of 28 older chicks contained 1,651 ants (23 birds), 20 knotgrass beetles (12 birds), 37 caterpillars of Lepidoptera (4 birds) and 10 of the plant bugs known as Sunn Pests (6 birds) (Poyarkov, 1955).

Sunn pests, a genus of plant bugs, are one of the most important pests of wheat and barley in south central Eurasia. Since the early 1980s their control has required the use of insecticides on a truly vast scale (Miller & Pike, 2002). Adult grey partridges are well known as predators of these pest insects (Nefedov, 1943) and chukar have even been reared and released to help control them in Iran (see Fig. 107), as have grey partridges in Bulgaria (Stoyanov & Ninov, 1995).

Heaths, bogs and moorland

The diet of chicks in heaths, bogs and moorland pastures is particularly interesting because, as we saw earlier in the fossil record, this was where many grey partridges lived near red grouse, willow grouse and even ptarmigan. The first study of grey partridge chick food in such a habitat was that by Claude Novoa in 1996 and 1997 in the French Pyrenees at an altitude of 1,880–2,270 m in an area dominated by juniper, broom, heather and various grasses. Thirteen faecal samples were obtained by radio-tracking nine adult females. Adult ants were the dominant group eaten, comprising 73 per cent of identified insects. The remaining insects in the diet were ant pupae ('eggs'), weevils and grasshoppers (Moreby *et al.*, 1999). The proportion of insects in the diet was 1.4 times higher

FIG 108. Grey partridge habitat in Upper Teesdale: walled fields with hay meadows or rough pasture with abundant *Juncus* where radio-tracked broods fed on sawflies and with grouse moor on higher ground. (Jemma Grant)

than in natural hybrid red-legged x rock partridges of similar ages living in similar habitats in the Alps (Didillon & Chapuis, 1987; Didillon, 1988).

It was not until 2010 that the diet of grey partridges was studied on moorland in Britain: the work of Tom Hornby in the GWCT's team based in Upper Teesdale, in the Pennines of northern England. I am indebted to Tom, Phil Warren and the Head of the GWCT uplands research, David Baines, for access to this unique information ahead of formal publication.

Through the summers of 2010 and 2011 the roost sites of five broods were located by radio-tracking the parents and the faeces collected and examined. By number of items consumed, the diet consisted of ants 37 per cent, sawflies 36 per cent (32 per cent caterpillars, 4 per cent adults), beetles 15 per cent, plant bugs and spiders (including harvestmen) 4 per cent each, ichneumons including parasitoids of sawflies 2 per cent and flies and leaf hoppers 1 per cent each. Given their higher value in nutrition than ants, sawfly caterpillars are clearly important; one brood aged four days had consumed at least 123 in one day. This chick diet is virtually the same as that of the black grouse in northern England (Starling-Westerberg, 2001).

The diet described from Upper Teesdale will have been the typical one through most of the long history of the species in Britain and it is interesting to compare it to three GWCT farmland studies using the same methodology. Whereas ants and sawflies made up 73 per cent of the diet in Teesdale, they made up only 18 per cent of the diet on farmland.

FARMLAND: THE MAIN STUDIES

Most partridge chicks live or die in cereal crops but most chick diets are calculated from chicks obtained whilst they are outside these crops. The exceptions are where diets are calculated from radio-tracked broods, a technique not available until the 1970s. We need to keep this in mind when examining the change in diets caused by modern agriculture.

The insect food of the grey partridge has been broadly known for at least two centuries. With a farm near the Elbe in northern Germany, the Naumanns, father J. A. and his two sons J. F. and C. A., knew the bird well; C. A. shot 9,000 during 1816–44 (Mearns & Mearns, 1988). J. A.'s book on the birds of northern Germany was completed in 1804. In the update of 1833, J. F. described the insect food of chicks as spiders, earwigs, grasshoppers, caterpillars, leaf beetles and predatory beetles, adults of wireworms (Click beetles), crane flies and ants. This is a better account than one can find in most books today. Since 1833 a remarkable variety of insects and other arthropods have been recorded in grey partridge diets on farmland.

Britain

Oxford study

The first extensive research on the food of grey partridge chicks on farmland was that at the University of Oxford carried out by Ford *et al.* (1938). They examined 69 chicks sent in by gamekeepers during 1934–37, the majority of which were killed by the mowing of hay, clover, sainfoin or lucerne. As they wrote: 'Probably more young partridges live in growing cereal crops than in grass and clover, but there was no means of obtaining specimens from cereal crops in June and July, during the first 6 weeks of the partridge's life.' The results show clearly the dominance in the diet of soft-bodied and green, slow-moving species. In the first week the chicks had clearly been feeding in legume-rich hay meadows gradually switching to ants as soon as they could fly short distances (10–15 days) and when they would not be so dependent on cover from predators. Nearly all the grasshoppers came from two chicks in their second week from the same brood found on 22 June 1934 in a part of the Sussex Study area, Amberley Mount (see Fig. 82). This is a small area of uncultivated downland with juniper bushes, very like the species natural habitat. Grasshoppers and partridges are still present in a remnant of what were described in the mid-nineteenth century as 'heathery summits' (Knox, 1849); however, the heather is no more.

The Oxford study has been misinterpreted because it appeared to suggest a rapid fall-off in the intake of insects in the category older than 21 days. As is clear from the detail of the paper, however, a good number of these 'chicks' were shot at the beginning of September bringing the average age of the older than 21 days' group to 60 days (Fig. 111). The amount of food needed by chicks obviously increases as they grow but the insect component tends to level off at about 25

FIG 109. Larva of the lucerne weevil; one of the most important insects in the diet of early studies of grey partridge chicks in England and Czechoslovakia. (Frank Peairs/ Colorado State University)

days, but it is still substantial. The remaining diet consists of seeds, especially those of annual meadow-grass and chickweed and later grain and seeds of black bindweed and knotgrass.

Sussex Study

The Sussex study began by studying spatial variation in chick survival within years, effectively controlling for the effect of weather; the large geographical scale adopted by the Sussex Study was chosen for this very reason. From the outset it was clear that there were good areas in poor seasons for chick survival and poor areas in good seasons. If weather could be virtually ruled out, and it was, what could have been the cause of the differences in chick survival? Also varying was the abundance of sawfly larvae in cereal crops (see Fig. 169) and it soon emerged that the best areas for chick survival in 1969 were the areas with highest density of sawfly larvae (Potts, 1970a). Unfortunately sawfly numbers fluctuate wildly and they have declined in importance in the chick diet and to survival.

During the Sussex Study we have analysed the crop and gizzard contents of 52 grey partridge chicks and a further 5 that were obtained during the Damerham study but not examined at the time. The diet of 37 red-legged partridge and 12 chukar chicks were also examined to bring the total to 106 chicks, and we deal with the results for these later. The results for the grey partridge are given in Table 16, illustrating the most important groups of insects and other invertebrates during two periods. The 57 grey partridge chicks had eaten 16,429 items and, overall, the analysis in Table 16 shows a good deal of consistency in diet between the periods 1948–76 and 2010–11. Although the sample sizes are very low, there are some notable differences highlighted in blue.

FIG 110. Sorted crop contents from a one-week-old grey partridge chick killed by a weasel in the Sussex Study area.

TABLE 16. Showing number of insects and other invertebrates eaten per chick by 5 chicks during 1948–55 from Damerham and 35 chicks from the Sussex study area during 1968–76 combined, compared to 17 chicks from Norfolk Estate in 2010 and 2011. The numbers are based on examination of the crop and gizzard contents.

	1948–76 eaten per chick (40)	2010–11 eaten per chick (17)	1948–2011 Totals (57)
plant items	135	57	6359
snails	0.8	0.9	46
woodlice	0.1	0.0	3
centipedes	0.3	0.1	13
spiders	<2.1	0.6	93
mites	0.1	0.1	5
harvestmen	> 0.3	0.6	11
earwig	0.3	0.3	5
lucerne flea	34.7	0.2	1391
other Collembola	0.9	0.0	37
grasshoppers	0.2	0.2	11
plant bugs	3.3	1.5	158
spittle bugs	0.8	0.2	34
Delphacid plant hoppers	0.5	0.1	20
Cicadellid leaf-hoppers	0.8	0.8	44
aphids	29.8	133.8	3468
thrips	0.1	0.8	18
lacewing larvae	0.1	0.1	6
ground beetles large	0.2	1.35	29
ground beetles small	0.2	0.1	10
predatory beetle larvae	0.2	0.1	8
blossom beetle	0.1	0.5	12
rove beetles	1.1	0.9	81
click beetles	0.2	0.0	6

other large beetles	0.1	0.6	13
very small beetles	0.2	1.6	34
weevils	2.4	7.1	217
knotgrass beetle	3.3	2.6	176
tortoise beetle	1.3	0.9	66
flea beetles	1.4	0.4	61
ladybirds (Propylea)	0.2	0.4	14
flies (crane flies; dancing flies)	2.1	1.1	103
hover fly larvae	0.2	0.5	17
Lepidoptera caterpillars	1.0	0.5	47
parasitoid wasps	1.1	1.0	62
sawfly caterpillars	3.7	1.0	165
ants	85.2	7.0	3526
total invertebrates per chick	**179.3**	**168.0**	**175.9**

The 17 chicks from 2010 and 2011, from an area with conservation headlands, had eaten almost as many insects and other invertebrates per chick as in the period up to 1976 despite a much lower intake of plant items (mostly seeds). The apparent large differences in the cases of the lucerne flea and aphids are mostly attributable to a minority of chicks eating a lot of these items and are not statistically significant. The increased importance of weevils is likewise due to chicks feeding in pea crops, not grown in the Sussex Study area during the first sampling period.

The most important change in the diet of chicks over the past four decades, with wide relevance as we shall see, has been the increase in number of large ground beetles coupled with the decrease of sawfly larvae. The reduction in the importance of sawfly larvae in the second period represents a serious loss of what can be an excellent food source. There was not a trace of these caterpillars in the diet of eight chicks from 2011 and we return to this in the next chapter. Finally, nearly all the ants in the early period were from three chicks in one brood aged 35 days hit by a car.

East Anglia studies

The greatest step forward came with the radio-tracking carried out in a GWCT study by Rhys Green in north Norfolk in 1979–81 (Green, 1984a), with the assistance of Steve Moreby. Partridge broods were radio-tracked with the roost sites located at night, usually well out into cereal fields. The following day the roost site was visited and the chick droppings collected for analysis. All the fields had been treated with herbicides, some with aphicides, and the densities of insects in the fields were estimated from vacuum insect net samples. The availability of plant bugs to chicks was difficult to estimate with a vacuum insect net, so a sweep net was used. Many plant bugs, namely the winged grass mirids, congregate in the canopy of cereal crops way out of reach of chicks. Nevertheless for the first time we had evidence about the insect food of chicks that hitherto had been out of sight, hidden in cereal fields.

Another GWCT study was carried out in Norfolk during 2001–03 by Stephen Browne, again with the assistance of Steve Moreby in Fordingbridge, identifying the insects from faecal droppings (Browne *et al.*, 2006). The work was partly financed by the National Gamekeeper's Organisation who were worried about the implications of their members finding chicks with gapeworm and other parasites. Stephen's radio-located clutches hatched 13.5±0.7 young each, very close to the 13.8 figure used in the Potts model, suggesting no problems at that stage. Chick survival was however poor. From thousands of fragments of faeces collected at chick roost sites, Steve Moreby reconstructed the diet. On the basis of the minimum number ingested, the diet in the first three weeks consisted of leaf beetles and weevils 9 per cent, sawfly larvae 2 per cent, plant bugs and leaf hoppers 3 per cent and, most numerous, ants 22 per cent. A wide variety of other insects and spiders had also been eaten and in general it did not look at first as though the chicks had been starving. However, the main foraging areas were determined for 30 broods and surprisingly the three that used an area of heath did least well, with a diet dominated by ants (64 per cent) and a chick survival of only 4 per cent. Other chicks had eaten earthworms, rare in partridge diets, and excluding ants, only 14 per cent of the diet was what Browne *et al.* termed 'good insects'. Overall these results indicate poor availability of preferred chick food both in crops and also on set-aside. As a result many chicks foraged outside cereal fields in less suitable habitats where they were exposed to other factors. Three entire broods were lost due to predation by stoats.

In 1972–4 the food of stoats and weasels in the Sussex Study area was studied in areas with a full complement of tunnel traps (Tapper, 1976). This study concluded that predation on partridge chicks by stoats and weasels could be important, probably more so when poor chick food supplies forced broods to range more widely than would otherwise be the case; something proven in several studies (e.g. Dahlgren, 1987; Rands, 1986a; Enck, 1986).

Czechoslovakia

In 1951–3 there was an extraordinary research effort on grey partridges in Bohemia, now in the Czech Republic, and probably the best grey partridge habitat in Europe. Part of the work involved diet, during which Jiri Janda examined 294 chicks to the age of nine weeks. Again, most of the birds were probably obtained as a result of the mowing of hay meadows including fodder legumes such as lucerne. The diet was similar to that found in England in the 1930s, with lucerne flea and lucerne weevil predominating, but with more ants in the first week. The ants were found on the narrow grass banks that then separated the tiny fields (Janda, 1959a) of the kind that had long gone from England and have now gone from Bohemia, as discussed in the previous chapter. The results are similar to those in Britain; one comparison is given in Figure 111. The higher consumption of insects in Britain may be due to gamekeepers only sending in chicks that obviously had food in their crops. Most authors do not report the percentage of empty crops, but even when chicks were collected at peak feeding times, 9 per cent were completely empty (Rueda *et al.*, 1993).

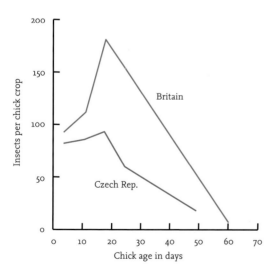

FIG 111. Changes in average number of insects found in chick crops in relation to age in days. Blue shows chick crops mostly from hayfields in England in 1930s (from Ford *et al.*, 1938), Red is from Bohemia, now part of Czech Republic, in the early 1950s (Janda, 1959a).

FIG 112. A pair of grey partridge with seven chicks at the edge of a carrot field in Norfolk. These chicks are two weeks old and although beginning to eat plant food they are consuming more insects than in their first week (see Fig. 111). (Chris Knights)

France

Research on chick food and the importance of insects in the diet has been investigated in France since the early 1970s, inspired by Dr Marcel Birkan of the then Office National de la Chasse. Working in the Gâtenais, just east of Orléans, in a detailed and thorough study Thonon (1974) examined the crop and gizzard contents of 20 chicks and at the same time measured daily changes in availability of the food species in winter wheat. In Aisne, Launay (1975) examined the crop contents of 14 chicks found in the larder of a stoat. The diet consisted mainly of crane flies, followed by hover-fly larvae and ground beetles (*Amara > Bembidion > Badister > Harpalus aeneus*). Sampling the crops, he described the food supply as abundant. A decade later, work switched to the Beauce in the vast plains between Orléans and Chartres famous for their grey partridges since before the French Revolution. By comparing chick food and insect availability, Marcel Birkan and entomologist Daniel Serre showed that chicks frequently ate aphids and plant bugs but not spiders, beetles and flies. As is clear from all studies that have been made, the chicks were not feeding on insects at random even if they could not find the preferred green caterpillars or larvae or nymphs of weed-dependent species. As an example, 279 of the small ground beetle *Trechus quadristriatus* were eaten by 13 chicks aged less than two weeks (Serre & Birkan, 1985).

FIG 113. The small ground beetle *Trechus quadristriatus*, frequent in the diet of grey partridge chicks, especially in France. (Josef Dvořák)

FIG 114. Despite the absence of weeds there were many *Trechus quadristriatus* in this crop of autumn-sown wheat in France.

It was easier to find *Trechus quadristriatus* in mainland Europe than in Britain. During 1978–83 I found 12–30 of this species per square metre in cereal crops in central Germany (the Wetterau). In the Po delta and Tuscany in 1984 I found 12 per square metre (Potts, 1986). In the Beauce, at the time one of the best area for grey partridges in France, on 24 June 1987 I found 15 per square metre in wheat crops free of weeds but with many aphids. Little wonder these beetles were prominent in the chick diet. In 2003 my personal record was of 60 on Jacques Hicter's farm at Savy in Picardie. In 2005 the main item in the diet of small chicks on the farm was *Trechus quadristriatus* and another small ground beetle *Bembidion* spp.

Denmark

A less detailed study than in England was carried out in Denmark in 1936 and 1937 by Hammer, Køie & Spärck (1958). The diet of 56 chicks and juveniles was investigated, mostly in late summer. Thirteen chicks were collected in July and these are of most interest. Twelve had been eating insects, with aphids, beetles, ants and 'other insects' dominating. Surprisingly, in view of their general abundance, no spiders were found but some woodlice had been eaten. Half the birds ate some insects into September, with seeds only gradually increasing in importance. In a study in 1985 and 1986 chick diets were described from analysis of the faeces of radio-tracked chicks (Steenfeldt et al., 1991; Rasmussen et al., 1992). Virtually no ants were eaten, with the diet consisting mainly of beetles: three genera of weevils, seven species of ground beetles including *Anchomenus*, *Amara*, *Harpalus*, the knotgrass beetle, cereal leaf-beetle, click beetles, flea beetles, a terrestrial water beetle and a vegetarian Silphid, *Blitophaga opaca*.

Poland

A great deal has been uncovered about the grey partridge at the Czempiń Research Station near Poznan, including in 1960/61 a month by month study of food eaten by a total of 420 adults and young by examining their crop and gizzard contents (Oko, 1963a, 1963b and 1971). At that time the cereal flora had not been affected by herbicides and there was an abundance of cornflowers, corn spurrey, black bindweed, knotgrass, pigweed (*Amaranthus*) and many other species. The food of the chicks aged about 32 days was mainly (93 per cent) ants.

From 1987–9 Marek Panek studied the relationship between insect food and brood survival. He found 50 per cent of the variation in chick survival related to plant bug abundance alone, but chick survival and plant bug abundance were both reduced by cool rainy days in June (Panek, 1992). His study showed very high chick survival rates in areas with high plant bug abundance (Fig. 115).

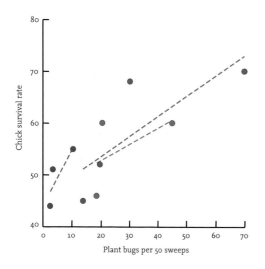

FIG 115. Relationship between plant bugs and grey partridge chick survival in study areas in Poland in three years (red, blue and green indicate separate years) (from Panek, 1992).

Finland

Before he became a member of parliament in Helsinki, Erkki Pulliainen began a great line of modern research on the grey partridge in his country and this continued when he moved north from the University of Helsinki to Oulu. To the east of the city there is an isolated block of 2,000 ha of arable land containing the most northerly population of grey partridge in the world (65°N). In the early 1990s, Ahti Putaala, Juhana Itämies and colleagues investigated the diet of chicks by locating the night roosting sites of three broods, following the methodology of Rhys Green, except that the densities of insects and spiders in the cereal fields were estimated by pitfall traps (which have to be cleared at dawn and emptied at dusk to avoid the many nocturnal species) and by sweep net. When the abundance of different invertebrate taxa was taken into account, chicks preferred plant hoppers, ground beetles, leaf beetles, various other beetles and aphids, whereas they avoided flies and spiders (Itämies *et al.*, 1996). The agreement between the two studies shows partridge chicks in north Norfolk and Finland are much the same in their choice of insect food (Fig. 116). Chicks were radio-tracked in both cases and ants did not dominate the diet.

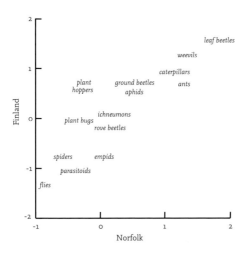

FIG 116. A comparison of the prevalences of insects and other arthropods in the diet of grey partridge chicks in north Norfolk (from Green, 1984a) and central Finland (from Itamies *et al.*, 1996). There is good agreement, although plant hoppers (especially Delphacidae) were selected more frequently in Finland.

Bulgaria

In a series of truly remarkable studies in Bulgaria, Georgiev astonishingly identified almost all plant and animal material in the diets of both young and old grey and chukar partridges. In 1950–51 he examined the diet of 42 young grey partridges finding 54 species of invertebrate, mainly various beetles, weevils, ground beetles and ants, with 24 species of plants (Georgiev, 1955).

FIG 117. Clip from the RSPB's 1976 film *Partridge Puzzle* showing a three-day-old chick about to devour a sawfly caterpillar *Dolerus haematodes*.

North America

Only in Utah were small chicks included: eight aged ~10 days had eaten mainly leaf beetles (Porter, 1955). Four other studies in the 1970s investigated the diet of chicks: 460 aged an average 43 days (Kobriger, 1980); 7 aged 52 days (Melinchuk, 1981); 46 aged 53 days (Hunt, 1974) and 40 aged 60 days (Weigand, 1980). In each case grasshoppers were the main insects eaten.

RED-LEGGED AND CHUKAR PARTRIDGE CHICK FOOD

Spain

A major study of the chick food of this partridge was carried out in 1985 on the Guedea estate in La Mancha, Spain, in the heart of the best area for the species, with a total of 143 chicks examined to the age of three weeks (Rueda *et al.*, 1993). These chicks had eaten 5,312 plant bugs, and these accounted for 58 per cent of all the invertebrates in the diet. By far the most important plant bugs were the very small lygaeids similar to the familiar cinch bug or milkweed bug. A wide variety of other insect food had been eaten too, including leaf hoppers and aphids

FIG 118. Field grasshopper, a preferred food of larger chicks. (Simon Litten/FLPA)

and, in the third week, grasshoppers and ants. A total of 120 species of insect and 39 species of other invertebrates had been consumed. The concentration on plant bugs is remarkable but they can be exceptionally numerous, dominating sweep net samples from grass-weed areas in arable land in La Mancha. The diet in the first week is summarised in Table 17.

One 20-day-old chick at Las Ensanchas, La Mancha, contained 89 insects and 23 seeds; 72 (81 per cent) of the insects were Harvester Ants. Most of the ant species that would be eaten occur in bare sunny areas where chicks would be vulnerable to predation at least until an age of 10–15 days when they would be able to fly from danger. This explains why few ants are eaten by small chicks despite the abundance of ants.

Portugal

My own investigations in southeast Portugal at Vale de Perditos near Serpa showed red-legged partridge chicks eating a lot of insects but very little vegetation or seeds. A total of 795 'insects' were identified from 8 small chicks collected in well-separated areas across the Vale de Perditos estate during

TABLE 17. Red-legged partridge first-week diet in Spain (Rueda *et al.* 1993) and Portugal.

	Spain (Guedea)	Portugal (Vale de Perditos)
chicks examined	56	8
insects etc. per chick	70	99
seeds and plant items	54 (44%)*	23 (19%)
total items per chick	**124**	**122**
more detailed items per chick		
snails	0.7	0.4
woodlice	<0.1	0
centipedes	<0.1	0
spiders, harvestmen	2	0.5
mites	3.1	0.8
springtails	0	0
grasshoppers	2.1	2.4
plant bugs	36.2**	4.4
leafhoppers	8.1	4.6
aphids	2.7	28.0
thrips	<0.1	0.1
lacewings	0.1	0.2
Cassida	0.5	42.0
other beetles	4.5	6.1
flies	7.7***	0.1
Lepidoptera caterpillars	0.7	2.0
parasitoid wasps	<0.1	0
sawfly caterpillars	0	0.3
ants	1.2	5.4
insects / all items	**56%**	**81%**

*Sisymbrium; ** *Microplax interupta;* *** *Chlorops pumilionis*

FIG 119. Rich floral diversity: plenty of chick food here. (Patricia Maldonado Vidal)

16–18 May 2011 (Table 17). Judging by the abundance of the different types of insects in the vegetation and eaten by the chicks, four groups were eaten preferentially in the order: *Cassida* larvae > aphids=*Cassida* adults > leaf-hoppers (Cicadellidae). By the same comparison four groups of insects were ignored or unobtainable; all were very small: flies, thrips (or thunder bugs), springtails (but not lucerne fleas) and parasitoid wasps. The frequencies of the remaining groups were more or less in line with their abundance in the vegetation.

The astonishing result from this work in Portugal was the very strong preference for the tortoise beetles (*Cassida* spp.), of which there were three species in the samples. Most of these live on leaves of dead nettles, thistles and a few other grassland species such as, in Portugal, the crown-daisy. The *Cassida* adults and larvae/pupae together comprised only 3.4 per cent of the insects in

FIG 120. Insects from the crop of a five-day-old red-legged partridge chick at Vale de Perditos in 2011: note lack of plant material. Most of the items are larvae, pupae and adult tortoise beetles. In 2012, Lepidoptera caterpillars predominated.

the sweep samples but 42.3 per cent of insects in the diet. In contrast only 30 (0.3 per cent) tortoise beetles were amongst the 9,129 insects eaten by red-legged partridge chicks in La Mancha (Rueda *et al.*, 1993). Remarkably, however, as we saw earlier, these scarce tortoise beetles have been recorded before in grey partridge chicks in Russia and a chick at Damerham in 1955 had eaten 50. In the Sussex study these beetles have very occasionally been found on chickweed but not in the diet.

One remarkable feature of the red-legged partridge chicks in Portugal was that they had eaten virtually no seeds. The reason appears to be that the vegetation in Portugal was senescing; any available seeds were ripe, hard and dry. Insects with soft parts, like caterpillars that are susceptible to desiccation, also become very scarce when the vegetation ripens and dries out.

FIG 121. Larvae and adult of a typical tortoise beetle; the larva has a supposedly protective covering comprised of their own faeces, but this does not deter partridges. (Roger Tidman/FLPA)

France

Results from the south of France based on an analysis of faeces showed red-legged partridge chicks had been eating aphids, ants, harvestmen, spiders, flies, beetles, grasshoppers and 'springtails' (Ponce, 1989). The full results are being prepared for publication.

Bulgaria

The diet of 113 young chukar with an average age of about 6 weeks contained 138 species of plants and 140 species of invertebrates. The main foods of 12 young chicks were plant bugs, aphids, grasshopper nymphs, weevils, tortoise beetles, Lepidoptera caterpillars but not ants (Georgiev, 1963). If we did not know these were chukar chicks we might easily guess from their diet that they were grey partridge chicks.

Britain: East Anglia

In Norfolk, red-legged partridge chicks radio-tracked by Rhys Green foraged in cereals like grey partridges but consumed fewer insects and more grass seeds. By dry weight the percentage of insects in the red-legged chick diets was 50 per cent at three days falling to ~5 per cent at the end of the third week. For comparison grey partridge chick diet was 80 per cent insects at three days dropping to 20 per cent at the end of the third week. By numbers of items, 95 per cent of the grey

FIG 122. Female red-legged partridge with ten chicks by carrots in Norfolk, a crop in which they usually do well. (Chris Knights)

TABLE 18. Comparison of chick food in grey, red-legged and chukar partridge from the Sussex Study during 1968–2011, also including eight chicks from Damerham, 1948–55.

	grey	red-legged	chukar
chicks examined	57	37	12
items per chick	288	506	172
plant	112	316	110
snails	0.8	0.2	0
woodlice	0.1	0.2	0.2
spiders, harvestmen	1.8	3.9	0.8
earwig	0.1	0.1	0
mites	0.1	0.1	0
lucerne flea	24.4	7.7	9.7
other springtails	0.6	0.2	13.0
grasshoppers	0.2	0.2	0.1
plant bugs	2.8	4.4	0.5
leafhoppers	1.7	0.9	0.2
aphids	60.8	138.4	28.0
thrips	0.3	0.4	0.2
lacewings	0.1	0.1	0
beetles	12.8	17.4	6.8
flies	1.8	10.2	1.3
Lepidoptera caterpillars	0.8	0.8	0.3
parasitoid wasps	0.8	0.9	1.0
sawfly caterpillars	2.9	0.7	0
ants	61.8	3.0	0
total insects etc. per chick	176	190	62
insects / all items	61%	38%	36%

partridge diet in the first week in Sussex was insects, compared to 28 per cent for the red-legged partridge chicks. In the third week the percentages had fallen to 49 per cent and 28 per cent respectively (Green *et al.*, 1987). In an important development it was found that many of the grass seeds eaten by grey partridge chicks less than ten days old were not fragmented, whereas most of those eaten by red-legged partridge were fragmented and therefore digestible (Green *et al.*, 1987).

Sussex

The data in Table 18 give a simple comparison of the diet of the chicks of the three species in the Sussex Study, adding in three red-legged partridge chicks from Damerham (as with the grey partridge). A total of 37,116 food items were identified. In Sussex in the early 1970s the red-legged partridge chick food in the first week was mainly cereal aphids and lucerne fleas followed by plant bugs and beetles but with very few ants, suggesting a possible difference from grey partridge chicks. In the main, however, there were few, if any, noticeable differences in the preference for different insects between the two species (Vickerman and O'Bryan, 1979; Moreby *et al.*, 2006).

ADULT *ALECTORIS*

From August 1968 to July 1972 the food of adult red-legged partridges was studied in southeast Portugal. Insects were eaten only from June to October and were entirely Grasshoppers and ants (Vizeu-Pinheiro, 1977). In a later study further north in November and December, adults had fed on only a few insects, 83 per cent of which were ants (Tavares *et al.*, 1996). In Greece the insect food of adult rock partridges was grasshoppers followed by leaf beetles and weevils (Sfougaris *et al.*, 2003). The main insect food of adult rock partridges in the Alps was grasshoppers (Didillon, 1988). In all these cases the groups of insects eaten were the same ones that dominated the insect diet of chicks. The diet of adult *Alectoris* partridges appears very similar to that of the grey partridges in warm, dry regions with many ants and grasshoppers but few soft-bodied caterpillars.

There appears to be the same agreement between the diet of chicks and adults as we found in the grey partridge, although there are far fewer data. Adult chukar in Bulgaria obtained through 1957 ate mainly ants including Harvester ants (*Messor* sp.), and no fewer than 15 species of grasshopper and bush cricket (Georgiev, 1961). In Nevada in 1963 the main insect food was grasshoppers followed by ants. In Kazakhstan in 1975 the main insect food was grasshoppers followed by leaf beetles, weevils and the sunn pest (Grachev, 1983).

OVERALL COMPARISON OF *ALECTORIS* AND *PERDIX* CHICK DIETS

A comparison of food found in the crops and gizzards of chicks from the major studies shows red-legged partridge chicks eat almost as many insects as grey partridges (Fig. 123). The plotted data give no support for the conclusion that the different partridge species differ in their requirement of insect food. The red-legged partridge chicks usually but not always (Portugal) consume more seeds, but the number of insects needed per chick appears to be the same.

For many years it has been assumed that red-legged partridge chicks have not been as adversely affected by shortages of insects as grey partridge chicks, but we have seen from crop and gizzard contents that they eat as many, or almost as many insects for a given age. The difference is not in the consumption of insects

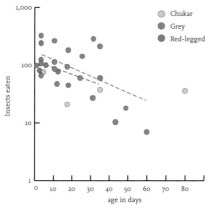

FIG 123. Some comparisons of the total number of insects (invertebrates) eaten per chick by grey, red-legged and chukar partridge of known age. The decrease with age is significant (P=0.005) but there is no significant difference between the species. From Ford *et al.* (1938), Janda (1959), Georgiev (1955), Georgiev (1963), Thonon (1974), Serre & Birkan (1985), Rueda *et al.* (1993), Sussex study and Potts, unpublished (Portugal).

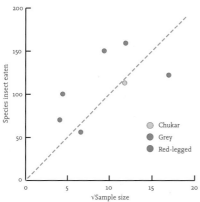

FIG 124. Number of species of insect eaten by samples of chicks of grey partridge, red-legged partridge and chukar as a function of sample size; there is no suggestion of a difference between the species.

but in the consumption of plant food, which is greater in the *Alectoris* species. Two lines of evidence support this.

Although the information is for obvious reasons very hard to obtain, six of the studies reviewed here managed to identify all the species of insects in the diet (Ford, *et al.*, 1938; Janda, 1957; Serre *et al.*, 1985; Georgiev, 1955, 1963; Rueda, 1988), and in 2010 and 2011 at least 70 species had been eaten by only 17 chicks from the Sussex Study area. If *Alectoris* chicks need fewer insects they might choose fewer species but the data for all seven studies given as Figure 124 do not suggest any differences between the three species.

The second line of evidence that insects are important to the red-legged partridge chick survival comes from the evidence of their response to conservation headlands.

Different gizzards

The gizzard is hugely important in partridges of all ages but particularly so in chicks, where it accounts for 12–15 per cent of the body weight, compared to 4 per cent in an adult. Thanks to very recent work in the Sussex study we now know that grey partridge chicks accumulate grit only gradually; virtually none in the first week. At this time most seed-eating weevils and the head and thorax of ants and some beetles pass through the gut intact; soft bodied insects are obviously preferable at this stage. By contrast red-legged partridge chicks in both Sussex and Portugal accumulate grit from day 1 with more than 40 pieces of grit already in the gizzards by day 2 (Fig. 126). This undoubtedly explains the more efficient fragmenting of seeds by the red-legged chick, but grass seeds are a relatively poor source of food for a rapidly growing chick.

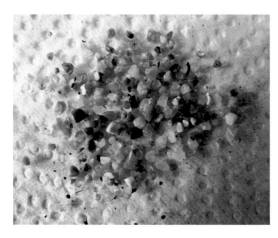

FIG 125. Natural grit, 181 pieces, from the gizzard of a grey partridge aged an estimated 40 days.

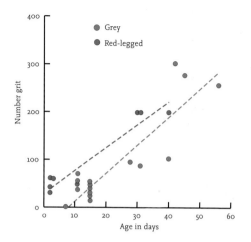

FIG 126. Higher uptake of gizzard grit with age in red-legged partridge chicks (red) compared to grey partridge chicks (blue).

The average number of grit in the gizzards of adult grey partridge in Sussex was 346±17 per gizzard, so the chick's 190 pieces of grit accumulated by 40 days is 55 per cent of the adult number. In the larger red-legged partridges the grit was almost double the size but smaller in number at 233.25±17.00 per gizzard. Thus the 40-day-old red-legged partridge chicks with 220 pieces of grit had already accumulated 81 per cent of the adult number. It would follow that in the absence of soft bodied insects feeding on green material, this extra uptake of grit is to deal with the hard parts of insects – the heads of ants and weevils, parts of armoured bugs, grasshoppers and similar insects – not necessarily to utilise unripe grass seeds.

The average number of grit per grey partridge gizzard in Sussex of 346 compares with 239 in Hungary (Thaisz & Csiki, 1912), 500 in Poland (Oko, 1971), 510 in Czechoslovakia (Bialas *et al.*, 1996) and 676 in Denmark (Rasmussen *et al.*, 1989). The number of grit in 98 adult red-legged partridges in Spain was 272 (Jiménez *et al.*, 1991). It has been argued that very hard seeds are a substitute for grit (Beer & Tidyman, 1942), but I could see no evidence for this.

WHAT INSECTS ARE PARTRIDGE CHICKS SEARCHING FOR?

It is firstly clear from the above studies that radio-tracked chicks in crops are not eating mainly ants. Secondly it is clear that partridge chicks are feeding selectively on insects, with some of the most abundant insects groups in cereal crops virtually ignored, for example thrips, small flies and the small parasitoid wasps. Yet somewhat paradoxically the chicks have a wide range of food species across

FIG 127. Sawfly larva. (GWCT)

the different habitats. It would help to interpret this finding if we knew what determined the chick's choice of food; how they develop search-images. In the 1950s the Dutch ornithologist Luke Tinbergen developed the hypothesis of search images, which essentially states that predators focus on a single kind of prey at any one time, ignoring equally rewarding prey that is not so numerous. The explanation is that it is difficult to search for several kinds of cryptic prey, such as moths on bark, at the same time (Dukas & Kamil, 2001). But partridges do feed on many kinds of insect in the same feeding bout. For example, in Sussex in 2011 four small chicks from the same brood accidentally killed in the half-light of dawn by a shepherd on the Norfolk Estate had eaten only 135 insects but these were of 47 different species. At the other extreme a red-legged partridge chick in Portugal in May 2011 had eaten 108 insects including 75 of a scarce tortoise beetle. Similarly in 1969 one chick in the Sussex Study area had eaten 40 large sawfly caterpillars, which I calculated was the food equivalent of at least 2,000 aphids. Some chicks feed almost exclusively on ants and especially ant pupae, or on aphids, to the exclusion of other prey. However, a pattern emerges from this kind of information and it is clear that several kinds of insect can dominate the diet *if they are available.*

Ants

The Sussex work correlating chick survival with insect abundance has been questioned because it took no account of ants, although these were recognised to be important at the start of the work (Birkan & Jacob, 1988), and this is fair. However, ants are very rare in cereal crops and cannot be monitored by sampling cereals. Three of the four radio-tracking studies (Green, 1984a; Rasmussen *et al.*, 1992; Itamies *et al.*, 1996) showed only a very small proportion of ants in the diet; only Browne *et al.* (2006) found them to be a significant part of the chick diet.

FIG 128. Numerically ants are the most important part of the grey partridge insect diet, mostly obtained as here from mounds of the yellow meadow ant. (right: Jef Meul/Minden Pictures/FLPA)

As in Stephen Browne's case the chicks must come out of cereal crops to find them and, as we have seen, this exploration can lead to predation by Stoats and collisions with traffic.

Over all the studies of chick food, ants comprise 20 per cent of the diet in the first week, with 84±17 adult ants per grey partridge crop and 155±50 pupae. After the first week ants constitute 36 per cent of the arthropods eaten by chicks and 44 per cent of arthropods eaten by adults. No other component of the diet comes near these percentages. Perhaps surprisingly, given that some ants can bite or sting, whereas their pupae cannot do either, the relative number of adult ants and pupae (the well-known ant eggs or 'cocoons') does not change with age. Unexpectedly, across 43 studies there was no decline in the proportion of the diet that consists of ants through the past 50 years if we discount the low frequency of ants in the diet of radio-tracked broods.

The relationship between ants and partridges is complex and often puzzling. For example, partridges often dust bathe in excavated ant hills but they have apparently never been observed 'anting', that is using the formic acid from ants to help control the numbers of feather lice. Ants carry parasites that infect partridges and we examine this in Chapter 7.

CHOICE OF FOOD SPECIES: LABORATORY TRIALS

In 1997 a series of feeding trials were carried out at the GWCT HQ in Fordingbridge confirming that plant bugs were highly selected by 5–10-day-old grey partridge chicks (Moreby *et al.*, 2006). Selection probabilities were calculated and were for live insects: plant bugs (mainly the grass mirid *Closerotomus*

FIG 129. *Closterotomus norwegicus* (formerly *Calocoris norvegicus*) the most numerous of the plant bugs in Sussex Study area. These plant bugs are the most preferred insect in food trials for both grey and red-legged partridge chicks. (Hans Lang/Imagebroker/FLPA)

norwegicus) 0.735; sawfly larvae 0.233; adult yellow meadow ant 0.027; the small ground beetle *Bembidion* spp. 0.014 (not often eaten) and seven spot ladybird 0.001 (hardly ever eaten). In trials with dead insects it was found that leaf weevils were less preferred than sawfly larvae but more preferred than the yellow meadow ant. Finally it was clear from trials with different coloured pellets that green-yellow was preferred over brown-black, with red avoided. Chicks imprinted on students in Minnesota, like the famous geese in Konrad Lorenz's work, ate plenty of brown or black hard bodied insects but did not do so when green or yellow leaf hoppers were available (Erpelding *et al.*, 1987). Studies on the pheasant by David Hill on the Damerham Estate (Knoll Farm) showed that preference is not the same as importance. Crane flies were the most preferred insects but only comprised 6 per cent of the chicks' diet by dry weight, whereas plant bugs were not preferred but were the second most abundant group of insects eaten (after sawfly larvae), comprising 18 per cent of the chicks' diet (dry weight) (Hill & Robertson, 1988). This also sums up the situation in partridges.

DIET OF VERY SMALL GREY PARTRIDGE CHICKS

In the first days of life it is clear that chicks are eating small insects, especially the springtail known as the lucerne flea and found on the feather-grass steppe; as we saw earlier, one chick had eaten 1,282. In the field studies on Lord Rank's Estate in the mid-1960s, 90 per cent of the diet of six grey partridge chicks in their first week was found to be aphids and the lucerne flea (Southwood & Cross, 1969). One chick collected from the Sussex Study area in 1969 had recently eaten

FIG 130. (left) Lucerne flea (Gilles San Martin) and aphids (Nigel Cattlin/FLPA): the two foods dominating the diet of very small chicks (see Fig. 131). One 40-day-old grey partridge in the Sussex Study area had the remains of 2,037 pea aphids in its crop and gizzard.

1,859 of a cereal leaf-dwelling aphid *Sitobion fragariae*, a species that summers on barley leaves and winters as an egg on twigs of bramble. In 2010 another chick from the same area had eaten 2,037 of the much larger pea aphid. There are no records of chicks eating black bean aphids. Work with chicks imprinted on humans in Minnesota showed that chicks aged 2–8 weeks consumed insects 0.5–5 mm long, and especially (as found later in Finland) plant hoppers (Erpelding *et al.*, 1987).

It seems obvious that some insects may be too big for chicks, but it is not so simple. Rebecca Taylor and colleagues working in Montana defined chick foods as species greater than 1 mm in length, with medium and large ground beetles and large grasshoppers excluded (Taylor *et al.*, 2006). Yet larger insects are killed and then dismembered to be eaten bit by bit. For example, a fourth-stage 25 mm sawfly caterpillar, full of easily digestible nutrients, would be half the length of a two-day-old grey partridge chick. The problems this presents to the chicks was well shown by the remarkable footage in the RSPB's 1976 prize-winning film *Partridge Puzzle* by Anthony Clay. Despite the bulkiness of the caterpillars the small chicks soon got the hang of it and ate many. The dismemberment of large insects was also noted in the Minnesota study.

Combining all studies, the importance of the lucerne flea and aphids in the first week is striking (Fig. 131). Both the springtail and cereal aphid have declined with agriculture (see Chapter 6) clearly presenting a problem for very small chicks. One basic cause of lower chick survival in recent decades may have been the scarcity of these insects. Ants are less important at this early stage, but apart from their lower quality as food there is no reason why some ants should

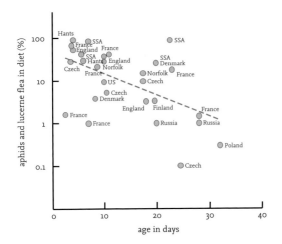

FIG 131. Emphasis on aphids and lucerne flea in the diet of younger chicks (P=0.003). (Authorities for Figs. 131 & 132 at foot of page)

not be eaten in the first week provided only that broods can obtain them with the necessary cover against predators. This appears to have been the case on the steppes, in the Czech studies of the early 1950s and in the already mentioned Spanish sub-species *P.p. hispaniensis*, where 88 per cent of the diet in the first week consists of ants (Moreby *et al.*, 1999).

INSECT FOOD OF YOUNG AND ADULT GREY PARTRIDGES COMPARED

It was explained earlier that parents guide the chicks to food and in general the correlation between the prevalence of taxa in adults and chicks is remarkably high, with a correlation coefficient of 88 per cent (P<0.001) (Fig. 132).

Authorities for chick diet: Browne *et al.* (2006), Bud'nichenko (1965), Erpelding *et al.* (1987), Ford *et al.* (1938), Georgiev (1955), Green (1984a) *ext. in litt.*, Hammer *et al.* (1958), Hunt (1974), Itamies *et al.* (1996), Janda (1959), Kobriger (1977), Launay (1975), Litun (1993), Melinchuk (1981), Moreby *et al.* (1999), Moreby (*in litt.*), Oko (1963b), Porter (1955), Potts (1970a), Potts (herein), Poyarkov (1955), Rands & Moreby (*in litt.*), Rasmussen *et al.* (1992), Serre & Birkan (1985), Southwood & Cross (1969), Thonon (1974), Vickerman (1976), Vickerman & O'Bryan, (1979), and Weigand (1980). Authorities for adult diet: Janda (1957), Kelso (1932), Khanmammedov (1962), Kuz'mina (1992), Middleton & Chitty (1937), Oko (1963a), Poyarkov (1955) and therein; Pulliainen (1965), Rörig (1900), Sussex Study, Thaisz & Csiki (1912), Vertse *et al.* and therein (1955), Yeatter (1934), Weigand (1980) and Dahlgren (1987).

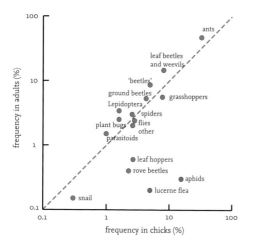

FIG 132. Grey partridge: insect groups eaten by chicks and juveniles are also those eaten by adults, with the exception of aphids and lucerne flea that are eaten mainly by chicks in their first week; all adult and all chick studies were combined.

WHY CHICKS NEED INSECTS

Studies on the causes of variation in partridge chick survival have long been subject to controversy; not founded on misplaced sentiment, as is often the case with predation, but on genuine difficulties with the evidence. There are two inter-related issues and both are complex in the extreme: the required composition of the diet and the urgency with which the required diet needs to be eaten. Both issues involve the weather. If conditions are warm and dry with little risk of predation, then there is more time to feed and fewer insects may be required. In poor weather more food is needed but the time available is shorter through being restricted by dripping vegetation and by the cold. Even today many insist that good weather in Ascot week (third week of June) ensures chick survival. The reason such correlations are difficult to quantify is that the time available to feed is determined not just by the cold and wet but by the abundance of insect food.

In the late 1950s Lord Rank, famous in so many different walks of life, began to worry about the nutrition of his grouse. He had peat and heather examined from different parts of his moor in Scotland and the results showed the best grouse numbers where there were the most insects. In March 1961 he contacted Dick Southwood at Imperial College Field Station, Ascot, with a view to further research, whereupon the grouse were apparently forgotten and the focus switched to partridges. It was to be 40 years before the role of insects in the grouse story was fully explored (Park *et al.*, 2001). Meanwhile the work at Imperial College set in motion a cascade of research that progresses decades afterwards, with the case that a plentiful accessible supply of insect food is essential to a good survival rate of grey partridge chicks becoming irrefutable. There are many fundamental reasons why the rapid growth of partridge chicks is dependent on a supply of insect food. Two days before hatching, the yolk sac, at that stage still 20 per cent of the chick's body weight, is drawn inside the body but not completely used up until the end of the first week. Partridge chicks hatch with good fat deposits that can maintain energy levels for a few days, but from the moment that the protein in the yolk is used up, chick growth is dependent on the food they can find and catch for themselves. There is no equivalent in partridges of the protein-rich 'crop milk' secreted by cells in the lining of the crop such as used by pigeons and the linnet and some other finches that makes them independent of a supply of insect food.

For partridges easily digestible insect food is essential because it supplies vitamin B_{12} and a balance of essential fatty and amino acids necessary for healthy growth, with sufficient sulphur amino acids (cysteine and methionine) for feather formation. Some of these nutrients cannot come from plant material no matter how well it is fragmented and digested. It is important to point out that Galliformes depend largely on the digestion of cellulose by bacteria in the caeca and that very little is known about the age at which this process can start. In adult chukars more than 90 per cent of cellulose is digested, similar to the situation in grouse (Inman, 1973), but it appears that the cellulose digestion efficiency is not known for chicks of any species of partridge.

Protein usually comprises around 50 per cent of the dry weight of insects, far higher than in available plant material. Fat intake is also important and it comprises 31 per cent of beetle larvae and 17 per cent of sawfly larvae (Southwood & Cross, 2002). As shown by several studies, weight gain and feather growth both improve greatly with a diet of insects, increasing the chick's resistance to chilling (see Fig. 5.1 in Liukkonen-Anttila et al., 2002). Newly hatched chicks fed natural diets but without insects did not grow and all would have died had the regime been maintained (Potts, 1986). Surprisingly the same was true of batches of chicks fed only one species of cereal aphid, although not when only one species of grasshopper was given (Borg & Toft, 1999). This species, the bird-cherry oat aphid, is also a low quality food for a wide range of spiders, harvestmen, beetles and ants compared to (for example) fruit flies (Toft, 2005). Fruit flies are often numerous in cereal crops but they are only very rarely eaten by partridges.

Chicks able to feed for longer and with a better diet of insects fly at an earlier age and, as shown by Jens Dahlgren in Sweden (Dahlgren, 1990), they may also be more resistant to toxic chemicals. It has now been demonstrated in six studies that broods have to search greater areas where insect supplies are poor, as in cereals treated with herbicides. Based on only a few samples from cereals at Highclere in Hampshire in 1963, Dick Southwood calculated that chicks needing to obtain 4 g wet weight of insects per day would have to walk 919 yd in weedy cereals but 2,919 yd in sprayed cereals: 3.17 times further. More than 20 years later, it was shown by radio-tracking that chicks moved 0.9 m per minute in weedy cereals but 2.35 m in sprayed cereals: 2.61 times further (Dahlgren, 1987), an astonishing agreement!

WEATHER

The extra searching time required when food is short means that chicks are more vulnerable to poor weather. During pioneering studies on the energy requirements of grey partridge chicks in France in the early 1980s, François Reitz found that small chicks needed to be brooded half the time even at 24°C (Reitz et al., 1984). Marjoniemi et al. (1995) showed that chicks aged 1–2 days were not able to maintain body temperature for more than 20 minutes at 25°C and wet chicks lost heat far more rapidly than dry chicks. Further research showed that 1–3-day-old chick grey partridges cannot maintain their body temperature unless they are brooded, or the ambient temperature is above 30°C; thermo-regulation begins only after the eighth day (Pis, 2001) and is not complete until the twenty-first day (Marjoniemi et al., 1995). Partridge chicks are only exceptionally rarely found dead even in radio-tracking studies and when they are found at roost sites, hypothermia is usually diagnosed (Enck, 1987; author, unpublished). Having watched broods feeding, it seems to me that most chicks that die are 'left behind' for whatever reason and so do not get brooded. Similarly the disturbance of a brood by predators, farming activities or dogs can separate chicks from parents and lead to disaster if the vegetation is wet or the weather cold. Wet vegetation often associated with sharply reduced temperatures means it is very difficult to obtain enough food without getting wet or risking hypothermia. In the much larger domestic fowl, chick foraging times are reduced about 40 per cent during rain (Wood-Gush et al., 1978). Even in hardy Willow Grouse chicks a drop in temperature from 19.5°C to 9°C with rain reduced the duration of foraging by 60 per cent, with chicks consuming almost twice as much insect food on warm, dry days compared to cold wet days. During warm weather chicks fed selectively on caterpillars, while in cold weather they ate smaller leaf hoppers, aphids and crane flies (Erikstad & Spidsø, 1982). It is easy to imagine the same in partridges, and Itamies et al. (1996) described how grey partridge chicks in Finland ate more vegetable material and fewer insects when it rained.

This interaction between weather and feeding behaviour is very difficult to study when the chicks are hidden in farm crops, but grey partridge chicks are surely more vulnerable to weather than the more robust chicks of domestic fowl or grouse. It is obviously the case that more insect food is required and harder to obtain in poor weather, but it is not at all obvious how this affects chick survival. Availability of food is crucial and severely limited where thick crops become impenetrable when soaking wet and chicks cannot see properly or walk over the ground. Nevertheless as Reitz (1988) concluded, poor weather probably reduces the survival of chicks significantly only in the absence of a good supply of food. In the Sussex Study the coldest and wettest post-hatch interval during the entire period 1957 to 2011 was in 1972 when chicks did well in an area with abundant sawfly larvae. Following this logic, in northern France food must have been scarce in the late 1970s and early 1980s because Reitz (1988) explained 93 per cent of the variation in the average number of young produced per female using weather alone. The intensity of rainfall and evaporation were selected as the key variables. The 93 per cent of variation explained cannot all be put down to chick survival however, because, as found earlier (Chapter 4), heavy rain can reduce nesting success, a component of the measure 'young produced per female' used by François Reitz.

Several attempts have been made to record weather in the Sussex Study area but none have been satisfactory: for example, thermo-hygrographs placed in cereal crops and an automatic weather station installed for some years at North Farm. Here I have used the longest near-continuous weather record in the public domain, that for Bognor on the coast 13 km to the southwest of the Sussex Study area. The Sussex Study area is 4.5 km from the coast and rises to a maximum of 236 m above sea level so has a different micro-climate but this does not matter if, as here, we are comparing the species rather than trying to explain all the variation in chick survival. The same goes for the role of the chick food index not being available prior to 1969. Here I have used the index derived from Sussex Study D-vac samples and stubble counts during 1970–87 and followed the method of Potts & Aebischer (1991). The combined weightings explained 52 per cent of the variation in chick survival up to 1987 but we now realise this index does not include some insects known to be increasing and important such as crane flies and harvestmen. For present purposes this does not affect our species comparison. The index is calculated as 0.0141 times the number of ground beetles, plus 0.120 times the number of sawfly and Lepidoptera caterpillars, plus 0.083 times the number of leaf beetles and weevils, plus 0.006 times the number of plant bugs and leaf hoppers, plus 0.0004 times the number of aphids (they are very small!). A different issue is that our chick food index was designed to represent availability to the grey partridge chicks, not red-legged partridge chicks.

For both species an analysis of variance (ANOVA) showed that only three variables accounted for a significant amount of the variation in chick survival. Surprisingly, neither average rainfall nor the number of rain days had any discernible effect. The significant variables were the chick food index, June mean daily maximum temperatures and whether there was predator control. This latter variable acted through nesting success increasing numbers of chicks hatched (as explained on p. 20) and not through reducing predation on the chicks.

In the case of the grey partridge, 47 per cent of the variation was explained by the chick food index (P=0.004), June temperature (P=0.008) and predator control (P=0.007). In the case of the red-legged partridge, 31 per cent of the variation was explained by the chick food index (P=0.034), June temperature (P=0.047) and predator control (P=0.063).

I had expected temperature to be far more important in the red-legged partridge. But this was not so. Instead the analyses show that insects may be equally important in determining the survival rate of chicks in both species. The lower amount of variation explained in the red-legged partridge is undoubtedly attributable to the presence of many reared birds, including chukar hybrids.

CHANGE IN THE GREY PARTRIDGE CHICK DIET WITH HERBICIDES

As we have seen, the results are dominated by the consumption of ants, with some studies showing virtually all the food as ants. After excluding ants (obtained outside cereal crops), the remaining diet shows a decrease in the frequency of

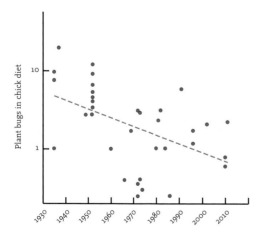

FIG 133. Grey partridge: decline in percentage frequency of plant bugs in diet of grey partridge chicks (after excluding ants, see main text) showing a marked decrease from the 1950s when herbicides use became widespread. Plant bug abundance in cereals is largely determined by abundance of broadleaved weeds.

plant bugs, a group that reflects the weediness of cereals (Fig. 133). This change becomes evident in the mid-1950s with the first widespread use of herbicides in cereals, following the same time course as with weed seeds in the diet (Fig. 67).

CONSERVATION HEADLANDS

We learned earlier about the first attempt to measure the impact of herbicides on partridge chick food at Highclere in Hampshire. Dick Southwood, who identified the insects in his and David Cross's study, was also first author of *Land & Water Bugs of the British Isles* published in 1959, and he knew better than anyone how much the common plant bugs of arable land depended on weeds such as fat hen, scentless mayweed and thistles that were rapidly disappearing from cereal crops. Yet in one of those strange twists regularly sent to divert ecologists from the scent, the work did not show more plant bugs in his untreated plots, the main benefit of not spraying at Highclere was to the plant hoppers.

It was 14 more years before the first large-scale experiments could begin. Herbicide use was a triumph for cereal growers. It had transformed cereal growing and no farmer appeared willing to turn the clock back on a sufficient

FIG 134. Typical conservation headland on the Norfolk Estate dominated by poppies.

FIG 135. Atypical conservation headland on the Norfolk Estate, Sussex Study area, with marsh woundwort despite being a dry site.

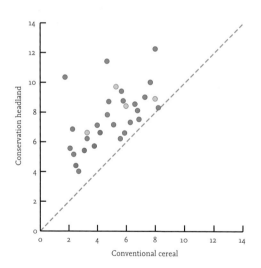

FIG 136. Comparisons of brood size with and without conservation headlands, showing a greater benefit at lower brood sizes. Results from Manydown (Rands, 1986), East Anglia (Sotherton, 1991) and the Sussex Study are shown in blue; Sweden (Chiverton, 1999) in yellow; and red-legged partridge shown in red (Sussex Study). All but one of 30 comparisons showed a benefit from conservation headlands.

scale until the Oliver-Belassis family at Manydown Estate near Basingstoke in Hampshire offered their facilities to the GWCT. The results were outstanding (Fig. 136), a convincing demonstration that herbicides were to blame for much of the poor survival of grey partridge chicks in recent decades.

Taken together, the trials showed that brood size is 1.8 times higher where chicks have access to conservation headlands than where they do not. The implications for restoration of partridge numbers are profound, an average of 5.20 (95 per cent confidence limits 4.42–5.98) fledged chicks per brood with conventional sprays and 8.00 (7.24–8.76) with conservation headlands, as we shall see in Chapter 10.

CONCLUSION

The above evidence all points to the high value of insects to the survival of grey partridge chicks, with a very strong likelihood that the same applies to the red-legged and chukar partridge chicks. For the grey partridge there has been a detrimental effect of herbicides that can be reversed by the use of conservation headlands. In the long-run, however, whether partridges can co-exist with agriculture will depend largely on how the insect communities in cereal crops respond to changes in farming; this is the subject of the next chapter.

CHAPTER 6

The Cereal Ecosystem and the Abundance of Chick Food in the Sussex Study Area (1968–2011)

THE SUSSEX DOWNS HAVE been farmed for thousands of years and provided good habitats for grey partridges until the advent of pesticides. After many incidents of direct toxicity in the 1950s and early 1960s the effects of pesticides became largely indirect, through food supplies. Detailed information about the invertebrates is only available from 1969 when the Sussex Study started its annual monitoring. As explained in the previous chapter however, many species of insect that traditionally feature in the diet of grey partridge chicks had declined considerably before 1969, in line with broadleaved weeds. Since then there has been remarkable stability with no overall trend in the abundance of chick foods – with decreases in the lucerne flea, small diurnal ground beetles and sawfly caterpillars offset by increases in the abundance of earwigs, grasshoppers, click beetles, crane flies, ants and Lepidoptera caterpillars. Cereal aphids were most abundant during 1968–76. The causes of these changes are reviewed here and they are complex, involving not just pesticides but changes in crop rotation and increasing spring temperatures.

Agriculture is essentially a natural process. Ploughing is not all that different to the rooting of wild pigs or even in former times to that of the huge mammoth-like shovel-tusker. Plants even have their own equivalents of 'herbicides' known as allelochemicals, as is the case with some species of gum rock rose (p. 117), and insecticides such as pyrethrum. What is important to partridges is not the fact of agriculture; it is instead the speed and scale with which it is changing. Looking to the future, the merits of genetic engineering, which also can occur in nature, are discussed.

A SHORT HISTORY OF FARMING ON THE SUSSEX DOWNS

The switch from hunter-gathering to farming occurred independently in at least seven areas of the world over a period of about 5,000 years (Smith, 1998). It took place on the Sussex Study area about 7–8,000 years ago. Quite why such fundamental changes happened is not known but supposed causes include over-hunting resulting in a scarcity of food. Whatever the cause, compared to the malarial swamps, thick forest and unworkable soils in the surrounding lowlands, the present study area, with light soils (i.e. with little clay) on free-draining land, was ideal for the purpose. The general area became 'one of the cradles of civilisation in Britain' (Brandon, 1998). Since the conversion to agriculture, nearly all the Sussex Study area has been ploughed at some time with the evidence clear today when newly ploughed land reveals the boundaries of former terraced fields created by the pre-Roman strip-lynchet field system (Fig. 137).

Farming divided the area so that the higher, steeper slopes were mainly used for grazing with the remainder devoted to arable. Sheep and cattle were shepherded and herded on the grasslands during the day, spending the night on the arable where they helped to provide manure. This kept the non-arable

FIG 137. Surviving part of the pre-Roman strip lynchet system of arable farming, Norfolk Estate.

area largely free of trees and maintained diverse, grazed, unfertilised semi-natural grassland that with the light grazing would have been ideal for flowers, grasshoppers, ants, partridges and a semi-natural biodiversity. In ancient times the fields on the lighter chalk rendzina soils with many flints were relatively square and about 4 ha, surprisingly large for the era. Whether cattle, small horses or mules were used at that time for ploughing is not known. On the heavier soils, instead of the larger fields there were hundreds of strips of about one acre (0.4 ha) – these being a furlong (201 m) in length and a chain (20 m) wide. Similar strips dominated the landscape throughout Western Europe, existing still in southeast Poland, parts of Spain and in the Balkans.

In Britain, following the English Civil War, there were innovations from mainland Europe with the farming turning to a rotational system of mixed stock and crops, underpinned by the use of nitrogen-producing clovers and other legumes and with spring-sown cereals planted with a nurse crop of grass and clover (Potts, 2008). This semi-natural system known as under-sowing is ideal for sustaining sawflies, clover weevils and many other insects; it is known as the 'traditional ley'. On some estates farm tenancies were made conditional on following rotations of this kind.

The farm records are particularly detailed at Applesham, long maintained by Christopher Passmore. On the lighter soils three-year grass and white clover leys were established by under-sowing spring barley and left down for three years, after which there was a spring fallow to control couch, onion couch, the perennial *Agrostis* grasses (black and creeping bents) and docks. In July the fallow was sown to forage rape followed by three years of cereals with the third of these under-sown, repeating the rotation. As well as maintaining fertility with the legumes and livestock, and controlling perennial weeds, this system provided fresh pastures that reduced infection of sheep with parasites. The system also maintained a 'patchwork quilt' farmland landscape with an intimate mixture of crops and livestock. Where the soils were heavier there was a variety of other crops, such as mangolds, vetches (tares), sainfoin, potatoes and grass and some kale for dairy cattle. All the light land farms on the Sussex Study area were farmed in more or less this way but most abandoned the system during 1965–80 with the notable exception of Applesham Farm. Dairy farming has gradually disappeared. Replacing the traditional leys there has been a wide variety of novel rotations, ranging from continuous winter wheat to continuous grass, with alternating winter wheat and oilseed rape a popular choice. New crops included, beans, peas and linseed, and set-aside came and went. Now we see a marked reappearance of ley farming, with a return to sheep and cattle, and superficially at least, the farmland landscape now resembles that of the early 1960s.

FIG 138. Applesham: Chris Passmore using a sweep net, with the annual monitoring in the background.

Modern farming essentially separates stock from crop and crop from pests, and produces polarised agricultures (Southwood, 1972). This occurs on several scales, from within fields to across continents. What has happened in Sussex has happened virtually everywhere in the grey partridge range; Shrubb (2003) has described the situation for Britain as a whole. Taking grass out of arable rotations has by itself caused problems for wildlife but it has also increased the need for anthelmintics and for herbicides to control perennial weeds. Since World War II four main classes of pesticides have been introduced in the Sussex Study area: seed dressings and then in sequence, the herbicide, fungicide and insecticide sprays. Each has had different effects on the insect populations in cereal crops.

THE SUSSEX STUDY'S LONG-TERM MONITORING OF INSECTS AND OTHER INVERTEBRATES

There was an outbreak of cereal aphids in the Sussex Study area in 1968 which many farmers and crop advisors believed to be unprecedented. This led to speculation that a scarcity of the aphid's natural enemies was part of the cause; nobody seemed to have seen ladybirds on farms for years. It was alarming because if the cause was a shortage of natural enemies, the outbreaks were likely to increase in frequency, eventually resulting in the use of insecticides in summer on a vast scale using aircraft. It was obvious the ramifications would go far further than mere partridges. Research to introduce natural enemies to control pests in greenhouses was under way just outside the study area at the Glasshouse Crops Research Institute, Rustington, funded by the then Agricultural Research Council. It was shocking to realise that this kind of work might eventually have to be done to reintroduce predators and parasites to the countryside. What little was known at the time came mainly from the Rothamsted Insect Survey (RIS). This uses two very different methods: light traps that trap mainly moths at night and aerial suction traps atop 12.2 m high towers.

Southwood *et al.* (2003) examined the plant bugs caught in a light trap at Rothamsted Experimental Station over a period of 67 years. This showed a big decline in abundance between 1933–49 and 1960–2000, with the main change being the loss of aquatic species following the filling of a pond near the trap! Surprisingly the least change was in *Lygus rugulipennis* and species associated with arable weeds. Much more extensive information has come from no fewer than 100 light traps across Britain. The results show that 222 (66 per cent) of the 337 species of larger moths monitored declined during 1968–2002 (Conrad *et al.*, 2006). The declines for 71 species were sufficient to classify them as endangered or vulnerable on IUCN criteria, similar to the situation with 'specialist' butterflies.

The suction traps sample the aerial plankton, such as aeronaut spiders that drift on their gossamer threads and tiny wind-driven insects such as thrips and

FIG 139. Sussex Study: the author sampling with a Dietrick vacuum insect net (D-vac) in 1971.

FIG 140. A few of the exceptionally large numbers of seven-spot ladybirds in cereal crops in the Sussex Study area in 1976.

frit flies and the larger free-flying species as well as aphids. The data from the RIS suction traps during 1969–88 showed there was no notable trend for six of seven species of cereal aphid with an increase in the seventh (Woiwood, 1991). Four traps in southern England showed no significant trend in aphid abundance from 1973–2002 (Shortall *et al.*, 2009).

Going back to 1968, it was clearly a problem that almost nothing was known about what was actually taking place in crops. A fair amount was known about the natural history of beneficial insects and a lot about some pest species, but virtually nothing was known about trends in abundance. When truly staggering numbers of seven-spot ladybirds appeared on sea fronts in the late summer of 1976, most people thought they had come from France. We knew through our monitoring that they had emigrated from the cereal fields of southeast Britain. The increase in numbers was caused by the short run of years with high numbers of cereal aphids and the subsequent return to normality was due to a shortage of aphids and a very high rate of infection with the parasitoid wasp *Perilitus coccinellae*. The Sussex Study was begun precisely to gain perspectives like this.

The GWCT began its annual monitoring of insects in the cereal crops of the Sussex Study area in 1969 and 1970. At first I thought ten years might be enough to settle the issue of the cause of cereal aphid outbreaks but there remain very important questions to answer after more than 40 years. Following various trials with nets and pooters we settled on a D-vac, originally designed for work in alfalfa (lucerne) fields in the US, as the best technique for sampling insects in cereal crops. More than 40 years ago we came to the same conclusion as Doxon *et al.* (2011), namely that the D-vac was more appropriate for game-bird chick food than sweeping. After sampling each field three times each year in early June, mid-June and early July, it was clear the second period was the most feasible. Earlier samples were often spoiled by too much soil being sucked-up by the D-vac, and later ones were overwhelmed by barley awns. To get a fair picture across the whole area we needed to sample at least 100 cereal fields and this sampling has taken place on 16 and 17 June (the work takes two days) or as soon as weather permits after these dates, and has continued for 43 years. Analysis of aerial suction trap catches at the University of Stirling shows the same overall downward trend in insect abundance as observed in the Sussex Study (Benton *et al.*, 2002). Given that the two sites are 640 km apart, it is clear the Sussex Study represents the situation on a national scale (see also page 226 for the situation with sawflies).

The sampling of cereal crops in the Sussex Study coincides with the peak hatch of partridge chicks. At Damerham the hatching dates were recorded for 1,939 clutches over the 11 years, 1948–59. The average hatch date was 15 June but this was not just a function of the date that the eggs were laid because it was also dependent on the nest success rate. If this rate was high there were correspondingly fewer repeat clutches that delayed the hatch dates by up to three weeks. Even with this variation, the earliest and latest average hatching dates over the 11 years at Damerham were only 2½ days apart. Analysis of the British Trust for Ornithology's nest record card scheme showed an average hatch date of 18 June for the whole of Britain from 1941–76 for the grey partridge and 22 June

FIG 141. Steve Moreby (with D-vac) and Julie Ewald (emptying D-vac) in drought-affected field with conservation headland: Sussex Study, 2011. (Peter Thompson)

for the red-legged partridge (Potts, 1980). Another study, this time in the region around Nantes, France, indicates nearly the same dates for both species during 1977–85 (Brun, 1991). The dates of hatching can also be estimated from the ages of chicks seen during the stubble counts, and this gave an average hatch date of 15 June in 2011, which had had the warmest spring on record. Through the study there has never been any reason to suspect that hatching dates have changed due to climate change. This is a different story to that with many song birds, where breeding seasons have advanced with increasing temperatures. The reason that partridge hatch dates have not changed in the same way is because their cue to start comes from increasing day length. This is well known in game farming where the laying dates of partridges, like those of domestic fowls, are brought forward with additional lighting.

PESTICIDES

Sulphur and other chemical have been used to control pests and diseases for more than 4,000 years (Conway & Pretty, 1991). From 1804 partridges have been found dead after eating seed grain treated with arsenicals, and in 1844 Hawker wrote: 'the farmers cutting up their grass banks for fuel, and thereby driving the

FIG 142. Spring-sown barley virtually impossible to harvest when infested with runch (wild radish), a weed readily controlled by the first hormone-based herbicides.

FIG 143. 1952: spraying with Denocate. (GWCT)

birds to breed in open fields, at the mercy of hawks, wet weather, and scythes – putting among their seed-wheat vitriol (copper sulphate to prevent smut), which poisons many birds, that would otherwise be left to breed – and mowing their wheat' (Young, 1804; Hawker, 1844). In 1938 mercury seed dressings were introduced that caused some mortality to grey partridges in Sweden (Borg *et al.*, 1969), but in general pesticides are not thought to have reduced partridge numbers until the 1950s. The first chemical to cause serious problems to game birds was the herbicide di-nitro-ortho-cresol (DNOC). Mortality peaked during 1950–53 but soon the compound had to be withdrawn following the poisoning of several tractor drivers (Bidstrup & Payne, 1951). Importantly this herbicide also killed insects directly and it was this that stimulated Dick Southwood's studies at Rothamsted mentioned earlier.

From 1956 to 1965 the organo-chlorine insecticide dieldrin, a relative of DDT, was used in seed treatments that caused significant mortalities to grey partridges and other species, most notably the bird-eating raptors, foxes and other predators. In March and April 1958 several grey partridges were found dead in the Sussex Study area after eating dieldrin-treated grain. Dieldrin was gradually phased out through the 1960s, first as a seed dressing, then as a sheep dip and finally as moth-proofing for carpets. When it reached the sea the highly diluted insecticide began to concentrate again as it accumulated through marine food chains. Amounts were

FIG 144. Colony of shags on Brownsman, Farne Islands, in 1963 when the eggs were found to be contaminated with pesticides.

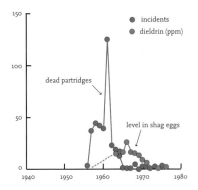

FIG 145. Incidents of partridges poisoned by dieldrin in Britain showing the peak in 1961, and levels in shag eggs on the Farne Islands, Northumberland, showing the peak in 1966. The use of dieldrin was phased out during 1962–66. (Coulson *et al.*, 1972; Potts, 1986)

monitored in eggs of the shag on the Farne Islands and this showed a peak about five years after the peak mortality on farmland (Fig. 145).

The important point here is that the grey partridge was the sentinel for a much wider problem of organo-chlorine dispersal around the globe. Farms are not isolated from other often distant ecosystems. Although modern pesticides have become much less persistent, not accumulating up food chains, they remain toxic and are being used on such a wide, indeed global, scale that problems continue to occur, for example with accumulation in ground water, a subject outside the scope of this book. It seems inconceivable that agriculture could ever again reach a position where it could manage without pesticides but there is a serious need for continued surveillance.

In the early spring of 1981 there were many reports of grey partridges dying in south-central Hungary. I was called in to investigate. The cause this time was the organo-phosphate monocrotophos, even more toxic than dieldrin and never authorised for use in Britain. In Hungary it was used to control maize leaf-weevils in very large fields. I proposed an immediate ban on its use near field margins, but incidents continued and it wasn't until 1996 that the chemical was completely outlawed from the country. In 1995–6 there was a large loss of wildlife in Argentina including more than 5,000 Swainson's hawks (Goldstein *et al.*, 1999), which led to a ban there and in Australia (Food & Agriculture Organisation).

The chukar partridge is the national bird of Pakistan, hence the many colourful paintings on the highly decorated trucks one sees everywhere. The bird itself has greatly decreased however, something that Imran Khan has drawn attention to in his 2012 book *Pakistan*. Whether pesticides are to blame for the

FIG 146. Modern sprayer with 36 m boom but used very carefully by Jacques Hicter to protect insect food of grey partridge chicks. (Markus Jenny)

decline of the partridge is not known, but in April 2004 I found monocrotophos was still being used. For some years now the international trade in pesticides has been regulated under the Rotterdam Convention, with Pakistan a signatory. In June 2006 the licence to import the chemical to Pakistan was revoked. I earlier calculated that it has usually taken 8–10 years for the regulatory authorities to phase out harmful agro-chemicals (Potts, 2000).

The first two hormone herbicides were the British MCPA and the American 2, 4-D. Some formulations of the latter were weakly insecticidal and in the Sussex Study area it was still being used in 1972 on winter wheat, with an isolated case as late as 1977 (Ewald & Aebischer, 2000). Dinoseb may also have killed insects directly; it was last used in 1970. Today the consensus appears to be that the impacts of herbicides are not due to toxic effects (Brust, 1990). So far as partridge chick food is concerned the most important changes in insect numbers in cereal crops are due to herbicides. These remove the food plants of many species. It was not until conservation headlands were employed in good numbers that we could confirm this. We now ask how the use of these and other pesticides and modern cereal growing generally have affected the cereal ecosystem invertebrates as a whole.

SYSTEMATIC REVIEW OF THE STATUS OF INSECTS AND OTHER INVERTEBRATES IN THE SUSSEX STUDY CEREAL CROPS

This review focuses on issues of direct relevance to partridges. Further details are to be found in Potts & Vickerman (1974) and in Aebischer (1991) and a comprehensive review covering 1970 to 2011 is in advanced preparation. The abundances in the graphs are the numbers per 5 D-vac samples overing 0.46 of a square metre of the cereal crop adjusted to 1 square metre.

Snails: Mollusca

Five species have been found in the sampling, with little change excepting a marked increase since 1990 (Fig. 147) largely attributable to the small conical snail *Cochlicella acuta*. Not much is known about it in Britain but it has become a serious pest of wheat in Australia, making separation of grain more difficult at harvest. Although the larger snails are too heavy to be sampled with a D-vac they are increasingly found feeding in and around game-cover crops, especially those containing kale.

Woodlice, centipedes and millipedes

One species of woodlouse (*Philoscia muscorum*), three of centipedes (*Lamycetes*

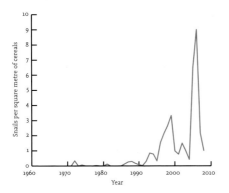

FIG 147. Abundance of snails in cereal crops from 1970 to 2008.

fulvicornis, Geophilomorpha sp. and *Lithobius* sp.) and one millipede in the group Polydesmida make up this group. Normally only the centipedes have featured in chick diets. There has been no significant overall change in the status of these mostly omnivorous species.

Arachnida

Spiders: Araneae

Keith Sunderland made a special study of these and found 29 species in the June samples out of a total number of 180 species recorded from cereal crops in Britain (Sunderland, 1987). The average density was 20 per square metre, with a slight decline perhaps reversed (Fig. 148).

Harvestmen: Opiliones

Although only 1 per cent as abundant as the spiders, these can be important chick foods. Four relatively large and active predatory species are found in Sussex Study

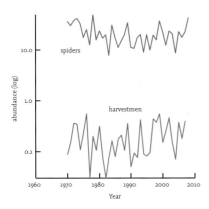

FIG 148. Trends in abundance of spiders (red) and harvestmen (blue) in Sussex Study cereals during 1970–2008. Note log scale, essential when comparing trends.

cereals: *Nemastoma bimaculatum*, *Homalenotus quadridentatus*, *Oligolophus agrestis* and *Platybunus triangularis*. These are amongst the most numerous of the 22 in Britain (Sankey, 1988). No overall change.

Pseudoscorpions

One species not identified; scarce with no change in abundance.

Insects

In the review that follows, all insect orders that occur in the Sussex Study are mentioned, but for the largest groups with thousands of species – the beetles, flies, wasps and allies and Lepidoptera – it is impossible to give more than superficial coverage here (more detail can be found in Potts & Vickerman, 1974). The orders and the numbers of accepted species are those of the Royal Entomological Society (Barnard, 2011).

Springtails: Collembola

There are two main types of these tiny primitive wingless insects in Sussex study cereals. The first type includes three suborders of springtails that as a group are the most numerous insects in D-vac samples, with more than 13 species averaging 642 per square metre. They may be most important as food of ground beetles (Potts & Vickerman, 1974; Brooks *et al.*, 2012). These species mostly feed on soil fungi and although they have declined since the mid-1980s, there is no decline over the period as a whole. Although abundant, these tiny insects feature rarely in partridge chick diets, with the most frequent being the larger yellow *Entomobrya* spp.

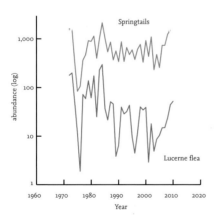

FIG 149. Trends in abundance of lucerne flea (red) and other springtails (blue) in Sussex Study cereals during 1970–2008 (log scale).

The second group is represented by a final suborder the Symphypleona with two species present, one of which is the lucerne flea, averaging 50 per square metre but with a marked decline since the mid-1980s. At one time featuring very frequently in the diet of very small chicks these insects are tiny and as commented by Ford *et al.* (1938): 'it is evident that the chicks spend much of their time in catching this minute insect, so it must be regarded as important'. The insect can be a pest in lucerne crops but in the Sussex Study area it feeds mainly on clovers and they have declined along with traditional under-sowing. There was however a dramatic but unexplained dip in abundance of all springtails in the mid-1970s.

Earwigs: Dermaptera

There are seven species in Britain, of which the ubiquitous common earwig *Forficula auricularia* is by far the more numerous of the two found in Sussex Study cereals. Usually considered omnivorous they are also predators of cereal aphids (later). The other species is *Labia minor*. Despite the lower number of aphids since 1976, earwigs have shown a ten-fold increase.

Grasshoppers and bush crickets: Orthoptera

This almost entirely herbivorous group is perhaps the one most likely to benefit from climate warming (Hickling *et al.*, 2006). By far the main species of two is the field grasshopper *Chorthippus brunneus*, with the meadow grasshopper *Chorthippus parallelus* found mostly in rough grassland. The speckled bush cricket *Leptophyes punctatissimahas* has also recently been found in conservation headlands near hedges. This group is under-sampled with a D-vac when compared to sweeping.

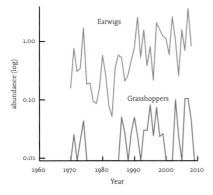

FIG 150. Trends in abundance of earwigs (blue) and grasshoppers (red) showing increases in Sussex Study cereals during 1970–2008 (log scale).

True bugs: Hemiptera
Plant bugs: Heteroptera

These insects tick all the boxes except one. After blossom beetles, they respond better than any other group to conservation headlands, where they usually account for about 17 per cent of all insects caught. They are preferred over all other insects in laboratory preference tests, they are the right colour and size and their variations in density explain a significant amount of variation in chick survival. As we have seen in the previous chapter, they are of similar importance in Norfolk (Green, 1984) and in Poland (Panek, 1997). The problem in Sussex – the box they do not tick – is that they account for only 1.6 per cent of the food items in the grey partridge chick diet; 2.3 per cent in the case of the red-legged partridge chick. In addition the increase from about 1985 (Fig. 151) due to a surge in some species of broadleaved weeds even in herbicide treated cereal crops (Potts *et al.*, 2010) was not reflected in improved chick survival.

By far the most important of the 37 species occurring in Sussex Study area cereal crops is *Closterotomus norwegicus* (formerly *Calocoris norvegicus*). This species accounts for 84 per cent of the plant bug community that in total averages 11 per square metre and it and other members of the genus are very widely distributed, including through the range of the red-legged partridge (Rosenzweig, 1997). In addition to *Closterotomus* there are eight predatory plant bugs, seven grass feeders and the remaining species that feed on broadleaved weeds. Some species overwinter as adults, others, including *C. norwegicus*, overwinter as eggs, but in both cases always in hedges, shrubs or dead vegetation. For this reason these insects avoided the hazards of the very widespread straw and stubble burning that was such a feature of the Sussex Study area until the ban became effective in 1992. The winged forms which fly out of the cereals in early July spend some time before leaving the crop in the canopy of cereals, especially winter barley, where they are far from the reach of chicks but ideally situated for corn buntings.

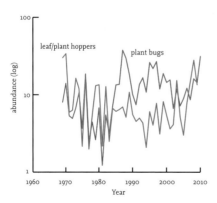

FIG 151. Densities of plant bugs (red) and leaf and plant hoppers (blue) in Sussex Study area cereal crops, 1969–2008, showing an increase in plant bugs in the late 1980s attributable to an increase in broadleaved weeds (Fig. 117).

Frog-hoppers, leaf-hoppers and plant hoppers: Cercopidae, Cicadellidae (formerly
Jassida) and Delphacidae

In many ways this is the opposite story to the plant bugs; they are less numerous,
averaging eight per square metre, but at least as important in every study of
grey partridge chick diet that has been made. Why this group did not fluctuate
in parallel with the plant bugs is not known but many species live at least part
of their time on cereals and grasses. Fortunately these insects respond well to
conservation headlands (Chapter 10).

Aphids (greenfly): Aphididae

Aphids, the most abundant items in the diet of both grey and red-legged
partridges in the Sussex Study area, account for 35 per cent, 45 per cent and 73 per
cent of the diet of grey, chukar and red-legged partridges respectively (Table 18).
On average, the predators that specialise in eating aphids, such as hoverfly
larvae, add a further 2 per cent of individuals to the diet. Predators not eaten
include seven-spot ladybirds because chicks find them distasteful (Whitmore
& Preuss, 1982; Moreby et al., 2006). Adult partridges eat ladybirds occasionally
and as mentioned earlier the similarly coloured fire bug. Almost 40 per cent of
predatory insects, mainly spiders and beetles, prey on aphids (Sunderland et al.,
1988) and many of these predators feature in partridge chick diets. Aphids are
clearly a key group.

In 1969 the Natural History Museum's Victor Eastop identified the aphids
from the crops of seven grey partridge and five red-legged partridge chicks,
with the results given in Table 19. In wheat most cereal aphids live on the ear
where they are unobtainable to partridge chicks. Nevertheless the results were
surprising; none of the most abundant species of cereal aphid Sitobion avenae had
been eaten. In the peak years of 1970, 1975 and 1976 there can be no doubt that

TABLE 19. Species of aphids eaten by partridge chicks in the Sussex Study in 1969 and their
host plants.

species	main host plant	grey partridge	red-legged partridge
Metopolophium dirhodum	cereals	97	0
Brachycaudus helichrysii	speedwells, clover	38	0
Sitobion fragariae	spring barley	226	2,509
Cavariella aegopodii; theobaldii	hogweed	0	483
Not identified	–	52	180

FIG 152. Numerous aphids on ears of wheat where they are out of reach of partridge chicks, but insecticides used to control them affect chick foods lower down in the crop. (GWCT)

cereal aphids which also occur on lower leaves were eaten; these were all good years for partridge chick survival.

So what determines the abundance of the aphids in cereal crops; could their natural enemies be important, as speculated at the start of the studies? The practical significance of the answer was enormous.

Forecasting the likelihood of such a spiral in insecticide use was a focus for the Joint Cereal Ecosystem Study. This was a complex issue, for there was a continual rain of winged aphid immigrants to cereal crops, especially on fine, warm days in mid-May to mid-June. On 1–4 June 1971, 590 newly arrived winged aphids were collected from a random sample of cereal fields and, again, identified by Victor Eastop. Thirty-four species were present only eight of which feed on cereals or grasses, but they accounted for 75 per cent of the individuals identified.

First we had to find out which predators ate significant numbers of aphids and the results were surprising. Far more species of polyphagous predators preyed on aphids than anyone imagined. Some rove beetles, thought to feed only on fungi, were found to climb cereals at night where they fed on aphids, with the best example being *Tachyporus* (Vickerman & Sunderland, 1975). This was discovered by camping by a cereal field and sweeping the crop every hour, day and night. Another surprise was the finding that a high proportion of the aphids on the ears of wheat fell to the ground before climbing another stem, perhaps disturbed by predators. During such excursions they could become available to ground beetles (Wratten & Powell, 1991) and of course partridge chicks. Some high-tech methods had to be used to detect liquid parts of aphids in predators, for example laborious enzyme-linked immunosorbent assays involving the rearing of rabbits (Crook & Sunderland, 1984). The work would now be easier because DNA can be used (e.g. Traugott *et al.*, 2008).

Parasitoid wasps and the aphid specialist predators played a part too, and it became clear that the cereal field insect community was rich and complex, not at all what anyone expected. The Joint Cereal Ecosystem Study resulted in a tremendous amount of work in the Sussex Study area during the late 1970s and early 1980s (Chambers *et al.*, 1983). Over six years cereal crops were sampled by sweeping 128 times day and night, by ground searching 136 times and by pitfall trapping 667 times. Keith Sunderland identified a total of 279 species of predator, mainly spiders and beetles, of which 110 species had fed on aphids (Sunderland *et al.*, 1988). The most numerous species of cereal aphid, *Sitobion avenae*, is the best known, and in Southern England this one species is infected by seven species of parasitoid wasp that in turn are infected by five of their own parasitoid wasps known as hyper-parasitoids (Wratten & Powell, 1991). In summary, almost all the field work on aphid predators and parasitoids pointed to them having an important role in keeping aphid numbers lower than would otherwise be the case, and it was the experimental evidence that was most persuasive.

Field trials where aphid enemies were excluded or augmented gave the most instructive results, with lower peak numbers of aphids found where generalist predators (mostly ground beetles) were most abundant (Fig. 153).

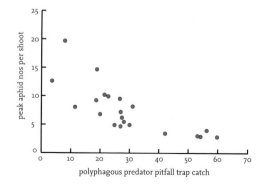

FIG 153. Lower peak numbers of aphids in cereal crops, with increased numbers of polyphagous predators, mostly beetles (Wratten & Powell, 1991).

FIG 154. Sussex Study area 1975: the first significant aerial spraying of insecticides to control cereal aphids.

All this labour-intensive work on aphids was very time-consuming, but as it turned out, establishing which natural enemies were important was easier than answering questions about long-term trends. We expected cereal aphid numbers and the use of insecticides to increase; the pesticide treadmill feared at the start. For the first seven years it appeared this might be the case (Fig. 155). Yet, for the next 20 years a substantial and highly significant decline was evident on all farms, equally so in winter barley, spring barley and winter wheat (Aebischer, 1991). Winter cereals are infested mainly by *Sitobion avenae* and this species overwinters on cereal crops, whereas spring barley is infested by aphids which overwinter as eggs on shrubs: for example, *Sitobion fragariae* overwinters on brambles. Winter wheat was sprayed in autumn and summer, winter barley in autumn and spring barley was not sprayed, yet the aphids declined in the same way in all three types of cereals. Moreover the decline of cereal aphids in Sussex has continued through the past two decades and it has occurred in other countries, for example in the Czech Republic (Honek & Martinkova, 2005).

The declines in aphid numbers have been forecast to continue into the future as CO_2 levels increase in the atmosphere, due to global climate change (Newman, 2005). This forecast is however based on laboratory work with the bird cherry aphid, which is uncommon in Sussex Study cereals, and it may not be

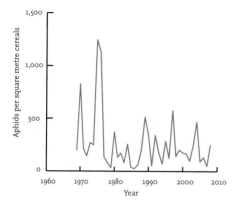

FIG 155. Numbers of cereal aphids in Sussex Study area cereal crops from 1969–2009.

valid. Any explanation for the existing decline would have to address changes in the resistance of new cereal varieties to aphids and in the height of crops, with more modern shorter crops more accessible to predatory beetles. Unfortunately because cereal aphids are no longer perceived to threaten cereal crops, there are too few scientists to settle these issues. Insecticides may be of overriding importance.

At the GWCT Julie Ewald has diligently compiled pesticide usage in the Sussex Study area from 1970 and much of the following information comes from a unique account of pesticide usage (Ewald & Aebischer, 2000). Apart from seed-dressings, the first insecticide used to control aphids was demeton-s-methyl in 1975. Most of this chemical was applied from crop-spraying planes. In trials on headlands, plant bug numbers were reduced 31 per cent (Sotherton, 1991). Because of this, and out of concern for ladybirds, some farmers used pirimicarb, which did not reduce plant bug numbers (Sotherton, 1991) but did reduce aphid predator numbers by about 50 per cent (Powell et al., 1981).

Essentially the modern era, in which all winter cereals are treated with insecticides, began in 1983 and 1984 with the aim of eradicating barley yellow dwarf virus from susceptible autumn sown crops. In subsequent years, despite the low numbers of cereal aphids in summer, insecticide use escalated with allegedly two new threats emerging in the 1990s, even though our monitoring showed no change: thrips and the orange blossom midges (Holland & Oakley, 2007). Cypermethrin, one of the new synthetic pyrethroids, was used to control them. These chemicals are toxic to a very wide range of beneficial and chick food insects; indeed they are advertised to control pest sawflies. They are slightly less harmful than dimethoate (Moreby et al., 2009), but they were used on a vast scale, sometimes in conjunction with chlorpyrifos. Short-term adverse effects on the

FIG 156. The Beauce, France, in the late 1980s: irrigation system and use of insecticides to control cereal aphids. Grey partridges are now in much lower numbers.

insect food supply of yellowhammers were reported for at least 20 days after application (Hart *et al.*, 2006). In Sussex there have been much longer-term effects on sawflies (Aebischer, 1990, 1992) and beetles (later).

Dimethoate caused 80–95 per cent mortality to field-layer invertebrates in field trials (Vickerman & Sunderland, 1977; Sotherton, 1991) and the GWCT advised its members not to use the chemical. In the 1993 evaluation of pesticides, under the 1985 Food & Environment Protection Act only two paragraphs in 214 pages dealt with our concerns, but Nicholas Aebischer's model that sawfly populations could take as long as seven years to recover from one application was mentioned. Only a small fraction of sawflies occur at field margins but the official government recommendation was not to use the chemical in the outer 6 m of cereal fields after April, a restriction of use of about 6 per cent. This was a huge breakthrough, with the invertebrate wildlife in cereal crops given some recognition, and it led directly to 6 m exclusion zones for the synthetic pyrethroids, the adoption of conservation headlands and greater care in giving approvals to new pesticides. We do not know exactly what the side effects of the synthetic pyrethroids were on partridge chick foods, but we do know that it takes many species more than one year to recover from adverse effects and sawflies remain very scarce where insecticides were most often used in the 1980s and 1990s. Dimethoate is no longer used in the Sussex Study area but it is widely used elsewhere. At least until recently it was extensively used to control caterpillar infestations in olives in Spain.

Nicotine has been used as an insecticide for 200 years but with the drawback that its effects were very short term. The neonicotenoids (nicotine-like) are much more persistent and ten new formulations were launched in 1991–2001 that together can adversely affect an extraordinary variety of invertebrates including slugs, aphids, leaf-hoppers, plant hoppers, thrips, flies, Lepidoptera, sawflies and beetles (Elbert *et al.*, 2008; Liu *et al.*, 2007) and, controversially, bees (Benjamin

& McCallum, 2009). Fortunately in our case these chemicals are used as seed dressings, so limiting the collateral damage that occurs with sprays. Chlothianidin has been used on most autumn-sown cereal crops in the Sussex Study area for five years but fortunately not on spring barley. Whether autumn use causes harm is difficult to say because it all depends whether the chemical retains enough activity six months after sowing. We investigated whether the failure of sawflies to recover on the Norfolk Estate could be due to Clothianidin. The clue that it was probably not the problem comes from the very wide range of insect groups the insecticide kills. It is very difficult to see how sawflies alone would be affected when other insects were doing well, even those that eat growing cereals such as crane flies and click beetles (adult wireworms). It has to be said however that, with 21 different insecticides used on cereals in the Sussex Study area since 1970, identifying specific adverse effects on non-target insects is virtually impossible.

The neonicotenoids can poison partridges directly and one of 43 birds postmortemed during the radio-tracking studies in France mentioned in previous chapters had died this way (Bro *et al.*, 2001). The neonicotenoid used in cereals, Clothianidin, is virtually non-toxic to bobwhite quail (US Department Agriculture) and no adverse effects have been suspected on partridges in Sussex. The neonicotenoids themselves are not likely to be used very far into the future; where used intensively, pests have quickly developed resistance (Elbert *et al.*, 2008).

Pea aphids can be a serious pest and when this happens almost all pea crops are treated with insecticide (see p. 335). On the Norfolk Estate the outer 10 m of pea fields are not sprayed with insecticide and most aphids eaten by partridge chicks in 2010 and 2011 were pea aphids, which are much larger than cereal aphids, more available to chicks and undoubtedly the reason why chicks do so well in pea fields with unsprayed margins.

Jumping plant lice: Psyllidae
These are somewhat similar to aphids. In Britain there are 80 species, with three species in Sussex Study cereals, and they are increasing.

Bark (book) lice: Psocoptera
At least 3 of the 100 species in Britain are found in study area cereals.

Thrips or Thunder-bugs: Thysanoptera
There are 179 species in Britain with only three regularly found in Sussex Study cereals at a combined average annual density of 160 per square metre; these are pests of cereals with no trend in abundance, at least in the studied area. These insects are too small to be a food for partridge chicks.

Beetles: Coleoptera

This is a vast group with c.4,000 species in Britain, with at least 151 species in Sussex Study cereals.

Ground beetles: Carabidae

The larger species in this immensely important group are not monitored effectively because the beetles are either too heavy to be sucked up with the D-vac or strictly nocturnal. The monitored ground beetles can all be eaten by partridge chicks. The most important species in the diet, *Trechus quadristriatus, Demetrias atricapillus, Notiophilus biguttatus, Bembidion guttula, Amara aenea* and *Anchomenus dorsale,* are monitored but the strawberry-seed beetle and *H. aeneus* are too large. One species increased: the Russian or corn ground beetle, sufficiently so to be a pest of winter wheat in the 1990s. The trend for all the monitored species is shown below, with a marked decline since the early 1990s (Fig. 157).

The most important species for partridge chicks, *Trechus quadristriatus,* is more abundant where there is more shade (Mitchell, 1963) but is most frequently seen on bare areas in sunshine, even though it is classified as being inactive in daylight (Holland, 2002). This beetle is predatory, feeding on other invertebrates, especially cereal aphids (Sunderland, 2002; Honěk & Jarošík, 2000), but when these are not available will feed on some species of weed (Goldschmidt & Toft, 1997) and it can also eat the eggs of frit flies (see Potts & Vickerman, 1974). As related in Chapter 5, European mainland densities were at least ten times higher than in Britain in the 1970s and 1980s. Whether this is still the case we do not know. So why has *Trechus quadristriatus* declined so steeply, especially since the year 2000? Most ground beetles in the Sussex Study area have been found to be

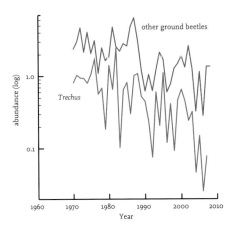

FIG 157. Trend in ground beetles (red) in Sussex Study area cereal crops from 1970 to 2008, showing a decline that coincided with the use of insecticides. The important chick food *Trechus quadristriatus* is shown in blue (log scale).

rather resistant to pesticides (Ewald & Aebischer, 2006) and the poor correlation with aphid abundance (cf. Fig. 155) suggests that the problem is not just a lack of aphid food.

This beetle is one of the few species that are active in the autumn when insecticides are applied to control aphids and the spread of barley yellow dwarf virus. Laboratory and field trials conducted in the autumn have shown that pyrethroid insecticides are toxic to this species (Wiles & Jepson, 1992; Pullen *et al.*, 1992). The newer insecticides such as the nicotenoid seed dressings might not kill the beetle directly but would still deprive it of its main prey. Whatever the reason, the ground beetles that spend the autumn in field boundaries, such as *Demetrias atricapillus*, *Bembidion guttula* and *Anchomenus dorsale*, escape the impact of farm activities by doing so (Sotherton, 1984).

Rove beetles: Staphylinidae

With their red elytra, *Tachyporus* beetles were the most striking insects in sweep net samples from spring barleys in 1969–71, with four species, *T. chrysomelinus*, *T. hypnorum*, *T. nitidulus* and *T. obtusus*. As we have seen from Rhys Green's radio-tracked broods in Norfolk, the beetles feature in partridge chick diet when their preferred insects are scarce. It would be difficult for chicks to find them in the Sussex Study area today. On the Norfolk Estate I estimated the number of all adult *Tachyporus* combined at 9 per 25 sweeps in 1969–70 and 0.2 per 25 sweeps in 2008–11, a 97 per cent decrease. Out of a total 22,606 insects I caught in sweep nets in 2008–11, only 16 (0.07 per cent) were species of *Tachyporus*.

This very substantial decline in the abundance of these beetles (Fig. 159) probably began in 1973 or 1974 and it exactly parallels the decline of mildew and

FIG 158. *Tachyporus obtusus*, one of four formerly abundant rove beetles in a genus of aphid predators that has all but disappeared from cereal crops. (© entomart)

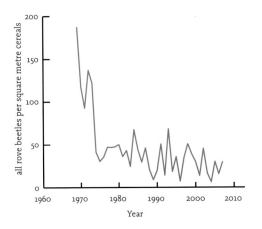

FIG 159. The decline of rove beetles, Staphylinidae, in Sussex Study area cereals from 1970 to 2008 (log scale).

yellow and brown rust in cereals (Aebischer, 1991). Other partly fungus-eating species appear to have been affected by the use of fungicides but none more so than *Tachyporus*.

Apart from a small trial in 1970, foliar-applied fungicides (that is sprays not the fungicidal seed dressings which had been used for decades) were first used in the Sussex Study area in 1971 when they were applied to 7 per cent of cereals to control barley leaf blotch (*Rhynchosporium secalis*) and mildew (*Erysiphe graminis*). Use rapidly escalated, with more than half of all cereals treated by 1976. By 1983 fungicides were used on all the winter wheat and winter barleys. By the late 1980s two applications per summer were normal.

It is difficult to judge whether insects have been adversely affected by any direct toxic effects of fungicides. Benomyl, used on some cereals during 1976–82, and carbendazim, used somewhat later, were suspected as having adverse effects based on laboratory work, but it has been impossible to measure such effects in the field against the background of many other changes in farming activity, such as the straw burning already mentioned, which was at its peak at the time. Only one fungicide was known to definitely increase mortality in insects in cereal crops, namely pyrazophos, introduced in 1983 as Missile to control mildew and aphids in cereals. The GWCT and University of Southampton carried out a large amount of research to quantify effects, against huge pressure from the agro-chemical lobby (Wratten *et al.*, 1988). The fungicide was highly insecticidal but not used in the Sussex Study area and it was rapidly outmoded. What would have happened if it had been a really good fungicide is anyone's guess. Today, hopefully, better safeguards are in place, so we will find out if herbicides or fungicides are insecticidal during the registration process.

Some rove beetles remain common, especially the genus *Aleochara*, which is eaten by partridge chicks. These beetles are parasites of flies and they are not affected by fungicides. Other species are known to prey on fly larvae including those of the orange wheat-blossom midge. The midges became more of a problem in the 1990s, as already mentioned, increasing the use of insecticides. Whether all this was due partly to the decline in rove beetles is not known (Holland & Thomas, 2000) but remains a possibility.

Leaf beetles: Chrysomelidae

A notable loss of a weed-dependent species from partridge chick food was the knotgrass beetle. The ecology of this beetle was unravelled in the late 1970s by Nick Sotherton, currently Director of Research at the GWCT. The species feeds on knotgrass and is entirely dependent on this one plant. His documentation of the collapse of the food chain – knotgrass > knotgrass beetle > grey partridge chick – inspired the BBC to commission special music. Sally Beamish's lament *Elegy to Knotgrass* was premiered during the Proms at the Royal Albert Hall in July 2001 – not many weeds have such a claim to fame.

Many other species have gone the same way as the knotgrass beetle, some perhaps beyond the point of no return. Fortunately, however, the knotgrass beetle has begun to return in conservation headlands (Chapter 10). This is remarkable, for the knotgrass beetle cannot fly, has low dispersal powers and was consequently thought to have been severely affected by stubble-straw burning.

FIG 160. Adult knotgrass beetle, an obligate breeder on knotgrass and subject of a performance in the Royal Albert Hall. (Charles Coles)

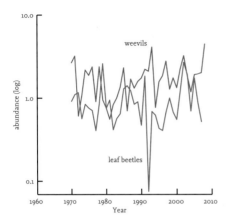

FIG 161. Annual abundance of leaf beetles (blue) and weevils (red) in Sussex Study area cereal crops from 1970 to 2008 (note log scale).

Fortunately a small stock must have survived somewhere, around other crops or in weedy corners.

We have not found the lucerne weevil in the Sussex Study, yet it was a major food of grey partridge chicks in England in the 1930s and in Czechoslovakia in the 1950s, as already described. This species can only breed prolifically on lucerne, where its green larvae (Fig. 109) feed exposed near the top of the flowers. Lucerne is grown in the Sussex Study area but not continuously, and a break in cropping is a good way of controlling the pest. With less lucerne grown than formerly, the species is in decline (Shamuratov & Deordiev, 1990).

As mentioned in the previous chapter, tortoise beetles have featured to a surprising extent in the diet of grey, red-legged and chukar partridge chicks overseas. Three species have been found in the Sussex Study cereals: *Cassida flaveola* on chickweed, *Cassida viridis* on dead nettles and *Cassida rubiginosa* on thistles. Although rare, they appear to be benefiting from conservation headlands.

Wireworm adults (click beetles): Elateridae

There are 73 species in Britain, with 5 species of click beetles found in our D-vac samples, the most numerous being adults of the notorious wireworms of the genera *Agriotes* and *Athous*. This group has increased markedly since the 1980s though still nowhere near their abundance prior to the use of effective seed dressings.

Other Coleoptera

There are many other groups such as the soldier, longicorn, flea and blossom beetles that feature in partridge diets and we look at these in Chapter 10 because they have come to prominence only with the use of conservation headlands.

Flies: Diptera

A vast group, with 7,000 species in Britain but with only 80 species identified in the Sussex study cereals, certainly a huge underestimate of the number that actually occur. Most flies are plant feeders, including important pest species such as frit flies, wheat bulb fly, wheat blossom midges, cereal leaf miners, saddle gall midges, various shoot-boring flies (*Opomyza, Geomyza, Chlorops*) and crane flies.

Crane flies: Tipulidae

Crane flies are the adults of the leatherjackets that used to be such a problem for cereal growers before the widespread use of insecticides. The two main pest species are *Tipula paludosa* and *Tiplua oleracea* but it is a third species that is the main one eaten by partridge chicks, the tiger crane fly *Nephrotoma flavescens*. The increase in crane flies seems to have paralleled that of the click beetles; the larvae of both have a similar diet of grass roots.

FIG 162. Tiger crane fly. (Graham Calow)

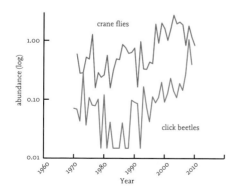

FIG 163. Annual abundance of click beetles (blue) and crane flies (red) in Sussex Study area cereal crops from 1970 to 2008 (note log scale).

Empids

Also known as dancing flies, these are the next most important in the chick diet.
The adults are predatory and easily identified as a group by the rows of hooks on
their legs used to hold prey.

Other flies

Adult flies eaten include the beautiful long-legged *Dolichopoda*, and the larvae of
hoverflies that prey on aphids feature strongly in chick diets.

Ants, sawflies, parasitoid wasps: Hymenoptera

Another vast group, with 7,000 species in Britain but with only 50 identified to
species in the study, again far below the true number of species present.

Ants

In the Sussex Study, ants have been found almost entirely outside cereal crops.
Although still rare in cereals there has been a significant increase in numbers
since the early 1970s; the vast majority being the yellow meadow ant *Lasius flavus*
(Fig. 164). The grazing by rabbits is important to this species, clearing vegetation
around the mounds, allowing sunshine to warm them; their original purpose.
This is especially important where light grazing by cattle or sheep is absent.
Rabbits also use the mounds as look-out posts, leaving many droppings and thus
fertilising the vegetation, but still maintaining it short (Fig. 128). In the Sussex
Study area rabbits were almost eliminated by myxomatosis in 1954. A slow recovery
then began, with numbers recovering to 30 per cent of pre-myxomatosis levels by

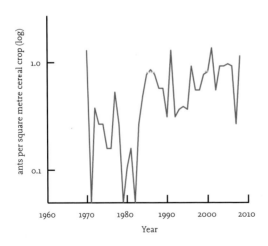

FIG 164. Change in density of
ants in Sussex Study area cereals
from 1970 to 2008 (note log scale).

1972 (Potts & Vickerman, 1974). The recovery has continued to the present, though probably with numbers in many areas still less than in 1953, most likely held down by fox predation. The increase in the abundance of ants since the early 1980s is therefore consistent with the hypothesis (Potts, 1970a) that decreased grazing was responsible for a decline after 1954.

Ants are of course very different from other chick foods in being found in large colonies on the ground. The most important species in the chick diet in southern Britain is the yellow meadow ant, followed by the small black garden ant *Lasius niger*. These species can form colonies of tens of thousands of individuals. Two *Myrmica* species, *scabrinodis* and *ruginodis,* are rarely eaten by chicks (Ford *et al.*, 1938), even though they are widely distributed in Britain, probably because they can sting. This is fortunate for the chicks because *Myrmica* ants are well-known intermediate hosts of a tape-worm that can infect partridges (Chapter 8). Many other species of ants are found in the diet of partridges overseas. Ants and their eggs (pupae) accounted for an astonishing 98 per cent of all arthropod food taken by 3–6-week-old chicks in Poland, mainly the European black ant *Formica fusca* that lives in colonies of 500–2,000 under stones and is also fairly common in southeast England. In Hungary *Lasius alienus* was the main species eaten; this is a small brown species of warm soils on heaths, limestone or chalk or along coasts, but it is uncommon in most of Britain. Yellow meadow ants and garden ants both tend aphids, even looking after hibernating aphid eggs. They do this to improve their supplies of honey-dew, much as we husband cows for milk. Ants are especially abundant in Mediterranean regions and the harvester ants feature strongly in *Alectoris* diets, even though they can result in significant infections with parasites (Chapter 8).

Sawfly larvae: Tenthredinidae

Trying to unravel the ecology and life histories of these insects, most of which belong to the genus *Dolerus* (incorporating *Loderus*), was a fascinating phase in the Sussex Study. These sawflies are found throughout the range of *Perdix* partridges including North America, with a third of about 80 species feeding on rushes (especially *Juncus*), a third on mare's tails (*Equisetum*) and a third on grasses or cereals. In a survey in Upper Teesdale in 1997 Alison Barker identified 51 sawfly larvae (Barker, 2006, and *in litt.*), 36 of which were species of *Dolerus*. *Dolerus madidus* was feeding on the rush *Juncus effuses*, *D. asper* on *Carex* sedges, *D. varispinus* fed on various grasses, and the remainder feeding on horsetails (*Equisetum*).

Sawfly larvae have been recorded as important in the diet of grey partridge, pheasant, black grouse, corn bunting and reed bunting. Notice something? On farmed land the numbers of all these species (even wild pheasants) have declined.

FIG 165. Adult sawfly *Dolerus puncticollis*. The caterpillar larvae, an important food of grey partridge chicks was first described by the GWCT's Alison Barker. (Sergio Storai)

Very early in the Sussex Study sawfly larvae were commonly found in grey partridge chick diets and a survey of the whole area was carried out, with the results shown as (Fig. 166). Because sawfly larvae had not been thought an important part of the diet of chick, I worried that the Sussex Study area may have been unusually suitable for sawflies. In 1969 and 1970 I therefore took sweep samples from cereals at Micheldever, Damerham, in north Norfolk, in Northamptonshire, on the family farm in North Yorkshire and in and around the Vale of Strathmore, Scotland. It turned out Sussex was not especially favourable and the highest density was on the family farm in North Yorkshire. I brought some larvae back from Scotland for rearing, to uncover their life cycles. Returning by plane I was alarmed to see, crawling on the hair of the lady in the seat in front of me, some larvae that had escaped.

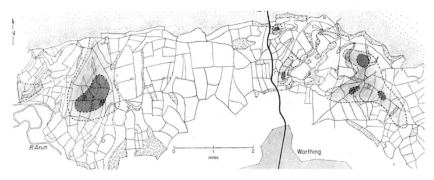

FIG 166. Distribution of sawfly larvae in cereal crops across the Sussex Study area in June 1969 showing areas of relatively high density; the main patch on the left is on the Norfolk Estate. Applesham, just off map in the southeast corner, was not included in the survey but numbers were highest there in 1970 and in following years.

FIG 167. (Clockwise from top left) Each female *Dolerus* sawfly deposits 32–34 eggs into slits cut into grass leaves using its saw, placing one egg in each slit (©Bruce Marlin); behind the head is the egg of an Ichneumon parasitoid *Tryphon* – an important source of caterpillar mortality (Peter Copeman); ploughing is another source of mortality; sawfly pupae exposed to gull predation by ploughing (Steve Moreby).

The life cycles of the *Dolerus* sawflies are similar. According to the species concerned, the peak date of emergence of adults from the soil in spring varies from 30 March to 2 June. The three most common species in the Sussex Study area all have their peak emergence during 8–14 May, with the males flying before females. The females emerge complete with eggs, usually 32 or 34, and these can be fertile even in the complete absence of males, as first shown in pioneering work by Frank Waterhouse in studies at the University of Dundee.

After World War II the land was restored to arable farming, pipes were laid and more than 200 metal water troughs put in place. *Dolerus* sawflies were attracted fatally to the water and during the springs of 1969–76 1,562 individuals of 11 species were retrieved from the troughs.

After short dispersal flights the adult females emerge, use their saws to cut pockets into the leaf edges, midribs or stems of cereal or grass leaves and then lay one egg in each. The eggs hatch in about 12 days, with the larvae reaching maximum size after 4–7 moults on or about the 17 June, just when the partridge chicks need them most. When growth is finished at about 30 mm in length the larvae, known as pre-pupae, burrow into the ground excavating a cell in which to pupate some months later. In the pre-pupa stage the larvae are vulnerable to disturbance and desiccation. They overwinter as pupae.

Sawfly larvae are an unreliable source of chick food with huge variations in abundance from year to year, from farm to farm and from field to field. More important the numbers have declined, although with a strong revival on the traditional ley farm at Applesham in the first years of the present century (Fig. 169).

The relationship between undersowing of leys and sawfly numbers was investigated in a series of detailed studies in the 1990s by Alison Barker at the GWCT, during which she first described the larvae of *Dolerus puncticollis* and greatly improved the key to identifying larvae (Barker 1998, 2006). Even before Alison started her work some early trials had shown sawfly larvae, including what was suspected to be *Dolerus puncticollis*, survived much better when grasses were present (Vickerman, 1978). With this in mind, Alison thoroughly studied the issue in all species with the results shown in Table 20. These show that most *Dolerus* either depend on grasses rather than cereals or prefer grasses to cereals (Barker & Maczka, 1996). The dramatic switch from spring barley to winter wheat on the Sussex Study area must have had a devastating impact on the *Dolerus* sawflies, none of which survive well on wheat although they can be successful on barley.

The purpose of undersowing is to use cereals as a nurse crop for grasses; with the main grass sown being perennial ryegrass. As this is the most efficient host for many sawfly species (Table 20), this is the first reason that undersowing

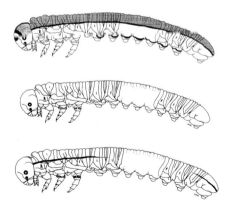

FIG 168. The three commonest species of sawfly in the Sussex study: *Dolerus haematodes* (top), *D. puncticollis* (middle), described for the first time by Alison Barker in 1998, and *D. gonager*. (drawings by Alison Barker)

increases the numbers of sawflies. The second reason is that ploughing and cultivation, absent with undersowing, destroy or expose the pre-pupae (Fig. 167). A single ploughing without the normal cultivation that normally follows reduces the numbers of pre-pupae by 52 per cent (Barker & Reynolds, 2005).

It is not known when farmers first used cereals as a nurse for grasses and clovers but the Romans are known to have used the method to ensure a pasture after harvest. It was certainly widespread in Flanders, Belgium, in the early seventeenth century and it was known in the Sussex Study area by the end of that century. At Applesham the traditional mix had been ryegrass, cocksfoot, timothy, white clover, alsike clover and black medick. As appreciated by Charles Darwin (Hector & Hooper, 2002), this mixture maximises growth at various stages in the rotation cycle and (with the cocksfoot) is an insurance against drought. The clover and other legumes provide growth without diverting nutrients from the grasses. None of the six species was redundant. One difficult issue is herbicide approval. Early in 2008 the Pesticide Safety Directorate decided that herbicides needed specific approval for each ingredient in the traditional seed mix. This is a serious blow for biodiversity.

At the start of our studies on sawflies, cycles of about four years were found in sawfly abundance driven mainly by Ichneumon parasitoids in the genus *Tryphon* spp., (Kasparyan, 1973; Barker, 1999, 2006; and Sussex Study). We have also found these Ichneumons on sawfly larvae in Upper Teesdale; whether the infection is sufficient to cause cycles in sawfly abundance is a very interesting but unanswered question. In Sussex the cycles seem to have disappeared but in the absence of long-term data on *Tryphon* spp. it is difficult to judge their effectiveness as parasitoids.

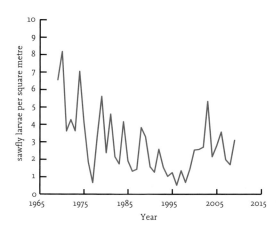

FIG 169. Sawfly larvae densities in Sussex Study area cereal crops from 1970 to 2008. The recovery that began in the late 1990s was confined to the farm (Applesham) that had continued under-sowing.

TABLE 20. The species of *Dolerus* found on gasses and cereals in lowland Britain showing relative abundance in the Sussex Study area during 1969–76 and most efficient hosts (from Barker, 1998; Barker & Reynolds, 2005). No species utilised autumn-sown wheat.

species	abundance in 1969–76	found in 1990s	most efficient hosts
D. puncticollis	575	yes	ryegrass, *Poa annua*, barley
D. gonager	560	yes	ryegrass, red fescue, barley,
D. haematodes	310	yes	barley, ryegrass, red fescue
D. aeneus	27	yes	red fescue, ryegrass
D. sanguinicollis	23*	no	?
D. liogaster	23	yes	ryegrass
D. nigratus	21	yes	ryegrass (many grasses)
D. niger	11	yes	ryegrass, barley
D. picipes	9	yes	red fescue, ryegrass
D. brevitarsus	2	no	?
D. anthracinus	1*	no	?
D. planatus	no*	no	?
D. possilensis	no*	no	?
Total	**1,538**		

* said to be common in lowland England by Benson (1950); have they disappeared? *D. anthracinus* has not been found in Britain since 1977 (*Sawfly Study Group Newsletter*, 2: 2007).

One sawfly that appears to be increasing is *Cephus cinctus* but its larvae live inside cereal stems and so are unavailable to chicks; it may have been held in check by straw burning.

Other parasitoid wasps
This is a huge group, with most species difficult to identify. Exceptions include the braconid wasps that infect cereal aphids already mentioned, resulting in the well-known aphid mummies. The remaining braconids mostly infect small flies. The next most important group is the chalcid wasps that infect the braconids as hyper-parasitoids. It was therefore a puzzle that the chalcids have increased recently, because we were unable to work out what insect group they infected. It

turned out they were Eurytomid wasps that mine the stems of grasses. Amongst the many other fascinating parasitoids are the beautiful but tiny fairy flies or mymarids. They have to be small because they infect eggs of species such as plant bugs.

Back from the dead: the turnip sawfly
In the nineteenth century turnips were important crops often devastated by the turnip sawfly and there was a serious infestation on the Norfolk Estate in 1837. For reasons unknown the species became apparently extinct in England in the 1920s (Benson, 1950). The pest then reappeared in the 1940s but remained very rare until 2003. The species is dependent on relatively high temperatures, preferably developing in the range 23–26°C (Afonin *et al.*, 2008); 2003 saw record high temperatures in Sussex and there was a notable immigration in 2006 (Holland & Oakley, 2007). In 2009, after a gap of 172 years, the sawfly was again found in stubble turnips on the Norfolk Estate on a sufficient scale to require some use of insecticide. This small black species is not eaten by partridge chicks. Another species with slug-like larvae that suddenly became common in 2011 is the Pear Sawfly, living not on pears but on the newly planted hawthorn hedges. Again the larvae are small and black and completely unlike the large green caterpillars of the cereal leaf-eating species that can be so important to grey partridge chicks. It seems perverse that these undesirable sawflies have thrived where the desired species have failed to materialise.

Caterpillars: Lepidoptera
Interestingly, in view of Conrad's work mentioned earlier, the trend in the Sussex Study has been in the other direction, upward (Fig. 170). Most of the species are moths, with larvae feeding on grasses.

Scorpion flies: Mecoptera
Four species in Britain – one, *Panorpa* sp., found in cereal samples.

Lacewings: Neuroptera
One species is commonly found, namely *Chrysopa carnea*, with the larvae an aphid predator eaten by chicks.

Strepsiptera
Again one species identified, *Elenchus tenuicornis*, which is a major parasite of the plant hopper *Javesella pellucida*, a food of partridge chicks (Potts & Vickerman, 1974). Most Strepsiptera are parasites of bees.

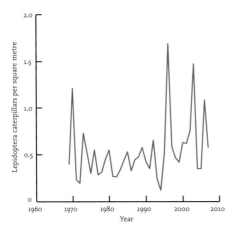

FIG 170. Lepidoptera caterpillar densities in Sussex Study area cereal crops from 1970 to 2008.

NUMBER OF SPECIES IN THE SUSSEX STUDY AREA CEREAL CROPS

The taxonomy of the invertebrates is daunting; in difficulty it is in a class of its own compared to the plants, birds and mammals. We do not know how many species we are monitoring in the Sussex Study but we can get an idea of what might be present by looking at the groups that have received the most attention.

The numbers found in Sussex cereals represent the following percentages of the total for Britain: springtails (5 per cent); spiders (5 per cent); harvestmen (18 per cent); plant bugs (7 per cent); ground beetles (9 per cent); weevils (2 per cent); leaf beetles (5 per cent); rove beetles (18 per cent) and sawflies (5 per cent). Excluding aquatic species, fleas and suchlike, the total number of species of arachnids and insects in Britain is about 23,500. The mean presence in the Sussex Study of the better known groups is 6.7 per cent (geometric). In Europe as a whole this figure was put at 8 per cent before deducting any losses to pesticides (Heydemann, 1983). On the same basis a completely different approach to calculating the fauna, based on the ratio of herbivorous insect species to plant species and predator and parasitoid to host in other habitats, estimated 698–1,776 species (Potts, 1991). These estimates seem to converge on about 1,500 species harboured by the cereal ecosystem in Sussex. We have identified only 486.

None of the estimated 1,500 species is red-listed, yet as we shall see many qualify, with others in the 'too late to save category'. Overall however, although many species declined to about 1990 and some have continued to decline, there have been recoveries augmented by conservation headlands. Some groups have recently reached their highest ever levels.

RELEVANCE OF TRENDS TO PARTRIDGES

Here the data reviewed and the discussion exclude conservation headlands, dealt with in detail in Chapter 10. The most important – heavily weighted – insects in the chick food index (p. 190) are the smaller ground beetles, especially *Trechus quadristriatus*, and this group has spectacularly declined since the mid-1980s (Fig. 157). In contrast to the situation in mainland Europe in the late 1970s and early 1980s, these insects were not common in Sussex, rarely more than one per square metre. The next most important group were the sawfly and Lepidoptera caterpillars. Sawflies have declined (Fig. 169) but this has been offset to some extent by the increase in Lepidoptera. The next most important groups, and the most numerous, the leaf beetles, weevils, plant bugs and leaf and plant hoppers, have not declined during more than 40 years, although much less abundant than in the days prior to the use of herbicides. The final group in the chick food index, the aphids, have declined but mainly through the influence of the cereal aphid outbreaks of 1970, 1975 and 1976, which included mostly *Sitobion avenae* on the ears out of reach of chicks.

Noting that the lucerne flea was not in the chick food index, it is apparent that the index has recently tended to recover even where conservation headlands were not present; the main reason why, at least in the Sussex Study area, that chick survival has trended upwards since about 1990 (see Fig. 26) – again excluding areas with conservation headlands. This appears to be due directly and indirectly to increasing spring temperatures, a change that has also led we believe, to increases of grasshoppers, earwigs, crane flies and click beetles and ants that were not in the chick food index (see p. 190).

FIG 171. Hogweed (left) and *Artemisia vulgaris*, two tall perennials currently increasing in Sussex Study cereals .

Thus comparing today with the start of the Sussex Study, many downward trends in insect abundances have been eventually balanced by upward trends. This is also what was found for weeds. Insects and weeds are both much less abundant than prior to the use of herbicides, but the basic story is one of relative stability, bumping along the bottom. Given all the changes in agriculture, this is surely remarkable. As we shall see, sawflies apart, we can still escape this by using conservation headlands, but are there other possibilities?

THE FUTURE: TRANSGENIC CROPS

In the early 1980s it became possible to add DNA to crops from other species of plant, bacteria or even animals. By 2011, some 160 million ha of transgenic crops (genetically modified, GMO or GM) were grown globally. In contrast to the situation in Britain and in some EU countries where they were dubbed 'Frankenstein foods', the US, Argentina and Brazil had few qualms about allowing the use of transgenic crops. Wholesale branding of GM crops in this way was understandable because genetic engineering was fundamentally altering the way in which our food was produced. In ecological terms it was, however, irrational to 'tar all with the same brush'.

Transgenic wheat has been developed to resist mildew and it has been shown there are no significant effects on cereal aphids or on their parasitoid and hyper-parasitoid wasps (von Burg *et al.*, 2011). In this case the transgenic crop has the potential to avoid the use of fungicides that might be harmful directly or indirectly to beneficial insects. No insecticide is entirely specific to an insect pest and all insecticides have some adverse effect on insect wildlife, but this is not necessarily true with transgenic insect pest resistance. A natural enemy of caterpillars is the bacteria *Bacillus thuringiensis*, known as Bt, and transgenic maize incorporating Bt was approved by the US's Environment Protection Agency (EPA) in August 1995. Within four years a note appeared in *Nature* claiming that Bt maize pollen could harm Monarch Butterfly caterpillars. There was a huge furore, but after a great deal of further research the EPA found that there were no adverse effects and renewed and extended their registration. To this day there is no proven case of a GM Bt crop directly harming a beneficial insect. So if Bt is incorporated into a crop, cotton being the best example, then the collateral damage caused by using insecticides can be avoided. There are however two problems with transgenic cereals from a partridge viewpoint.

The problem with GM from a partridge viewpoint is most likely to come from the herbicide-tolerant crops where the herbicide can kill important non-crop plants. For example, the GM Roundup-tolerant wheat could in theory remove *all* the weeds that are the food base for partridges and the associated insect food because Roundup (or glyphosate) kills a very wide range of weeds.

Field trials with transgenic wheat began in 1994 and Monsanto expected to bring glyphosate-tolerant wheat to the market in 2003. The potential was enormous; wheat is grown on 65 million acres in the US alone, but a number of issues needed to be addressed: the impact on weeds and on insects. There was also the possible toxicity of glyphosate and of some early surfactants used to enhance its activity. Finally there was the speed with which weeds would become resistant to glyphosate.

In 2003/04 it was proposed to sample invertebrates in Monsanto's Roundup-ready wheat trial plots with a view to evaluating the possible impact on grey partridge chicks in the US. After initial support for the idea, Monsanto subseqently claimed that there was no need for the work because 'the US and Canadian approval systems do not require information on farmland biodiversity'. Then 'out of the blue' on 11 May 2004, Monsanto declared that it was not proceeding with glyphosate-tolerant wheat 'for commercial reasons'. Research continues, especially in China, so this is very unlikely to be the end of the story and we need to examine the likely damage of herbicide-tolerant cereals.

In Europe four transgenic crops had cleared most regulatory hurdles by 1998 but there was growing concern about the farmland wildlife. In response the UK government funded what became known as the Farm Scale Evaluations. The detailed results were set out in a theme issue of *Philosophical Transactions of the Royal Society, London, B.* (2003). During 2000–03 herbicide-tolerant crops were sown in half of 60–70 fields across Britain, with conventional varieties on the other half. No small grain cereals could be involved because there was no commercially available variety for trial and we have to estimate what might happen in small grain cereals from observations in sugar beet, oilseed rape and the large grain cereal, maize.

So far as weeds were concerned it was concluded that herbicide-tolerant sugar beet and oilseed rape would lead to more effective weed control, with the opposite effect in forage maize. Maize is an important crop for partridges but the potential has not been realised in recent decades because of the extensive use of atrazine, a most effective herbicide. The transgenic maize was tolerant to glufosinate-ammonium, which is less harmful to the flora than atrazine. Thus the conventional maize crops contained an average 9.7 species of weeds, whereas the transgenic maize had 15.5. Some comparisons amongst insects that are important foods for partridge chicks are given in Table 21, but it is important to recognise that it was not an aim of the work to evaluate the food of partridge

TABLE 21. The farm scale evaluations of transgenic (GM) maize in Britain; numbers per sampling unit of plant bugs and ground beetles potentially important to partridge chicks.

species	conventional	transgenic
plant bugs	3.53	3.14
Amara spp.	1.88	3.58
Anchomenus dorsale	5.46	9.32
Loricera pilicornis	2.95	5.93
Trechus quadristriatus	1.19	1.46
total	**15.01**	**23.43**

chicks. Nevertheless some comparisons of chick foods can be made and they show that transgenic maize was better than conventional maize due to the hyper-effectiveness of the conventional herbicide.

So what might happen in the vast areas sown to small grain cereals, far greater than maize, sugar beet and oilseed rape combined? Some species of weed that are beneficial to partridges may increase such as pigweed, which is resistant to glyphosate, but the future is very uncertain. The early indications were that Bt cotton would help to conserve Bobwhite quail populations. Less use of insecticide would allow intercropping with lucerne that supports many chick food insects. But some boll weevils are already resistant to Bt cotton and in some areas, particularly in China, there have been outbreaks of mirid bugs in Bt cotton requiring insecticide treatment not used for conventional crops. Transgenic crops are relatively few and they have been around for only two decades, yet problems seem to be crowding in. In the absence of even short-term impact assessments, it is simply not possible to forecast the impact that transgenic cereals may have on farmland wildlife; in the long term the portents are not good for GM or partridges.

Transgenic wheat is currently being developed at Rothamsted that would repel aphids and it will be interesting to see the results of current field trials. The new wheat could avoid the need for aphicide and thus increase the chick food supply. But the loss of cereal aphids would also have a large impact on their predators, many of which feature in partridge chick diets. The net effect cannot be forecast. In many cases however, for example salt tolerance or drought resistance, transgenic crops could improve farm outputs and reduce the need to destroy natural habitats.

We now turn to another aspect of insect food: their role as parasite hosts.

CHAPTER 7

Parasites Lost?

In many ways, parasite species appear as hidden 'dark matter' that holds the structure of the (food) web together.

Dobson *et al.* (2008)

P ARASITES AND DISEASES ARE usually ignored in contemporary bird monographs, presumably on the assumption that they are not important. Every now and again however, an epidemic shows this is unwarranted: for example, the recent infection of the greenfinch with the protozoan *Trichomonas*. The story with partridges is unusual because their parasites are relatively well known, due to sharing so many of them with domestic poultry. We therefore have a good understanding about the extent to

FIG 172. Domestic fowl and partridges share many parasites and pathogens but when did these species of Galliforme first meet? (Arthur Scott)

which the various parasites infect partridges, although, in marked contrast, we have far too little information about their impact, and nearly all the life cycles are incompletely known.

Some idea of how long parasites and partridges have co-existed comes from the extent to which the same species of parasites are shared by different host species. Such parasite sharing has been used, for example, to place the Seriemas of South America close to the bustards because they share similar tapeworms. If so, that sharing must have begun when South America finally separated from the Old World about 80 million years ago. From Chapter 2 we know that New World quails and partridges have not had a common ancestor for about 30 million years, yet the bobwhite quail shares 43 per cent of its parasitic worm species with grey and red-legged partridges (this work, later, c.f. Kellogg & Calpin, 1971; Peterson, 2007). The *Perdix* and *Alectoris* evolutionary lines are thought to have diverged perhaps 10 million years ago (Chapter 2), yet they share only 29 per cent of parasitic worm species. Whatever the evolutionary significance of this contrary evidence it is clear that some partridge parasites must have co-existed with their hosts for tens of millions of years, evolving together in long-term co-existence. Many parasite species may have evolved before their present day host species.

On these long timescales parasites will have little effect on host populations. On much shorter timescales, with the disrupted ecosystems of today, it is not surprising to find many host–parasite relationships that are not harmonious. Where parasites and diseases have serious adverse effects on partridge populations the chances are that there has not been enough evolutionary time for a stable natural resistance to develop. Alternatively it may be that the parasite encounter with its host is unusual in some way or even unprecedented, as with introduced species, such as the well-known case of avian malaria in Hawaii. On this basis the disease strongylosis, which we deal with later, could be seen as a consequence of unusually high densities of partridges due to conservation management. For the parasites we are dealing with here, the death of the host would be the end of the line and not a sensible strategy. This is the opposite of the insect parasites, such as the parasitoid wasps that emerge from their host caterpillars or aphids after consuming them.

In humans slight infestations of tapeworms are often symptom-less, so maybe the same is true with partridges? How would we know? In the 1952 'New Naturalist' volume *Fleas, Flukes and Cuckoos*, Rothschild & Clay were to the point:

> *Although many species of parasitic worm appear to have little or no effect on their bird host, this is in all probability because we cannot ask them about their symptoms. Heartburn, dizziness, insomnia, optical illusions, general nervousness,*

*flatulence, abdominal discomfort, reduced perspiration, palpitation of the heart …
(are) scarcely likely to be recorded for birds.*

Some tapeworms of partridges are large: *Raillietina tetragona*, a species using
ants as a vector, is typically 10 cm long, but even so partridges appear to tolerate
numbers without problems. The same is reported for grouse, where tapeworm
burdens did not affect body condition either in Scotland or Canada (Watson &
Moss, 2008). Tapeworms have no mouthparts, absorbing nutrients through their
epidermis, and usually any tissue damage is limited to the point of attachment
to the gut wall. During 1933–58 at the GWCT, Dr Phyllis Clapham found only one
case that caused death in 167 infections. Browne *et al.* (2006) reported an 18 per
cent infection of tapeworms in wild grey partridges in East Anglia and later we
look at a possible explanation for this relatively high level. With nematodes the
picture varies, with some species or stages burrowing through tissues causing
obvious damage but with others apparently feeding harmlessly on caecal bacteria.
At one time it was even thought that small numbers of the caecal nematode
Heterakis actually benefited domestic fowl, though how is hard to say. Otherwise
benign nematodes can facilitate harmful bacterial (Panasyuk *et al.*, 1972) and
protozoan infections like blackhead, so the interactions are complex.

Partridges acquire most tapeworms and many nematodes through eating
insects or other invertebrates, so given the evolutionary arms race between
parasite and host, partridges could be expected to reduce the risk of infection by
preferring to eat insects that rarely carry the intermediate stages of parasites. Why
do partridge chicks starve in habitats where, with a little litter scratching, their
parents could easily provide many snails, slugs, earthworms, woodlice, beetles,
earwigs, centipedes, millipedes and the like? Domestic fowls and many other
Galliformes scratch, so why not partridges? Partridges do scratch for food but
nearly always this is specifically to expose ants or ant pupae ('eggs'). There are few
answers yet because host behaviour in relation to parasite life cycles is a subject
much neglected since the 1950s when research turned from epidemiology to the
development of modern chemical anthelmintics. It remains fascinating, and in
evolutionary terms potentially important, in explaining preferences for certain
kinds of food. Other things equal, evolution should have favoured partridges that
avoid eating the invertebrate hosts of parasites. This is investigated here.

Rothschild and Clay called for a compilation of the known life-cycles of
parasitic worms, with lists of known intermediate hosts. This was in 1952, with
the main change since then being that the need for such a compilation is much
greater today. From 1922–88 host–parasitic worm records were kept by H. A.
Bayliss at the Natural History Museum, London, and this has continued (Gibson

et al., 2005), but the gaps are many. To put the issue in perspective, the number of known species of roundworm (nematode) parasites of vertebrates is about 13,000 (Anderson, 2000). Many parasites that infect partridges have had no research carried out on them beyond basic taxonomy and even that is not settled. In future this will change for the better. Due especially to work on food webs in a salt marsh in California, the importance of parasites to ecosystem structure has finally been realised (Lafferty *et al.*, 2006), so stimulating much more research. In the past, working out life cycles was really tedious; Wisniewski examined 1,537 vertebrates and 119,300 invertebrates to fathom parasite life cycles in a single Polish lake (Esch, 2004). Today even very low rates of infection with parasites are detectable using DNA (PCR)-based probes, for example detecting tapeworm larval stages (cysticercoids) in ants (e.g. Padgett & Boyce, 2005).

The prevalences of some parasites and pathogens are often under-represented. This is especially true of bird malaria and nematodes found in blood, because it is not practicable to search for them in congealed blood, postmortem. Some flukes are also easy to miss, for example *Prostogonimus ovatus* that occurs inside the oviduct. Parasites have also been recorded from the bursa of Fabricius, a blind sac leading from the cloaca, deeper in immature birds, which can be used to distinguish old and young pheasants – the 'bursa test'. The organ is involved in the development of the immune system but it is rarely searched for parasites.

In the 1970s the then Natural Environment Research Council turned down an application for funds to carry out experiments to study the causes and effects of strongylosis in grouse on the grounds that parasite infestations were not important to birds. Just over 100 years ago the Committee of Enquiry on Grouse Disease had concluded otherwise, but the consensus in the 1970s was that strongylosis was not ultimately caused by *Trichostrongylus tenuis* but was instead the result of stress and adverse conditions. It was agreed that spiny-headed worms caused mortalities for some eider populations, but this was thought to be an exceptional case amongst birds. So far as red grouse are concerned the GWCT was determined to investigate the realities, funds were raised and in 1979 Peter Hudson began to put the record straight, first in his pioneering studies in the Pennines and then in Scotland.

In the early 1970s a four-year study of red-legged partridges in southeast Portugal revealed high rates of infection with parasitic worms, for example 52 per cent were infected with the nematode *Allodapa suctoria*, with 17 worms per bird infected (Varela, 1974). The 1974 revolution led to over-hunting of partridges and a crash in numbers to as low as three pairs per 100 ha (Borralho *et al.*, 1997) and the research on game birds ceased. Meanwhile in Spain a great deal of research has been carried out quantifying the role of parasites in the ecology of the red-legged partridge, especially by the team of scientists at the Institute for Research into Ecological Resources (IREC) affiliated to the University of Castilla-La Mancha, La Ciudad. So the subject is getting the attention it deserves. As we shall see however, the detail is massively complicated not just by amazing life cycles, sometimes with two intermediate hosts, say a snail and an ant, but by many species having several alternative scientific names (synonyms). Virtually all organisms suffer from the same problem, for example a recent attempt to resolve plant names halved the number (see www.theplantlist.org). A similar study of parasites would probably have a greater proportional impact on the number of known species. Further difficulties include the fact that much of the older literature is in difficult scripts and obscure publications.

Despite these shortcomings a useful picture emerges showing the changing prevalence of the internal parasites and diseases, their effects on individuals and populations and how the risk of acquiring parasites could influence the choice of foods.

LONG-TERM TRENDS IN PARASITISM AND DISEASE

The GWCT archives contain 2,972 records of postmortems of partridges carried out during 1933–82, mainly by Phyllis Clapham up to 1958 and John Beer from 1970. John compiled his results in two reports (Beer, 1976, 1982) and his results are compared to those of Dr Clapham in Table 22; in both cases non-specific, systemic conditions such as 'inflammation of the intestines' are excluded.

Grey partridges accounted for 88 per cent of the postmortems up to 1969 but only 20 per cent after that, illustrating both the extent of the decline in the

FIG 173. Dr John Beer, gamebird pathologist at the GWCT from 1970 to 1992. (GWCT)

TABLE 22. Postmortems of wild and pen-reared grey and red-legged partridges found dead in the wild, carried out at the GWCT during 1933–1981 giving percentage causes of death by specific parasites and pathogens, with shading indicating the main causes.

	1933–69		1970–81	
	grey %	red-legged %	grey %	red-legged %
sample size	1280	182	305	1205
Histomonas	16.6	24.2	4.0	8.7
Heterakis	1.0	1.1	1.8	1
strongylosis	6.6	0	0.4	0
coccidiosis	1.3	2.2	2.4	23.5
gapeworm	10.4	10.4	4.9	4.6
tapeworm	0.4	0	0	0.3
Capillaria (former)	0.2	0	0	3.2
parasites total	**36.5%**	**37.9%**	**13.5%**	**41.3%**
aspergillosis (fungal)	0.9	1.6	0.8	0.8
moniliasis (fungal)	0.1	0	7.0	1.7
avian tuberculosis	1.5	2.7	0.6	0.8
Pasteurella/Yersinia	3.2	6.0	1.0	2.8
E. coli /Salmonella	3.8	1.1	4.2	10.4
Clostridial infection	0.4	0	0	4.3
staphylococcosis	1.4	0	1.1	0.1
Hexamita/Trichomonas	0.4	0.5	0	0.6
Mycoplasma spp.	0.2	0	0.7	0.5
erysipelas	0	0	0.5	0
leukosis (cancers)	2.2	3.8	0	0.4
pathogens total	**14.1%**	**15.7%**	**15.9%**	**22.4%**

Note: Among the bacterial diseases avian tuberculosis is caused by *Mycobacterium avium*, *Pasteurella* is also known as fowl cholera, *Yersinia* is avian pseudo tuberculosis, *E. coli* is *Escherichia coli* and *Salmonella* includes fowl typhoid.

grey partridge and the increased rearing of the red-legged partridge. The most important change from 1933–69 to 1970–81 was the 62 per cent drop in the percentage of grey partridges that died primarily from infection with parasites. The red-legged partridge showed the same large decrease in *Histomonas* infection as the grey partridge but this improvement was offset by a large increase in coccidiosis. There was little change in the prevalence of diseases over the two periods except for a marked increase in *E. coli* and *Salmonella* in red-legged partridges.

CAUSES OF MORTALITY IN SUSSEX STUDY AREA PARTRIDGES

During the Sussex Study, postmortems have been carried out on 177 grey partridges and 52 adult red-legged partridges aged over six weeks. There are few significant differences between the species or from the first period to the second (Table 23). The main changes were the disappearance of blackhead (histomonosis) and the huge increase in raptor predation, as analyzed further in the next chapter. Strongylosis and blackhead are both conditions involving nematodes and they appear to be in remission. Tapeworms infecting the duodenum are the other main parasites. Another nematode genus, *Capillaria,* is found with a low prevalence but did not cause death. There were only three cases in which strongyles were present, with the maximum number in one bird of only three, compared to the many thousands that used to occur, as we see later in this chapter.

The gapeworm

The best-known parasite of the grey partridge is the gapeworm, the nematode *Syngamus trachea* (formerly *S. trachealis*). It is different from the other parasitic worms in that it is the only one that is currently a problem in the Sussex Study area. Gapeworms infect the windpipe, with their presence revealed by the behaviour known as 'snicking' in which birds try to cough up the worms, which is why it is so well known; they are a serious impediment to breathing and cause obvious distress. This worm was first noticed in domestic fowl and turkeys in Baltimore in the US in 1797. When found in Europe in 1806, it was at first considered to be a non-native introduced with domestic fowl from America to England and France. Later, given reports of the worm in dozens of species of birds and their abundance in crows, starlings and especially rooks, this view was dropped.

Meanwhile concern about mortality caused by the worm grew and Lord Walsingham, from his estate in Norfolk, offered a generous cash prize to carry out research. The French parasitologist Mégnin won the prize. His report to the

TABLE 23. Most likely prime cause of mortality in grey and red-legged partridges older than six weeks given postmortems in the Sussex Study area, 1952–2011; blackhead (histomonosis) is no longer found; raptor predation has become the dominant cause of mortality. The shading indicates these changes.

	grey		red-legged	
	1952–77	2003–11	1952–77	2003–11
histomonosis	12	0	15	0
strongylosis	1	0	0	0
coccidiosis	4	0	2	0
gapeworm	5	5	4	0
tapeworm	1	2	0	1
aspergillosis (fungal)	2	0	0	0
moniliasis (fungal)	3	0	0	0
avian tuberculosis	1	0	1	0
E. Coli	1	0	0	0
gut protozoa	0	2	0	1
mycoplasma	1	1	1	0
cancers	1	1	0	1
renal failure	1	0	0	1
dieldrin	3	0	0	0
lead shot ingestion	6	3	1	1
raptor	7	56	1	6
fox/dog/cat	4	7	0	0
injury	24	10	5	3
unknown	7	6	7	1
postmortems	84	93	37	15

Société de Biologie in 1880 filled in many aspects of the worm's life cycle, for example confirming that the males and females spend all their lives attached in permanent copulation. But it was left to Walker in New York to discover that the earthworm was an effective intermediate host (Walsingham, 1888; Walker, 1897).

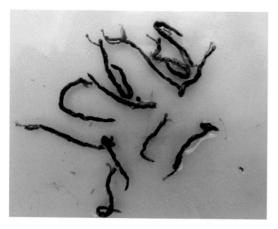

FIG 174. Sussex Study area, Norfolk Estate, 2011. These 12 pairs of gapeworm were the sole cause of death of a 28-day-old grey partridge chick.

In cool, damp conditions or where faeces cover the ground, the intermediate host is not necessary (as shown by Dr Phyllis Clapham in the early 1930s). In hot, dry summers the parasite is protected in its earthworm hosts from desiccation and gapeworms are much less frequent in drier countries with hotter summers. For example the parasite has not been found in the Daurian partridge in Kazakhstan (Gvozdev, 1957) or in the grey partridge in Turkey.

The incidence of gapes was recorded from 1947 to 1959 on the Damerham Estate, Fordingbridge, and the results show a remarkable increase of infection in young grey partridges. In one locality, Boulsbury, gapes was particularly prevalent reaching 80 per cent in 1958 but with 'little effect on production rates and the young to old ratios on areas with high infection have been no lower than elsewhere' (ICI *Game Research Station Annual Report* for 1958). This did not appear to be the case in Sussex in the late 1960s. On the North Farm shoot the prevalence of gapes was localised and centred on pheasant release pens where the parasite had been a serious problem in pheasants for about ten years. Earthworms, snails and slugs from this area fed to red-legged partridge chicks each produced a 100 per cent infection with gapeworms. Grey partridge chick survival rates were lower in the fields surrounding the release pens, but most chicks died before they reached the earliest age of 14–19 days at which the gapeworm can first be found in the windpipe. After a series of laboratory trials the chick deaths were considered to be due to food shortages, with the gapeworms mostly indicating poor food supplies rather than a direct cause of death (Potts & Vickerman, 1974). In this case it appears that reared pheasants were acting as a reservoir host for *Syngamus trachea*, much as domestic fowl can act as a host for the parasite when it is endemic in domestic turkeys. This was one reason why, in the days before poultry medicines, poultry keepers were strongly advised not to rear turkeys and domestic fowl together (Ransom, 1921). Gapeworms can persist encysted in earthworms, which are long-lived, and the recent occurrences in the Sussex Study area appear to be due to the large numbers of pheasants released in the days before modern medicines and rearing methods, or possibly to large numbers of Rooks.

In the 1930s Phyllis Clapham attributed the deaths of 2.0 ± 0.6 per cent of male grey partridges to the gapeworm, compared to 7.8 ± 1.2 per cent for young females (Clapham, 1939c). Other things equal, these death rates would produce a surplus of males of 6.3 per cent. In Sussex in 2010 and 2011 there was a surplus of young males of 7.6 ± 1.1 per cent, almost all of which can be attributed to the gapeworm, because the sex ratio on hatching is even (Potts, 1980). So, although a problem, it is no more so than it was nationally in the 1930s.

Heterakis gallinarum carrier of blackhead (histomonosis)

About ten years ago considerable arguments broke out about whether the caecal nematode *Heterakis gallinarum*, the carrier of blackhead (histomonosis), was a significant problem to wild grey partridges. Some newspapers carried articles claiming that the increase in numbers of reared pheasants would be the 'last nail in the coffin of the grey partridge'. This was based on the hypothesis from the University of Stirling that pheasants spread the parasite to grey partridges on a scale sufficient to cause population reduction through both increased adult mortality and reduced productivity (Tompkins *et al.*, 2000b).

Validation of the Stirling hypothesis was sought by replicating the Stirling experiments (Sage *et al.*, 2002) and by using the GWCT postmortem records (Potts, 2009). In the experimental work, 26 hand-reared grey partridges were given an experimental infection with the caecal nematode *Heterakis gallinarum*, and these were then compared to 26 uninfected controls. Under the laboratory conditions, no measurable clinical effects of the infection were found during 91 days. The results were different from those at Stirling, where there were significant negative impacts on eight infected birds but none on six controls, albeit with unexplained deaths in both groups (Tompkins *et al.*, 2000b).

Turning to the postmortems, after excluding birds younger than 15 days, there were 12,056 records for grey and red-legged partridges and pheasants found dead from 1912 to 2003. Throughout this period the levels of infection with *Heterakis* was found to vary in parallel among wild, reared, young and adult partridges of both species and in young reared pheasants but not adult pheasants. Except among adult pheasants, the prevalence of *Heterakis gallinarum* (henceforth simply *Heterakis*) declined by 91–100 per cent from 1952 to 1991

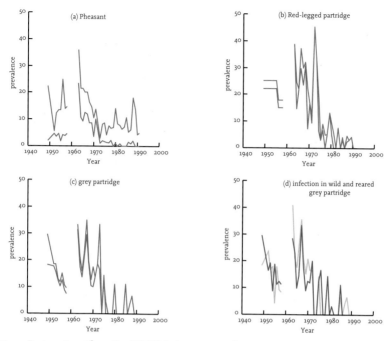

FIG 175. Postmortems from the GWCT during 1952–91: the summed prevalence of blackhead (*Histomonas*) (red line) and *Heterakis* spp. (blue line) for: (a) the pheasant, (b) red-legged partridge and (c) grey partridge. Prevalence of infection with *Heterakis* spp. and *Histomonas* in reared (yellow line) and wild grey partridges (green line) are compared at (d) (from Potts, 2009).

(Fig. 175). During the same period similar declines took place in the rest of Europe. Overall the evidence from almost 18,000 postmortems was a decline in prevalence of *Heterakis* during the very period when pheasant rearing expanded (Potts, 2009). The evidence implicating the pheasant in the partridge decline was not stacking up.

Domestic poultry

The once universal use of hens and bantams to incubate eggs and rear game-bird chicks has been shown to be responsible for infections of *Heterakis* in grey partridges and also in bobwhite quail, where it was found in 'almost all birds reared either with bantam hens or in close proximity to chickens but not at all in wild birds' (Cram *et al.*, 1932). Pheasants are never used to foster partridges (though it sometimes happens naturally), ruling them out of this link in infection.

Until the mid-1950s, large numbers of domestic fowls ranged freely across farmland throughout Europe, with wild grey partridges frequently feeding amongst them. There were several warnings about the dangers of allowing domestic poultry to glean stubbles where the partridges could pick up infection (Maxwell, 1911). The density of these truly free-ranging domestic fowls was high: for example, on a typical mixed farm in Yorkshire in 1939 up to 1,000 per 100 ha (Long, 1969). Such truly free-ranging, unfenced poultry are now very rare in Western Europe, although they can still be seen in some places, for example Albania (pers. obs.). In some areas partridges still join household flocks in severe weather and in the Caucasus this has resulted in the spread of *Heterakis* to chukar partridges (Kozhokov, 2007).

The most serious cross-infections were however from domestic fowls to turkeys, as was first recognised in 1893 at Rhode Island in the US. In 1920 *Heterakis* spread *Histomonas* from domestic turkeys to the heath hen, a sub-species of the greater prairie chicken. Already depleted by a number of factors the *Histomonas* reduced heath hen numbers by 92 per cent and ensured its extinction (Johnsgard, 2002). Domestic fowl carry more *Heterakis* than pheasants, for example an average of 180 in the 1930s (Morgan & Wilson, 1939), and at one time domestic fowl outnumbered pheasants in the UK countryside nine-fold (Potts, 2009). As described above, these domestic fowls shared the countryside with partridges and pheasants in a way that is inconceivable today, especially considering the much larger number of foxes now present. Put simply, the modern methods of rearing (vitamin supplements, deep litter and broiler and battery hen systems) and electrification of farms in the mid-1950s enabled domestic poultry to be brought indoors. By the early 1970s the number of traditionally free ranging poultry had dropped 90 per cent (Fig. 176). Domestic poultry, broody hens and bantams virtually disappeared from game-rearing

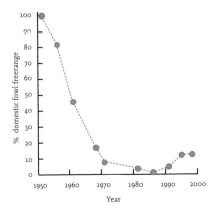

FIG 176. The decline in numbers of free-ranging domestic fowls in Britain as a percentage of all domestic fowls from 1950 to 2000, from MAFF June returns and Museum of the British Poultry Industry, Cambridge.

TABLE 24. Tests of nine species of Galliforme birds to show their relative efficiency as hosts of *Heterakis gallinarum* and *Histomonas meleagridis* (from Lund & Chute, 1974).

captive game-bird	tests	efficiency producing *Heterakis*	efficiency *Histomonas* transmission
peafowl	1	0	0%
Japanese quail	4	0.01	0%
grey partridge	1	0.08	0%
chukar	5	1.1	0%
bobwhite quail	3	0.17	33%
turkey	14	1.9	43%
guinea fowl	5	9.7	60%
domestic fowl	30	5.2	80%
pheasant	4	19.4	100%

facilities at the same time for the same reasons. Finally the anthelmintics and anti-blackhead drugs have been used extensively and standards of hygiene greatly improved. For example, earthworms are no longer available when birds are indoors on concrete floors.

Experimental evidence of Blackhead transmission

The *Heterakis–Histomonas* (blackhead) system is surely one of the wonders of nature. Firstly the *Heterakis* and its host have to co-exist, involving some degree of harmony otherwise it would not be sustainable. As work by Madsen (1962) and Lund & Chute (1974) has shown, this extends to the protozoan (*Histomonas*) because infection can be so great that the *Heterakis* have to leave the caeca and die without perpetuating either their own kind or the protozoan host. It seemed that neither the turkey nor the heath hen had resistance to blackhead; in all likelihood *Histomonas* was introduced to America sometime after 1492 (Schorger, 1966). Pheasants and domestic fowl on the other hand can tolerate far higher burdens of *Heterakis* than grey partridges, so presumably they were exposed much earlier. Further explanation was sought in a remarkable series of 67 trials in the US involving more than 4,000 galliformes and 282,000 infective *Heterakis* eggs over a period of 18 years (Lund & Chute, 1974). The essential results are given in Table 24.

Although few tests were available, for some species the picture obtained has stood the test of time; namely that common pheasants and domestic fowl are the most likely candidates to spread *Histomonas*. The turkey and guinea fowl are not so important simply because they are much less numerous, although locally they can be important, as on game-rearing areas.

Until the arrival of dimetridazole (Emtryl) in the late 1970s, game birds were susceptible to blackhead infection in roughly the order domestic turkey > red-legged partridge > grey partridge > pheasant > domestic fowl. In the Sussex Study area from 1952–77 histomonosis was the main cause of death for 9 per cent grey partridges, 21 per cent red-legged partridges and 67 per cent of chukars.

For resistance to be acquired by the host it has to be impacted by significant mortality caused by the parasite. In North America turkeys probably first encountered *Histomonas* when they were reared on farms alongside domestic fowls, perhaps 200 years ago. At the other end of the scale, domestic fowls could have spread *Histomonas* to pheasants in China at any time back to 58,000±16,000 years ago (Sawai *et al.*, 2010). Where and when grey partridges first encountered *Histomonas* is unknown, but in France and Britain (where most mortality was reported) it must have been after domestic fowls were first introduced to these countries, less than 3,000 years ago (Kyselý, 2010). So the exposure may have been in the order domestic turkey < grey partridge < common pheasant < domestic fowl; the reverse of susceptibility. It follows from the susceptibilities in Sussex that the *Alectoris* partridges have only been exposed to significant *Histomonas* in recent times, perhaps through rearing.

At present the evidence shows that blackhead is no longer a significant problem for wild grey partridges. *Heterakis gallinarum* itself is not currently a problem in Sussex but in some areas it still turns up, including an area with the highest densities of partridges in England (Draycott & Ármenteros Santos, 2012). The species still occurs in black grouse and relatively high prevalences have recently been found in rock partridges in the Alps (Fabro *et al.*, 2011; Formenti *et al.*, 2011).

STRONGYLOSIS

This parasitic worm is now recognised as the cause of the disease strongylosis of red grouse that became well known from about the middle of the nineteenth century and is caused by the nematode worm *Trichostrongylus tenuis*. Recorded in red grouse as early as 1854 this parasite was not associated with disease in grey partridges until 1900 (Portal & Collinge, 1932). To this day *T. tenuis* is the only parasite known to have (in the past) caused population fluctuations in the grey partridge. Although the nematode that causes the problem is effectively the same in both partridge and grouse, there are some striking differences in the current impact on populations of these game birds. The grouse disease persists in red grouse, with significant effects on reproduction and population size, especially where medicated grit is not used, but it has not even been suspected of having any adverse effect on free-living grey partridges since 1962 (Potts, 1986). Arguments persist about whether *T. tenuis* in red grouse causes population quasi-cycles or is partly a consequence of them. The situation is simpler in the grey partridge because this species has never shown quasi-cyclic fluctuation (Tapper, 1992).

Although some of the life cycle details remain unknown, *T. tenuis* has no invertebrate transport hosts. This distinguishes it from the gapeworm and *Heterakis*, although most infection is probably direct even in these. It is claimed (e.g. by Freehling, 1993) that *T. tenuis* may be several species or sub-species or forms. Whether *T. tenuis* was imported into North America with infected pheasants (Anderson & Moore, 2000) is still not verified and seems unlikely. Some of the supposed *T. tenuis* in the US were later shown to be *T. cramae*, and *T. pergracilis* is taken to be the same species as *T. tenuis*, although the differences in the caudal ray are marked (Portal & Collinge, 1932). This is another case where DNA analysis could solve the issue. In the meantime the consensus appears to be that *T. tenuis* is, for practical purposes, one species with many host species, including some ducks and geese. Although widespread and often with high prevalences, the numbers are usually very low at low population host densities, for example in Ptarmigan in Scotland (Watson & Shaw, 1991), in Red grouse in Ireland (Byrne & Moles, 2002) in Willow Grouse in Norway (Madsen, 1952) and in grey partridges in recent decades (Potts, 1986). The highest numbers in grey partridges are today found on moorland fringes, where a prevalence of 81 per cent, with nine per bird, has recently been reported (GWCT). This compares to a prevalence of 24 per cent in England and 15 per cent in Denmark during the late 1930s and early 1940s (Madsen, 1952). Whether the infection rates at moorland fringes owe anything to red grouse is unknown, but in this particular grouse numbers can be very high before population crashes, often up to an average 6,000 worms per bird. The comparable figure for the smaller grey partridge, 3,500 worms per bird, represents roughly the equivalent worm burden. Effects on the host were similar in partridges and grouse, with serious caecal damage and in consequence, poor incubation and breeding success (Hudson, 1992).

Given that higher numbers of this worm are found at higher host densities in the wild, we should expect infestations to be much more serious in penned birds. Prior to the use of modern anthelmintics this was indeed the case. The most thorough investigation was that by Páv and colleagues in Czechoslovakia when 1,261 grey partridges were investigated between 1958 and 1960 (Páv *et al.*,

1961). Prevalence of *T. tenuis* was 14 per cent in 812 pen-reared birds but with none found in 196 wild birds. In Czechoslovakia and Poland during 1949–1957 the prevalence of *T. tenuis* in 868 shot wild grey partridges was found to be only 1–2 per cent, about one-fifth of that found in Britain at the time (Bezubik, 1959; Páv *et al.*, 1961). This fits the general geographical distribution both in partridges and grouse, with more of these worms in areas with more Atlantic climates. Thus in Scandinavian willow grouse, infections were highest on coastal islands and in west Norway and lower further east (Holstad *et al.*, 1994; Schei *et al.*, 2005). Similarly in the grey partridge, prevalence was 9 per cent in East Anglia with low rainfall (Browne *et al.*, 2006) but 81 per cent in upper Teesdale with high rainfall.

T. tenuis had not been found in grey partridges in the Sussex Study area since 1958 until two larvae were discovered in one caeca of a bird killed by a hen harrier in December 2010. Should numbers increase due to restored grey partridge numbers, then medicated grit, which has been so successful in raising grouse productivity (Cox *et al.*, 2010), could be used more easily than on a grouse moor. It would be relatively easy to introduce medicated grit where partridges are already using provided grit.

SPREAD OF PARASITES AND DISEASES FROM PEN REARED PARTRIDGES?

We have seen how reared pheasants can spread the gapeworm to the grey partridge and how domestic fowl can spread *Heterakis gallinarum* to reared gamebirds. Millán (2009) went further, claiming that the intensive management of red-legged partridges in Spain was 'promoting the release and transmission of infectious and parasitic diseases'. With colleagues he had earlier reported three cases of avian tuberculosis (*Mycobacterium avium*) in wild partridges (Millán *et al.*, 2004), concluding that 'the aggregation of partridges and woodpigeons around bird feeders and watering points probably favored the transmission of the infection'. The GWCT postmortems show no increase in prevalence of avian tuberculosis (Table 25) and Millán's further suggestion that *Salmonella* was spread by farmed partridges is also not substantiated by the experience in Britain. The well-known disease psittacosis (*Chlamydophila psittaci* and *C. abortus*) has been found in grey, and chukar partridges on game farms (Kaleta & Taday, 2003) and it has recently been found in wild Rock partridges (Bertoletti *et al.*, 2005). As with all these organisms it is important to remember that although they may become much more of a problem with rearing, all these parasites and pathogens must always have existed somewhere in the wild; they are not new but only in a new role.

Could parasites spread to non-game birds? There was great consternation in La Mancha, Spain, when the nematode *Eucoleus* (formerly *Capillaria* etc.) *contortus* was found in a little bustard in an area where many pen-reared red-legged partridge were being released. Found in 8 per cent of the reared birds it was concluded that 'the release of farm-reared gamebirds can eventually introduce new pathogens to wild populations of different species, many of which are of conservation concern' (Villanúa *et al.*, 2008). This parasite can have a marked adverse effect on body condition. It had apparently not been reported in the little bustard before but it has been reported from a very wide range of hosts, including the stone curlew, lapwing, starling, gulls, many ducks and waders, as well as the domestic fowl and many galliformes (Madsen, 1952).

The data most likely to illustrate the risks are John Beer's diagnoses from 1970 to 1981, where wild and reared birds were rigorously identified and separated (because payment was required for reared but not wild birds). Rearing was rapidly increasing and postmortems were becoming expensive. After 1981 the postmortems were overwhelmingly of intensively reared red-legged partridges and from 1991 routine postmortems were no longer carried out by the GWCT.

The results comparing the causes of death in wild and reared partridges are given in Table 25. The overall rates of death due to parasitism were similar in wild and reared birds but coccidiosis was much more frequent in reared partridges, especially red-legged partridges. This disease is due to non-flagellated protozoans in the genus *Eimeria*, with ten species in pheasants and with red-legged and grey partridges each having their own species (Beer, 1988). Each *Eimeria* species is restricted to a particular part of the intestines where normally they cause no problem. Occasionally however, they multiply vastly and become pathogenic. What propels *Eimeria* from a harmless co-existence with its host to lethality is not understood but usually explained as 'stress' reducing immunity. In red-legged partridges *Eimeria* infection is a major cause of paleness of the normally bright red beak and eye ring and the reduced immunity this indicates (Mougeot *et al.*, 2009). Despite *Eimeria* developing resistance to early coccidiostats used to treat infections they were eventually brought under control in the 1980s by the use of clopidol (dichlor-dimethyl-pyridin) (Beer, 1989). For both species of partridge the incidence of disease was two to three times higher in pen reared birds than in wild birds (Table 25).

Pen-reared birds seem particularly at risk from the protozoans *Trichomonas* and *Hexamita* that each possess long whip-like structures, the flagella that enables them to move about quickly. The diseases caused by these mobile (or motile) protozoa, known as flagellates, were a problem in France as early as 1969–74 when they were the main cause of deaths of partridges prior to release (Schricke, 1978),

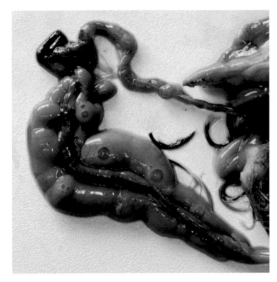

FIG 177. Caeca infected with protozoans *Hexamita*, *Trichomonas* or *Spironucleus* or all three (see text), a common syndrome in the red-legged partridges much less common in grey partridge.

though strangely not recorded during 1972–84 (when *Staphylococcus* was the main cause of death (Louzis *et al.*, 1988).

Many pathological conditions are caused in humans, fish and other animals by flagellates but here we are mainly concerned with *Trichomonas phasiani*, which can affect the intestines and caeca of partridges. *Trichomonas gallinae* also occurs in game birds but is mainly known as a disease of budgerigars and pigeons, except that around 2005 it spread to greenfinches, chaffinches and house sparrows, with a notable reduction in greenfinch abundance (Robinson *et al.*, 2010). *Trichomonas phasiani* occurs mainly in red-legs but its prevalence and effects are confused by its frequent association (in the same bird) with a similar organism, *Hexamita meleagridis*. These parasites were effectively controlled by the use of Emtryl until the EU banned its use in 2002, but since then improved hygiene appears to be keeping the situation under control. Coccidiosis may be one of the most important diseases of partridges in captivity, especially in the red-legged partridge, when it can be associated with another flagellate, *Spironucleus*. This highlights mixed and multiple infections, whereas many biologists tend to address disease as a single species problem.

Another illness, apparently new to the grey partridge, was caused by *Cryptosporidium*, a widespread group of protozoa invading cells, in this case in the air sacs, causing respiratory disease (Sironi *et al.*, 1991). On some Spanish game farms *Alectoris* have been heavily infected (Pagès-Manté, 2007) but the organisms have not been reported as causing a problem for any wild partridges.

An important cause of death in reared grey partridges used to be moniliasis caused by the fungus *Candida albicans* perhaps growing in response to an imbalance in the diet: an absence of ants was blamed and certainly formic acid

TABLE 25. Postmortems of wild and pen-reared and released grey and red-legged partridges, carried out at the GWCT during 1970–81 giving percentages of diagnoses where the principal cause of death was specific parasites or pathogens.

	grey		red-legged	
	pen reared	wild	pen reared	wild
sample	217	88	1,106	99
Histomonas	2	9	7	25
Heterakis	3	0	1	1
strongylosis	1	0	0	0
coccidiosis	3	1	25	2
gapeworm	5	5	4	7
tapeworm	0	0	0	3
Capillaria (former)	0	0	4	0
parasites	**14%**	**15%**	**41%**	**38%**
aspergillosis (fungal)	0	3	1	0
moniliasis (fungal)	9	1	2	0
avian tuberculosis	1	1	3	7
Pasturella/Yersinia	1	1	2	2
E. coli/Salmonella	6	1	11	3
Clostridia	0	0	5	0
staphylococcosis	2	0	1	0
Hexamita/Trichomonas	0	0	1	0
Mycoplasma	1	0	1	0
erysipelas	0	0	1	0
leukosis (cancers)	0	0	0	0
pathogens	**20%**	**7%**	**28%**	**12%**

TABLE 26. Mean abundance of parasitic worms in game-farm and wild red-legged partridge in Spain (results of Millán *et al.*, 2004, and Villanúa *et al.*, 2008, are combined). Shading is blue for flukes, amber for tapeworms and green for roundworms.

	farm (167)	wild (180)
Dicrocoelium petrovi	0	13.1
Raillietina tetragona	0.11	0.67
Raillietina (S.) bolivari	0.27	0.00
Ascaridia compar	31.51	0.00
Heterakis gallinarum	0.25	0.01
Aoncotheca caudinflata	1.95	0.00
Eucoleus contortus	0.38	0.00
Cheilospirura gruveli	0.51	2.80
Cyrnea seurati	0.00	0.33
Trichostrongylus tenuis	0.00	0.66
totals	**34.98**	**17.57**

alleviated the problem (Wood, 1969; Keymer & Austwick, 1961). One symptom is characteristically twisted feathers, so it is easy to recognise the disease, and since the early 1980s it has virtually disappeared.

Studies in Spain have helped to explain the reasons for the different suites of parasites in reared and wild partridges (Table 26). Millán *et al.* (2004) examined 5 mm slices of the livers of 231 red-legged partridges in Spain. They found no flukes in the game-farm birds, but a very surprising 51 per cent of 109 wild birds were infected with an average 18 *Dicrocoelium petrovi* per bird or 13 when combined with the data of Villanúa *et al.* (2008).

The fluke *Dicrocoelium petrovi* was almost certainly acquired by eating ants that had in turn eaten plant material infected by snails. Such a food chain is not likely on a modern game farm. The same applies for one of the most abundant nematodes in red-legged partridges in Spain, *Cheilospirura gruveli*, a species that lives behind the hard horny lining of the gizzard and is the cause of significantly poorer body condition (Millán *et al.*, 2004). Grasshoppers are the hosts of closely related species in the US and this is likely to be the case in Spain, explaining why the species is much less frequent on game farms. The 52 per cent infection of wild red-legged partridges in southeast Portugal with *Allodapa suctoria* and 18 per cent infection with *Cyrnea parroti* were probably attributable to grasshoppers, given their importance in *Alectoris* diets (Varela, 1974).

Conversely, parasites that do not have intermediate hosts can thrive on game farms, with an example being the thin white roundworm *Ascaridia compar* (Table 26). This nematode can reach 12 cm in length and lives in the duodenum but has a very strange geographical distribution. It is extremely rare in grey partridges in Britain (one record, Shipley, 1909) and Denmark but is found frequently in Finland (Lampio, 1946; Raitis, 1970), Poland (Bezubik, 1959), Czechoslovakia (Páv, 1961), Armenia (Hakhumian & Khanbekian, 1982) and Kazakhstan (Gvozdev, 1958). This worm is very rare in red grouse in Britain (Watson & Moss, 2008), yet very common in Scandinavia, with 50–70 per cent of willow grouse infected (Madsen, 1952). Whether these worms are or were having a significant adverse effect is not known, but on the Spanish game farms the mean abundance (Table 26) is near the level where adverse effects on domestic fowl growth become measurable (Reid & Carmon, 1958). Rosa *et al.* (2011) report a lower hatching success in captive rock partridges carrying 2–40 worms per bird. In free-living rock partridges in Italy the abundance of *Ascaridia compar* was considered sufficient to provide some support for the hypothesis that these parasites cannot be ruled out as generating population cycles (Rizzoli *et al.*, 2003; Rosa *et al.*, 2011); the overall prevalence was 33±5 per cent with an average nine per bird infected. Notwithstanding the cycles, rock partridges have declined in most areas and this indicates that some other factor or host of the worm is at least partly responsible for the infections. The well-known large round worm of the small intestine of domestic fowls is *Ascaridia galli* and its prevalence in wild grey partridges usually ranges around 1 per cent (Clapham, 1936; Madsen, 1952).

Perhaps the clearest example of a direct life-cycle nematode causing problems in captivity but not in the wild is *Heterakis isolonche*, which is or was (prior to the availability of modern medicines) a very serious problem for pheasants in zoos and collections, especially for the Ruffed pheasants. It remains a problem on game farms in Serbia (Pavlović *et al.*, 2003) and Slovakia (Goldova *et al.*, 2006) and has a cosmopolitan distribution, but has only very rarely been reported from wild partridges. It is much more pathogenic than *Heterakis gallinarum* (Hennache & Ottaviani, 2005).

Two decades ago John Beer referred to a strong feeling amongst pathologists and veterinarians that diseases caused by viruses, e.g. Rotavirus, would soon become more important due to large numbers of game birds being intensively reared (Beer, 1992). He found that the rate of increase in the number of postmortems of game birds (at that time he was carrying out 27 per cent of the UK annual total) was higher than the rate of increase in numbers of game birds reared nationally. There are no more recent comparable data, partly because the UK's state veterinary recording scheme VIDA does not distinguish game birds by species or rearing methods. Occasionally however, there are reports of infectious sinusitis and the joint disease synovitis in wild partridges, conditions much more frequent in reared birds and attributable to the primitive bacteria known as *Mycoplasma* spp. There are five species, the most important of which infect the air sacs as well as the sinuses and is the cause of the well-known 'bulgy-eye syndrome'. All are now much more effectively controlled by antibiotics and by sourcing eggs from flocks free of the disease.

One disease of partridges not connected with rearing programmes is caused by an avian pox virus carried by mosquitos. Francisco Buenestado and colleaugues (2004) reported a notable outbreak of avian pox in southern Spain but they could not find any difference between survival of partridges with pox and those without it. Reported mortality rates from this infection varied only from 0.6–1.2 per cent; most birds clearly recovered.

The malaria-like parasites are spread by biting flies such as black flies, midges and mosquitos, and recognising the impracticality of detecting them at postmortem, it has to be said there are astonishingly few reports in partridges. In 1977 a survey of 187 species of birds in Kazakhstan discovered cases of *Haemoproteus chucari*, in both grey partridges and chukar. Originally named after the chukar, for reasons not clear the name was later changed to *H. perdix* (2nd All-Union Conference of Protozoologists). A survey of freshly shot birds in Iraq found a 13 per cent prevalence of *Haemoproteus danilewskyi* in chukar partridges (Mohammad *et al.*, 2001) and at the 5th Meeting of the European section of the Wildlife Disease Association, in Heidelberg, 2002, Javier Millán announced that *Haemoproteus* had been found in red-legged partridges (*Alectoris rufa*) in Spain.

THE DIFFERENT GROUPS OF PARASITIC WORM THAT INFECT PARTRIDGES

In addition to those mentioned in the text the sources used for this account are: Anderson (2000), Avancini & Ueta (1990), Avcioglu *et al.* (2008), Bendel & Lisk (1957), Bezubik (1959), Bondarenko *et al.* (1979), Calvete *et al.* (2003), Chiriac *et al.* (1972), Clapham (1933–61), Cram (1928), Ergun & Merdivenci (1953), Fagasinski (1964), Foronda *et al.* (2005), Gagarin (1954), Gibson *et al.* (2005, BMNH), Gvozdev (1956, 1957, 1958), Hakhumian & Khanbekian (1982), Inglada (2007), Jones & Horsfall

(1935), Kazimov (1956), Keymer *et al.* (1962), Kozakiewicz *et al.* (1983), Kozhokov (2007), Kurashvilli (1956, 1957), Kurtpinar *et al.* (1954), Lampio (1946), Madsen (1941, 1945, 1952), Mendelewska (1982), Millán *et al.* (2004a, 2004b), Nadakal *et al.* (1973), Pav (1961), Raitis (1970), Schmidt (1986), Skrjabin & Udinzew (1930), Sonin & Barus (1996), Stoimenov & Trifinov (1964), Tibbets & Babero (1969), Tolgay *et al.* (1960), Varela (1974), Vasiliev (1992, 1995), Vrazic (1957) and Yeatter (1934).

The flukes (Trematodes)

Flukes are found in many parts of the body but especially in the liver. A total of 24 species have been recorded from *Perdix*, red-legged and chukar partridges: 11 species were recorded 32 times from *Perdix* and 17 species were recorded 59 times from *Alectoris*. Ignoring cases with only a single record of a parasite in *Perdix* or *Alectoris*, then only three species of fluke, 12 per cent of the total, are found in both groups of partridges. Most flukes infect snails during their life cycle, infecting partridges directly or via ants that eat snail effluvia.

The tapeworms (Cestodes)

Tapeworms are usually found in the intestines but with one genus in the liver. A total of 33 species have been recorded, with 21 found 60 times in *Perdix* and 30 found 66 times in *Alectoris*. Again ignoring isolated records, ten species, 30 per cent of the total, are found in both groups of partridges. It is relatively easy to find the encysted immature stages (known as cysticercoids) of tapeworms in the intermediate hosts such as beetles and ants and so most is known about them. Muir (1954) describes how he found cysticercoids free in the body cavity of 8 per cent of *Myrmica* ants on a grouse moor where the grouse were infected with tapeworms. Non-infected ants had a dark reddish-brown tint, whereas infected individuals were dark chocolate in colour. Partridges are infected directly by eating infected ants.

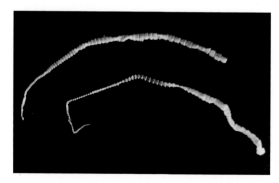

FIG 178. Sussex Study area, Norfolk Estate: two tapeworms from 42-day-old grey partridge chick in very good condition killed by collision with a farm vehicle. Infection by this species, *Raillietina cesticillus* is the result of eating ground beetles.

A species of *Mesocestoides* has a high prevalence of 36–56 per cent in Rock partridges (Manios *et al.*, 2002) and can cause mortality. This is the one that lives in the liver and peritoneum not in the gut.

The roundworms (Nematodes)

The round worms are found in the eye, eye-orbit, trachea (windpipe), oesophagus, gizzard, intestines, caeca, air sacs and blood, depending on the species. As larvae, many of these parasitic worms migrate through the body tissues until they reach the site where they can mature and reproduce. A total of 48 species have been recorded, with 37 found 103 times in *Perdix* and 40 recorded 81 times in *Alectoris*. Thirteen species, or 28 per cent of the total, have been found in both groups of partridges. Few authorities appear to have investigated the possibility of parasites infecting the brain or spinal cord of partridges but cerebral nematodiasis has been reported from a chukar (Sass & Gorgacz, 1978). The different species of roundworm infect partridges that eat infected invertebrates or in some circumstances directly by eating eggs or larvae.

Spiny headed worms (Acanthocephala)

A total of four species recorded: all four from *Perdix* and one from *Alectoris*. Little is known of the life cycle of the species reported from partridges, but the intermediate hosts are likely to be woodlice and their relatives in the case of *Prosthorhynchus transversus* and grasshoppers in the case of *Mediorhynchus micracanthus*. These two species are rare in the grey partridge and only the second of them has been reported from *Alectoris*. In the Ukraine two further species of *Mediorhynchus* have been reported from the grey partridge, *M. papillosus* and *M. petrotschenkoi* (Lisitsyna, 1994). Infection is through eating invertebrates.

EXTERNAL PARASITES

Not much is known about the effects of the many species of external parasites, such as biting and chewing feather lice, ticks and flat flies that are found on partridges.

Feather lice; biting lice

Some 543 species of feather lice have been found on Galliformes (Price *et al.*, 2003) and Niethammer (1942) listed 9 species from the grey partridge. In Croatia Vražić (1957) found 7 species of lice on grey partridges but not including *Lipeurus caponsis*, typical of partridges in the UK (Clay, 1949), and in Turkey there were 4 species on only 36 birds (Aksin & Oncel, 2011). The number on red-legged partridge may be higher, with 11 species listed (Millán, 2009). The situation with game-farm partridges varies; in Spain only two species were found but in the Czech Republic there were heavy infestations, with seven species on Chukar (Sychra, 2005). Echoing the geographical distributions found with parasitic worms, none of the species found in the Czech Republic were the same as the species found in Spain. One species, *Goniocotes microthorax*, was however found on red-legged and grey partridges in Portugal (Martinez-Nistal *et al.*, 1986), something impossible to check because the grey partridge is now extinct in Portugal (Atlas Equipa, 2008). Ryder (1967) found ten species on domestic fowl in northern England but none of these species were found on partridges in the region. The impact of these lice is unknown; one nematode, *Paraornithofilaria lienalis*, found in the blood of partridges belongs to a group that have feather lice as intermediate hosts. Lice are often abundant on birds that have died of other causes, especially on lightweight individuals (Millán *et al.*, 2004b), but this is usually put down to poor preening consequent on bad health. Some of the eggs of these parasites are beautifully intricate, with structures to prevent their removal by preening.

Partridges spend a lot of time dusting and at one time it was thought this was to rid their feathers of lice. However, an alternative view was that dust baths are where the lice spread from host to host and it seems now to be accepted that dusting is to reduce the greasiness of feathers and to aid an even distribution of lipids (fats) (Borchect & Duncan, 1974). Gamekeepers have in the past dusted insecticides on dust baths but no research was done to show whether this was effective. Given the importance of ants to partridges and the possible

FIG 179. Eggs laid by some species of feather lice are highly complex structures designed for accurate placing on the feathers and to resist preening and dusting. (John Beer and University of Southampton)

role of 'anting', the smearing of feathers with ants as a method of reducing lice abundance, it is surprising that the behaviour has never been reported in partridges (Simmons, 1957).

Ticks, fleas, louse flies and feather mites

Other arthropod parasites found on partridges include the sheep tick *Ixodes ricinus*, host of louping ill, which is a serious problem for red grouse in some areas (Duncan *et al.*, 1978) but not known to infect partridges. Two further species were found on red-legged partridges in Spain (Millán *et al.*, 2004). At least three species of feather mite have been found on partridges, a mite that lives under the skin, *Pterolichus obtusus*, and several species of quill mites (Acari: Syringophilidae) (Skoracki & Sikora, 2011).

The only species of flea regularly on partridges is the duck flea *Ceratophyllus garei*, although the rabbit flea is also found (Rothschild & Clay, 1952). Some infestations can be heavy: in 1950 one successfully hatched nest at Damerham contained 392 (Ash, 1952). These fleas spray blood onto nest material as food for their larvae, which explains the blood spotting sometimes found on partridge eggs.

Examining a freshly shot partridge bag usually turns up at least one louse fly. As well as identifying feather lice, ticks and fleas during the Damerham study, John Ash also recorded Louse flies. He found two winged species, *Ornithomyia avicularia* and the finch louse fly *Ornithomyia fringillina* on both grey and red-legged partridges, but the first of these was found only on the grey partridge (Ash, 1960) and this is the species that occurs in Sussex. A third species, *Ornithophilia metallica*, is found on red-legged partridges in Spain (Millan *et al.*, 2004). Louse flies sometimes have their own parasitic mites attached (Shipley, 1911) and can transport feather lice to new hosts (Warburton, 1928).

Viruses

Discovered in Java in 1926, Newcastle disease is nevertheless named after Newcastle upon Tyne where it was also described. It is caused by a virus in the same group as myxomatosis and it has been found in many species of bird. The disease occurs in poultry on a worldwide scale and appears to be naturally endemic in some seabirds, including the gannet, cormorant and shag. Until the 1950s sea birds were regularly shot for food, with the inedible parts left for poultry to scavenge. In consequence there were outbreaks of the disease in poultry in northwest Scotland (Blaxland, 1951). Again this illustrates the point that disease is more serious in 'unnatural' situations. There was a severe case in wild pheasants in 1963 but the first dramatic outbreak started in 1970, with a marked peak in the summer of 1971. Many pheasants were affected in Britain, France, the Low Countries and Germany but very few partridges (Louzis, 1978) and the disease was controlled by mass vaccination. During the past decade there have been reports of the disease on game farms in Europe, including in Denmark where grey partridges became infected. Imports resulted in three outbreaks in Britain, one each in grey partridge and pheasants, but these were contained with no spread to wild birds.

Another world wide virus, bird flu, has a highly pathogenic strain that has caused a great deal of concern in recent years because it can affect humans as well as birds. It was distinguished from bacterial diseases in 1878 and originally termed fowl plague. This virus apparently can affect all kinds of birds but is particularly associated with congregations of ducks, geese and swans with natural hosts, including shorebirds and gulls. Gamebirds can be infected. What caused the mutation that changed the natural low pathogenic strains to the highly pathogenic H5N1 is not known but this variant probably originated in domestic quail in Hong Kong in May 1997. In the original outbreak some domesticated *Alectoris* partridges were infected, although tests have shown that, unlike turkeys, they can recover well (www.fao.org/avianflu). Presumably Asiatic chukars have been exposed to earlier variants of the disease so have acquired some resistance not available to turkeys.

In August 2010 there was an outbreak of Bagaza virus (Bagaza is in the Central African Republic), a close relative of West Nile virus, in the Cadiz area of southern Spain, with unusually large numbers of red-legged partridges found dead on a number of properties. This was an unusually wet year in the area, so the mosquitoes that carry the virus may have bred where they could not have done in drier years. Nevertheless this was the first report of the virus in Spain. There have been several reports of West Nile virus in chukars, but it is thought they are resistant to such an extent that they might spread the virus (which reached the US in 1999) to sage grouse (Walker & Naugle, 2011).

GEOGRAPHICAL VARIATION IN PREVALENCE OF SPECIES IN THE GREY PARTRIDGE

Suppose we travelled overland to Mongolia observing grey partridges along the way. We would be hard pushed to see any differences in the outward appearance of the birds, greyer perhaps as we pushed on eastwards. But suppose we could see inside the birds! As we travelled east familiar parasites would disappear and new ones appear until at journey's end all would be different (Fig. 180).

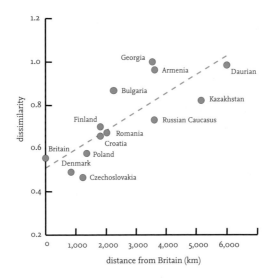

FIG 180. Grey partridge: the changing prevalence of parasitic worms from west to east. **Note:** The Dissimilarity index (Bray–Curtis) was obtained by reference to Clapham's results for the 1930s (the largest investigation). The other authorities are Denmark (Madsen, 1941, 1952), Czechoslovakia (Páv, 1961), Poland (Fagasinski, 1964; Bezubik, 1958; Kozakiewicz *et al.*, 1983), Croatia (Vražic, 1957), Finland (Lampio, 1946; Raitis, 1970), Romania (Chiriac *et al.*, 1972), Bulgaria (Stoimenov & Trifinov, 1964), Russia (Kozhokov, 2007), Armenia (Hakhumian & Khanbekian, 1982), Georgia (Kurashvilli, 1957), Kazakhstan (Gvozdev, 1958), and Daurian partridge (Gvozdev, 1957).

For the grey partridge, the typical roundworms of Western Europe include the gapeworm, strongyle worm, the caecal worm *Heterakis gallinarum*, the threadworm *Capillaria* (now *Avesaoncotheca*) *caudinflata* and the tapeworm *Hymenolepis linea*. Roundworms becoming more abundant travelling east are *Ascaridia compar*, the proventriculus worm *Cyrnea eurycerca*, gizzard worm *Acuaria gruveli*, the caecal worm *Allodapa suctoria*, the eye-orbit worm *Oxyspirura schulzi* and two tapeworms, *Davainea andrei* and *Lyruterina nigropunctata*.

In summary the similarity between *Perdix* and *Alectoris* parasites increases eastwards. The common feature here is climate, with very low rainfall in summer associated with grasshoppers and ants but an absence of earthworms. We return to this subject later.

DOES THE RISK OF INFECTION WITH PARASITES DETERMINE THE DIET OF PARTRIDGE CHICKS?

In the US in the 1920s Eloise Cram began an amazing series of experiments by extracting eggs from the uteri of worms parasitising domestic fowls and game birds. Keeping the species separate, these eggs were mixed with green food or finely ground cereal grains and fed to invertebrates that she had collected from fields, again keeping the species separate. A proportion of the grasshoppers and other invertebrates were then dissected at various stages before the remainder was fed to the birds. In this way the life cycle could be explored at every stage. For example, eggs of the gizzard worm *Dispharynx spiralis* which has been widely recorded in the grey partridge were fed to snails, slugs, earthworms, millipedes, grasshoppers, leaf hoppers, crickets, cockroaches, ground beetles, various beetle larvae and two species of woodlouse. The eggs hatched and developed in both species of woodlouse but not in the other ten groups of invertebrates. When the woodlice were fed to ruffed grouse, bobwhite quail and a pigeon, these birds became infected with the gizzard worm, but when fed to domestic fowl infections did not result. Thus woodlice are likely intermediate hosts of this gizzard worm in the grey partridge (Cram, 1928).

Here we are considering all 109 species of parasitic worm that infect partridges. There is very little information about the life histories of many species, but by extrapolation from what is known about species in the same genus we can estimate the intermediate hosts of 61 species. A further five, all nematodes, have no intermediate hosts. Many of the records of intermediate hosts are from experimental feeding, but this seems a valid and robust approach, consistent with what we know about natural infections. As an example, it is known from natural infections that the important tapeworms *Raillietina (R.) tetragona* and *R. (R.) echinobothrida* are transmitted by ants, whereas *Raillietina (S.) cesticillus* is transmitted by beetles. Two researchers in India confirmed this in the field by examining almost 9,000 ants and 1,400 beetles, finding none of the first two species in beetles but each of them in ants; no *R. (S.) cesticillus* were found in ants, all were in beetles (Gogoi & Chauderi, 1982).

Snails

Investigating grey partridge diet in Czechoslovakia, Farský (1926) drew attention to the extent to which snails were eaten, which he thought, probably correctly, was to gain calcium, especially as the snail eating seemed to coincide with egg laying. The snails that were eaten included members of Limnaeidae, Succinidae, Paludinidae and Sphaeriidae, which all live in wet or damp places not usually

FIG 181. Red-legged partridges frequently drink water and are affected by flukes whereas grey partridges rarely drink water and are rarely infected by flukes. Snails are intermediate hosts of these flukes but red-legged partridges mainly eat air-breathing land snails, not water snails. (grey partridges by Chris Knights)

associated with the bird. It was even thought that the partridges might help to control the intermediate host of the sheep liver fluke *Fasciola hepatica* (Farský *et al.*, 1928). The four species of snail found in grey partridge diet in North Central Europe all live in damp or wet places; Janda reports the Amber Snail *Succinea putris* and *Zonitoides nitidus* from Czechoslovakia, Thaiz & Csiki (1912) reported *Chondrula tridens* from Hungary and Oko (1963a) *Limnea truncatula* from Poland. This last species is the intermediate host of the common liver fluke.

Some flukes have two hosts; a common example is the lancet fluke of the liver and bile duct of sheep. In this fluke the first intermediate host is a land snail that secretes infected slime balls that are eaten by the ant *Formica rufa*. Infected ants deliberately climb grasses to complete the cycle when the grass is eaten. There are few other reports in the literature of snails in the diet of the grey partridge, which is strange given the numbers eaten in the Sussex Study area. With all this in mind it is surprising that the snails eaten by chukars in southeast Bulgaria and Azerbaijan were door snails *Clausiliidae* and species of *Vitrea*, air-breathing land snails adapted to living in dry habitats (Georgiev, 1961, 1963).

At the genus level something is known about the life cycles of 19 of the 24 species of fluke found in *Alectoris* and *Perdix*. The life cycle of four of the nine flukes found in *Perdix* involve freshwater snails. In *Alectoris* only one involves freshwater snails. These results are the opposite of what we would expect from the different drinking habits of the two species, but they do fit what is known about the diet. The reasons for the greater prevalence in *Alectoris* are not at all clear and too little is known about life cycles to speculate further, but ants may hold some clues. A study involving the fluke *Dicrocoelium petrovi*, snails, ants and red-legged partridges would be a mouth-watering prospect? In the meantime it seems to defy explanation that grey partridges, which very rarely drink water, eat freshwater snails and that *Alectoris* partridges, which drink regularly, feed on land snails.

Earthworms

The first study of partridge food in the UK gave a significant frequency of earthworms in the diet (Collinge, 1917). Dr Walter Collinge worked at the University of St Andrews for many years before joining the *Country Life* inquiry into strongylosis in the early 1930s. His methods appear reasonable enough but there is insufficient explanation:

> *careful examination of the crops and stomach* [gizzard?] *contents of a large series of adult and young birds* [how many? presumably shot?], *obtained from various parts of the country during the past 6 years* [Scotland? and when?], *examination and experiments on captive birds* [sample size not given] *and numerous field investigations* [what were these?].

The percentage of the diet consisting of earthworms is given for each month throughout the year; overall it was for the pheasant 8.7 per cent, for the red grouse 3 per cent (with 2 per cent slugs) and for the grey partridge 6.5 per cent (with 4 per cent slugs). In the same work animal matter was said to comprise 22.5 per cent of the diet of the red grouse! On this last point Collinge is out of line with every other study. When his results were challenged, he maintained that the diet had changed since 1917, with fewer invertebrates eaten (Collinge, 1938), but no supporting evidence has emerged.

Three of 156 grey partridges shot in Finland in 1964 had been ill and one had eaten one earthworm (Pulliainen, 1965). Erkki Pulliainen considered that these ill birds were deliberately seeking invertebrates to restore their protein levels. This could apply to one adult female grey partridge found in the Sussex Study area suffering from lead shot ingestion that had eaten a number of ground beetles and an earthworm. Stephen Browne found some earthworm remains (chaetae) in his 2001–03 investigations of chick food in East Anglia (Browne *et al.*, 2006) in an area of poor chick food supply with relatively high rates of parasitism.

Lucerne flea: *Sminthurus viridis*

Just as World War II started, during which she was switched to other duties, Phyllis Clapham examined a number of invertebrates in an area heavily infected with gapes (Clapham, 1939b). To a well-known list of worms and snail vectors of the gapeworm she added a centipede, *Scolopendra* sp., the larvae ('leatherjackets') of the crane fly, *Tipula* sp., and the lucerne flea, *Sminthurus viridis*. It is the lucerne flea that concerns us here most because it is a preferred item in the diet of young chicks. She found gapeworm larvae had migrated from the gut of the lucerne fleas into the surrounding tissues. Unlike all other vectors of parasitic worms, the lucerne fleas live on vegetation and not on the ground. It seems therefore that her observation may be due to the unusual circumstances in which the lucerne fleas were living, in a well-known hot-spot for gapes. Here it is assumed that the lucerne flea is not an important vector of gapes. Phyllis Clapham also showed that the maggots of house flies *Musca domestica* and green-bottles *Lucilia sericata* can be vectors of the gapeworm (Clapham, 1939a), but these maggots are at best very rare in the diet of partridges. They will eat them when they are offered but they are not natural foods.

Grasshoppers and crickets

This is the group of insects that above all others feature strongly both in partridge diets and as intermediate hosts of partridge parasites. So why do partridges eat them? Ten species have been shown to harbor Tapeworm cysts or parasitic nematodes (Schmidt, 1986; Anderson, 2000) but not all were natural infections; some were the result of laboratory feeding. At least 31 species of grasshopper and cricket, including bush crickets, have been recorded in partridge diets but few of these species has been shown capable of transmitting parasites. The main species eaten on steppe grassland is *Calliptamus italicus*, which as an adult has striking red warning colouration on the wings, but it has not yet been shown to be a host of a tapeworm that could infect partridges. Unfortunately most relevant research has been done in the US using such species as rice grasshoppers and others existing outside the range of the grey partridge.

Most grasshoppers and crickets have been recorded in the diet of partridges in Mediterranean countries, Eastern Europe or Asia where experimental research on parasite transmission has been minimal. At the generic level the genus *Melanoplus*, which includes the abundant grasshopper pests of North America, and *Chorthippus*, which includes the common field grasshopper of Europe, are eaten by partridges and are known carriers of tapeworms. How the grasshoppers are infected by the parasites is unknown except perhaps incidentally as they chew herbage, for very few grasshoppers feed on other invertebrates (some tettigonids do).

Beetles

Studies of grey partridge diets have identified 242 individual ground beetles to the level at least of genus. The total is small given the abundance of beetles and in the most extensive investigation only 2 per cent of the insects eaten were ground beetles. Most ground beetles are nocturnal or too large and strong, which may explain much of this.

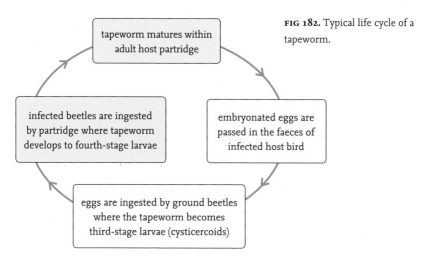

FIG 182. Typical life cycle of a tapeworm.

tapeworm matures within adult host partridge

infected beetles are ingested by partridge where tapeworm develops to fourth-stage larvae

embryonated eggs are passed in the faeces of infected host bird

eggs are ingested by ground beetles where the tapeworm becomes third-stage larvae (cysticercoids)

At least 91 species of insect have been shown to carry immature stages of tapeworms known as cysticercoids, and they include 64 species of ground beetles (Enigk & Sticinsky, 1959). Working at the Veterinary Research Institute, Hannover, in the 1950s, Enigk and Sticinsky collected beetles far away from areas with domestic fowls and then fed tapeworm eggs (as tapeworm segments or proglottids) to the beetles whilst they were kept in insectaries. After a suitable time for development the beetles were then dissected and the next-generation tapeworm cysts (known as cysticercoids) counted.

Two of the three main diurnal species in the diet of grey partridge chicks, *Bembidion lampros, B. quadrimaculatum*, were not found to carry cysticercoids but the third and most important, *Trechus quadristriatus*, was not tested. The larger diurnal beetles *Amara* (the sun beetles) and *Calathus* account for 17 per cent of the ground beetles in the grey partridge diet and 93 per cent of these contained cysticercoids of *Raillietina cesticillus*, the most abundant tapeworm in grey partridges. The genus *Harpalus* accounted for 42 per cent of ground beetles in the diet in Hungary, but only 8 per cent carried cysticercoids and the main species eaten, *H. chalceatus*, was not tested. The main species eaten in the Sussex study, the predominantly vegetarian *Harpalus rufipes*, was also not tested. If partridges are infected by ground beetles, then *Amara* and perhaps *Harpalus* are the ground beetles likely contributing most risk of infection. The only other beetles infected were dung beetles. Only two of these, both the small *Aphodius* often found under sheep droppings, were present amongst the 3,341 insects listed in the grey partridge diet in Hungary (Vertse *et al.*, 1955) and none were found in Sussex.

Ants

Although sometimes absent from diets, ants are, over all the diet studies, by far
the most abundant insects in the diet of partridges, with 32 species recorded.
Why should partridges eat so many ants if they carry parasites?

Of 18 records of *Raillietina* tapeworms that can be transmitted by ants, 14 are of
the closely related *R. tetragona* and *R. echinobothrida*. A number of older studies in
the US (Jones & Horsfall, 1935) and France (Joyeux & Baer, 1939), and a more recent
study in India already mentioned, all implicate or confirm that species in the
European and North American ant genus *Tetramorium* can transmit tapeworms,
as can some species of the genus *Pheidole*, the 'big-headed ants' (Horsfall, 1938). A
total of 10,006 adult ants in partridge diets have been identified to species. Only
one individual has been found in the diet of partridges (red-legged partridges in
Spain) that is known to transmit a tapeworm. This is *Tetramorium semilaeve* that
can transmit *Raillietina tetragona*. At the generic level however, 18 of the 10,006 ants
(0.2 per cent of the total eaten) are known to be capable of transmitting *Raillietina
echinobothrida* and *R. tetragona*. Harvester ants (*Messor* sp.) are the most common
ants in the diet of red-legged partridges and they appear not to be able to carry
cysticercoids (Mohammed *et al.*, 1988). As part of his studies in Norfolk, where
harvester ants do not occur, Brown *et al.* (2006) fed more than 10,000 *Lasius flavus*
to grey partridge chicks without any evidence of infection. Thus on the evidence
available, the most frequent species of ants in the diet appear safe, but where the
other species mentioned above occur this may not be the case.

The question at the head of this section is difficult to answer. There is
however enough to sustain a working hypothesis. All available data from

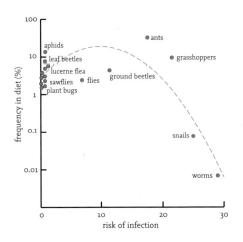

FIG 183. The composition of the
invertebrate diet of grey partridge
chicks in relation to the risk of
infection with parasitic worms.

the 28 studies of the diet of grey partridge chicks up to six weeks of age (Chapter 5) were divided into age by weeks to give 39 estimates of the composition of the diet. These were given equal weight and the average percentage composition calculated. The risk of parasite infection was obtained by allocating all known published records of each of 109 flukes (Trematodes), tapeworms (Cestodes) and Nematodes in grey partridges to their intermediate hosts (where known). For example, four separate analyses finding the tapeworm *Raillietina cesticillus* would all be allocated to ground beetles. This is necessarily a broad brush approach involving some 80 separate studies of varying quality and frequent unknowns.

The working hypothesis mentioned above comes from a comparison of the diet with the risk of infection. This is done in Figure 183. It seems clear, despite all the complication above, for example that most ants might actually be safe; it seems that moderate risk does not reduce the consumption. In fact, as we have seen, grasshoppers and ants are preferred items in the diet. However, the significant miscellaneous group of snails, slugs, woodlice, millipedes and earthworms do not feature much in the diet. It follows that grey partridges do not scratch to make food available to their chicks or feed on earthworms because the risk is too great. Overall a balance has to be struck between starving and being infected. The evidence of a shift in the diet away from weed-dwelling insects, described in Chapter 5, does explain why rates of parasite infection, especially with the gapeworm, can be higher where insect food is scarce.

OVERALL CONCLUSIONS

Many species of parasites and disease organisms are found in partridges, with the species changing markedly from Western Europe to China. The postmortem results show a dramatic decline in the level of blackhead and strongylosis in wild grey partridges but higher levels of parasitism and disease in red-legged partridges. The parasites found to predominate on modern game farms are not the same as those found in the wild due to the differing availability of intermediate hosts. There is substantial evidence of reared game birds and poultry spreading parasites but not diseases to wild game-birds. Currently there is a very low degree of parasitism in wild grey partridges. There seems sound evidence that most invertebrate foods in the diet carry little risk of infection, though there is some evidence that infection with the gapeworm is higher where preferred foods are scarce. Those groups such as earthworms and snails that carry most risk of infection are rare in the diet.

CHAPTER 8

Living With Raptors

Tis unnatural,
Even like the deed that's done. On Tuesday last,
A falcon, towering in her pride of place,
Was by a mousing owl hawk'd at and killed.

Macbeth, Act II Scene IV

IN THE RECENT PAST, nothing has divided bird protection and hunting lobbies more than their differing attitudes to raptors. Yet, in future, raptors could be the glue that binds the two lobbies together. Raptors need food and with modern agricultures there is less and less food for wildlife every year, except where wild game-birds are conserved, as we shall see in Chapter 10. Only three species of raptor have been shown to prey on significant numbers of partridges; sparrowhawks in England, hen harriers in France and goshawks in Germany, Poland and Spain. In each case we could wish for more convincing evidence, but with a likely absence of experiments far into the future, information will remain sparse. Many other raptor species have been recorded killing partridges, and collectively they may have a significant impact, but here the data are even more elusive. The larger raptors and owls also kill smaller raptors and owls and this needs to be factored in, with profound implications that we review here. Partridges appear to be suffering high predation rates partly through an absence of top predatory birds, just as we saw with the absence of top-predatory mammals in Chapter 4.

THE SUSSEX STUDY

There are detailed records of the circumstances of the deaths of 307 partridges in the Sussex Study area (248 grey partridge, 43 red-legged partridge and 16 chukar [including one hybrid]) during 1953 to October 2011. In the period up to

FIG 184. A female sparrowhawk attacks the defending male of pair of grey partridges with small chicks; more males than females are killed at this time, but this male has had warning and the attack is unlikely to be successful. (Painting by Richard Robjent)

the year 2000 there were only 5 raptor kills (all grey partridges) in 160 deaths, or 3 per cent of deaths. Since 2000 there have been 62 raptor kills in 147 deaths (47 grey partridge and 15 red-legged partridge), or 42 per cent of deaths. Whether this predation has significantly reduced partridge numbers or could do so in the future has been studied in several ways. Some 18 species of raptors and owls have been seen in the Sussex Study area and these, and those owls that were seen in daytime, have been recorded annually since 1970. Finally, the predation on partridges by raptors has been related to the partridge population and the habitat. Mark Watson from the GWCT studied the effects of raptor predation on the grey partridge on 20 sites including the Sussex Study area.

Identifying the raptor responsible from the kill

Since the year 2000, female sparrowhawks have been observed killing grey partridges on 13 occasions in the Sussex Study. On the basis of the features of known sparrowhawk kills, a further 22 grey partridges were considered killed by sparrowhawks.

The 13 partridges seen to be caught by sparrowhawks were not killed outright but eaten alive, typically from one shoulder downwards, with the hawk standing on top of the partridge to hold it down. On two occasions the partridge escaped during the process only to die days later from deep wounds. The victims were usually near trees, large bushes or tall hedges, in which case the bird was dragged under cover before being eaten to prevent other raptors, ravens and carrion crows stealing the prey. The mean weight of partridges in spring is ~400g, 1.5 times heavier than a female sparrowhawk. The same partridge would however be 2.6 times the weight of a male sparrowhawk, which is in consequence too small and weak to catch adult partridges. Grey partridges cannot be carried even by female sparrowhawks and so adult partridges are not normally found at regular plucking sites or brought to the nest by sparrowhawk males. This is probably the main reason why in Germany in the 1930s, when grey partridges were super-abundant, only 79 (0.2 per cent) were found amongst 42,261 prey items at plucking sites (Uttendörfer, 1939).

FIG 185. This not quite fully grown grey partridge was attacked by a female sparrowhawk and traumatised. The sparrowhawk was driven off and after a time the partridge recovered.

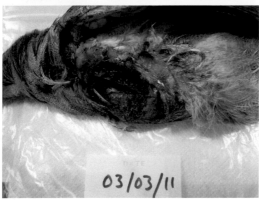

FIG 186. This adult male escaped after being partly eaten by a female sparrowhawk, but died later.

FIG 187. Typical sparrowhawk kill, with the majority left uneaten.

FIG 188. Sometimes this is all the evidence one sees of a sparrowhawk kill, the partridge having been dragged into a secluded spot to avoid other raptors stealing the kill.

In typical sparrowhawk kills the bulk of the flesh is uneaten. This is because the sparrowhawk crop capacity of a maximum ~120g is only 30 per cent of the body weight of a grey partridge. Such a meal would suffice for two days, during which time the remaining carcass will have been scavenged. Sparrowhawks scavenge the kills of other predators, but only rarely (Watson, 2004).

The remaining 27 partridges not killed by sparrowhawks appeared to have been killed outright, with extensive bone damage, including a much damaged sternum, with feeding beginning from the underside and the skeleton picked clean in the open. In four of these cases this type of predation was seen to be due to hen harriers, with a further four almost certainly due to hen harriers. Two grey partridges were seen to be killed by peregrines and in both cases the cervical vertebra (neck) was neatly cut through, and a further five were attributable to peregrines. Many of the remaining 12 kills were near trees with 2 known to be killed by a buzzard and the remainder killed by buzzards or harriers, including marsh harriers. In conclusion sparrowhawk kills are easily distinguished from other raptor kills, but with the exception of the peregrine I was unable to identify most predation by other raptors. I am reminded of the Earl of Warwick: 'Who finds the partridge in the Puttock's [red kite] nest/But may imagine how the bird was dead/ Although the kite soar with un-blooded beak' (*Henry VI, Part II*, Act III Scene II).

Relationship of predation on grey partridges to the number of sparrowhawks
Female sparrowhawks accounted for 11 per cent of raptor sightings but 56 per cent of raptor kills of the grey partridge. The characteristic spring peaks of predation by female sparrowhawks is shown in Figure 190 as also is the

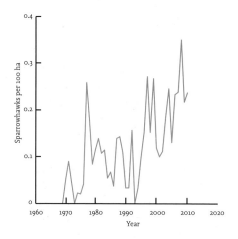

FIG 189. Sussex Study area stubble counts: the number of sparrowhawks has increased, recovering from the indirect adverse effects of insecticide seed dressings in the 1950s and early 1960s.

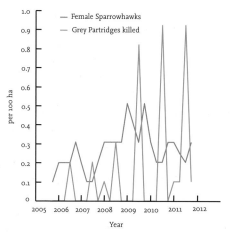

FIG 190. Density of female sparrowhawks in spring (red) and their kills of grey partridge (blue) by quarter from 2005 to 2011.

number of female sparrowhawks; both were measured on the Sussex Study area used by Mark Watson. It is clear that the number of sparrowhawks is more or less constant but with strong 'peaks' of spring predation on grey partridges.

From 11 trials in 3 winters at 8 of 20 sites, Watson (2004) calculated his raptor kill search efficiency as 28 per cent (range 10–60 per cent). It is surely the case that this is less than the incidental searching efficiency of the gamekeepers. Although they are not searching deliberately on set occasions, they are on the ground almost continuously. Erring on the side of caution, however, Mark Watson's 28 per cent is assumed to hold in the calculations below. Foxes scavenge sparrowhawk kills and by removing carcasses they can reduce the search efficiency substantially, but foxes were well controlled on the Norfolk Estate. In the calculations below, the raptor kill efficiency of 28 per cent is not altered on account of fox scavenging.

In 2009–11 the average number of grey partridge known to be killed by sparrowhawks during the spring peaks was 8, 9 and 11 respectively, which represented, with the Watson correction above, the loss of 33 per year. Usually three female sparrowhawks are resident partly or wholly on the Norfolk Estate. The loss of 33 grey partridges therefore amounts to 11 per female sparrowhawk during the ~85 days between covey break-up and the start of the sparrowhawk clutch. This would represent perhaps a quarter of their diet during that time. Between February 2000 and March 2001, Mark Watson found 188 kills made by all raptors, mostly female sparrowhawks, in the Sussex Study area. There were nine grey partridges, with their low density at the time, comprising 5 per cent of prey items. Song thrushes appear to be the dominant prey on the Norfolk Estate, less so blackbirds; both are numerous, easier to catch and much easier to handle than partridges. In year-round observations at Manydown in the 1990s Andrew Williams found that sparrowhawks fed mainly on wood pigeons, with grey partridges accounting for only 2.3 per cent of sparrowhawk kills, but these kills accounted for 40 per cent of grey partridge bodies found (A. Williams, *in litt.*).

Elsewhere things may be different. At Kurikka in Ostrobothnia, Finland, Erkki Pulliainen followed 12 coveys through the snow of 1964–5 and found a rather low loss of 30 birds (23 per cent) to all causes in 10 coveys, but in the other 2 a female sparrowhawk, a rare predator in Finland at the time, killed 12, a 46 per cent loss to this predator alone (Pulliainen, 1966). We do not know the context of these events but there a number of cases in the literature where raptors have specialised on partridges, even one case, again in Finland, where a female Merlin apparently wiped out an entire grey partridge covey. At the GWCT Francis Buner, simultaneously radio-tracking grey partridges and sparrowhawks, is filling important gaps in our understanding of the context of predation.

SOME ESTIMATES OF OVERALL LOSSES TO RAPTORS FROM FIELD WORK IN SUSSEX

During the winter and spring of 1999/2000 Mark Watson found that all raptors combined killed 11 per cent of grey partridges on the Norfolk Estate at a density after shooting of only 4 per 100 ha. Jumping forward to 2010/11 we can make the same calculations on the same assumptions, in which case all raptors combined killed 3 per cent at a density of 150 per 100 ha. Thus the impact of predation, by female sparrowhawks, decreased three-fold while grey partridge numbers increased 38-fold.

A key limitation of the impact of sparrowhawks is that their numbers did not respond to the increase in partridges (see Fig. 190). This is almost certainly because the territory the sparrowhawks establish in spring is chosen largely by the males (Newton, 1986). Male sparrowhawks stay almost entirely in and around the woods. Of 73 separate sightings of sparrowhawks on the Norfolk Estate since 2005, 65 (89 per cent) were females.

At Damerham, in the early 1950s, before poisoning with the insecticide dieldrin began to reduce sparrowhawk numbers, they comprised 13 per cent of raptor sightings. Since 2005 this percentage has been virtually the same in the Sussex Study, with sparrowhawks accounting for 11 per cent of raptor sightings through the year. This is an amazing agreement given that before they were protected, sparrowhawks were trapped and killed at every opportunity at Damerham (especially males caught to finches).

Sex ratio of partridges predated by raptors

In spring grey partridge populations usually have a sex ratio biased towards males. This is mainly due to the loss of females during incubation the previous year; in the Sussex Study mostly fox predation. In autumn the surplus can be large, for example 2.7 'old' males per female over nine years in Lithuania (Logminas & Petraitis, 1970). In spring the surplus males move around looking to form pairs and they have a high visibility. At Damerham 39 per cent of unpaired males (65) died compared to 12.5 per cent of paired males (365), a highly significant difference, but with the mortality attributable to all causes. During three years in Schleswig Holstein, goshawks killed 75 males and 62 females (1.21 males per female), but this does not indicate a higher predation rate on the males because these were in surplus, with, for example, 68 males and 51 females (1.33 males per female) in the bag. From all his study areas combined Mark Watson determined the sex of 676 birds in winter coveys and found 55 per cent of them to be males (Watson,

2004). On the same areas 62 per cent of 42 raptor kills retrieved by gamekeepers were males. On the Norfolk Estate 72 per cent of 32 raptor kills were males. In North Dakota John Carroll captured 64 males and 46 females for radio-tracking and found mortality rates into May to be 34 per cent for females and 67 per cent for males, with the main cause of mortality being raptors (Carroll, 1989, 1990). In Watson's study the excess of males amongst the raptor kills was not significantly different from the excess in coveys and this seems generally to be the case, but with the exception of North Dakota. If this is generally true the excess of males amongst predated partridges is ultimately attributable to the loss of females during incubation (or to gapes, see p. 246) the previous season and not to sparrowhawks finding males easier to kill. If all surplus males were to be predated, then some paired females would not be able to replace lost partners and in a study in France, where raptors caused significant loss of adults in spring, 34 per cent of the initially unpaired males eventually replaced lost paired males (Aufradet & Birkan, 2001).

When sparrowhawks attack grey partridge broods, a frequent event just after winter barley crops are harvested, the male uses a frantic flee and distraction display to attract the hawk away from the chicks. It is suspected that some fatherless broods may have been the result of sparrowhawks killing males at this time. Female grey partridges have been seen to thwart attacks by harriers in Sussex, and in Ireland one drove a sparrowhawk away from a chick it held (Kieran Buckley, pers. comm.).

Age ratio of partridges predated by raptors
Excluding chicks and juveniles that were aged less than four months, the average age of grey partridges killed by raptors was 9.4 months and dying by other causes was 10.5 months; no significant difference.

Was the predation attributable to partridges being in poor health?
It is well known amongst hunters that birds injured by shooting are quickly picked off by raptors, especially goshawks (Lampio, 1949). There is even a case of a Kestrel killing such an injured grey partridge in Sussex (Knox, 1845). It was also well known during the episode of deaths to dieldrin seed dressings in the late 1950s and early 1960s that raptors killed birds suffering from poisoning by seed dressings, thus accumulating lethal doses themselves. For these and similar reasons the idea that raptors acted as 'health police' took hold. It is a nice idea but, like the balance of nature itself, the evidence suggests otherwise.

Mark Watson examined 41 adult grey partridges killed by raptors and found that the condition of 95 per cent was average to excellent (score 3–5). At the GWCT Chris Davis examined 77 kills with organs intact and found only 7 parasitic nematodes (0.09 per bird). Repeating this work on 16 adult birds from the Norfolk estate during 2005–11, I found 94 per cent had excellent condition scores, with a total of 7 nematodes found (0.44 per bird). There was no suspicion that the parasites (5 *Capillaria*, 2 Strongyles) were contributing to the causes of death. Can we reconcile this with the hunter observations? Yes we can. Injured and poisoned birds can be out in the open flapping in obvious distress, whereas moribund birds hide away quietly out of sight of raptors.

Timing of predation by raptors

The main period of predation by sparrowhawks, accounting for 45 of 56 (80 per cent) kills, is in February to April inclusive (Fig. 190). The sudden start of this period of highest predation by sparrowhawks follows pair formation. The first pairs are seen in early January but the vast bulk of pair formation is in the last week of January and first week of February. Most predation by raptors is later, during the competitive nest site 'exploration' phase when nest searching is carried out through the day. The end of the risk period is when crops provide cover and when sparrowhawks begin to lay and incubate, a period of about 41 days, during which time the female is fed at or near the nest by the male (Newton, 1986), and therefore not on partridges. This increased vulnerability in spring is much less pronounced in the red-legged partridge for reasons not understood (Watson, 2004).

HARRIERS

Whether harriers can depress partridge populations through preying on adults or young is a vexed question for hunters and ecologists alike. To try to answer it we turn again to the remarkable studies in north-central France during the three years 1995–7 based on radio-tracking 1,009 females caught during early spring and followed until September (Bro *et al.*, 2000). Unfortunately the males were not radio-tracked and so their rate of loss is not known. This work showed that the breeding success was most restricted by loss of females during incubation, almost all attributable to predation. As described in Chapter 4, 64 per cent of this predation was due to ground carnivores, especially stone martens. A further 29 per cent of the predation was caused by raptors and the overall predation rate on females doubled as the number of marsh harriers and hen harriers increased four-fold (Bro *et al.*, 2001). There was no sign of pre-existing conditions such as disease that might have exacerbated the predation, and the mortality caused by the harriers was considered to be additive to the other predation, with a clear effect on grey partridge numbers (Fig. 192). Elizabeth Bro and her colleagues

FIG 191. A beetle bank (above left) offering very little protection against raptors; (above right) remains of grey partridge killed by a female hen harrier on 7 December 2008 on the same beetle bank.

considered that the raptor predation might have been increased by the larger fields of contemporary agriculture, but the average field size in their studies ranged from a tiny 1.5 ha to only 10 ha, small compared to the field size in Britain and near the optimum for partridges.

From a strictly scientific viewpoint it is unfortunate that the strongest evidence that could be brought to bear on the problem, the results of experimental reductions of harrier abundance, is ruled out for social and ethical reasons. Accepting this, the circumstantial evidence from the studies in France, particularly the high overall mortality of healthy females during spring and summer, is certainly pointing to the harriers, especially hen harriers, having an important role. Without doubt it was sufficient to consider reducing the impact through habitat management, as discussed in Chapter 4.

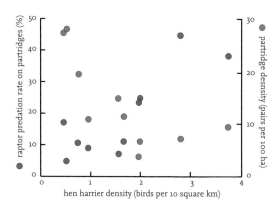

FIG 192 Grey partridge numbers in France were lower when predation by the hen harrier (mainly) and marsh harrier was higher (from Valkama et al., 2005).

FIG 193. This first autumn pallid harrier straying from a route that would normally take it from Kazakhstan to East Africa stayed on the Norfolk Estate through September 2011. Here it is shown carrying a female house sparrow caught in an unharvested conservation headland. (Dorian Mason)

FIG 194. Lapwing driving a marsh harrier from the Boora – an area of cutaway bogs in central Ireland where partridge numbers have been restored. (John Murphy)

GOSHAWK

There is only fragmentary information about the impact of the goshawk on grey partridge populations. Heinz Brüll studied a partridge population in a 1,700 ha area to the west of Hamburg occupied by half of the territory of one pair of goshawks and three of sparrowhawks. The study began on 1 March 1950 and continued for ten years. Brüll estimated that the number of male grey partridge calling in spring at a total of 171 for the three years 1952–4, probably representing 228 males (Kasprzykowski & Goła, 2009). The grey partridge density was therefore low, with only ~4.5 nesting pairs per 100 ha. The partridge population appeared stable at the time so we can estimate their total number at about 1,200 birds per year in September. The number killed by the goshawks in the two years when the bag was known was 50 (4.2 per cent) per year compared to 220 (18 per cent) in the bag. Of the total 3,785 birds and mammals killed by the goshawks grey partridges accounted for 9 per cent, very close to the 11 per cent obtained in the wider study in Germany by Uttendörfer (1939), mentioned earlier.

Near Frankfurt goshawks killed 33 grey partridges mainly within 70 m of trees from where the ambush originated (Döring & Helfrich, 1986). These kills accounted for 15 per cent of all birds killed in the area by the goshawks and as with sparrowhawks most predation was in early spring, but the impact on the partridge population could not be determined due to a very substantial dispersal of pairs. Dudziński studied the winter home ranges of grey partridges in a 1,500 ha area in central Poland with several areas of forest, fields in strips only 28 m wide with boundaries of brambles and other shrubby cover. He found that the partridges died or were killed at the rate of one every 47 days per covey. Losses were least near roads, orchards, buildings and dogs and greatest near the forested areas. The average number of predators per 100 ha was fox 0.6, pine marten 0.2, buzzard 0.7 and goshawk 0.3. Predation was the main cause of death, with goshawks responsible for 75 per cent of deaths (Dudziński 1988, 1992) and with the density of partridges lower in the areas regularly used by goshawks. In a major study Santi Mañosa examined of the impact of raptors on the red-legged partridge in northeast Spain and found that the goshawk predation reduced numbers by 22 per cent (Mañosa, 1994).

Other raptors

The *Buteo* buzzards are by far the most numerous raptors in partridge range, accounting for 26 per cent of the 5,330 sightings mentioned below. In October 1977 and 1978 a stubble count in the Wetterau near Giessen in Germany revealed an average 158 grey partridges and 50 buzzards. Such figures alone certainly indicate

FIG 195. Male red-legged partridge killed by a buzzard in Portugal; buzzards typically tear off the head.

that the two species can co-exist to some extent! We saw earlier that buzzards have killed both grey and red-legged partridges in the Sussex Study area but unlike with other raptors there is some evidence that they have difficulty catching wild partridges. They readily prey on reared and released partridges, on birds weakened after prolonged snow (Hell, 1965) and one red-legged partridge killed was certainly very ill. Another had hit a fence whilst being chased by a buzzard and two grey partridges were killed against a rabbit-proof fence. In Germany at the end of the nineteenth century the stomachs of 1,237 buzzards contained 18 grey partridges (1.4 per cent), whereas those from the stronger 386 rough-legged buzzards contained 8 (2.1 per cent) (Rörig, 1896, in Kokeš & Knobloch, 1947). The rough-legged buzzard is a tundra species that feeds mainly on lemmings and voles and normally is only an occasional winter visitors to the Sussex Study area, with only three wintering in the past ten years. Numbers were however exceptional from the end of October 1974 to the beginning of March 1975, with a maximum of 12 present at any one time. At least initially the partridges were very frightened of these birds, but there were no recorded deaths to them.

A number of raptors have been recorded preying on grey partridges in North America. In Washington State's Palouse Prairie, the great horned owl and Cooper's hawk killed near trees, whilst the prairie falcon and hen harrier did so in open country (Yocom, 1943). In Montana hen harriers were thought the most important predator on grey partridges, followed by rough-legged buzzard and prairie falcon in winter and Swainson's hawk in spring (Weigand, 1977). In North Dakota John Carroll found that 79 per cent of the mortality of grey partridges in winter and spring was predation. Great horned owls and snowy owls caused most losses, with hen harriers and Swainson's and red-tailed hawks (similar to but larger and stronger than a buzzard) causing 'some mortality' during their spring migration (Carroll, 1989). No losses were attributed to falcons or smaller hawks. In Wisconsin great horned owls and Red-tailed Hawks were most important (Church et al., 1980). In the north Gyr falcons and bald eagles as well as snowy owls come into the reckoning (Dekker & Court, 2003) but with the latter at least not responding to grey partridge density (Gollop, 1965).

Puga et al. (2002) listed seven raptors and four owls reported by others as predators of adult red-legged partridges but including such species as the hobby and barn owl that seem extremely unlikely. Similarly Calderon (1977) mentioned the Short-toed Eagle but this specialises on the same snakes and lizards that are a significant cause of egg losses (Otero, 1999). In the south of France Cheylan (1977) found that red-legged partridges were the main item in the diet of the rare and generally declining Bonelli's eagle. A study of the diet of Bonelli's eagle in Cyprus showed chukars also the main item of prey but this included some game-farm birds, so the impact is not clear (Iezekiel et al., 1997). Notwithstanding the relatively high frequency of red-legged partridges in the Bonelli's eagle diet, a major study in Spain has shown the impact to be a negligible 1.26 per cent of the

FIG 196. 14 September 2011: the first of many short-eared owls that wintered in the Sussex Study area in 2011/12, hunting night and day. (Neville Kingdon)

FIG 197. New Year's Day 2005: John Carroll with a wing from a male grey partridge retrieved from a peregrine kill brought back to the spire of Salisbury Cathedral. (Eileen Carroll)

numbers counted at pair formation, with a bias towards males, and 0.42 per cent of numbers after the breeding season (Moleón *et al.*, 2011).

The peregrine falcon (Porter & White, 1973), golden eagle (Bloom & Hawks, 1982), bald eagle (Robinson, 2007) and prairie falcon (Boyce, 1985) have all been recorded preying on chukars in the US but their impact is not quantified. Working in the western Alps Ariane Bernard-Laurent tracked 50 rock partridges, finding that predation accounted for 85 per cent of deaths, with golden eagles the main predator (Bernard-Laurent, 1989). Since then it has become clear that this eagle is a super-predator with more other predators in its diet than even the goshawk, Bonelli's eagle or eagle owl (Lourenço *et al.*, 2011). We look at the implications later.

Valkama *et al.* (2005) summarised a large number of studies of the diet of raptors in Western Europe and listed the percentage prey items that were gamebirds. There are problems with these kinds of figures if only because the impact of raptors on gamebirds depends on far more than the composition of the diet, but they do allow an approximate ranking of importance in the diet. The species with the highest frequency of game birds in the diet was the golden eagle, followed by Bonelli's eagle > goshawk > hen harrier > booted eagle > peregrine > eagle owl > marsh harrier > buzzard.

FIG 198. Sussex Study area: although numerous in surrounding fields, grey partridges shun this valley where they could easily be ambushed by predators.

Incredibly Valkama and ten co-authors omitted the sparrowhawk, because 'all authors consider that the impact of this species on game species is negligible'. Based on my own direct observations of kills of grey partridges in Sussex, the order should be sparrowhawk > hen harrier > (then in no particular order) buzzard, peregrine and marsh harrier.

EFFECT OF RAPTOR PREDATION ON GREY PARTRIDGE POPULATION DENSITIES

This was investigated in a combination of field studies and the Potts computer model (Watson *et al.*, 2007). If you know how many partridges are killed by raptors it seems at first sight easy to calculate the effect on the population. It is however far from easy because we also need to know two additional things. Firstly, how many of the birds would die in the absence of the predation and secondly, how the raptors respond to changes in the partridge population density. This last response has two components: changes in feeding habits (known as the functional response) and changes in the number of raptors relative to the number of partridges (known as the numerical response).

From what we know about the sex, age and good health of the partridges killed by raptors, it seems that the raptors are not benefiting the partridges much by acting as a 'health police'; in fact we can put the issue on the shelf for now. Dispersal is another thing and because it is higher when the numbers in winter are relatively higher than normal due to large numbers of young birds in the population, it could be that the effects of raptor predation are cushioned. This was allowed for by calculating the losses before spring dispersal when the cushioning was possible and after the dispersal, when it was not. Here these two have been averaged, representing the situation in nature. Finally, it was assumed the raptor population would not increase if the partridges increased. The computer model was run under many different scenarios with various combinations of farming and predator control, with each scenario run with and without raptors.

The findings were very clear: the effect of sparrowhawks was greatest at the low densities we observe with modern farming and no game management, and lowest with conservation headlands and game management; the higher the partridge population, the smaller the effect of sparrowhawks. The modeling showed that at worst their predation could reduce long-term average numbers by 26 per cent, at best by 11 per cent. In the model, raptor predation is however set at a constant 15 per cent per year, whereas we know from the direct observations above that when partridge numbers are restored, this percentage can reduce to 4 per cent.

AVOIDING RAPTOR PREDATION

Many were surprised when it was first shown that Vervet Monkeys give different alarm calls on sighting eagles and snakes, even though it is self-evident that this should be so, given natural selection. Gamekeepers and poultry keepers have known for generations that the reaction of gamebirds to ground predators is a low-intensity 'crouch and freeze call' evolved with camouflage so as not to reveal the caller, and that the response to hawks is a sharp 'prepare to flee call'. The 'crouch and freeze call' is retained for quartering harriers where cover is scarce. Raptor avoidance behaviour is very highly developed; it has to be with so many raptors around.

Predator avoidance can be instinctive, acquired through experience or taught by parents, taught by others or permutations of all these. In the 1970s it was discovered that the reaction of partridges to alarm calls was only partly instinctive and that learning and experience were necessary to fine-tune the instinct (Menzdorf, 1976). Instinctive reactions are genetically based and evolve relatively slowly, but acquired behaviour can evolve very quickly through non-genetic inheritance. Ethologists Laura Beani and Francesco Dessì-Fulgheri at the University of Florence studied the role of grey partridge parents in the development of anti-predator behaviour of chicks (Beani & Dessì-Fulgheri, 1998). They found that freezing and crouching were more predictable and maintained more strictly in the parent-reared birds. So, although anti-raptor behaviour in partridges is instinctive, partridges learn as chicks to behave in ways that give the best defence against specific predators. For some time this has been exploited by fostering brooder-reared chicks onto wild birds that have no chicks.

One ancient group of galliformes, the megapodes, the familiar mound-builders of Australasia, are like the cuckoo, not reared by their parents and so cannot benefit from parental tuition. When the megapode chicks emerge from the mounds they instinctively react to the alarm calls of song birds (Göth, 2001). This being so, we must ask why anti-raptor behaviour in young partridges is dependent on their parents. The answer has to be that the parents can provide much more precise help than song birds. In red-legged partridges it has been found that the alarm calls for fox and raptor are different and probably convey significant information about the context of the danger (Binazzi et al., 2011).

David Jenkins showed how in coveys sentinels were always on the look out for raptors and that this became less demanding for individuals as covey size increased (Jenkins, 1961a). Mark Watson showed that coveys could easily improve vigilance when needed to cope with raptors but could not do so when paired (Watson, 2004). In grey partridges males are more vigilant than females, looking out for male competitors as well as predators, but there is very little difference in the red-legged partridge (Binazzi et al., 2011).

The value of vigilance in coveys has been shown by an interesting study of snowy owls in winter in Alberta (Boxall & Lein, 1982). Although female snowy owls killed grey partridges, which were very visible against the snow, only 1 of 11 attacks that were observed was successful and this was on a lone partridge. In all, 14 partridges were known to have been killed, representing 9 per cent of prey items in the diet, all in one winter (of two studied) when small mammals, the main prey of snowy owls, were uncommon. The value of being in a covey in a snow-covered landscape is the reason that pairs re-group into coveys if snow returns after pairing. These coveys are quite different from earlier coveys and the pairs are distinct and readily discerned. Against a background of snow-raptor predation is not only more likely but easier to study. Far less is known about raptor predation at other times of year.

Nevertheless, with partridges paired up in spring, vigilance is obviously more demanding and in addition the males have to guard against unpaired or opportunistic male neighbours. It is at this time that protective cover is vital.

COVER

Perhaps the most seminal paper ever produced on this subject was that by Errington & Hamerstrom (1936). In an extremely detailed study of the bobwhite quail on farmland in Wisconsin and Iowa, they quantified predation by the Cooper's hawk (a slightly larger version of the sparrowhawk) and great horned owl (a slightly smaller version of the eagle owl). They came up with one of the most enduring of statements: 'The population in excess of the carrying capacity is dangerously exposed and hence doomed, be there few or many predators.' This simple statement came to define what was known as the doomed surplus. It was grabbed by protectionists as proof that predator control was not necessary, by hunters as evidence that shooting did not depress numbers and just for good measure the useful concept of carrying capacities was derided by fence-sitting ecologists and theoreticians. Close inspection of the paper shows that none of these reactions was justified.

In fact Errington & Hamerstrom had advocated planting suitable cover against predation to raise the carrying capacity. To be effective, they said, the cover needed to protect against raptors and be close to roosting and feeding places. They recommended strips of raspberry, prickly ash, roses, coral berry, sumac and hawthorn, to produce scattered thickets, and the encouragement of tall weeds along fencerows. Bobwhite quail are much more at home in woodland than grey partridges, but on open farmland their cover requirements are similar. It is remarkable how often thorny vegetation is considered important whether for nesting, as we saw in Chapter 4, or as cover at other times. In Sussex the most protective cover is provided by blackthorn, but brambles, hawthorn and wild roses are used. South of the Caucasus, thickets of Christ's thorn provide the main daytime cover of grey partridges (Dement'ev & Gladkov, 1952). In mountainous areas junipers are widely used as cover, as we saw with the Pyrenean partridge. In Tadjikistan losses of chukar partridges between nesting and winter were far lower in areas with patches of juniper than in predominantly rocky areas (Lebedev, 1976).

Mark Watson referred to this type of vegetation as 'concealing cover' and he examined its use in relation to the risk of predation by raptors. He found that the 'first line of defence' of the grey partridges was to remain in taller cover, with this especially the case where sparrowhawks, but not buzzards, were most frequent.

FIG 199. Partridges hidden under kale are safe from raptors.

FIG 200. Royston: grey partridge covey emerging from kale to feed on stubble. (Malcolm Brockless)

There was insufficient information about the response to harriers to draw any conclusions, but in France it had been shown that hen and marsh harriers killed more partridges further away from permanent cover and where crops were shorter (Reitz & Mayot, 1999). In China I found that sea buckthorn bushes protected two Daurian partridge coveys from hen harrier predation. In general partridges have to be more vigilant as crop vegetation grows (Watson & Aebischer, 2007) until the point where it is tall enough to give canopy cover, whereupon the vigilance becomes largely unnecessary. It is important when planting game-cover to aim to provide a suitable canopy from the time of pairing until crops can provide it. Unfortunately by the time of pairing, crop cover, such as maize and sugar beet have gone and oilseed rape is usually too thick and often too wet.

The value of cover strips of maize (and sometimes kale) based mixtures was investigated in a six-year study on four almost hedgeless areas in France (Bro *et al.*, 2004). There were four managed areas of 387–1148 ha and four control of 440–1002 ha, with three years of observation before the strip cover was planted and three after. The results showed that overwinter losses were higher where strip cover was planted and the authors considered only that their results pointed to the need for 'replicated field experiments at a farm scale'. Further analysis shows that when in coveys the grey partridges were 800 times as numerous in the strips as in surrounding fields. Moreover the overwinter losses increased strongly with density, which is why the areas with strip cover had higher percentage losses than elsewhere.

Sometimes the strips have been referred to as predation traps but the evidence suggests this is unwarranted. We return to the value of cover strips in Chapter 10.

NIGHT-TIME

Simon Dowell of the GWCT studied the roosting of 11 wild coveys on the Shaftesbury Estate near Damerham (Dowell, 1988b). In 1987 and 1988 the daily pattern was almost invariably a move towards hedgerows and shelter belts during mornings and away from them in the evenings. The final move to the roost site about 20 minutes after sunset usually involved a short flight. Perhaps as a response to higher predator numbers, the roost sites were 80 m out in the field, further than the 25 m found in a hedged part of Saskatchewan in the early 1970s (Hunt, 1974). Near Frankfurt, roosting was always on ground without vegetation cover, or at least no vegetation more than 12 cm in height, to ensure a clear view (Döring & Helfrich, 1986). In North Rhine–Westphalia and lower Saxony in 2005 and 2006 Jörg Tillmann of the Institute of Wildlife Research, University of Veterinary Medicine, Hannover, carried out a unique study of the behaviour of 102 coveys of grey partridge at night using thermal-imaging cameras (Tillmann, 2009a, 2009b). No coveys roosted on grassland; all were on arable fields with crop cover less than 12 cm in height and on average 60 m from field margins. Predators were very frequent, with coveys disturbed by, in order: fox, domestic cat, badger, stone marten, polecat, stoat, domestic dog and, locally, eagle owl. When disturbed the coveys took flight, raining droppings on the disturber and, despite the dark, they always seemed confident of finding an alternative roost site. As in Britain the main predator at night was the fox, although the rate of predation was low compared with during nesting. Jörg concluded that the partridges were responding to their 'landscape of fear of predation' by foxes at night and by goshawks during the day. This was why the coveys avoided cover at night but hid in it during the day. Feeding had to be squeezed into the two switchover periods.

FIG 201. Dusk, partridges feed whilst many raptors have begun roosting. (Olga Potts)

The hours around dawn and dusk are especially important to partridges, indeed this appears to be the case with most Galliformes. Some observations on the Palouse Prairie in the US had shown autumn flights as early as 50 minutes before sunrise and more than 30 minutes after sunset (Haugen, 1941). In the same area, 40 years later, Rotella & Ratti (1988) carried out 138 sunrise and 140 sunset surveys. Peak calling was 15–45 minutes *before* sunrise and 15–45 minutes *after* sunset. Calling was infrequent during nesting and brood rearing to avoid revealing locations to predators. Similarly, the restriction of calling to hours of near darkness can be assumed to be a way of reducing the risk of predation, but this has not yet been studied in partridges. The time of leaving the roost in the morning and return in the evening has been recorded for radio-tracked Cooper's and sharp-shinned hawks in the US (Roth & Lima, 2007). In the sharp-shinned hawks there was very little activity before sunrise or after sunset but this was not so with the Cooper's hawks, which fed in well-lit urban areas. In Britain peak hunting of female sparrowhawks is 4–5 hours after first light in spring and summer and 2–3 hours after first light in winter (Newton, 1986). This fits well with my experience in Sussex.

Owls were the main cause of mortality in the sharp-shinned hawk and Roth & Lima suggest that because of this, owls may release small birds from predation risk just before sunrise; if so, the same could apply to partridges, but only if owl predation on partridges was exceptional. Reports of owls, other than

FIG 202. Grey partridge pairs roosting while facing in opposite directions to spot approaching predators, something that is much easier for a covey. Predation by owls has not been shown to be important. (Jörg Tillmann)

eagle and snowy owls, preying on partridges are almost as rare as hen's teeth; only two unconvincing cases for the abundant tawny owl (Dal', 1944; Mastrorilli & Barattieri, 2001). With at least six short-eared owls wintering on the Norfolk Estate and hunting mainly at night but also in the day, we have no evidence of predation on partridges. A major study in Britain and Ireland during 1964–1973, when grey partridges were still numerous, showed the normal predominance of field voles in the diet, with 36 species of small birds but no partridges (Glue, 1977).

FIG 203. Finland: a goshawk carries off a male grey partridge. (Markus Varesvuo/naturepl.com)

In Sussex the hunting activity of harriers is apparently similar to that of the African marsh harrier, where foraging began in the mornings only after about an hour of sunning and preening and stopped about an hour before roosting (Simmons, 2000). In Sussex, kestrels were the only raptors to forage after sunset, although sparrowhawks hunted at an urban Starling roost later than in the rural areas. Most foraging by foxes occurs after the evening calling and before the morning calling.

We can now relate partridge activity to that of its predators. It is clear that the partridge calling periods are the times with the least predation risk from raptors. Morning feeding starts out in the fields near the roost sites where the visibility is much better and it is more difficult for the raptors to surprise partridges, especially if they are in coveys with well-organised sentinels. By peak sparrowhawk activity, grey partridges should be concealed in cover either in the field or in field edge cover. Evening feeding begins in cover and needs to be completed before the move to roosting sites. A late evening visit of pairs to the feeders is obvious behaviour on Jacques Hicter's farms and in the Sussex Study area. In fact in March and April a quick way of assessing pair numbers is simply to drive by the feeders.

On contemporary farmland with a shortage of waste grain and weed seeds, it must be much more difficult to find food in the morning and evening windows of opportunity than was the case formerly. Today, with abundant raptors, the situation is worse for the partridges and it is partly because of these changes that hopper feeding has recently become necessary.

HOPPER FEEDING

We saw how important this has become in Chapter 3 as a result of declines in weeds seed and waste grain, but is there more to it than that? My contention is that because feeders so greatly reduce the time necessary for feeding, they result in partridges being less vulnerable to raptor predation. It is strange that there has been so little research on the subject of feeding grain to partridges, with no controlled and replicated practical experiments to justify the way feeding is now practised on many areas for both *Perdix* and *Alectoris* partridges. However, the use of automatic infra-red cameras near feeders is filling in some of the story for other species (Rollins *et al.*, 2006). At Loddington cameras also showed the extent of the use of grain at feeders by other species of bird, particularly the yellowhammer (see also Chapter 10 for Sussex). In Portugal the cameras also showed that rabbits fed at feeders during the night, something that was pretty obvious from the amount of rabbit droppings. Rabbits have been seen feeding at hoppers in Sussex but only rarely. Wood pigeons, rooks and jackdaws are more of a problem at Sussex feeders.

The possibility of competition between common pheasants and grey partridges at feeders has not been studied thoroughly, although in Sussex in March 2006 the numbers of pheasants and partridges were counted within 30 m of each feeder. With a total of over 100 pheasants and 28 grey partridges at 55 feeders, there was no discernible competition, at least up to 5 pheasants per feeder. The reason was that in the evenings the pheasants used the feeders before the grey partridges; they were often roosting in trees before the partridges fed. No hostility was seen. Grey and red-legged partridges used the same feeders and more than one covey and more than one pair could use the same feeders. Normally however, one pair of grey partridge would include a hopper in its home range, excluding others. It is therefore the aim on the Hicter farms, and elsewhere, to have one hopper per pair.

Although the benefits of feeding are fairly obvious, some possible disadvantages of feeding wheat to game-birds should not be ignored. No comprehensive studies have been made but several aspects were studied in red-legged partridges in Spain in 1999–2001 (Millán et al., 2003). Feeding with wheat which is low in fibre lowered heart weights by 8 per cent and reduced the length of the caeca by 15 per cent. Whether these differences persisted or made any difference to survival or productivity after release was not studied. Chicks hatching from eggs laid by captive pheasants on a high-fibre diet were 2 per cent heavier (Dessi-Fulgheri et al., 2001) but again the practical significance is unknown. It is known that a diet of wheat alone leads to fatal vitamin A deficiency, as we saw earlier, but with a good supply of wheat, partridges still eat a lot of natural food, especially in the early mornings. Despite the alleged disadvantages of hoppers, the advantages are easy to see in addition to improving the effectiveness of anti-raptor behaviour. One hen crushed by a cultivator within a week of hatching her eggs had recently eaten 169 grains of wheat as well as abundant green food. She weighed 445 g, well above average, whereas normally weight declines substantially during incubation (Olech, 1971). This goes some way to explaining the higher incubation success with hopper feeding observed in France (Aufradet, 1996). Fred Guthery summarised a number of experiments with hopper feeding in the bobwhite quail, showing that there was no effect on autumn numbers (Guthery, 2002), although feeding is clearly beneficial in the California quail, as first shown on the Macmillan Ranch (Leopold, 1977).

Whatever the uncertainties it is absolutely clear from my experience that both grey and red-legged partridges utilise feeders to an extraordinary extent. The use obviously reduces the time necessary for feeding and it is so concentrated in the period of twilight when raptor predation is limited (Chapter 3) that it must have reduced the risk posed by raptors. Hopper feeding is today a major part of wild partridge management on the estates with the highest densities of the grey partridge in England and France and of the red-legged partridge in Spain. It may have multiple benefits, for example in reducing spring dispersal at high densities.

REDUCING DISPERSAL

In 1999–2003 Mark Watson studied the interactions between vigilance, predation by raptors, dispersal and feeding at 20 sites across eastern England, including the Norfolk Estate. Confirming earlier work (Pulliainen, 1966), he found that vigilance of individuals decreased with covey size. It follows that individuals in pairs have to be more vigilant than individuals in coveys. In his classic studies in the 1950s David Jenkins found that the male and female in a pair very rarely feed at the same time. The birds alternate; one looks out for predators and competing males while the other feeds, and vice versa. This is a good system but predation risk is higher for individuals in pairs than individuals in coveys and understanding the causes of this is vital to explaining the spring pulse of raptor predation. The basic argument in what follows is that unsettled partridges will be most at risk of raptor predation.

The procedure of pairing was discovered by David Jenkins at Micheldever with meticulous observations on individually marked birds of known sex and age. He found that the first pairings within coveys was by renewal of the pairings of the previous year, if both birds had survived. It also occurred in coveys if the female was the initiator, but importantly there was no record of females pairing with their fathers or brothers. Most pairing was with birds from other coveys, started by young males leaving their natal coveys and then 'haunting' other coveys, sometimes displaying. A responsive hen within the covey would then select a male and once the pairing was bonded, the pair would go off together (Jenkins, 1961a).

The next phase, 'exploration', was described from the study of birds in Wisconsin marked with solar-powered radios. This is not a crepuscular activity, it can last up to three or four weeks, does not stop until a suitable nest site is found (Church et al., 1980) and is the time of most successful attacks by raptors. For reasons not fully understood red-legged partridge females leave the parental covey and not males (Green, 1983). Unlike in grey partridges the sex ratios of red-legged partridges are much more balanced and this may be part of the explanation.

When partridges were more numerous than they are today, most movement of young pairs appeared to be the result of searching for nesting cover. In studies in the US a shortage of nesting cover increased the dispersal distance of pairs (Weigand, 1977; McCrow, 1982), but as numbers fell during the 1990s it became obvious that this was no longer a valid explanation for some extraordinary distances covered at very low densities. Very high rates of pre-nesting dispersal were reported from areas with plentiful nesting cover, in Finland (Putaala & Hissa, 1998), in Ireland (O'Gorman, 2001) and in the eastern Pyrenees (Novoa & Dumas, 1994). In Finland and Ireland the view was that the birds were searching for more appropriate habitats, especially brood-rearing habitats. Most movements were made by pairs (Weigand, 1977; Church *et al.*, 1980; Putaala & Hissa, 1998; Reitz & Mayot, 1999; O'Gorman, 2001; and Salek, Marhoul & Pintir, 2002). This means that most movements were not caused by the difficulty of finding mates although, because females are in short supply, some males never find mates, and they travel furthest (Potts, 2002; Aufradet & Birkan, 2001; Salek *et al.*, 2002). In France Reitz & Mayot (2000) found evidence of greater dispersal at low partridge densities and concluded that partridge density and landscape diversity are no longer sufficient to explain variation in partridge dispersal. We can use 12 studies during 1949–2003 to see whether they were right. Reared and released partridges have been excluded.

1. Damerham 1949–59 (GWCT archives)
The data used here form part of a study of 598 birds that were fitted with individually numbered and colour-coded back tabs that survived the pre-nesting period. In this study the positions of the marked birds were plotted and the straight-line distances calculated between the autumn/winter trapping site and the nesting site, or in the case of unpaired young males the site where they were last seen. The area studied was 14 km² and searches were made by resident gamekeepers and farmers as well as GWCT up to a distance of 10 km.

2. Micheldever 1952–6 (Jenkins, 1956, 1961)
The techniques were the same as in study (1.) and 375 birds of both sexes were marked and studied on an area of 2.6 km². The young males moved furthest, but no frequency distribution of distances moved is available for either sex. It was estimated that 90 per cent of the marked birds stayed within the area (Jenkins, 1961) which had a maximum distance to the boundary of 750 m. Partridges older than one year 'rarely moved further' than 400–800 m, whilst 'few' young male partridges moved more than 2000 m. All this is consistent with the mean distances moved being the same as those at Damerham, 50 km

to the west. The surrounding area was searched, so far as practicable, up to a distance of 17 km.

3. Montana 1969–74 (Weigand, 1977, 1980)

Some 320 birds of both sexes were individually marked with vinyl ponchos, plus 9 with radios, the first such use in the partridge. The study area was 140 km²; young males moved furthest but 86 per cent of birds spent their lifetime moving <604 m.

4. Iowa 1975–7 (McCrow, 1982)

Ponchos were attached to 31 birds but only 8 were re-sighted and some birds may have left the area, though it was 21 km². Radios were attached to six birds located four or more times. The mean pre-nesting dispersal distance of six pairs was 630 m; this excludes movements undertaken during pairing, and an unpaired male moved 6 km. The average distance of 1,397 m is retained partly because of the underestimation. The mean distance between the centres of winter and summer home ranges was about 1,500 m but this included some extensive movements made in late summer.

5. Wisconsin 1979 (Church et al., 1980)

A pioneering study of nine radio-tracked females carried out in an area of 72 km². The maximum movement between home ranges was 2,200 m which was equivalent to a mean distance between home range centres of 1,386 m.

6. North Central France 1980–90 (Reitz & Mayot, 2001)

As part of the largest study to date, 85 females were radio-tracked from August to the location of the nest site in the following year. Three different areas were considered. Maps showed 12 females moved an average 430 m between November and nesting. The mean distance between the position of all birds in January/February and the nest site was ~388 m, ~385 m and ~150 m on the three areas.

7. Beauce 1985–6 (Birkan & Serre, 1988)

Another detailed radio-tracking study, this time over an area of 20 km². Males moved furthest. Dispersal distances were calculated as the extreme limits of the home ranges. These were 800±120 m for eight females and 1625±426 m for nine males. Subtracting the radius of the (presumed circular) home ranges from the beginning and end of the calculated movement gives 464 m for females and 1,213 m for males.

8. Eastern Pyrenees 1990–93 (Novoa & Dumas, 1994; Novoa et al., 2006)
Fourteen individuals were radio-tracked in mountainous country at an altitude of
1,650–2,450 m over an area of 58 km². Dispersal was the distance between the winter
capture site and the nesting home range. In winter and spring relative habitat use
was highest where there was a shrub-canopy of broom and juniper covering 60 per
cent of the ground (Novoa *et al.*, 2002). In summer more open habitat, sparse shrubs
and montane grassland was used, but woodland and bare rocks were avoided at all
times. Six young males never paired and these moved furthest.

9. Finland 1991–6 (Putaala & Hissa, 1998)
Twenty-four females were radio-tracked in an area of 20 km² to the east of Oulu
at 65°N with 50–55 per cent in spring-sown cereals and an average field size of
4.4 ha. Dispersal was between winter capture site and nest site.

10. Central Ireland 1997–9 (O'Gorman, 2001)
Only males were radio-tracked, with the best data for four paired birds. The
distances were re-calculated from maps and estimated at 4,000 m; one unpaired
male moved 7 km, others may have moved even further. The density was much
lower than in other studies.

11. Prague 1997–9 (Sálek, Marhoul & Pintir, 2002; Sálek & Marhoul, 2008)
This study was carried out on a highly diverse area of only 1.5 km² just to the
southwest of the city with a high density of pairs: 24–33 pairs per 100 ha. Eleven
partridges were tracked from 1997–9, from pairing to nesting. Here the distances
were calculated from the maximum spans of the home range using the relationship
between this measure and distance as found in Study 5 above. This work continues
and Mirek Sálek reports that a single male moved 6 km in spring 2010.

12. Eastern England 1999–2003 (Watson, 2004)
For present purposes the data from all 20 sites are combined, and only males
were radio-tracked by Mark Watson on 20 estates scattered through southern and
eastern England, one of which was the Norfolk Estate in the Sussex Study area.

DISPERSAL IN RELATION TO DENSITY

The above studies have greatly expanded our understanding of dispersal by
showing that it can be very important in very low-density populations. Hitherto
dispersal had been seen as the result of competition for nest sites (Potts, 1986),

but it has now become clear that another factor is responsible when wintering numbers drop below about ten males and females, or one covey, per 100 ha. It seems inconceivable that this could be due to a shortage of nest sites. Instead it seems that a shortage of other partridges could be the problem. As discovered in the mid-1950s, independently at Damerham and at Micheldever, pairings do not occur between siblings. Males pairing for the first time must therefore look to neighbouring coveys for a mate. With a density of one covey per 100 ha, this could involve a journey of 1 km or more. The key here is that this journey to the nearest neighbour becomes disproportionately longer as the density goes down; it can be estimated from the Clark & Evans equation (Southwood & Henderson, 2000) as $= 1/2\sqrt{D}$, where D is the density of birds.

The analysis of the results of the 12 studies shows a clear increase in distance dispersed with the distance to the nearest neighbour (Fig. 204); the relationship explains 58 per cent of the variation in distance dispersed (P=0.004). At Damerham, a high-density population, the old males moved 265 m, the young males moved 525 m; twice as far, partly due to a small proportion of males that never found mates moving farthest of all, as also well shown by Aufradet & Birkan (2001). This is not to suggest that young males leave coveys to search blindly for females. From listening to coveys many times in the half-light of dawn and dusk, it seems to me that coveys need to maintain contact with one another. The coveys are linked in a network of calling in the half-light of dusk and dawn. This explains why, on fine mornings in mid-January to early February, it is relatively easy to see pairing taking place when coveys are in close proximity. At very low densities this social behaviour could be crucial.

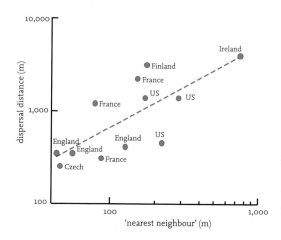

FIG 204. The increase in dispersal distance by grey partridges with greater distance to the nearest neighbour, from the 12 independent studies reviewed on pp. 298–300.

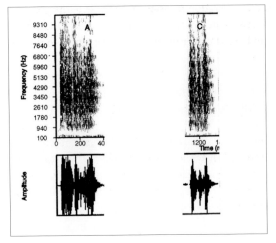

FIG 205. Rusty-gate call of male (left) and female (right) grey partridge, from Beani *et al.* (1995). Recordings can be heard at www.xeno-canto.org.

Not knowing whether you have a nearest neighbour must be like falling off a cliff. In good conditions the human ear can detect the rusty-gate call at 300 m (Tillmann *et al.*, 2012), but for us it is not at all easy to distinguish male and female (Fig. 205).

Almost as soon as biologists began to focus on competition between animals as limiting the increase in their numbers, attention was drawn to the opposite: the need for social cohesion at very low densities (Allee *et al.*, 1949). The significance of Allee effects, as they have long been known, is largely unknown but for dispersing partridges but it is clear that their exposure to raptors could be very high at low densities.

In 2001 the home range of radio-tracked grey partridge pairs on the Norfolk Estate had diameters of up to 2 km and pairs covered areas that now contain up to 80 pair home-ranges. Predation increasing as density decreases is often thought to illustrate what is known as a 'predator trap' or 'predator pit'. In our case this would be misleading because the causes of the low pair density are factors other than raptor predation. Cure them and the problem may be solved.

Relatively long-distance movements can, however, be highly successful. For many years the range of the grey partridge in North America was expanding, unaided by further introductions, at an average 3.3 km per year (Traylor *et al.*, 2001). Seven of the studies in their literature survey gave the maximum recorded distance and these averaged 8.8 km per year, consistent with rapid range expansion and successful dispersal. The grey partridge is often regarded as an extremely sedentary bird, spending its entire life in a few fields. If it was so sedentary it would never have colonised North America in just a few decades.

Once a range is occupied the conservation message in the case of the grey partridge is that it is possible to reduce dispersal and build up stocks locally by bringing the essential features of habitat closer together, and we return to this in Chapter 10.

TRENDS IN RAPTOR ABUNDANCE IN SUSSEX

One of the most striking and unexpected discoveries in the Sussex Study was the rapid increase of raptors on the Norfolk Estate following biodiversity restoration, in contrast to the numbers remaining constant where biodiversity had not been restored. Only the Montagu's harrier and little owl have declined. The trends for all the species combined are given in Fig. 206.

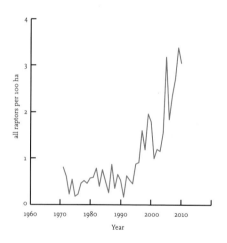

FIG 206. Sussex Study area stubble counts: trends in numbers per 100 ha for sparrowhawk, buzzard, all harriers and other raptors, 1968–2011.

The evidence suggests that the goshawk, sparrowhawk and hen harrier can cause significant mortality to grey partridges. At present only the sparrowhawk breeds on the Norfolk Estate. Is it likely that in future the other species could do so?

Goshawk

The combination of persecution and loss of woodland led to the species becoming extinct in England soon after 1800, though hanging on in Scotland and Ireland until about 1850 (Kenward, 2006). Breeding again took place from 1965 due mainly if not entirely to introductions from Finland, with the population estimated at 250–300 pairs (Ogilvie & Rare Breeding Bird Panel, 2004). A pair bred successfully in Sussex in 2009 (SOS).

Hen and marsh harriers

The hen harrier was probably extirpated from Sussex before 1802, before it was first recognised as a different species from the Montagu's harrier. Numbers overwintering in Sussex, originating in Scotland and the near Continent, have slowly increased, with an average of about 10 records per year from 1947–61, rising to 190 in 2010 (SOS Report). In recent years birds have been later to leave and earlier to arrive, with records in all months in the Sussex Study area. Hen harriers nest regularly in cereal crops as close as northern France. Whether or not hen harriers will establish themselves in cereals on the Sussex Downs is unknown, but field voles are their common prey in the arable areas of France and these are not found in England. Nevertheless, according to Natural England there have been three attempts at nesting in cereals in 'southern England' in recent years, with one chick reared in 2009 in a locality not yet divulged. Marsh harriers nest commonly in cereals in East Anglia and especially in Hungary, where they may threaten partridge stocks. Like the hen harrier, the marsh harrier has increased greatly in recent years in Sussex, nesting since 2004, and individuals have begun to summer in the Study area.

Eagle owl

Today it is claimed that 12–40 pairs of eagle owls nest in Britain, with one pair rumoured to be breeding in Sussex. This has caused a great deal of controversy, with many regarding these birds as alien. A detailed inquiry by the World Owl Trust concluded this was unfair.

The fossil record suggests that whenever the climate was suitable, this owl has been present, for up to 700,000 years extending into the last 10,000 years. The latest fossil dates from the period 700 BC to AD 43 but it may be an unreliable

FIG 207. Eagle owl, Las Ensanchas. (Patricia Maldonado Vidal)

identification (Stewart, 2007). Nevertheless the bird had names from ancient times in Gaelic, Manx, Welsh, Cornish and Irish. In the fourteenth century good representations of eagle owls were carved in wood in Gloucester and Worcester cathedrals. Blome (1686) describes the use of eagle owls as decoys to catch birds such as the magpie, a practice which may have been widespread for centuries, including in England (Eastham, 2005). Melling *et al.* (2008) reviewed records from 1678 but because birds were kept in captivity even earlier than this, doubt was thrown on many records because of insufficient information. The authors clearly believe most of the birds had escaped from captivity, but 23 were found on the east coast mostly in autumn, consistent with a crossing of the North Sea. In their first autumn these birds can disperse 400–1,000 km or more over land and the crossing from Norway to Shetland (where 4 of the 23 were found) is only 350 km. This crossing is regularly made by weaker owls (and birds as small as the goldcrest!), and eagle owls have no difficulty negotiating high mountain passes in Switzerland, so the crossing is feasible. Stable isotope analysis of a specimen found in Norfolk in 2006 was consistent with the birds having an overseas origin (Kelly *et al.*, 2010). However it is true that there was no regular breeding of proven wild birds from some time prior to 1800 through to the 1990s. Birds that bred successfully at Arundel in the nineteenth century were described as eagle owls, but these were great horned owls imported from North America. Two mounted specimens are still to be seen in Arundel castle.

In conclusion goshawks, hen harriers, marsh harriers or eagle owls, or all four, could conceivably nest in or near the Sussex Study area in the near future. The raptor community will become more similar to that in the rest of Europe. What then would be their impact? Would it be tolerable? The answer depends on how the various raptors compete with one another.

INTERACTIONS BETWEEN RAPTORS

Echoes of Macbeth's sentiment at the head of this chapter, where one predator eating another is considered unnatural, are still to be found in the policies of bird and mammal protection organisations. A generation has passed since it was clearly shown that large owls prey on small owls (Mikkola, 1976, 1983) but even today it is not well known that raptors and owls can prey on one another. Meanwhile many landowners have given up hope of restoring grey partridge populations because they fear that predation by protected raptors would eventually override their conservation work. This is based partly on the experience with hen harriers (and later other raptors) on the grouse moor at Langholm, southwest Scotland.

FIG 208. João Costa, farm manager at Vale de Perditos, with a buzzard killed and eaten by an eagle owl.

For this book I have compiled counts during which 5,330 raptors of 45 species have been sighted during work on partridges in 8 countries (Appendix 4). Sparrowhawks comprised only 386 (7 per cent) of the raptor total. We cannot directly compare numbers because the time spent on the various studies and size of the areas covered varied hugely. So the expected number of sparrowhawks and goshawks for each study was calculated by assuming that they make up a similar proportion of the total raptor community through all the studies. The differences between the expected and observed abundances are plotted in Figure 206 showing that many fewer sparrowhawks than expected are found when more goshawks are seen than expected ($P<0.011$). This is not to say sparrowhawk numbers overall are potentially depressed by goshawks, only that this appears to be the case in areas where partridges have been counted. Nevertheless in a heavily wooded area of 34,200 ha in Germany in the 1930s in which there were nine goshawk nests, the density of sparrowhawks was only 0.08 per 100 ha (Uttendörfer, 1939), a quarter of the density in the Sussex Study area. In Brüll's studies of the goshawk mentioned earlier, the sparrowhawks were also at 0.08 per 100 ha, with 4 killed by goshawks, along with 43 other raptors killed.

In partridge habitats goshawks have much larger territories than sparrowhawks and the impact on partridges of both raptors together might be less than with sparrowhawks alone, although a lot could depend on whether

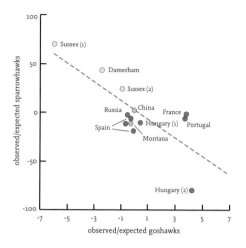

FIG 209. Raptors sighted during work on partridges showing that higher numbers of goshawks are associated with lower numbers of sparrowhawks (P<0.001, see text for method). Sources are given in Appendix 4.

eagle owls were in the vicinity depressing the number of goshawks. Some results of the incredibly detailed work on the food of raptors in northwest Germany in the 1930s already mentioned are summarised in Table 27. These show that the sparrowhawk is not capable of killing other raptors, but it is preyed upon by the goshawk, which does prey on other raptors.

Goshawks were found in the prey of the eagle owl, as were many other raptors and owls. This is surely an area for much more research. The limited data used to investigate the effect of goshawk numbers on sparrowhawk numbers were not sufficient to show other relationships. There appeared to be fewer harriers where there were more eagles, but this may have been an effect of habitat. Although they were often seen during counts in Spain and Portugal there was little useful information about eagle owls because they are so nocturnal.

A total of 681 captive-bred eagle owls were released in Schleswig-Holstein during 1981 to 2006, resulting in a large, self-sustaining breeding population of ~300 pairs. Using data from long-term raptor studies, Rutz *et al.* (2006) showed that there were marked and consistent adverse effects on goshawks, which

TABLE 27. Summary of early studies on the food of hawks and eagle owls in Germany (Uttendörfer, 1939).

predator	partridges in prey	other raptors and owls in prey
sparrowhawk	79	0
goshawk	835	365
eagle owl	200	166

declined by about 50 per cent as eagle owls took over their territories (Busche *et al.*, 2004). At the point of halving of the density of goshawks and eagle owls their densities in Schleswig-Holstein were similar. When the population of goshawks was halved presumably their predation on partridges was also halved, but grey partridges are now so scarce in the region that further study is impossible.

The occurrence of all game birds averaged 10.4 per cent in 28 studies of goshawk diet compared with 4.2 per cent in 16 studies of the eagle owl (Valkama *et al.*, 2004). Using an adjustment to allow for its greater size, the eagle owl relative food consumption increases from 4.2 per cent to 5.6 per cent. From this, we might conclude that the probability of an eagle owl eating a game bird is (5.6/10.4) or 54 per cent that of a goshawk. Thus, the goshawk take of 13 per cent of partridges, halved with the addition of eagle owls, becomes 6.5 per cent + 54 per cent of 6.5 per cent = 10 per cent (or 3 per cent lower than that which was observed without eagle owls). This could be very important because F. J. Koning reported (to the World Working Group on Birds of Prey and Owls) that at an exceptionally high density of 0.3 pairs of goshawks per km², the sparrowhawk was 'almost exterminated' (Koning, 2003). Prior to the arrival of the goshawk there had been 0.2 pairs of sparrowhawk per km².

Most crucial here is the role of the eagle owl. As it recolonises Germany, clear evidence of very substantial adverse effects on the breeding success of goshawks and buzzards has emerged (Chakarov & Krüger, 2010). As mentioned earlier in relation to rock partridges, the golden eagle is even higher up the food chain and

FIG 210. Top predator of predatory birds in partridge range: the golden eagle. (Patricia Maldonado Vidal)

its impact could be greater still. More and more evidence is also accumulating that these top raptors and owls prey on smaller more numerous raptors and owls when their preferred food is scarce (Lourenço et al., 2011). I expect the interactions have become more serious with agriculture and other developments reducing prey populations so much, but nobody seems to be monitoring the effects on small game.

The top predators such as the wolf and lynx are missing from almost all partridge ranges and this appears to distort the picture for raptors as much as for partridges (discussed in Chapter 4). In the absence of top predators, ground-nesting raptors can benefit greatly from the presence of gamekeepers. At Langholm grouse moor it was shown that red grouse could not co-exist with a high density of the ground-nesting hen harriers (Redpath & Thirgood, 1997), but when fox control ceased, because there were too few grouse to make it worthwhile, the nesting success of the hen harriers declined from 78 per cent to 41 per cent (Baines et al., 2008). This did not result in more grouse because the foxes had an even greater effect on the grouse than did the harriers. So the harriers were clearly benefiting from predator control, but removing the need for it was not a sustainable solution! Whether this would have been the case if one of the absent top-predators, the golden eagle, had been re-introduced, is unfortunately not known. The reintroduction was proposed but unfortunately rejected.

The difficulties of managing predation in the absence of direct predator control or top predators are exemplified by the triangular relationship between the fox, grey partridge and hen harrier in north-central France. As we have seen, the evidence shows that relatively high densities of hen harriers in France (though far lower than the harmful densities at Langholm grouse moor) may have had a severe impact on partridge densities. At the same time, even in France where foxes are relatively scarce, it appears that the fox is a significant predator at the nests of the hen harrier. Comparisons of maps of harrier abundance and fox-hunting bags and data about the recent trend of the three species in France suggest that there may be a negative interaction between the two predator species but without benefit for the partridge. It is sad that so little practical research is being done on these interactions. A modeling approach concluded that hen harrier numbers on the Langholm grouse moor could be reduced if the moor was managed to reduce vole populations (New et al., 2011); whereas a better approach would be to focus on the ecosystem as a whole; management so that harriers cannot find food would eliminate a host of species.

The eagle owl kills far more potential egg predators than the goshawk. In one particularly detailed study of eagle owl diet, partridges accounted for 8.4 per cent of items and pheasants for 2 per cent, with their potential egg predators accounting for over 31 per cent of items (Bezzel *et al.*, 1976). The most important egg predator, the hooded/carrion crow, features in eagle owl diets more than twice as often as in goshawk diets (Uttendörfer, 1939; Brüll, 1964; Bezzel *et al.*, 1976). In Michigan great horned owls killed broods of red-shouldered, red-tailed and Cooper's hawks and had a major effect on the distribution of the first two, relatives of the buzzard (Craighead & Craighead, 1956). These authors added: 'So great was the effect of the horned owls' presence on nesting crows that they ranked as a major factor limiting crow productivity', and the density of crows was amazingly low compared to Britain: just over one pair per 100 ha. It is clear from these interactions that more species of large predators may not mean more partridges killed. In Spain, in the best area for the red-legged partridge, four species of eagle and the eagle owl can be seen in a single partridge counting session and at least three of these species are important predators of partridge predators (see Borralho *et al.* 1992). Those involved in small-game management are usually distrustful of raptors, yet Patricia Maldonado Vidal at Las Ensanchas in La Mancha, Spain, is protecting the larger eagles and eagle owls from power-line electrocution in the belief that this helps control the smaller, more harmful raptors. It also appears that eagle owl nesting success can be higher where ground predators are controlled.

FIG 211. Eagle owl clutch predated by a polecat or stone marten.

FIG 212. Stone marten, a major predator at nests of partridges in Eurasia, although not present in Britain. (Horst Jegen/Imagebroker/FLPA)

Establishing the true position in the field in a comprehensive study of predators, prey and their foods will be challenging and appears not to have been attempted since the work of the Craighead brothers in the US in the early 1950s. Buzzards, for example, are probably significantly adversely affected by predation from larger raptors (as we have seen with the great horned owl and buzzard relatives) and by competition from the goshawk (Hakkarainen *et al.*, 2004), but goshawks also provide the buzzards some protection from egg predation by corvids (Krüger, 2002). Ravens frequently prey on crow broods (Ratcliffe, 1997) and generally benefit farmland bird numbers (Tryjanowski, 2001). The breeding success of a number of middle-sized raptors can also be adversely affected by larger raptors, for example the breeding success of Tengmalm's owls is reduced in the presence of Ural owls (Hakkarainen and Korpimäki, 1996), and pygmy owls collect smaller food stores for the winter in the vicinity of Tengmalm's owl territories (Suhonen *et al.*, 2007).

One complication is the degree of prey specialisation among raptors and owls. Some eagle owls may specialise in killing raptors; in 1948, Hagen reported that a pair in Norway had killed 13 raptors and owls in one nesting season (Bannerman and Lodge, 1955). In France a pair of peregrine falcons killed 17 other raptors in one season (Kayser, 1999), and in Kielder forest, Northumberland, goshawks killed 115 kestrels. Raptors and foxes together predated 36 per cent of tawny owls during the post-fledging period (Sunde, 2005). Of a total of 36 empirical and experimental studies on 45 raptor and owl populations belonging to 10 'killer species' and 13 'victim' species, effects on victim numbers were statistically significant in 60 per cent of cases (Sergio & Hiraldo, 2008).

FIG 213. Imperial eagle feeding on rabbit with other rabbits unconcerned. In Spain, many have concluded that the density of rabbits has declined to an extent where its numbers are now too low to support predators such as the Iberian lynx and some raptors. Where ground predators are controlled to conserve partridges however, rabbits can still be exceptionally abundant. An ecosystem approach to raptor conservation would pay dividends. (Patricia Maldonado Vidal)

A final complication is that where there are genuine specialists among the predator population a different approach to predator control might sometimes be practicable. For example, Bayes *et al.* (1964) found that only 1 of 232 pairs of great skua had fed on arctic terns (killing 11) and that removing only 1 pair of the great skua could have saved 200 kittiwake eggs, 63 per cent of the total predated. From J. A. Naumann onwards, many commentators have mentioned raptors specialising in killing grey partridges in winter but the subject is virtually unexplored.

In summary it is clear from this review and from the earlier review of ground predators (Chapter 4) that we have a pauperate community of predators in Britain, with the grey partridge likely trapped by the absence of top predators. It could be that the role of the gamekeeper is to restore the balance and we return to this later.

CHAPTER 9

Hunting

The (grey) partridge of the war zone [Western Front, World War I] *shows no signs of such sensitive nerves. The rattle and rumble of transport, the constant coming and going of troops, the incessant rattle of musketry and the deafening explosions of the artillery, the night-long flare and flicker of star-shells, have not sufficed to scare the local birds from their chosen feeding grounds, and to all appearances they have not been deterred from rearing their broods.*

Saki, in Gibson (2005)

THE EFFECT OF HUNTING ON partridge populations has been much misunderstood, with decisions turning on whether the mortality caused by hunting is or is not 'compensated' by increased survival or productivity of the birds that survive the shooting. The assumption has usually been that if the shooting losses are compensated, then there is no effect on the population. The same has been applied to arguments about raptor predation; it doesn't matter if there is compensation.

Such assertions are incorrect for reasons that have been clear to some for many decades: 'A fishery, by thinning out a fish population, itself creates the production by which it is maintained' (Baranov, 1918). In order to achieve compensation for shooting in partridge populations it is first necessary to reduce ('thin', in the words of Baranov) the size of the population. An important consequence follows. Since shooting reduces the size of a partridge population, to claim that management for shooting benefits partridge populations, it is necessary to show that partridge numbers after shooting are higher than they would have been had there been no shooting and that this is due to conservation. It was not necessary to show this in the past but it is now when so many question the links between hunting and conservation. Fortunately it is easy.

MAN HAS BEEN HUNTING PARTRIDGES FOR AT LEAST A QUARTER OF A MILLION YEARS

As we saw in Chapter 2, many grey partridge fossils have been found in the caves occupied by the first European humanoids, *Homo antecessor*, about a million years BP, at Atapuerca, near Burgos, Spain. Whether the partridges had been brought to the caves by humans or by predators is not known for certain. That early man ate game, both mammals and birds, is indisputable but the evidence is mainly from the larger animals (such as the horses at Boxgrove). There is also some evidence that remains in some caves do not derive from hunting by humans. The bones from an estimated minimum 1,454 individual grey partridges in the caves at La Fage in the Massif Central, France, accumulated about 242,000–300,000 years ago showed a lower proportion of the wing bones and thigh bones than that which would indicate human use (Mourer-Chauviré, 1993). If humans did not bring the majority of the partridges to La Fage caves, what did? An interesting feature of many partridge fossil bones is that they show holes and marks similar to those caused by predators (Jánossy, 1991). The same may be true of the Boxgrove partridge in Figure 32, p. 40.

The best evidence that humans were catching and eating hares, partridges and other small game dates to about 250,000 years ago (Eastham, 2005), with the first certain records of humans cooking small game birds dating from 150,000 years ago (Blasco & Peris, 2009). From ~35,000 years ago, as human populations developed further, there was a pronounced emphasis towards the consumption of grey partridge and quail in Italy and towards chukar partridges in Israel (Stiner *et al.*, 2000). Chukar partridges have been reared for fattening for millennia (Christensen, 1970). In Eastern Europe, with cold snowy winters, partridges were at one time housed in barns for release in spring (Kokeš & Knobloch, 1947). Given that *Gallus* (chicken) species and hybrids have been domesticated independently on five occasions, it is puzzling that partridges have never been domesticated.

How the first partridges were caught is not known but we can be pretty sure snares and nets were used in prehistoric times, as is the case with most bush meat hunting today and even with traditional hunting in China (Zhao *et al.*, 1992). Centuries before shotguns were used for small game in Britain, Germany, Czechoslovakia and no doubt elsewhere, nets were used to catch birds. Sometimes large numbers would be caught, a well-known example being the 2,100 grey partridges provided for Henry III's Christmas banquet of 1251. Sport hunting as we understand it began with falconry, about 6,000 years ago (Macdonald, 2006), but with considerable uncertainty about the dates (Kenward, 2006). There is however consensus that the sport originated within the range of the chukar partridge. When partridges were first shot for sport is not known. The musket gun invented in China and used from the fifteenth century was used to shoot partridges on the ground, and this was widespread in Europe by the late seventeenth century. At this point we need to make a clear separation of the shooting of birds found with dogs, 'walked-up shooting', from shooting birds driven over a team of guns. Shooting at driven birds required modern (faster-loading) shotguns and only became feasible in the 1860s.

Because dogs are so efficient at locating partridges, a high proportion can be found and shot even at low densities. Usually the proportion of young birds shot is higher. In contrast, driven partridge shooting only becomes realistic at densities over a threshold of about 120–40 birds per 100 ha and a higher than expected proportion of old birds is found in the bag, especially so with males (Potts, 1980). The release of pen-reared birds (grey or red-legged) increases the numbers so that driven shooting takes place below the threshold level. As we shall, see this can bring problems. So far as a partridge population is concerned however, it does not matter a jot how they are harvested, it is the proportion harvested that is important, and crucially so.

DRIVEN SHOOTING INCREASED BAGS

Generally there was an improvement in bags when driving began, as we saw in Chapter 1. We can see this in the annual totals for the Holkham Estate in north Norfolk, with an increase from the late 1870s after driving was adopted

FIG 214. A formal driven grey partridge shoot requires a lot of people! In early October 2010 this was the first such shoot on the Norfolk Estate in 49 years. (Jake Eastham)

FIG 215. Red-legged partridges in Spain: this might look to have more impact than walked-up shooting with dogs but it does not; a lower percentage of partridges are shot to the extent that it is not worthwhile shooting unless at least one bird per ha is available, thus preventing shooting bringing about a population decline. (Patricia Maldonado Vidal)

(Fig. 216). This sustained yield of partridges over 150 years also emphasises the unprecedented collapse of bags in the 1950s, as described in Chapter 1.

There are even earlier bag records from Czechoslovakia. Those at Třeboň from 1666–1920 show a large increase from 1856 (Nováková, 1966) and there was a doubling of numbers during 1727–1909 at Krumai (Wing, 1953).

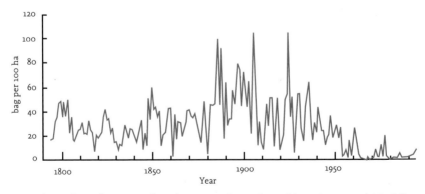

FIG 216. Numbers of grey partridges shot per 100 ha on the Holkham Estate, north Norfolk from 1793 to 1993.

During the Damerham study all grey partridge shot were birds driven over the guns by a line of beaters. The number of grey partridges shot per year ranged from zero to 80 birds per 100 ha, closely related to the number of birds present before the shooting commenced (Fig. 217). Including the red-legged partridges, the threshold for shooting was 133 birds per 100 ha on 1 September, the opening of the partridge season in Britain. At North Farm, in the Sussex Study area, the numbers shot in relation to the numbers present were almost identical to those at Damerham from 1957 to the mid-1960s, until the releasing of pen-reared birds began. On the famous partridge manors at the beginning of the twentieth century about 160 birds per 100 ha was thought to be the threshold for shooting, which gave an average bag of about 40 per 100 ha per year over a whole estate, which might be 2,000 ha or even much more (Alington, 1904; Maxwell, 1911).

Importantly the shooting of wild driven grey partridges largely regulates itself and it cannot cause a decline in numbers because shooting is effectively banned at numbers less than the threshold for shooting. The basis of traditional shoot management was to raise the numbers of partridges to their highest sustainable level. At this point the numbers shot will not reduce breeding stocks because if not shot, the birds would disperse or not breed so well. The trick in shoot management is therefore to keep numbers, and in consequence bags, as high as possible over a sustained period, without reducing the number shot in future years. Well-managed shoots adopting this principle, such as Damerham and North Farm, were plentiful until the early 1960s. Then as the numbers of wild partridges fell, shooting stopped altogether, continued when it should not have done, or continued with the release of pen-reared birds. Where shooting continued, the numbers shot were no longer determined by the numbers of partridges present; it was the other way around: shooting determined the number of partridges.

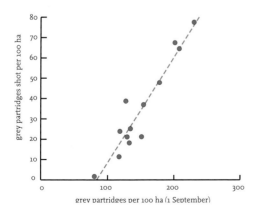

FIG 217. The number of grey partridge shot at Damerham per 100 ha in relation to the numbers present on the opening day of the partridge season, 1947–59.

SHOOTING TOO MANY

In the partridge simulation model with the driven shooting scenario, no partridges were shot below 120 per 100 ha. However, the release of pen-reared birds were brought in as an option, with the data based on the experience at North Farm during 1963–79. In this case a level 25 per cent were shot per annum through the range from zero to 120 grey partridges per 100 ha. Data presented by Watson *et al.* (2007) from 1979–2001 showed 23 per cent shot per annum in the Sussex Study area. Where the shooting rate was higher, shooting inevitably reduced breeding stocks. Thus on one farm in the Sussex Study area during 1997–2003 the density of pairs in spring declined by 1 per cent for every 1 per cent increase in the percentage shot the previous autumn (Watson *et al.*, 2007). This was in agreement with the model predictions, but on this farm the average of 52 per cent shot per annum was far above any recommendations based on the model. The reason for this relatively high rate of shooting was solely the release of pen-reared red-legged partridges. At this point we need to see the relationship between shooting rates, bag sizes and breeding stocks.

The basic relationships were set out in four scenarios. In each the breeding stocks of grey partridges decreased as the annual percentage shot increased. Despite this the bag increased with the percentage shot up to 30 per cent shot *per annum* and then fell. At the point of highest sustained bags the breeding stocks were in each case reduced by half (Fig. 218).

On the basis of these modelled scenarios, which also explained the situation in the Sussex Study area mentioned above during 1979–2001, it is clear that shooting rates above 30 per cent cannot be justified any more than can over-fishing in the North Sea. Stocks will not be reduced by half but driven at least to local extinction. With the low chick mortality in the pre-herbicide period the percentage shot could be higher than 30 per cent, perhaps up to 45–50 per cent (Potts, 1986; Birkan & Jacob, 1988). These figures include the relatively few birds shot or injured but not retrieved.

The 1986 conclusions derived from the Sussex model have been re-examined, most notably in an extensive review by De Leo *et al.* (2004). This work strongly supported the model, in particular with hunting not being compensated by lower autumn-winter losses at current densities. They describe a 'continental population' effectively the same as the top right scenario in Figure 218, defined as high mortality no predator control. In this scenario there is a sharp drop, with shooting 30 per cent per annum and extinction with shooting 40 per cent per annum. With a 30 per cent shooting rate, the De Leo *et al.* model predicts

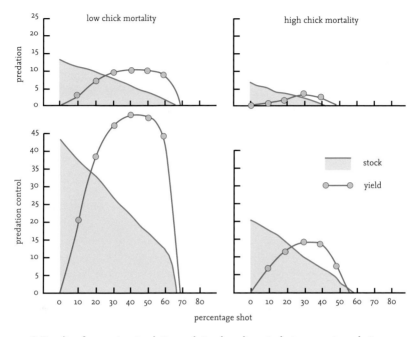

FIG 218. Results of computer simulations relating breeding stocks to percentage shot per annum for four scenarios: with and without high chick mortality; and with and without nest predator control. In all cases shooting reduces breeding stocks but with management these stocks are much higher despite the shooting (from Potts, 1986).

a 40 per cent chance of extinction in 50 years, which rises to almost 100 per cent with 40 per cent shot per year; the same. Another computer population-simulation model was created for the Beauce grey partridge populations, from information about survival rates and production of young available for 1979–92. The maximum sustainable bag was modelled lower than with the Sussex model but with spring stocks higher (Letty *et al.*, 1998).

There are fewer than 15,000 pairs of the Pyrenean sub-species but it remains a popular game bird. The impact of hunting was studied during 1992–2001 using 67 radio-tracked birds (Besnard *et al.*, 2010). Predation accounted for 71 per cent of the mortality of these birds, with hunting 22 per cent. Models suggested the population could not sustain this level of hunting and hunting quotas were introduced in 1995. This measure increased the population size and after the recovery, the bag. This is precisely what we would expect from the Sussex model.

Whereas driven shooting effectively maintained good stocks in the past, it cannot be relied on to the same extent today where the percentage of grey partridges shot is now largely determined by the density of pen-reared birds; it is no longer determined by the number of wild partridges present. Worse than that, the release of pen-reared birds can obscure the status of wild birds. Kieran Buckley of the National Parks & Wildlife Service points out that it was only after the shooting of partridges was stopped in 1995 that the perilous state of the species in Ireland became evident. By the autumn of 2001 only 23 birds remained, all in the Boora, an area where peat had been harvested. With a number of colleagues and a campaign by the Irish Grey Partridge Conservation Trust, Kieran has worked on saving the grey partridge in Ireland with outstanding success, although hampered by the lack of an appropriate agri-environment scheme in the country. By the autumn of 2011 the population had grown to 956 birds. A huge effort was made, including predator control, translocation and re-stocking.

Where red-legged partridges are reared for shooting, grey partridges can be protected from most of the shooting. At Royston a great effort was made and a red-legged partridge shoot was maintained with only negligible losses of grey partridges. From 2004–8 the annual rates of shooting were 60 per cent for the red-legged partridge and only 2.7 per cent for the grey partridge, not the expected 30 per cent (Aebischer & Ewald, 2010). It is to be hoped that more are now following this lead. To do this, the line of guns has to be warned, for example with a whistle, if grey partridges are about to fly over them. Once pairs begin to form, from Christmas onwards, this is impossible, with the grey partridges no longer discernible in tight coveys.

WALKED-UP SHOOTING

The evidence that hunting can depress numbers and even cause local extinctions comes mainly from shooting with the use of dogs and counter-intuitively this can be as harmful as the release of pen-reared birds. In many parts of Italy partridges are shot with the use of dogs and pen-reared birds are a main target. Perhaps not surprisingly grey partridges and rock partridges are now found in reserves where shooting is banned. High losses to hunting were recognised in the early 1970s (Renzoni, 1974) and the term 'hyper-hunting' was used. The annual loss of ringed released birds to shooting was calculated to be ~65 per cent per annum (Potts, 1985). In the case of the rock partridge in the western Alps, better regulation of hunting has enabled numbers to recover (Bernard-Laurent et al., 2012). Meanwhile hyper-hunting in Albania almost wiped out grey partridges

FIG 219. Sadie, a Llewellin Setter: the 'best of nineteen bird dogs I've trained'. (John Ratti)

FIG 220. Bill Palmer of Tall Timbers Research Station, Tallahassee, and Calvin Barstow, with the bag of six guns over several days using pointers and flushing dogs, Moss Bank, Saskatchewan, in 2004. (Dennett Jackson)

by 2008, despite the presence of some of the best habitat I have ever seen: small fields and traditional cropping virtually unaffected by modernisation.

With hybrid driving–walking, some surprisingly high rates of shooting have been reported from mainland Europe. In one study in Germany during 1976–8 the shooting rates were 50 per cent per annum with correspondingly low breeding densities (Döring and Helfrich, 1986). Similar percentages have been reported from Czechoslovakia (Kokeš & Knobloch, 1947), the Netherlands (van Troostwijk, 1968) and Poland (Olech, 1971). Up to 1985 the information I had available showed annual shooting rates in Britain for driven shooting averaged 25 per cent, in mainland Europe with walked-up shooting (with or without dogs) also at 25 per cent and in North America with many bag limits 8 per cent. These figures were from study areas (and areas wholly or partly managed) and they exclude areas releasing pen-reared birds.

RED-LEGGED PARTRIDGE

If shooting can adversely affect wild grey partridge stocks, the situation is worse for wild red-legged partridges. In the original partridge simulation model the percentage of red-legged partridges shot was set at 1.87 times the percentage for the grey partridge. This was based on the longest run of records for a mixture of purely wild partridges of both species: the records of West Barsham in north Norfolk. The explanation is simple and it is due to the different ways in which the two species fly over the guns. Grey partridges fly over in tight coveys, whereas red-legged partridge coveys fragment and scatter, making easier targets. At North Farm in the Sussex Study area the percentage of red-legged partridges shot was 1.8 times that for the grey partridge up to 2001.

The most spectacular example of over hunting followed the 1974 'Revolution of the Clovers' in Portugal in 1974 when private estates were opened up to hunters, Italian style, and red-legged partridge numbers suffered a massive decline. Records made available to me by the de Mello Estate at Vale de Perditos indicate a density after shooting (December) of 80–90 birds per 100 ha in 1973–4. The Estate was taken over in April 1974 but reclaimed in December 1988, by which time the numbers had dropped to 7–8 birds per 100 ha. This drop of ~92 per cent was almost certainly the result of the combination of casual predator control with a high rate of hunting. In Israel the number of chukar partridges has increased markedly since their protection from hunting (Salit Kark, *in litt.*). In Huesca, Spain, 24 per cent shot per season on an area with no hunting regulation reduced spring numbers by 13 per cent, whereas on a regulated area 12 per cent were shot and spring numbers did not decline (Nadal *et al.*, 1996). Working in southern France, Peiro & Blanc (2011) argued that it was only necessary to know the young: old ratio in August to calculate the harvestable surplus. They assumed however that the mortality rates of old and young are not related or varying together and that the number of old birds is satisfactory.

The *Reclamo*

As with grey partridges the two main methods of shooting are driven and walked-up, but there is also a third method with a long tradition known as the *Reclamo*, which simply means 'decoy'. The basic method is that for a few days in early spring a red-legged partridge is placed in a cage in an area where surplus males ('torados') are known to be present. The hunter then sits in wait for these birds to come close enough to shoot. This is a very small-scale locally regulated method of hunting, highly valued as a tradition especially in southern Spain but which falls foul of the EC rule that no birds should be hunted in their reproductive season, depending on how this is defined (Vargas *et al.*, 2012). The test should not be an EC rule but the arguments should turn on whether there is any benefit to biodiversity. As is generally true with the hunting of small game species, sooner or later the relevant legislation will have to catch up with ecology. The issues are easier than with North Sea fishing.

INGESTED LEAD SHOT PREVALENCE AND SIGNIFICANCE

Right from the start there was scepticism about whether ingested lead shot can cause significant lead poisoning in game birds. Famously in the *Field* magazine of 19 February 1876 a Mr J. Hindle-Calvert wrote that, after killing a partially paralysed hen pheasant, 'I found 13 leaden pellets of various sizes; the grinding action of the gizzard had disseminated the lead with the food', adding that he had found traces of lead in the blood. Two days later he found four pellets in another pheasant that 'would soon have died from lead poisoning'. These definite reports from autumn 1875 compare to a vague assertion that ducks in Texas were poisoned by lead shot as early as 1874, which is considered the first time the problem was noticed (Bellrose, 1959). The Grouse Inquiry team considered in 1911 that, 'it is fairly common to find shot pellets loose among the contents of the crop or in the gizzard'... 'but the suggestion that lead poisoning has ever resulted either in this way or any other way from the scattering of leaden shot over a moor must not be taken too seriously.' Citing two cases of lead ingestion, including one pellet in a six-day-old chick, Stoddard (1932) concluded that ingestion of lead shot was 'just one of the many causes, some insignificant in themselves, that contribute to quail mortality'.

So what is the position today? In all, there are 29 separate estimates of lead shot ingestion – 16 for the grey partridge, 8 for the red-legged partridge and 5 for the chukar partridge – by twelve investigators (Fig. 221). We now also know that at least 75 per cent of the partridges that ingest lead shot will die as a result (Potts, 2005). The amount of lead in bones is the best measure of background contamination with lead. The levels of lead were determined in a substantial sample of femurs from the Sussex Study by Professor Andrew Meharg of the University of Aberdeen. This confirmed that the level of lead in partridges that had not ingested lead shot was extremely low.

There was a large amount of variation in the 29 estimates due to different sample sizes and methods but no statistically significant differences in uptake between the three species (Fig. 221). Given the amount of shooting and its increased popularity, we would expect an increase in the rate of ingestion. The increase is indeed highly significant ($P<0.001$), however inspection of the graph

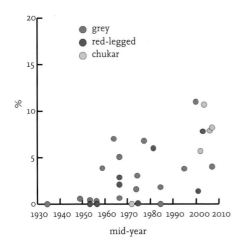

FIG 221. Prevalence of ingested lead shot in grey (blue), red-legged (red) and chukar (yellow) partridges from all known investigations. *Sources*: Bingham *et al.* (2008); Butler (2005); Clausen & Wolstrup (1979); Ferrandis (2008); Grondahl (1959); Kreager *et al.* (2008); Larsen *et al.* (2007); Potts (2005) and Sussex Study (unpublished); Tony Scheuhammer (2004, *in litt.*); Soler *et al.* (2004), Walter & Reese (2003).

suggests under-representation in the 1930s, especially since by that time game had been shot on a large scale for at least a century. So we cannot be sure about the rate of increase; all we can say is that it is increasing at 0.05 percentage points compound per year (zero in 1860, representing driven shooting dominant) to 0.12 percentage points (in 1947; first record was in 1948) and that it now stands at 7–8 per cent per annum.

Obviously we need to know more, and this is one of the vexed issues that deeply divide the bird protection and hunting interests. More than 130 species of birds, including endangered species, are known to have been poisoned by eating lead shot (Watson *et al.*, 2009). The International Council for Game and Wildlife Conservation (CIC), the senior international organisation representing hunting interests in more than 84 countries, is concerned, and determined that hunters should be seen not as the cause of the problem but as creating the solution. At its 56th General Assembly in Paris in May 2009 a resolution urging governments to work in close cooperation with international and national hunting organisations to solve the problem associated with lead shot and calling on the industry to give priority to the development and production of satisfactory alternatives to lead shot was adopted unanimously. This 'co-operation' is going ahead with the arms and ammunition interests in negotiations to solve the few remaining issues.

In the meantime some evidence is emerging that ingestion in partridges may be reduced by a combination of feeding with grain and grit, reducing the risk of lead shot being eaten in mistake for grit or seeds, many of which are virtually indistinguishable in size and appearance from lead shot. To do this the grit must be the right size (<2mm) whereas the grit sold for red-legged partridges and pheasants is larger. When this was done on the Norfolk Estate the supplied

FIG 222. Comparison of two lead shot from a partridge gizzard with two seeds of knotgrass and six seeds of black bindweed. Do partridges ingest lead shot thinking it is seed or grit?

grit soon accounted for about 65 per cent of the total grit in gizzards without any increase in the total numbers of grit; the provided grit replaced the natural grit. The number of birds shot on a wild bird shoot is also far less on a shoot stocked with pen-reared birds, again reducing the risk. Whatever the reason, against my expectation, the levels of lead shot ingestion in the Sussex study currently appears to be little higher than in the 1970s (Table 23).

CONSERVATION IMPLICATIONS

The natural reaction of many people to these statistics is to ban shooting. This would be a disaster because it would remove the incentive farmers and landowners have to restore partridge numbers. To restore partridge numbers on modern farmland, serious conservation measures have to be taken (the subject of the next chapter) and somebody has to give the commitment and supply the funds in the long term. Active conservation measures with a realistic chance of success have to be driven by results and revenue. The revenue that could come from wild bird hunting is surely the key to partridge survival into the future. Anyone interested in hunting has a vested interest in the quarry and destroying this link will throw the baby out with the bathwater. It is however a complex link because in order to restore partridge numbers, as this book has shown, it is necessary to improve habitats and control predation. The incredibly low densities of grey partridge in Germany are a case in point. The bird is classified as critically endangered in three states (Länder), endangered in eight and vulnerable in three, with shooting greatly restricted or banned by law or voluntarily in half the

FIG 223. Charlie Mellor, Head Gamekeeper, (right) and Beau Whitney keeping hoppers in good condition. Many have had difficulty regarding the job of gamekeepers as the equivalent of wildlife wardens, but that is what they can be.

country (Jörg Tillmann, *in litt.*). Predator control is severely restricted in all states. Similar farmland in France where predator control has been feasible has far more grey partridges. The wonderful biodiversity restoration on the Norfolk Estate would not have happened had there been a ban on partridge shooting or predator control: the bird and a huge swathe of wildlife would be gone for ever.

It is easy to see that uncontrolled fishing affects the larger more slowly reproducing predators first, species such as cod, halibut, tuna, swordfish and marlin. At first this benefits the fishes of lower trophic levels such as herring, sardine and smaller fishes and prawns, until the hunting switches to them (Pauly & Maclean, 2003). There is however a similar story from terrestrial habitats that is less well understood. Hunting (in its widest sense) at first affected the larger species such as the bigger carnivores and elephants (such as the five extinct species that were found in North America) and then switched to tapirs, monkeys and antelopes and larger game birds (Donlan *et al.*, 2006). Today even smaller species are now threatened in tropical rain forests by what is known as bush-meat hunting. Until recently the reaction of conservationists has been to call for bans backed up by swingeing punishment or sanctions. The only problem being that this approach has usually not worked.

This was recognised at the United Nations Convention on Biological Diversity's Liaison Group on Bush-meat that met in Buenos Aires in October 2009, with the following included in its recommendations:

> *Access, rights and associated accountability, as well as the responsibility to sustainably manage wildlife resources should be transferred whenever possible to local stakeholders who have a vested interest in maintaining the resources and who can deliver sustainable, desirable solutions.*

These principles are appropriate in our own countryside.

CHAPTER 10

Norfolk Estate: Restoration of Biodiversity

I do not want the grey partridge to go extinct on my watch.
Edward Duke of Norfolk, 21 November 2001

FROM 1959 TO 1962, COUNTS of wild grey partridges by gamekeepers in the Sussex Study area including the Norfolk estate show average September densities of grey partridges of about 135 per 100 ha. Since then, as elsewhere, there has been a massive decline, reaching 98 per cent on the Norfolk Estate by 2003. At that time, with a large surplus of males and no potential immigrants over the boundary, extinction appeared to be imminent. Fortunately the Estate was determined to reverse the situation and, as will be explained, public funds had become available to help. This story is essentially about a partnership between private and public investment giving returns in biodiversity that neither can achieve on their own.

GOVERNMENT MEASURES

Government funds to alleviate the impact of modern farming on wildlife were slow to evolve. There were several reasons for this. Through the 1970s it was clearly evident that wildlife conservation lobbyists were preoccupied with safeguarding, expanding and protecting designated areas of very high value such as nature reserves. In the 1980s there was real concern that the European Union's Common Agricultural Policy was fundamentally damaging the environment by

FIG 224. The central part of the Norfolk Estate partridge conservation area in late August 1977 (left) and early September 2010 (below left).

encouraging more and more intensive systems but, as it turned out, the case for reform did not hinge on wildlife. By producing more food it was clear that the more intensive agricultures actually save natural habitats from being cleared for agriculture. There was some sympathy for the plight of the grey partridge, but it was imagined to be an isolated case. Some commentators even considered the problems of toxic chemicals to have been exaggerated. The momentum for change in the early 1980s did not come from any real concern for wildlife; it came from the food surpluses, the 'milk lakes' and 'grain mountains' that the CAP's price support system had generated.

From 1984 a rapid radiation of developments ensured that change would eventually arrive. One of these was the designation in 1987 of the Environmentally Sensitive Areas (ESAs), one of which included the Sussex Study area. Some measures it financed, such as arable reversion, were harmful to partridges (Potts & Aebischer, 1998) but in its 1992 revision beetle banks and conservation headlands were listed as options that would qualify for subsidy. No beetle banks were installed because of a muddle in the government's Integrated Administration and Control System about whether beetle banks involved a 'significant area of the field'. If they did, the 'area payment subsidy' would be forfeited for the whole field if a claim was made to support the beetle banks. Bureaucratic obstacles like this were overcome. Conservation headlands and beetle banks were at first only grant-aided in selected ESAs, but from 1996 they also became an option in the government's Countryside Stewardship Scheme.

Even with government payments available, the take-up of conservation headlands and beetle banks was very poor. By 1994 conservation headlands covered only 0.3 per cent of cereal headlands (Potts, 1997), and a decade later accounted for only 0.35 per cent of Entry Level Stewardship points in England (Hodge & Reader, 2009). Apart from a few small short-term trials, there were none in the Sussex Study area. For the vast majority of farmers, not spraying headlands was an unnecessary step backwards.

THE MANAGEMENT PACKAGE

The area here termed the Norfolk Estate comprises 4 of the 12 original farms in the Sussex Study area and one of these (North Stoke) was the first anywhere to put into practice all the main recommendations from the Sussex Study, when it was taken 'in hand' by the Estate. Funds were obtained for conservation headlands and beetle banks through the area being in the South Downs Environmentally Sensitive Area. Later these were incorporated into the higher level part of the national Stewardship Scheme known as HLS. I have used the term HLS+ to cover an enhanced version implemented with a mixture of 15 private and publicly funded measures designed to work together, for example extra nesting cover and nest predator control as explained in Chapter 4. HLS+ began in February 2003 on 224 ha (145 ha arable), with full implementation on this part in 2004. In February 2006 280 ha (120 ha arable) was added, with a final 526 ha (435 ha arable) in February 2007, bringing the total to 1,030 ha (700 ha arable). These are the vital parts of the HLS+ management package:

1. Field size: beetle banks
The first aim is to divide large fields to reduce crop area size to a maximum of a rectangular 8 ha. In fact the average field size was reduced from 21 ha to 9 ha. Different types of crop were planted in the newly created fields on the two sides of the beetle bank to produce a patchwork-quilt or chequer-board pattern (see below).

The height of a beetle bank should be 0.4 m after seeding and settling, so that initially it needs to be higher (depending on the type of soil). The banks should follow contours so far as practicable to avoid soil erosion, which can be a problem where slopes are more than 12°. The second aim is to provide tussocks of tall grasses, especially cocksfoot, suitable for over-wintering predatory beetles and nesting partridges.

KEY: red = winter wheat; dark blue = winter barley; light blue = spring barley; dark green = non-rotational grass; light green = rotational grass.

FIG 225. Map on the left shows cropping in June 2003 when the grey partridge was approaching extinction on the area. Map on right shows cropping in 2011, with field size reduced from 21 ha to 9 ha and when all cereal field margins were in conservation headlands.

FIG 226. Norfolk Estate: (left) Peter Knight establishing a beetle bank; and (right) eight-year-old thorn hedge ready for layering.

FIG 227. Norfolk estate: a finished beetle bank with new thorn hedge.

FIG 228. Norfolk Estate: bank converted to cereals in 1977, restored in 2008 with many species, including poppies and sun spurge.

2. Strip cover

These strips are planted alongside beetle banks to provide escape cover until thorn hedges can do so or help them do so between February and April. At this time other cover is scarce and partridges are at most risk from raptors during their searches for suitable nest sites and until the pairs have 'settled down'. In December 2007 the opportunity came to compare 16 kale-dominated strips and 15 chicory-dominated strips. The strips were established at the same time in the spring of that year. Excluding woodpigeons, most numerous on the kale, the kale contained 1,024 birds and the chicory 324. The grey partridges preferred the kale, with 88 per cent of them found in the crop with the other species showing a similar preference being song thrush (83 per cent) and corn bunting (86 per cent). Kale is by far the best species to sow, as it not only gives the best cover in spring but also is accessible to chicks during wet weather.

There are however difficulties with kale. Sometimes the strips can be rendered useless by foraging woodpigeons or cannot be established without

FIG 229. Chicory mixtures are easier to establish than kale mixtures and can give good winter cover in dry conditions; hares like them too.

insecticide to control flea beetle, obviously to be avoided if at all possible. Trials have shown that strips can be established under fleece but this is expensive and may not be necessary in non-drought years. The rules also stipulate a mixture with other species less desirable than kale, although this can be overcome by specific derogation. The rule is to prevent harvesting the kale for seed. Popular mixes are chicory, melilot (often known as Canadian sweet clover) and quinoa. The latter is a good nurse species and chicory from the previous year can be good cover for partridges in early spring where it has been vigorous enough to withstand gales or snow.

The fundamental issue with all these strips, as with conservation headlands, is that the crops should give a canopy over the birds but not be too thick in order to give access when damp or wet. For example, reed canary-grass can provide excellent cover but in summer after heavy rain it can stay wet and impenetrable for days.

FIG 230. Strips of reed canary grass can improve winter and nesting cover.

FIG 231. Snow can all too easily render weak cover useless; however in this case, January 2010, the partridges were in coveys and not susceptible to raptor predation.

3a. Conservation headlands

Here the specifications have evolved with experience. Sotherton (1991) set out the first details for the management of the outer 6 m of cereal fields. Herbicides to control broadleaved weeds (dicotyledons) were allowed but only fluroxypyr for control of cleavers where absolutely necessary. Five herbicides to control grass weeds were also allowed, namely those that did not also control broadleaved weeds. Fungicides were allowed except the insecticidal pyrazophos (see p. 220) as were growth regulators. Insecticides were allowed in autumn if great care was taken to avoid drift into hedgerows and grass banks, but not at other times. Fertiliser use was as normal. It is easy to see here that in the absence of specific payments for not using fertilisers, farmers were trying to maximise yield whilst retaining benefits to wildlife; a difficult trick at the best of times.

On the Norfolk Estate, with the government payments, the 6 m specification was widened to 10 m and fertiliser was not used. Another change was that conservation headlands were not placed alongside woods or near rows of trees. This was to discourage pheasants and offset rabbit damage. Grass-weed herbicides were used but much more sparingly than before.

At first amidosulfuron was allowed in winter wheat between 1 February and 31 March where absolutely necessary to control cleavers. This recommendation was based on a huge amount of work (Clark *et al.*, 2007) at several sites where its use left the best control of cleavers with least harm to other broadleaved weeds and clovers. The reduction of 40 per cent in total invertebrate numbers was less than with other herbicides but it was a very substantial loss. In the dry conditions of March 2009 it was used in some conservation headlands on the Norfolk Estate, causing reductions of 61 per cent in the broadleaved weed index, 68 per cent in the number of species of broadleaved weeds, 50 per cent in the abundance of the main partridge chick foods and a 10–20 per cent points reduction in chick survival rates. The chemical is no longer used on conservation headlands on the Estate. Finally, if the aim is to save rare arable weeds, it is not advisable to use any herbicide. For obvious reasons the research to show the necessary selectivity has not been done; it would not be financially viable.

On many farms the main weed problem with conservation headlands is creeping thistle but, as in the pre-herbicide era, on the Norfolk Estate it is, like other perennial weeds, held in check by the ley-rotation. The most damaging grass weeds and cleavers are also held in check by the fact that no nitrogen fertiliser is used. If fertiliser is used in conservation headlands, the resulting thick growth of weeds can become a death trap for chicks in wet weather.

FIG 232. Some characteristic plants of conservation headlands on the Norfolk Estate: (clockwise from top left) Venus's looking-glass, an uncommon species; cornflower, still rare but kept going with conservation headlands; perennial sow thistle, this is one of the most abundant and troublesome of weeds on the estate; superficially like the abundant yellow charlock, the bastard cabbage is locally abundant, having been introduced with clover seed from the south of France in the 1920s.

Where absolutely necessary to control black grass, clodinafop-propargyl is allowed post-emergence in winter wheat and pinoxaden is allowed in winter barley. These chemicals do not control broadleaved weeds or, importantly, annual meadow-grass.

No insecticides were allowed in cereals in spring or summer and 10 m wide margins were left around peas with the rest treated with pirimicarb if absolutely necessary. Insecticide and fungicide seed dressings are used on conservation headlands as on the rest of the field. Whether this causes a problem was reviewed in Chapter 6. The neonicotinoid insecticide used as a seed dressing can increase mortality rates in a very wide range of invertebrates. The fact that insects responded so well to conservation headlands on the Norfolk Estate is clear indication that, used as a seed dressing in autumn, it has little if any adverse effect the following season.

3b. The unharvested option

Another factor minimising the impact of weeds is that wherever possible the conservation headlands are not harvested, for example where the following crop does not demand autumn cultivation. The payment under HLS compensates for the loss of the yield; in 2011 the payment for ordinary conservation headlands was £247 per ha rising to £440 for unharvested conservation headlands. One-third of conservation headlands were in the unharvested option.

3c. Wide-spaced rows

On several occasions broadleaved weeds were suppressed by a vigorous crop of winter barley. To overcome this, the crop was drilled at double the normal row width. The technique was also tried in other cereals but without any measurable benefit. In the Sustainable Arable Farming For an Improved Environment (SAFFIE) project it was considered that wider rows doubled the number of beetles in samples and that this was beneficial to skylarks, but in general the benefits from wider spaced rows was small (Clark *et al.*, 2007) and it can result in a linear growth of weeds that would be a serious impediment to small chicks if damp or wet.

4. Undersowing

The aim of the under-sowing is to install the traditional grass clover leys to control perennial weeds that otherwise make conservation headlands difficult and to encourage sawflies affected by cultivation, especially during their pre-pupae stage, although as yet it hasn't done so (Chapter 6).

5. Overwinter stubble

This is particularly aimed at skylarks but it is also useful to partridges, especially if the stubble follows low input of herbicides, has a good amount of Polygonums and chickweed and is not sprayed with a total herbicide such as Glyphosate until just before ploughing or seeding.

6. A patchwork quilt of crops

Big fields restrict nesting space for partridges, which are essentially birds of the edge of crops, as reviewed in Chapter 4, but although hugely unattractive to partridges, big fields are only actually harmful if the crop is unsuitable for them. In that case it can be impossible for pairs to avoid the problem without deserting the nest, as we saw with irrigation. It can also be too far to guide chicks to a suitable supply of insects. If fields are smaller, when winter barley is harvested, broods can easily move into unharvested crops nearby. When a crop is sprayed or harvested, escape is that much more difficult with large fields. With the currently fashionable practice of block cropping, this becomes very difficult if not impossible. When asked to quantify the cost of smaller fields, one well-known farm management company tried to draw up costs but in the end said it was the 'hassle' that was key and not the cost!

FIG 233. Oilseed rape: block cropping like this has to stop if wild partridges are to be encouraged.

7. Hedgerows

All of the new hedgerows were planted with a mixture of hawthorn, blackthorn, spindle – a traditional species in the area even though it is the host of black aphids – holly and field maple When dividing a field to plant a new hedge across the middle, there is often a choice between east–west or north–south alignments. Which is best? At Great Witchingham the exact site was determined for 283 nests and the east–west hedges had 36 per cent fewer nests, with the fewest nests on their north side.

The areas given over to the key habitat options are given in Table 28. Other options such as stubble turnips are geared to helping ensure a mixed farming pattern that includes 1,100 breeding ewes.

TABLE 28. The scale of utilisation in 2011 of key HLS+ options on the Norfolk Estate.

option	area	comment
conservation headlands	97 ha	9% of farmed area, one-third unharvested
beetle banks and hedges	25 km	cocksfoot with thorns
under-sown spring barley	86 ha	40% of spring barley
overwinter stubble	121 ha	22% of cereal area harvested
wild bird cover	21 ha	kale, chicory, canary grasses etc.

8. Fencing

With livestock on the farm, stock-proof hedges or fences are essential. As well as keeping dogs away from sheep they also reduce the impact of dogs on partridges. The Norfolk Estate is criss-crossed by more than 20 km of footpaths and bridleways. Fences reduce any disturbance, especially by unrestrained dogs, and they provide corridors along which to move livestock to new grazing. When new, wire fences are a hazard to partridges, with a risk of collisions with the top wire, but replacing this barbed wire with a single strand appeared to reduce the problem.

9. Grain feeders

The aim with feeders was to provide each pair with a feeder operated from October to July; normally they were at 70 m intervals along beetle banks and existing cover, but not under trees used by raptors. Where necessary, rats were caught using bromadioline-treated grain in box traps placed near feeders.

Even at feeders partridges can be vulnerable to predation by raptors. To reduce the hazard the feeders need to be hidden just inside kale or protected with branches of *Cupressus* or equivalent. Wild boar or deer can overturn feeders, so they may need to be well secured.

10. Grit

There is no suggestion that grit is short on the Sussex Study area and the aim here, as with the provided wheat, is to reduce the amount of time that the partridges are searching for grit, during which they may be at risk of raptor predation. Most partridge grit sold today is for red-legged partridges and is too large for the grey partridge. Only when smaller grit averaging 1.5 mm was used was there a notable take-up. Now the majority of grit (>65 per cent) in the gizzards is provided grit. The total number of grit per gizzard has not changed as more grit was provided.

11. Set-aside

To this day there is no convincing evidence that grey partridges or any of the other bird species dependent on arable farming in Europe have benefited from set-aside except locally and temporarily. It was above all a temporary measure when the government-controlled market could not control surpluses. Set-aside was compulsory, involving all significant cereal growers, yet the declines of 13 of 15 red-listed widespread farmland birds continued through to at least 2009 (*The State of the UK's Birds 2011*); the policy was abandoned in 2007/8. Only the Song Thrush and Tree Sparrow increased during the period of set-aside and neither has been shown to benefit from it. On the Norfolk Estate, set-aside was abandoned as soon as it became possible to do so.

12. Releasing other game-birds for shooting

There is a history in the area of large-scale releases of pheasants and red-legged partridges, and in consequence diseases such as gapeworm and bulgy-eye syndrome (see Chapter 7) were known to be present. However, much the most important consideration, it was clear that gamekeepers cannot devote sufficient attention to wild grey partridges if they also have to pen-rear birds for release. Accordingly all rearing and releasing was stopped.

13. Predation control

This was crucially important. Predator control was well organised and carried out by three gamekeepers. The number of foxes and some other predators that had to be removed per 100 ha to restore the partridge population increased

TABLE 29. Predators removed showing the changes in numbers per 100 ha over the period 1961–6 to 2007–10.

year	weasel	stoat	fox	brown rat	grey squirrel	magpie	carrion crow
1961–66	11.4	5.58	1.85	26.51	1.17	1.71	4.06
2007–10	9.53	9.41	14.83	28.92	2.11	7.02	25.86
change	–16%	+68%	+702%	+9%	+80%	+311%	+537%

eight-fold from 1961–6 to 2007–10 (Table 29). Fenn Mk IV tunnel traps were placed at strategic locations along beetle banks and hedgerows and operated from February to July. The latest snares that enable badgers and deer to escape without harm were used during the nesting season and Larsen traps were deployed to catch carrion crows and magpies in spring. Foxes were shot at night mainly in spring. In general the methods were the same as those employed in the Salisbury Plain experiment (p. 22) but over an area twice as large.

These increases in the number of predators that had to be controlled were not confined to the study area and the GWCT's National Game Bag Census shows the number of foxes killed through southeast England increased from 0.5 per 100 ha in 1961 to 3.8 per 100 ha in 1990 (Tapper, 1992, with latest results at www.gwct.org.uk/ngcmammals). Predator control, always a hard, unpopular job, is harder than ever today, but as we shall see it does produce spectacular results for partridges and other ground-nesting birds.

14. Shooting

There was no shooting of grey partridges in the seven years from 2002 to 2009, but there was shooting of red-legged partridges and pheasants. A trial one-day shoot of grey partridges was held in October 2009, with two days in 2010 repeated in 2011. In each season the bag of grey partridges was managed to equal the 'harvestable surpluses'. This 'surplus' was the number that would leave enough birds after the shooting to allow for 'winter losses' of 45 per cent and an increase in the breeding stock. In 2012 there were 375 pairs but the aim, when the nesting cover matures, is to have 500 pairs.

The size of the bag (=surplus) was determined as the number on 1 September minus the required stock divided by the annual survival rate (0.55) excluding shooting. Say you have 2,000 birds and require 500 pairs, the bag = 2,000–(1,000/0.55) or 182 birds. The figure 0.55 represents an annual non-shooting mortality rate of 45 per cent (it can be higher). It is easy to see from this that the bag goes up with the number of birds available but that the stock goes down as more birds are shot.

15. Translocation

At the start of the restoration on the Norfolk Estate in February 2003 the grey partridge population in the western half of the Sussex Study area was two pairs in the area in hand, the North Stoke farm, and seven pairs in the surrounding 2,000 ha. By September of that year there was only one adult female remaining on North Stoke (0.9 per 100 ha), the other being killed by a dog and four old and four young in the surrounding area (0.2 females per 100 ha). There was no shooting allowed on North Stoke but it continued on the surrounding area, inevitable since it was a red-legged partridge shoot. Thus by February 2004 there were only three pairs in the entire area (0.3 females per 100 ha), with one pair just over the boundary of North Stoke. A likely stock of one pair on 224 ha of North Stoke was too risky a basis on which to invest significant amounts of money to restore numbers.

Pen rearing for release was considered either of birds in autumn or spring with or without fostering broods onto 'barren' pairs. This subject has been studied extensively and intensively by Francis Buner and colleagues at the GWCT in work at 12 sites in East Anglia and 12 in central southwest England (Buner et al., 2011). Whereas at North Farm in the 1960s survival rates of pen-reared birds were almost 40 per cent per annum including shooting (Potts, 1986), they encountered survival rates of 7–20 per cent per six months, clearly due to much higher predation. Brood production rates were also low: only 17 per cent in southern England. Given the high raptor population at North Stoke it seemed clear pen-rearing was not an option. There are concerns about trapping for translocation (Letty, 2007), but I knew of several cases where it had been successful in the US, including with chukar partridges (Sandfort, 1963), and that it was the key ingredient in the restoration of wild turkey numbers in North America. Even in captivity pairs that form freely are more successful (Beani et al., 1992), and so we would have to catch naturally formed wild pairs for release at about the time they would be choosing a nest site.

By kind permission nine such pairs were caught on the Sandringham Estate in Norfolk, 220 km north of the Norfolk Estate in Sussex, on 3 March 2004, translocated and trickle-released after a very short period in holding pens. Later in the spring another pair immigrated to give a foundation stock of 11 pairs. These bred very well, with only 1 adult of the 18 translocated birds lost during six months, and no further translocation was necessary. By the spring count of 2012 the 11 pairs had grown to 375.

PLANT BIODIVERSITY AND RARE ARABLE WEEDS

*Prof. Newton sent me the leg of a red-legged partridge which had been wounded and
could not fly, with a ball of hard earth adhering to it, and weighing 6½ ounces. The
earth had been kept for three years, but when broken, watered and placed under a
bell glass, no less than 82 plants sprung from it: these consisted of 12 monocotyledons
including the common oat, and at least one kind of grass, and of 70 dicotyledons ...*
Charles Darwin, On the Origin of Species, 1859

The original aim of increasing weediness with conservation headlands was to
increase the abundance of insects, but they have also turned out to be crucial to
the conservation of many plant species. The flora has been defined to include 215
wild species that have been recorded since the seventeenth century, after excluding
certain species such as mosses and shrubs (Potts, Ewald & Aebischer, 2010). So how
was the composition of this plant community affected by the use of herbicides?

As we saw in Chapter 3, in the Sussex Study the plant diversity of cereal crops
has been measured annually in two main ways: (1) weed abundance has been
measured on a scale of 0–5; and (2) species presence. The example for broadleaved
weed abundance is given in Table 30, comparing the weediness of headlands in
conventional cereal crops with conservation headlands. General weed abundance
and the occurrence of species have been measured throughout the Sussex Study.
Over the past four years the average broadleaved weed abundance has been 1.3 in
the headlands of conventional fields and 3.0 in conservation headlands, and the
number of species was almost four times higher in conservation headlands.

TABLE 30. Broadleaved weed abundance on the Norfolk Estate conservation headlands
compared with conventional headlands on the remainder of the Sussex Study area, 2008–11.

year	broadleaved weed abundance in conventional cereal crops		broadleaved weed abundance in conservation headlands on Norfolk Estate	
	index	fields sampled	index	fields sampled
2008	1.5	52	2.9	48
2009	1.0	82	2.5	39
2010	1.2	53	3.0	41
2011	1.5	71	3.6	38
average	**1.3**		**3.0**	

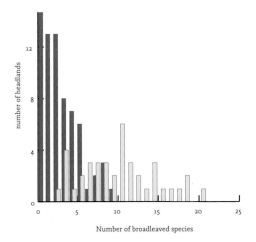

number of headlands

Number of broadleaved species

FIG 234. Overall abundance of broadleaved species in conservation headlands on the Norfolk Estate (green) compared with that in conventional cereal headlands on the remainder of the Sussex Study area (red).

A headland could score very high for weediness with only a few dominant species present, with the opposite also occuring. Nevertheless on average the number of species present rose from an average 2.52±0.28 in conventional headlands to 9.62±0.73 in conservation headlands. Interest here first centres on how many species of rare arable flowers can be saved with these headlands and then we look at the community as a whole.

THE UK RED-LISTED PLANT SPECIES AND HLS+

The aim here is to draw up a balance list of species that can be saved and those that cannot be saved.

1. Corn buttercup (*Ranunculus arvensis*)
Critically endangered, this species was recorded at Burpham in the 1930s at a time when it was generally too common in cereals to mention in detail (Wolley-Dod, 1937). It was recorded on Kithurst Hill in 1952 but has not been seen since.

2. Pheasant's eye (*Adonis annua*)
This beautiful but endangered species was once as common 'in the cornfields of Sussex as to have been collected and sold in Covent Garden' (Salisbury, 1961). From about 1880 there was a severe decline but it persisted near Peppering High Barn until about 1917 (Rev. C. Toogood). It has not been recorded on the Norfolk Estate since then.

FIG 235. Pheasant's eye, not recorded on the Norfolk Estate since 1917: this group was at Knoll Farm, Damerham. (David Hill)

3. Prickly poppy (*Papaver argemone*)

Superficially similar to pheasant's eye, this species has survived despite being 'rather rare in cornfields' (Wolley-Dod, 1937). Prior to the conservation headlands roll-out, there had only been 3 records on the Norfolk Estate from the Sussex Study in more than 30 years and one from the Sussex Botanical Recording Society (SBRS). It is hoped that conservation headlands will save this species on the Norfolk Estate, where it remains but is rare. Meanwhile the rough poppy (*Papaver hybridum*), which has greatly declined elsewhere, is thriving on the Norfolk Estate.

FIG 236. Rough poppy is thriving in conservation headlands.

4. Fine-leaved fumitory (*Fumaria parviflora*)

This has always been considered a rare to very rare species on the Sussex Downs. It was only recorded three times prior to 2007 but identification requires careful examination of seeds and flowers with a magnifying glass. In 2007 and 2008 it was found to be present on many of the newly installed beetle banks, especially in the Drier Barn area, and has been confirmed in conservation headlands (Frances Abraham). Although the species is not easy to monitor, it can no longer be considered rare on the Norfolk Estate.

5. Corn spurrey (*Spergula arvensis*)

Only recorded three times in the Sussex Study and only once on the Norfolk Estate with the last record in 1986. A species that does not like calcium-rich areas, it has always been very local and it is now considered locally extinct.

6. Night-flowering catchfly (*Silene noctiflora*)

No record in the Sussex Study area until 2008 when first found in conservation headlands on the Norfolk Estate. Since then it has been found commonly, at times even abundant on conservation headlands in spring barleys over a well-defined area of about 150 ha (see Fig. 238). This is a key species in defining the community of species in cereal crops (see later). 'Catchfly' refers to its covering of sticky hairs that are intended to repel or trap insects potentially harmful to the plant. The extent to which this is effective say in comparison to white campion, would make an interesting study. Pollination is by night-flying insects but the flowers also open in very dull conditions.

FIG 237. Night-flowering catchfly can be abundant in conservation headlands but only in a limited area (Fig. 238).

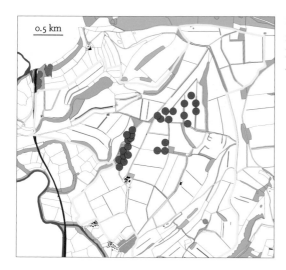

FIG 238. All known sites of night-flowering catchfly; none have been found elsewhere in the Sussex Study area.

7. Dwarf spurge (*Euphorbia exigua*)

Near threatened, there were only seven records in the Sussex Study during 1968–2005, all but one from the Norfolk Estate. This is now the most widely distributed of the red-listed species in conservation headlands, game cover and at field margins.

8. Shepherd's needle (*Scandix pecten-veneris*)

This species was abundant in autumn-sown cereals until the 1950s, so much so that it was a serious pest, impeding harvesting and threshing (Frank Penfold). It is still found in some years in a very restricted part of the Study area but it has disappeared apparently without trace on the Norfolk Estate.

9. Spreading hedge-parsley (*Torilis arvensis*)

Formerly an important weed on arable land, it was found on the Norfolk Estate in 1974 but not since.

10. Corn gromwell (*Lithospermum arvense*)

Endangered in the UK and only just hanging on at two sites in the Sussex Study area, one of them only 400 m from the Norfolk Estate.

11. Red hemp-nettle (*Galeopsis angustifolia*)

Critically endangered this striking plant was still abundant in 'chalky cornfields' on the Norfolk Estate in the 1930s (Wolley-Dod, 1937) but more recently only recorded there in 1959 (Frank Penfold), with the last single plant found in 2001.

FIG 239. It appears to be too late to save the corn gromwell on the Norfolk Estate, though a small patch survives on Amberley Mount.

12. Corn cleavers (*Galium tricornutum*)

There was one occurrence in the Study area during 1966–1978 but never on the Norfolk Estate and it has not been seen anywhere in Sussex since then (SBRS); critically endangered.

13. Narrow-fruited cornsalad (*Valerianella dentata*)

This is the most numerous of the red-listed species on the Norfolk Estate and it is sometimes abundant in conservation headlands in spring-sown barley. In 2011 the species was badly affected by mildew.

FIG 240. The narrow-fruited cornsalad is locally abundant in conservation headlands.

14. Corn chamomile (*Anthemis arvensis*)

Endangered yet found 'rather frequently' on the Norfolk Estate in the 1930s (Wolley-Dod, 1937) but not seen during the Sussex Study, i.e. since 1967.

15. Stinking chamomile (*Anthemis cotula*)

Not recorded from either the Norfolk Estate or the Sussex Study area since 1972.

This review of the fifteen red-listed species that have occurred in the Study area shows that the HLS+ management was unable to save two species because the Norfolk Estate was not in their range. It began too late to save a further eight species but has almost certainly saved five species (numbers 3, 4, 6, 7 and 13). Only 7 per cent of the broadleaved weeds are listed however, and we now turn our attention to the remaining 93 per cent.

THE NON-RED-LISTED SPECIES

Although many lists of cereal weeds have been made in Britain dating back to William Pitt's in Leicestershire in 1809, none provided species frequencies prior to the use of herbicides. Sandars (1939) listed the top ten cereal weeds, headed by charlock, thistles, docks and poppies, but obviously not representing the flora from a biodiversity standpoint. We have to turn to the work of Wasscher (1941) at Groningen in the Netherlands as the nearest we can get to a description of

FIG 241. After 60 years of herbicide use the soil seed bank obviously has abundant poppy seeds.

the flora of cereal fields prior to the use of herbicides. Studying associations of species in cereal and flax crops on formerly marine loams and fertile sandy clays, Wasscher identified a flora in the Hunsingo area that he called the common poppy–night-flowering-catchfly association. The association was characterised by the dominance of the poppy and the presence of the catchfly but with substantial amounts of knotgrass, chickweed and scentless mayweed. This is a reasonable description of the current flora in conservation headlands on the Norfolk Estate but the two areas, chalk hills and ancient polders, could hardly be more different.

Wasscher's community of weeds is indeed remarkably similar to that in non-herbicide-treated cereals in the Sussex Study (Potts *et al.*, 2010) and in conservation headlands on the Norfolk Estate (Fig. 242). So much so that, a bit like archaeology, we can investigate what might be missing on the Norfolk Estate conservation headlands. All Wasscher's 41 species have been found in the Sussex Study but some are no longer present. From the survey of red-listed species we should not be surprised that he found shepherd's needle and corn spurrey but there are also two that we should add to our 'too late to save' list: long-headed poppy and corn mint, not recorded from the Norfolk Estate and now extremely local on neighbouring farms. The most characteristic grass of Wasscher's association was couch and this was the most serious weed in the Sussex Study area in the 1960s, now uncommon for more than 30 years through intensive measures aimed at eradication such as burning the rhizomes and use of specific herbicides.

The startling conclusion from these comparisons is that the major features of the soil seed bank are still intact and have not yet been eradicated by 60 years of herbicide use. Apart from the ten 'too late to save species' the flora can be very quickly restored with conservation headlands. Considering the entire cereal ecosystem flora of the Sussex Study, the picture is still brighter. It is true that 16

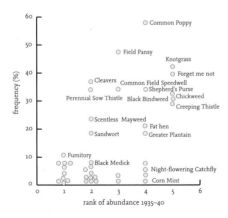

FIG 242. Comparison of frequencies of species in cereals in 1935–40 in the Netherlands (Wasscher, 1941) with those in 2011 in conservation headlands on the Norfolk Estate (R=0.56, P<0.001).

FIG 243. (left) Norfolk Estate, June 2007; (below left) the same spot, June 2010.

species have been lost since the seventeenth century, but 15 have been gained. Moreover a feature in recent years has been an increase in abundance of tall perennials such as hogweed, mugwort and lesser burdock (Potts *et al.*, 2010) that have considerable ecological importance, for example the hogweed for aphids, mugwort for plant bugs and the burdock providing food for goldfinches. The conservation headlands on the Norfolk Estate are probably floristically more diverse than cereal field headlands at any time previously.

INSECTS AND OTHER INVERTEBRATES

In mid-June during each of the four years 2008–11, sweep-net (Watkins & Doncaster E) samples were taken from 22 cereal fields on the Norfolk Estate, with the insects identified (so far as practicable). On average the samples contained 254 insects per 25 sweeps, with 116 considered chick foods and 138 non-chick foods.

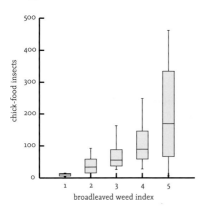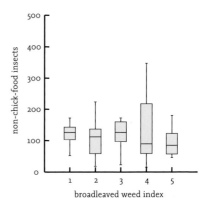

FIG 244. Insects in conservation headlands on the Norfolk Estate during 2008–11 in relation to the abundance of broadleaved weeds: (left) chick food species; (right) the remaining species.

The total number of chick food insects found in the samples was determined by broadleaved weed abundance, not by the number of species of weed present or by grass weed abundance, and it was clear that non-chick foods did not increase with broadleaved weed abundance (Fig. 244).

The response of individual insects to increased weediness was measured as the slope obtained from a plot of the logarithm of their abundance against the weed index scale of 0 to 5. This was after allowing for any year effect that was statistically significant (P<0.05). The response to the increased weediness was the same in the first year as in year four (2011), suggesting a large pool of potential immigrant weed-dwelling insects each spring despite 60 years of herbicide use.

With the observed weed index of 1.3 in conventional headlands in the rest of the Sussex Study area and 3.0 in conservation headlands on the Norfolk Estate, we can calculate that the conservation headlands increased chick food abundance by 102 insects (88%) per sweep sample. Virtually all of this increase was due to the ten groups listed in Table 31; essentially those that declined in importance in chick diets during the 1960s (Chapter 5). Ground beetles are only exceptionally caught in sweep-nets.

Several species have been noted in conservation headlands in recent years that have hitherto been extremely rare in cereal fields. These include the malachite beetle, various soldier beetles, the thistle longhorn, tortoise beetles and the bright bronze-green *Oedemera nobilis*. Some butterflies, especially the painted lady, and moths, most spectacularly the humming bird hawk moth, fall into the same category.

TABLE 31. Increases in abundance of individual groups of invertebrates in conservation headlands on the Norfolk Estate during 2008–2011. The groups are listed in order, with non-listed groups not statistically significant. All the listed insects feature in the diet of grey partridge chicks.

group	insects added with conservation headlands (per 25 sweeps)	Statistical significance of correlation (P)
blossom beetles	62.9	0.003
plant bugs	21.0	<0.001
weevils	5.0	0.001
other beetles	4.9	<0.001
leaf hoppers	2.2	0.004
empids & dolichopods	1.5	0.021
Lepidoptera	0.7	0.013
sawflies	0.5	0.019
harvestmen	0.4	0.013
grasshoppers	0.3	0.009

BIRDS

Excluding birds seen only when flying over the area, ~165 species have been recorded on the Sussex Study area. This includes the great bustard, which was lost sometime prior to 1820. Other species that formerly bred but no longer do so are ringed plover, wryneck, whinchat, red-backed shrike, cirl bunting and woodlark. The turtle dove, numerous at the start of the Sussex Study, has rapidly declined and was not seen in 2010 or 2011. Whether one or two pairs of wheatear breed regularly is not known for certain and grasshopper warbler no longer breeds on the Norfolk Estate but may do elsewhere in the Sussex Study area occasionally. The situation of the tree sparrow is uncertain but even when numerous it was confined to a small area in the extreme southeast of the study area. Another species more common in the east is the stonechat. One or two pairs breed on the Norfolk Estate and additional birds over-winter. Species lost from the area and then regained are red kite, buzzard, raven and, tentatively, stone curlew.

In 2007, with HLS+ beginning on the full area of the Norfolk Estate, 1,442 'pairs' of birds of 64 species were counted in summer and considered to be

FIG 245. Grey partridge family. (Malcolm Brockless)

breeding. This excludes the exceedingly numerous woodpigeon. Surprisingly 371 (26 per cent of the total) of these 'pairs' were red-listed species, with one of them, the skylark, the single most abundant bird with an estimated 181 singing males present. By 2011 the number of pairs of breeding birds had increased to 2,411, including 1,058 (44 per cent of the total) pairs of red-listed species. Whereas non-red-listed species had increased by 26 per cent, the red-listed species had increased by 285 per cent. After four years, in 2011 the skylark remained the most numerous species but now with 470 singing males, an increase of 160 per cent. Overall these results show that, as intended, HLS+ benefited the red-listed species most.

Grey Partridge

The most important single factor in the management package HLS+ was the control of nest predation and the results are given as Table 32. For the grey partridge there were no significant differences in nesting success between the Norfolk Estate and the rest of the area until 2004 when predator control started. Predation control raised the percentage of pairs that hatched chicks from 38 per cent to 86 per cent (Table 32). Nesting success was therefore more than doubled by predation control and by the provision of extra nesting cover. Add in the effect of saving first clutches and the number of young produced per pair increased from 4.6 to 11.9, a dramatic 159 per cent increase.

TABLE 32. Survival of incubating females and brood production rate on the Norfolk Estate and remaining Sussex Study area, 1968–2010

	survival females and SE	brood production and SE
Sussex Study area 1968–2003 control (36 years)	69±1%	43±2%
Sussex Study area 2004–10 control (7 years)	74±3%	38±3%
Norfolk Estate 1968–2003 control (36 yrs)	68±2%	54±4%
average of controls	70%	45%
Norfolk Estate 2004–10 managed (7 years)	87±1%	86±2%
gain as percentage points	**17%**	**41%**

This improvement in the number of chicks hatched and the higher survival achieved with conservation headlands (Chapter 5) led to very large increases on all Norfolk estate farms, beginning where HLS+ began, on North Stoke (Fig. 246). The annual rate of change averaged 50 per cent per annum, although declining as the population rose.

There were no such recoveries in the rest of the Sussex Study area. The numbers on the Norfolk Estate during 2004–10 were spectacularly different from those on the other four farms, whereas during 1968–2003 they had been similar

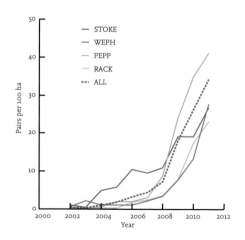

FIG 246. Increase of grey partridge on the four farms comprising the Norfolk Estate since 2002. The HLS+ management was implemented in two phases between 2003–2007 (green line North Stoke) and then subsequently on all four farms from 2007.

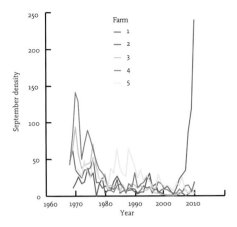

FIG 247. The trends in grey partridge numbers in September: 1968–2010. Farm 1 is the Norfolk Estate with the other groups of farms in the core zone of the Sussex Study area for comparison.

(Fig. 247). In 2011 numbers also began to increase also on North Farm (farm 3) following the adoption of conservation headlands.

The response of the grey partridge to the management package was spectacular (Fig. 248) and a little better than forecast at the start. It will now level off somewhat with the inauguration of shooting as described above. I estimate the carrying capacity of the Norfolk Estate at 500 pairs (2.7 on the logarithmic scale below).

The increase in numbers on the Norfolk Estate is compared to some other well-known increases in Figure 249. It is very similar to the earlier increases at Damerham and North Farm and at Savy, but the latter went on to double the densities achieved elsewhere. The challenge is obviously to maintain the trajectory on the Norfolk Estate.

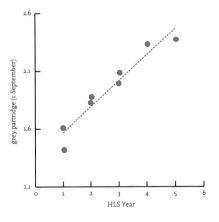

FIG 248. Grey partridge (log scale) on the Norfolk Estate since 2004 (i.e. beginning with the translocation) with number of years in HLS+, an increase of 50 per cent per annum.

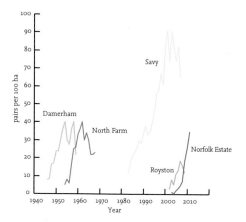

FIG 249. Comparison of five successful examples of grey partridge conservation in Britain and France.

RED-LEGGED PARTRIDGE

In the recent past the numbers of red-legged partridges on the Norfolk Estate has been determined by heavy rearing and kept low because of a high rate of shooting and poor breeding success. This management ceased as each phase of HLS+ began, whilst continuing on neighbouring farms. Because so many pen-reared birds immigrated onto the HLS+ areas, shooting of this species was allowed, as was also the case with pheasants. Despite the presence of pen-reared birds, nesting success dramatically improved and against expectation, red-legged partridges chicks benefited from conservation headlands. Numbers increased strongly (Fig. 250). The dip in numbers in 2011 is attributable to shooting in the autumn of 2010, but numbers increased again in 2012.

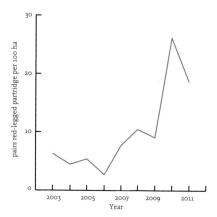

FIG 250. Red-legged partridge spring pairs on the Norfolk Estate showing the increase in density. The releasing of pen-reared birds ceased in 2006 where HL+ was introduced in 2007.

QUAIL

The number of calling males in the whole Sussex Study area has varied from nil to about 15 (in 1989). During all this time only seven broods were encountered in the stubble counts. On the Norfolk Estate a record 12 males were heard calling in 2007, with 8 the following year when 2 broods were fledged, the first in living memory. No males were heard calling in 2009 and 2010 but at least twelve called in 2011, though with no broods seen. This is fragmentary information but it does suggest quail may benefit from HLS+.

METHODS OF CALCULATING THE RESPONSE OF BIRDS TO HLS+

Bird density surveys began in the spring of 2003 and continued through the winter of 2012, which I carried out myself. The counts were obtained by walking along all linear features (fencerows, hedges, beetle banks, woodland edge) and where necessary across fields, up to 25 km per visit. For example, the lines of beetle banks were walked before as well as after their creation. Woodland and gardens were avoided. Encounters (sightings, songs and calls) were plotted in notebooks and transferred to 1:10,000 maps, with the aim throughout being an even spatial coverage of the entire area rather than a complete count. For birds that are more secretive when nesting such as the bullfinch and tree creeper, more time would inevitably have led to the discovery of more birds. At the other extreme were the red kite and raven, with total encounters three times the maximum number seen together. In this case the latter number was used. It was impracticable to assess the numbers of woodpigeon with large flocks at all times of the year. Numbers along farm boundaries were allocated equally to both sides. As far as possible, overlap and duplication were avoided. Counting began as soon as there was enough light to identify birds seen in cover, usually about 15 minutes before sunrise. There were strong seasonal and daily patterns, for example with robins tending to sing most in spring and early in the day, and yellowhammers most in summer and later in the day, but spring and summer counts were not combined to avoid duplication. Many skylarks moved from winter cereals in spring to spring-sown cereals in summer, so combining spring and summer numbers field by field would have given an over-count. It was not possible to assess the number of pairs of the Cardueline finches. Throughout the spring and summer flocks of goldfinches gathered on dandelions and burdock, linnets on knotgrass and linseed and greenfinches on ripening oilseed.

In spring 2003 surveys were undertaken on North Stoke (224 ha) and on two plots totalling 100 ha on Lee Farm almost adjoining North Stoke. Shoot management and farming had been similar on the two farms for 26 years. The counts showed remarkably similar densities of resident birds (density on North Stoke = $0.023\pm0.446 + 1.108\pm0.084$ y, r=0.83, p= 0.001 where y is the density on Lee Farm). This supports the use of the counts at North Stoke in 2003 as the baseline from which to measure annual changes.

Trends were calculated for 30 species from counts in the two phases of implementation: (1) from March 2003 to January 2007, ten visits per year covering all 224 ha at North Stoke – three in winter, three in spring and six in summer, averaging 4 hours each; and (2) from February 2007 to March 2012, 18 visits per year covering just under 1,000 ha (including only part of North Stoke) – six in each season averaging 10 hours. Importantly the areas covered and the time spent both changed from phase (1) to phase (2) and they are not combined for the analyses here.

The percentage annual increase or decrease was calculated for each species for each year to give eight annual changes over the nine years for breeding numbers. No winter or spring counts were done in 2003/04 and no spring count in 2011. The snow in the winters of 2009–10 and 2010–11 clearly reduced the number of skylark and some other species, indicated by * in Table 33 (pp. 359–60).

TRENDS, FOCUSING ON THE BIODIVERSITY ACTION PLAN BIRD SPECIES

Out of a possible 21 red-listed bird species 16 occurred on the Norfolk Estate during 2003–2011. Here we investigate the status of 12. The four other red-listed species were either too scarce to estimate trends (marsh tit), too erratic in numbers (cuckoo, with numbers highest in 2010) or only frequent in late summer (yellow wagtail). One pair of willow tits was seen, in the springs of 2004 and 2005, but none have been seen since.

As mentioned already no turtle doves were seen after 2009. The disappearance was disappointing because one of their favourite foods, fumitory, has become abundant in conservation headlands and in peas, nesting sites remain abundant and because in what appear to be poorer habitats in Hungary the bird remains abundant. There is a good deal of evidence that the breeding success has declined in Britain (Browne & Aebischer, 2003) but the Norfolk estate would appear to be ideal habitat; the bird was common there in the 1970s. A six-year study has shown that the overwinter survival of turtle doves breeding in France increases with the amount of cereals harvested (indicating also the availability of wild seeds), in Mali–Senegal (Eraud *et al.*, 2009). The explanation may lie in West Africa where our birds but not the Hungarian birds overwinter (Aebischer, 2002). Another migrant overwintering in Africa, the nightjar, breeds just over the boundary of the Norfolk Estate and these birds and bats are increasingly seen flying over conservation headlands at dusk.

The bird surveys summarised in Table 33 showed that 11 of the 12 monitored species on the red list were stable or increasing compared to only 1 nationally. Moreover at the time of writing, British Trust for Ornithology statistics are only available until 2009 and so exclude the recent cold winters. One of the red-listed species that is increasing on the Norfolk Estate, although not monitored (see methods), is the house sparrow, with four thriving colonies around farm buildings and another in a village. Six of the seven species on the amber list were stable or increasing compared to four nationally and only one species, the meadow pipit, has shown no response. However, two further amber-listed species have strongly increased on the Norfolk Estate in contrast to the situation nationally: the whinchat and wheatear. These species are however monitored

FIG 251. Linnets are very attracted to knotgrass, here on Alderney *Polygonum maritimum*. (Nicholas Aebischer)

TABLE 33. The annual changes in the numbers of 30 species of bird monitored on the Norfolk Estate after the adoption of HLS+. Percentages are the average of the annual changes during the four years 2003/4 to 2006/7 at North Stoke and the annual changes during the five years 2007/08 to 2011/12 on the Norfolk Estate as a whole, giving essentially the average response to the first four or five years of HLS+ respectively. The species indicated by shading in the first column are generally considered to be declining; those shaded in the body of the table have declined on the Norfolk Estate. * indicates numbers reduced by snow; counts were not made in autumn; n/p is not present.

red list			
	Summer	**Winter**	**Spring**
grey partridge		+48%	
lapwing	n/p	+23%	
turtle dove	lost	n/p	n/p
skylark	+32%	+7%*	+23%
song thrush	+1%	+56%	−4%
redwing	n/p	+37%	+39%
fieldfare	n/p	+58%	+47%
starling	0%	−20%*	+2%
house sparrow		strong increase	
linnet	−4%	+61%	+15%
yellowhammer	+7%	+70%	+66%
corn bunting	+5%	+40%	+5%

amber list			
	Summer	**Winter**	**Spring**
meadow pipit	lost	−17%*	−20%
stonechat	0%	−5%*	0%
mistle thrush	+19%	+4%	+9%
dunnock	+16%	+13%	+14%
whitethroat	+11%	n/p	n/p
bullfinch	+25%	+16%	0%
reed bunting	0%	+7%	20%

	Summer	Winter	Spring
not listed			
pied wagtail	0%	+38%	
wren	0%	0%	−12%
robin	−7%	+18%	+25%
blackbird	+8%	+4%	+11%
blackcap	+26%	n/p	n/p
chiffchaff	−23%	n/p	n/p
blue tit	+5%	+4%	+54%
great tit	+7%	+13%	+12%
chaffinch	−1%	−11%	+23%
greenfinch	+10%	−30%	+10%
goldfinch	+20%	−29%*	+60%

only during stubble counts. Ten of eleven of the non-listed species were stable or increasing, with only one declining, namely the chiffchaff. The annual rate of increase of many species has been very high.

GROUND-NESTING BIRDS: WADERS

Fourteen species of wader have been recorded in the Sussex Study area. A flock of usually more than 100 golden plover and a group of about 25 curlew wintered until 1980, both frequenting under-sown leys grazed by sheep and cattle respectively. One curlew that was shot in 1972 had eaten a large number of dor-beetle larvae obtained from the ground beneath cattle dung, and the curlews stopped wintering when this herd of out-wintered cattle was disbanded. A small flock of golden plover present in March 2011 was the first to stay in the area since at least 1999. Only three waders have bred: stone curlew, ringed plover and lapwing.

Stone curlew
Stone curlews have been recorded breeding on the Sussex Study area since at least the time of Gilbert White. But it may not always have been common and in 1900 W. H. Hudson writes of it having 'trembled on the verge of extinction

for 25–30 years', and 'it is now, like the great bustard nothing but a memory' (Hudson, 1900). If it had disappeared it soon recovered and up to 60 pairs bred on the Sussex Downs until 1937, at a little less than 0.2 per 100 ha (des Forges & Harber, 1963). In 1968 six pairs were nesting in the study area: 0.1 per 100 ha. The last pair nested successfully in 1980 (Prater, 1986). A very few may have been present in some subsequent years but there was no recorded successful breeding until 2007–11 and none have bred on the Norfolk Estate since 1975, although in recent years single birds have been seen.

Ringed plover

Two or three pairs nested annually on arable fields, with the last brood seen in 1973 on the Norfolk Estate.

Lapwing

With the great bustard, stone curlew and ringed plover lost as breeding species and the golden plover and curlew lost as resident in winter in significant numbers, the position of the lapwing had become of great concern; would it too be lost? The prognosis was not good. There has been a long decline in breeding numbers in Sussex since 1885 (*Birds of Sussex*, 1996). In Europe as a whole the

FIG 252. Male lapwing. (Olga Potts)

FIG 253. Lapwing nests (left) are very vulnerable; (right) on the Norfolk Estate tractor drivers avoid lapwing nests.

lapwing decreased by an average 3.3 per cent per year from 1980–2006, the fourth most severe decline of a farmland bird. Although only half the annual rate of decline of the grey partridge (Voříšek *et al.*, 2010); it was serious. Rather belatedly the lapwing was placed on the red list in the United Kingdom in 2009.

Counts of spring pairs across 2000 ha of the Sussex Study area in 1970 showed 64 pairs, giving an overall density of 3.2 pairs per 100 ha, with the density on the Norfolk Estate the same as that on the remainder of the area. Further counts in 1971–5 showed a decrease to two pairs per 100 ha, with the rolling of spring cereals believed to be a major cause of clutch loss. This practice virtually ceased in the mid-1970s but brought no reprieve. Neither did set-aside, which increased the amount of nesting habitat.

On the Norfolk Estate, the number of lapwing pairs has increased ten-fold to 40 (4 per 100 ha), considerably more than in 1970. Elsewhere in the Sussex Study area breeding numbers have continued to fall, with only 0.5 pairs per 100 ha in 2011. Despite the increase on the Norfolk Estate, the main feature is not the number of pairs but their high breeding success. This is difficult to measure with chicks hiding in growing crops, but broods of three or four full-grown young are frequent and in 2008 and 2009 the young to old ratio in post-breeding flocks was 1.5:1 – very high for the species. One reason why it is difficult to measure breeding success more accurately is the absence of wet areas attractive to lapwings, whereas these are abundant in the adjacent Arun valley. The recent springs have been unusually dry and in June the lapwings have left to join flocks on the wetlands as soon as they can fly. Winter flocks have recently increased from zero to 150–220.

The food of lapwing chicks was summarised by Shrubb (2007) and found to consist mostly of species found on damp grazed areas, habitats quite unlike the chalk downs of the Sussex Study area. I examined the food of 6 chicks in 1969 that had eaten 215 invertebrates. The most frequent species were the infamous wireworms or larvae of the click beetles (*Agriotes* spp.), followed by larvae of crane flies, the Tipulidae. Once very serious pests of cereals, the Sussex Study shows that click beetles declined to very low levels from the early 1970s through to about 2004, since when there has been a remarkable recovery, possibly due to the adoption of less toxic insecticide seed dressings. As we saw in Chapter 6, crane flies have increased strongly too. Beetles eaten by lapwing chicks included the ground beetles *Anchomenus dorsale* and *Amara aenea*, and the rove beetle *Stenus similis*. Since 1969 all three species have declined.

One reason for the high survival of young is considered to be fox control; there had been many cases of predation on unfledged chicks prior to 2007. There is support for this from recent ingenious studies that quantified chick survival separately for day and night with fox exclusion using electric fences (Rickenbach *et al.*, 2011). Further support comes from the extraordinarily high density (57 nests per 100 ha) and high breeding success in the Irish Grey Partridge Research Project where foxes and other predators are controlled (Buckley *et al.*, 2009).

GROUND-NESTING PASSERINES

Corn bunting

The corn bunting is a red-listed bird that has declined virtually throughout Europe since about 1976, with the decline averaging 3.2 per cent per annum during 1980–2006 (Voříšek *et al.*, 2010). A survey in Sussex in 1993–4 showed 1.3 singing males per 100 ha, with a reduction of 53–62 per cent since the mid-1970s (James, 1996). Numbers of corn buntings were much higher than this in the eastern part of the Sussex Study area, especially on Applesham, a traditional ley farm. Although not monitored annually until 2003 a number of counts have been made and all are plotted in Figure 255.

Surveys of the Norfolk Estate give 28 singing males in 1970 and 21 in the same area in June 1994. Surveys in 1995 and 1996 by Nick Brickle showed 8 and 7 pairs per 100 ha on Applesham and 2.3 and 1.8 on the other farms that did not have a traditional ley rotation (Ewald & Aebischer, 1999). In 1976 there were 16 singing males on a part of the Norfolk Estate that held 5 in 1993 and 9 in 2006. In 2003 during the first summer of biodiversity restoration there were 12 singing males at North Stoke, which increased to 20 over the next 3 years. Many of these birds moved to Peppering when HLS+ was extended there in 2007 (Fig. 257). North Stoke is 22 per cent of the Norfolk Estate but it held 63 per cent of the corn buntings in 2006, 46 per cent in 2007 and 10–25 per cent in subsequent years;

FIG 254. Corn bunting bringing moth caterpillars to chicks in a winter wheat field from a field of linseed. (Chris Knights)

the birds were spreading out to the east as conditions greatly improved there. In summary, the overall numbers on the Norfolk Estate have shown a substantial increase since 2003, but with a drop in 2011 (Fig. 255).

The composition of the insect food of corn bunting nestlings in the Sussex Study was studied from 1994–7 (Brickle & Harper, 1999). The main groups were Lepidoptera and sawfly caterpillars, grasshoppers, spiders and ground beetles and click beetles. After an impressive initial response to HLS+, numbers of corn buntings have steadied and one reason could be the virtual absence of sawflies, which comprised 16 per cent of the diet. Although increasing, grasshoppers remain scarce in and around most cereal fields on the Norfolk Estate and this, combined with the virtual absence of sawfly caterpillars, could impoverish food supplies, by about 30 per cent compared to the areas studied by Nick Brickle. Sawfly larvae were abundant on the Norfolk Estate in 1969 and judging by the food I saw carried to nestlings at the time they were the main food of corn bunting chicks. This could not be the case today. The relationship between sawfly numbers and corn bunting numbers would re-pay further study.

Where ground predators are not controlled nest predation appears to be high,

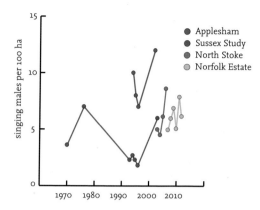

FIG 255. The number of singing corn buntings on the traditional ley farm, Applesham (with sawflies), remainder of Sussex Study area (red) excepting North Stoke (blue) with HLS+ from 2004 and Norfolk Estate as a whole (yellow) with HLS+ from 2008.

with up to 40 per cent losses at Applesham where however numbers remain high due to good food availability (Brickle & Harper, 1999; Brickle *et al.*, 2000).

Skylark

In May/June 1995 Andrew Wakeham-Dawson estimated the numbers of singing skylarks (= singing males; the females have only a weak sub-song) on a number of farms on the Sussex Downs, including fields in the Sussex Study area, to give an overall mean of nine pairs per 100 ha (Wakeham-Dawson & Aebischer, 2001). The density of skylark pairs at Applesham Farm, with its traditional system at the top end of favourability, was put at 27 per 100 ha in 2000 and 21 per 100 ha in 2003. Lower densities were expected on the Norfolk Estate, with no traditional ley farming on most of the area since 1970. In 2003 10.3 pairs per 100 ha were counted on North Stoke and 11.0 pairs per 100 ha on the neighbouring Lee Farm. By June 2011 there were 47 pairs per 100 ha on the Norfolk Estate, with the response to HLS+ shown in Figure 257.

A density of 47 pairs per 100 ha is high even for 'natural' heaths and steppes (Donald, 2004). On typical farmland numbers are very close to those at the start of HLS+ on the Norfolk Estate: about 10 pairs per 100 ha (Donald & Vickery, 2000). There were 14 pairs per 100 ha at Loddington in 1992 after four years of extensive voluntary set-aside (Stoate & Leake, 2002), and 6 per 100 ha on the RSPB's Hope Farm, before increasing to 15 after skylark plots had been installed for several years. The almost five-fold increase of the skylark on the Norfolk Estate, with an extra 370 pairs added since 2003, is remarkable against the background of continuing decreases elsewhere and the phasing out of set-aside, and we should be able to determine the reasons as it is an iconic, well-studied bird, and its decline has caused much public concern.

FIG 256. (left) Skylark densities are lower in oilseed rape than in cereals; (below left) the singing of many skylarks is what most people remember about a visit to the Sussex Study area. (Markus Jenny)

There are more than 300 papers in the scientific literature reporting studies on the skylark, but it is at once obvious there is no consensus about the relative importance of nest predation and the supply of insects for the chicks. The first modern study of skylarks, in an ideal habitat of mature grassy sand dunes, found nest predation rates of 90 per cent, with higher predation at greater nest densities (Delius, 1965). A major study of almost 1,000 nests in cereal crops during 1996–98 showed that almost half of nests were built near the tramlines. These nests were heavily predated, contributing greatly to an overall nest loss rate of 76 per cent (Donald *et al.*, 2002). On one farm in Norfolk where most variables (such as crop height) remained constant, predator control reduced nest losses from 88 per cent to 59 per cent. It was however doubted that predation was important because an increase in predators nationally had coincided with an increase in nesting success. This is however exactly what has happened with partridges where, other things equal, nest predation increases with nest density

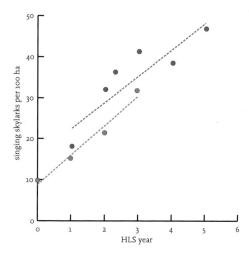

FIG 257. Response of the skylark to HLS+, the Norfolk Estate: pairs breeding per 100 ha on a log scale. Note that the slopes of increase are the same in phase 1 (North Stoke – blue) and phase 2 (Norfolk Estate – red), as a whole, but the intercepts on the vertical axis are different, reflecting the more wooded habitat at North Stoke.

and vice versa. The studies of relatively low densities of skylarks during the SAFFIE project from 2002–6 found nest losses low at 40 per cent but with at least 33 per cent due to predation, with filmed evidence showing the badger involved (Morris & Gilroy, 2008).

Skylark chicks are fed in the nest by parents able to forage over a large area and thus feed in the more insect-rich areas (Davis, 1967); even so, starvation of the chicks has been reported and it now may be a factor (Wilson *et al.*, 1997). Donald (2004) summarises what is known. As with the partridge chicks that forage for themselves, the diet is roughly in proportion to availability and not specialised, reflecting 'not only the type of habitat parent birds are foraging in, but also the human impact (such as pesticides) upon that habitat'. Despite much variation it appears the diet is mainly spiders, sawfly, butterfly and moth caterpillars, ground beetles, grasshoppers and crane flies. One brood of chicks in the Sussex Study, all killed by a stoat, had been fed almost entirely on *Pterostichus melanarius*, a ground beetle remaining common in herbicide-treated cereals (Clarke *et al.*, 2007). This diet differs from partridge chick diet in the absence of aphids, plant bugs, plant hoppers and weevils but there is considerable overlap.

The diet outside the breeding season is also well known; it is highly varied but the birds are heavily dependent on weedy winter stubbles, especially those with waste grain (Donald *et al.*, 2001). One study of seeds in skylark remains in hen harrier pellets (Clarke *et al.*, 2003) revealed that knotgrass and black bindweed obtained from game cover were important.

In its susceptibility to nest predation, reliance on insects at the chick stage and with a diet based on stubble weeds in winter, the skylark is like a miniature partridge. Paul Donald nonetheless concluded that there were five solutions to the skylark decline: more spring cereals; leaving small patches of ground clear of crops; more winter stubbles; more mixed farming and reduced pesticide applications. On the Norfolk Estate all these solutions have been implemented together with predator control, and the extraordinary rapid increase, almost paralleling that of the grey partridge, leans heavily towards predator control being a key factor. Whether it is or it isn't, the key is that the skylark has benefited enormously from a package of measures to rescue the grey partridge.

Meadow pipit

The story here is very different. From being a common breeder in the 1970s only a few pairs are now found on the Sussex Study area. Prior to the implementation of HLS+ only one count was made on the Norfolk Estate but it indicates the bird's former abundance. On 5 and 7 July 1971 'pairs' of birds that were seen from a Land Rover in the area included skylark (99), corn bunting (28) and meadow pipit (24). A few meadow pipit pairs remained in 2003 but only one by 2008 and no pairs have bred since then. In 2011 a search found only three pairs breeding on the nearby Amberley Mount where the species was numerous in the 1970s. This is very difficult to explain given that its main food – crane flies – have markedly increased in recent years. The species is declining on farmland virtually throughout Europe and it is on the amber list. Unfortunately, as remarked in *The Birds of Sussex*: 'the meadow pipit has a reputation for being an uninteresting species'. Given that the meadow pipit is a major host for the cuckoo, this is doubly unfortunate. Hen harriers can have a marked adverse affect on meadow pipit abundance on grouse moors in Scotland (Amar *et al.*, 2008) and although they have strongly increased in abundance, few of them have summered in the Sussex Study area, ruling out this as a cause.

OTHER RESIDENT SPECIES

Song thrush

It soon became obvious from the counting that the Norfolk Estate had suddenly become highly attractive to song thrushes in the winter and spring. In the first winter of the expanded programme of HLS+, 137 were counted, 95 per cent in strips of kale. The kale was thickly populated by garden and Kentish snails and many anvils were well used (Fig. 259). The increase in winter has not been evident in spring or summer, so it must be assumed that most of the attracted birds are migrants from continental Europe. Weediness encourages snails and so numbers in conservation headlands are also often high in summer.

There has been much concern about the status of the song thrush, mainly because the reasons for its decline from the late 1970s are poorly understood. The implications of a long-term decline in egg shell thickness are not known (Green, 1998) and the Biodiversity Species Action Plan mentions a host of problems: shortage of food and nest sites, predation, severe winters, dry soils, competition with the blackbird and for good measure, in France, shooting. Snails are not mentioned.

Yellowhammer

The main impact has been in the numbers in winter and spring, with numbers counted rising from 42 in 2005–6 to more than 200 in 2011–12 when almost all these birds were found feeding on wheat at partridge feeders. Breeding numbers have not responded significantly, with pairs currently found in tall hawthorn and

FIG 258. Kale cover strips for partridges result in abundant snails.

FIG 259. Evidence of the extent to which the song thrushes eat snails is evident at the numerous anvils.

blackthorn hedges which are atypical of the Norfolk Estate. This species is out of line with other farmland birds that have declined, with its decline starting later in the 1980s. Although the adults feed on grain if available, the chicks are fed a range of invertebrates, mainly caterpillars of moths and butterflies, crane flies and beetles (Stoate *et al.*, 1998). Insecticides were increasingly used on cereals in early summer through the 1980s (Ewald & Aebischer, 1999) and there is evidence that this had harmful effects on the chick food supply (Hart *et al.*, 2006). As part of HLS+ this use of insecticide no longer takes place on the Norfolk Estate and if there has been improved survival of nestlings as a result, it could also help to explain why winter numbers have increased. Why breeding numbers have not increased significantly is not known. As the new hedgerows become suitable for the species, a large increase is expected.

Goldfinch

This species is one of the very few that benefited from set-aside but when this system was abandoned and replaced by HLS+ their numbers did not fall as expected, they rapidly grew. The reasons are not understood but they are greatly attracted to the unharvested conservation headlands where they feed on lesser burdock, thistles and teasel.

Summer migrants

The blackcap and whitethroat have both shown large increases, but not the chiffchaff. The increase of the blackcap may have nothing to do with HLS+ but the increase of the whitethroat certainly has. In 2007 when 79 pairs were counted on the full area, only 3 (4 per cent) were breeding in newly created habitats, whereas by 2011 when 173 pairs were counted, 53 (31 per cent) were in newly created habitats, mostly game cover crops alongside beetle banks.

Raptors and owls

In many ways the response of raptors and owls is the most remarkable result of all. Some of the detail was given in Chapter 8 but the overall totals per 100 ha are given as Fig. 260 showing a five-fold response compared to stability in the remainder of the Sussex Study. A pallid harrier stayed from 14 September to 4 October 2011. It was seen by more than 1,000 people during the weekend of 17–18 September and by many others at other times. Many of the keener birders recorded ten species of raptors whilst looking for the harrier. The implications are profound; it appears these birds are short of food elsewhere.

How do these numbers of raptors and owls seen in daytime compare with those on farmland landscapes before pesticides were used and when raptors were not

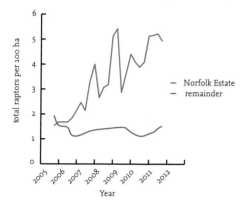

FIG 260. Numbers of raptors and owls seen in daytime on the Norfolk Estate for each season and on the remainder of the Sussex Study area for autumn only.

subject to persecution? Here the very detailed study by the Craighead brothers in a 9,300 ha of open farmland in south-central Michigan gives comparable data to that in Sussex (though, uniquely, they also quantified the food of the raptors and the numbers of prey available). During 1941–9 eight species were regular at combined seasonal densities, with an average 0.98±0.14 per 100 ha (Craighead & Craighead, 1956). This is very close to the situation in the Sussex Study area, apart from on the Norfolk Estate, where densities are now almost five times higher.

CONCLUSIONS

Birds

The red-listed birds have done well, especially ground-nesting species and raptors. Of the 968 non-raptor pairs added in four years, 687 (71 per cent) were red-listed species.

The increase of both species of partridge was due to increased survival of nests, chicks and the raising of the carrying capacity by the provision of grain and nest sites. All boxes were ticked, but what of the other species? The evidence suggests that the skylark, lapwing and possibly corn bunting have benefited from the control of ground predators. Food shortage, the lack of sawfly caterpillars, may have limited the effectiveness of this in the case of the corn bunting. The provision of game-cover crops has helped increase the song thrush in winter. The whitethroat has benefited from extra nesting cover, the goldfinch from game cover and unharvested conservation headlands, and the yellowhammer has benefited from the provision of grain. The results

FIG 261. Yellowhammer in blackthorn, an excellent protective cover. This species has benefited from HLS+.

were somewhat similar to those at Loddington, where there were strong increases in the seed-eating goldfinch, tree sparrow, greenfinch, linnet and bullfinch. The extra biodiversity has transformed the situation of the raptors and owls.

Mammals

Brown hare

In the early 1950s there were very few brown hares on the Sussex Study area but with a surge in numbers after myxomatosis drastically reduced rabbit numbers and as predator control was initiated to increase grey partridge numbers. Brown hares peaked in 1958, with 44 shot per 100 ha on North Farm, whereupon a slow decline set in as rabbit numbers increased, with very low numbers reached on most of the farms by 2004.

Brown hares seen during the bird counts on the Norfolk Estate increased 2.4-fold in the first year of HLS+ at a time of dramatic increases in the number of rabbits. In subsequent years however, the hares became difficult to see in daytime due to the extra cover in overwinter stubbles, stubble turnips and fodder beet. Tapper (1999) calculated that late-winter densities in optimum habitats can be expected to be 5 per 100 ha rising six-fold to 30 per 100 ha with fox control and to 40 with 'improved' optimum habitats.

In night counts in February 2012 53 per 100 ha were counted on the Norfolk Estate, about 21 times the numbers before HLS+. The UK's Biodiversity Species Action Plan originally aimed for a doubling of numbers, now somewhat revised downwards. After extensive investigations over many years in a combination of field work and computer modelling, Reynolds & Tapper (1995) concluded that foxes play a major role in brown hare population dynamics in many environments. In their validated models the final density of hares was three to six times higher than when fox predation was set to zero. Reviewing the evidence about the brown hare it was later concluded that, 'when predation control was stopped, hare densities fell, even where the habitat improvements remained in place' (Reynolds *et al.*, 2010).

FIG 262. Harvest mice were fairly common in the early 1970s, with signs they are coming back. (Chris Knights)

FIG 263. Sussex Study area: dormouse in 1973, one of the least known species, still present.

Small mammals

These were not measured directly but a comparison of small mammals in barn owl pellets collected from the whole study area in 1971–2 with those collected on the Norfolk Estate in 2010–11, indicates few differences (Table 34).

Barn owls are frequently seen hunting along beetle-banks on the Norfolk Estate, and, as we should expect perhaps, bank voles are common. This brings them out into the arable crop habitats where most wood mice are also found (despite their name). An investigation of barn owl diet across Britain comparing 1974 with 1997 concluded that the common shrew had decreased in importance in the diet, whereas wood mouse and bank vole had increased (Love *et al.*, 2000). Ideally these investigations should be related to the approximate four-year cycle in field vole abundance. In the Sussex Study area, this cycle may be partly related to weasel abundance (Tapper, 1979).

TABLE 34. Barn owl prey items from analysis of pellets in the Sussex Study area, comparing 1971–2 with that on the Norfolk Estate in 2010–11. The diet composition is indicated by percentage frequency of occurrence.

year	1971–72 (%)	2010–11 (%)
mole	0	0.4
common shrew	8.8	14.1
pygmy shrew	1.0	1.3
water shrew	0.0	0.4
rabbit	0.9	0.4
bank vole	1.2	8.5
field vole	47.2	29.9
water vole	0	2.1
wood mouse	11.1	32.9
yellow-necked mouse	1.7	1.3
house mouse	5.9	0.8
harvest mouse	15.4	6.8
brown rat	3.6	0.8
birds	3.3	0
total	**100.1**	**99.7**

Most interest centres on the harvest mouse, which in the early 1970s was the subject of a major investigation in the Sussex Study area (Trout, 1976), with numbers found to be highest on the Norfolk Estate in some unploughed downland with tall grass and brambles that was bulldozed flat in the mid-1970s. Numbers have probably increased with HLS+ where habitats have remained but they still appear to be low judging from their scarcity in barn owl pellets.

CONCLUSION

As a result of the desire to restore the numbers of a game bird for shooting, a whole ecosystem has been brought back to life: rare arable flowers, insects, mammals and birds, including raptors.

CHAPTER 11

Resetting the Barometer

T HE BAROMETER HAS SWUNG wildly. We have seen how the grey
partridge was driven from Britain by successive ice ages, only
returning each time as things warmed up. During the most recent
glaciation, grey partridges were cooped up along the northern shore of the
Mediterranean along with red-legged and rock partridges that could not escape
to North Africa. What happened in the east is far less clear, but before agriculture
it appears all these partridges were thriving.

FIG 264. These deep soil ridges are prepared for stone–soil separation prior to planting with
potatoes: wildlife can co-exist with modern agriculture, but only with skill and stewardship.
This lapwing successfully hatched chicks. (Chris Knights)

We have seen how agriculture affected grey partridges in several ways, from the first conversion of natural grasslands to the developments in arable farming. For thousands of years farming actually conserved the savannah-type landscapes formerly maintained by the mega-herbivores and the resulting biodiversity was high well into the twentieth century. Stock farming however means war on the top predators and as they were extirpated there could have been a problem with an upsurge of smaller predators but this was prevented by an army of poultry keepers, gamekeepers and fur hunters. So despite some parasites spread by poultry, partridges continued to thrive.

A few kinds of insecticide have been on the scene for centuries, with some deaths of partridges. However, even when dieldrin hit in the 1950s, partridge numbers were not affected overall. At the same time the early adverse effects of herbicides on the supply of insect food of chicks were hidden behind the good weather and excellent seasons of 1959–61. From 1962 onwards things were never the same again; chick survival rates dropped and gamekeepers found they could not keep numbers high enough for driven shooting and so turned increasingly to pen-reared birds. These were the first dramatic signs that modern agriculture was affecting wildlife badly. In their warmer, drier, less cultivated habitats the *Alectoris* partridges have been less affected but they too have declined in some former strongholds, particularly in the main arable areas of Spain and in areas where mountain pastures are no longer grazed using traditional methods. So, what can be done?

In the early spring of 1968 when the Sussex Study began there were 3.5 billion people on earth and whilst this chapter was being written the number passed 7 billion. By itself this would have put enormous pressures on biodiversity due to the increased food supply necessary, but it is much worse than this, because every inhabitant is using, and demanding, more resources, from water to bio-fuels, and land is continually being lost to infrastructure developments, particularly roads. For partridges the barometer is not set to 'fair'. On present trends the human population is expected to level off at between 9 and 10 billion. Consequently all the agricultural pressures that have led to the precarious position of partridges and the thousands of plants and animals that have in the past shared their habitats will increase. Many would argue that far too many natural habitats have already been cleared to feed the extra 3.5 billion since 1968. It follows that globally it is essential to increase intensification to save the natural habitats not yet destroyed by cropping and grazing. In Europe however there is pressure to reduce the impact of modern agriculture on wildlife; some aspects of agribusiness have become unacceptable to the tax-payers and here there is no burgeoning population.

FIG 265. Pakistan wheat harvest 2004: as the population of the Indian sub-continent continues to grow the need to produce wheat from every available bit of countryside is certain to bring huge pressures on wildlife.

As a schoolboy I was concerned about the effects of sprays; a tractor driver died from Denocate poisoning on a neighbouring farm, we found dead hares and knew about the partridges poisoned in the south. In the Faroe Islands in 1960 I collected a great skua chick dead in shell. Later I sent it with some shag eggs for analysis. I was galvanised when I learned that the chick, from a most oceanic location, contained significant levels of two insecticides and became determined to reduce the effects of pesticides on wildlife, the partridge giving me the opportunity. I never for one moment thought I might end up defending hunting, let alone predator control.

The central question is who is going to pay for any restoration of partridge numbers on farmland? Who is going to pay to compromise some aspects of modern farming in the long term? To me, not a hunter, it is starkly obvious that the future of red-listed partridges and the other species sharing their habitats will generally depend on enlightened hunting producing sustained revenue for habitat management. But hunting cannot do this on its own, without public support, and hunters themselves will have to generate a lot more enthusiasm for wild as opposed to pen-reared birds, entailing a much more sensitive but focused and efficient control of nest predators. In the long-run hunters of wild quarry will be incentivised only by self-interest, and numbers are crucial here.

What is needed is often a counter-intuitive approach. As already mentioned above, it makes no sense to oppose the further intensification of agriculture because it is this that could save many natural habitats. It is difficult for those who have done such a brilliant job for wildlife by protecting it from harmful pesticides, persecution and over-hunting to come to terms with conservation through hunting, but if they are not able to do so then I cannot see a way ahead. The fact that 11 red-listed birds species have increased during the restoration of partridge numbers described in the previous chapter, compared to only 1 out of 12 nationally, should help put to rest such difficulties.

FIG 266. Grey partridge, Boora, 2011: saved from extinction in Ireland in the nick of time. This male was in a pair that raised ten young. (Kieran Buckley)

The Stewardship Scheme that was introduced in the UK in 2005 has a basic Entry Level (ELS), taken up by the majority of farmers, and a Higher Level (HLS) for areas with a high biodiversity value. The aim of many organisations, including DEFRA and the EU, had been to halt biodiversity loss by 2010 with varying degrees of restoration of former numbers by 2015 or 2020. By general consent the ELS has not stemmed the general decline of farmland birds despite a wide uptake. The fact that even the first of these aspirations had not been met went unchallenged at the Nagoya CBD Conference, 18–29 October 2010. Agricultural intensity had caused the collapse of Europe's farmland bird populations during 1970–90 (Donald *et al.*, 2000) and its impact continued.

HLS on the other hand, with 100 top-up options for farms with a higher biodiversity value, provides more scope. In the ESAs it enabled various options to continue, as in the Sussex Study area. The most useful options for partridges are conservation headlands and beetle banks, and within HLS:

- HF14 – 'unharvested, unfertilised conservation headlands' @ £440 per ha;
- HF12 – wild bird seed mix @ £475 per ha; and
- HG6 & HG7 – for low-input cereals to enable under-sowing and the creation of an arable mosaic or patchwork quilt in the landscape; these last options currently pay £250 per ha.

These are the options that restored biodiversity to the Norfolk Estate but progress elsewhere has generally been at a snail's pace. This is particularly so in mainland Europe.

In January 2009 Council Regulation 74/2009 article 29 enabled 'innovative operations to support the conservation of biodiversity'. Legislation was therefore still moving in the right direction, but all these measures assume some matching funds from the member states and with the economic crisis deepening, these

FIG 267. Goldfinches benefited from set-aside but increased even more with HLS+. (Jacques Hicter)

were often not forthcoming, for example in Hungary, and may not be so for decades. Overall the public funds available have begun to decline, and this is likely to continue for the foreseeable future. On the other side of the fence the profitability of cereal growing has improved and will do so further as consumers drive markets underpinned by the diversion of grain to bio-fuels, for example in the major case of maize in the US.

In their proposed reforms to the rules about what farmers will have to do in return for public sector payments for the period from 2013, the EU Commission for Agriculture in October 2011 acknowledged the need to diversify landscapes. It was proposed that all farmers should grow at least three different kinds of crops with no crop exceeding 70 per cent of the cropped area. More relevant to partridges they also proposed:

> 1) *Farmers shall ensure that at least 7 per cent of their eligible hectares* [defined], *excluding areas under permanent grassland, is ecological focus area such as land left fallow, terraces, landscape features, buffer strips and afforested areas* [as referred to]
> 2) *The Commission shall be empowered to ... further define the types of ecological focus areas and to add and define other types of ecological focus areas that can be taken into account for the respect of the* [7 per cent].

Where the 7 per cent originated is not clear but it had been adopted earlier in the year in Switzerland's agri-environment legislation; it seems completely arbitrary. On the one hand could such a policy stick in the face of growing demand for food? On the other, is 7 per cent enough?

Conservation headlands on the Norfolk Estate cover 9 per cent of the farmed area, and it is not such a stretch to reconcile this with the 7 per cent referred to by the EU, although at the time of writing the envisaged composition of the percentage was not clear.

At present, conservation headlands are confined to an ever vanishing small part of arable farmland in Britain. The situation is even worse in the rest of Europe and in North America. Much more should be done to conserve this part of our biodiversity and cultural heritage. It is now extremely unusual to find cereals planted without any herbicides used anywhere in Europe and the valuable role of game conservation in preserving representative ancient farmland floras needs to be recognised far more than it is. There have been many schemes to encourage rare arable plants in Germany, but they have not been linked to grey partridge conservation. In the long run, conservation has to be fitted in to a consumer-driven agriculture, but far more could be done.

When *The Partridge* was written, 27 years ago, there were arguably around half a million pairs of grey partridge in the UK. The current figure has been estimated at around 60,000 pairs. One idealistic target might therefore be to increase present numbers by around 440,000 pairs, equivalent to more than 1,000 times what has been achieved on the Norfolk Estate in eight years. To put this in perspective, to restore numbers to the pre-1940 level would be equivalent to more than 5,000 times what has been achieved on the Norfolk Estate. Even the lower of these targets is not remotely realistic, but what kind of scenario can we envisage?

This book has shown that the restoration of the cereal ecosystem that sustained grey partridges and the associated biodiversity in the past would not have happened without the motivation of shooting wild partridges and the support of public funding. Had shooting been banned, it would never have happened at all. Whatever the aim is in the restoration of numbers, the higher the densities that can be achieved on an area, the lower the number of areas that will require public funding. On the Norfolk Estate, with HLS+ partly funded by government, grey partridge pair densities increased 34-fold in eight years. This is a ten times higher increase than could have been achieved without predator control, and such higher numbers are needed to justify the private part of the funding. We have a win-win-win situation. The taxpayer benefits, the ecosystem benefits and the private investment is rewarded.

What I am proposing is a deliberate private–public partnership to co-fund partridge habitat management. This would be economically efficient and unlike many agri-environment schemes currently operated, it would produce a spectacular amount of sustainable biodiversity. Far better to target management where it will produce results than spreading the effort far and wide in the hope it would produce results, as with the 7 per cent contemplated by the EU. If agriculture is eventually going to result in biodiversity deserts, it will be far better to have some oases. For many however, a sticking point would be predator control. Without predator control, restoring partridge numbers

FIG 268. The Albany Quail Project in Georgia, US, has demonstrated that a very high density of wild quail can co-exist with uncompromised crop production and irrigation if fields are divided with strips of nesting and brood-rearing cover. This kind of management driven by the desire to hunt wild quail has restored very significant biodiversity. (Clay Sisson)

sufficiently to enable shooting will be as difficult for shoot owners as it is expensive for tax-payers. Shoot owners will not have the motivation to invest in habitat improvement and replace pen-reared birds with wild birds. Without predator control, it will be impossible to raise enough revenue to put partridge conservation on a sustainable course. The issue has to be addressed.

With the release of a seminal review, *The Trophic Downgrading of Earth* by Estes *et al.* (2011), Michael Soulé, co-founder of conservation biology, commented: 'Why is it taking so long for ecologists to understand that the stripping of top predators from the earth's marine, freshwater and terrestrial communities is probably a greater threat to biodiversity than other forcing agencies such as climate change.' Similarly, Prugh *et al.* (2010) had concluded that the restoration of top predators to areas where they have been extirpated in the past could do much to stem the tide of undesirable meso-predator (e.g. fox) increase.

Many conservation authorities have dismissed the direct control of predators, completely ignoring the possibility that hunters, gamekeepers and others might to some extent be replacing the top-predators. Recognition of these effects could

FIG 269. Many public footpaths and bridle-ways criss-cross the Norfolk Estate.

FIG 270. The Norfolk estate has become a highly popular site for bird watchers. More than a thousand came to see the pallid harrier in September 2011. This group are delighted at having seen so many raptors, including a wintering rough-legged buzzard that stayed six months in 2011–12.

put predator control in its true ecological perspective and deal with some 'vexed issues'. Compensation for stock losses caused by wolves, cougars, bears and lynx may be appropriate where conserved wildlife is valuable or highly desirable, but even if was affordable it is impracticable in the lowlands of Europe. Even in the more marginal habitats, where there is no compensation for farm stock lost to the top predators and no licences to shoot them, they continue to be illegally poisoned, for example in Portugal where at least 33 wolves have been poisoned in recent years. In contrast, where licensed hunting of wolves is allowed there is no need for compensation or poisons, for example in parts of Spain.

It is becoming ever more obvious that the strictly protectionist approach can be counterproductive. Management is necessary and accepted for herbivores (Levy, 2011) and sooner or later it will become necessary for predators. Adopting this ethic might have saved the Langholm grouse moor and its harriers, grouse and gamekeeper livelihoods. After summarising the issues in their 'New

Naturalist', *Grouse*, Watson & Moss (2008) concluded: 'In British and Irish conditions some predator control is a necessary part of conservation.' They went further, exploring an 'ethical basis' for predator control, concluding this could be achieved 'if it could be shown that the predator (needing to be controlled) is unnaturally abundant and is suppressing desired creatures to unacceptably low levels'. By now, readers should know I agree.

There are vast areas where many ground-nesting farmland birds are declining, declines that are usually assumed to be almost entirely due to changes in farming. The evidence in this book suggests that this is not justified and that

FIG 271. Conservation headland, Norfolk Estate. (Olga Potts)

legal predation control substantially benefits the lapwing, corn bunting, skylark and several other species including the hare, as well as underpinning the whole ecosystem approach. In general, the situation of farmland birds is getting worse not better; so many previous prescriptions are not working. The publication *The State of the UK's Birds 2011* should make us all think. After declining since the 1970s the national trends for the years 1995–2009 remain: lapwing –13 per cent; skylark –11 per cent; linnet –23 per cent; corn bunting –29 per cent and grey partridge a staggering –50 per cent. These five species are amongst the ones that have increased most on the Norfolk Estate.

We need a farmland ecosystem approach to save at least some of the rich biodiversity that was formerly found on farmland. We have seen how 217 species of plants have been recorded in cereal crops in the Sussex study but that we can only view most of them now in conservation headlands. The seeds of key species have persisted remarkably well in the soil and species have been saved from local extinction on the Norfolk Estate, but a steady depletion continues elsewhere. Some 165 species of birds have been recorded in the Sussex Study area and these have been comparatively well studied. I have argued there are ten times as many insects and other invertebrates as there are birds (even excluding the soil micro-fauna such as free-living nematodes, worms and mites). The future of most of these species is dependent on intervention. Looking down through the food chains from partridges it is obvious that our knowledge of the invertebrates is woefully inadequate. Looking up it is also obvious that our knowledge of the net effect of competition amongst predators is equally wanting. Neither has been explored properly but from the glimpses we have had in this book there are many exciting things to discover.

In the current economic climate it is more important than ever to focus resources on the urgent and practical issues. The continued funding of long-term comprehensive research is however needed to inform and underpin practical research and it should be a top priority, by definition protected from temporary 'economic downturns' and political fashions. I hope the Sussex Study can continue.

Finally, I am absolutely convinced that a great deal of countryside biodiversity can be regained without compromising food production and with public acclaim. It can only happen however if the agribusiness, protectionist and hunter lobbies genuinely co-operate to solve the vexed issues. Too often these tribes play marbles in the middle of the road unaware of the juggernaut.

Research Data

APPENDIX I: DAMERHAM SOME BASIC INFORMATION COMPILED BY JOHN ASH AND ROGER BRAY IN 1969

TABLE 1.1. Grey partridge counts 1946–69.

| Year | March | | August sample | | September count | December count |
	Pairs	Single males	Total counted	Young to adult ratio		
1946	114	?	–	–	–	–
1947	121	?	384	3.57	1164	1156
1948	242	?	778	3.55	1991	1360
1949	248	25	643	4.31	3083	1696
1950	351	23	769	2.30	2636	1356
1951	350	38	863	1.85	2277	1351
1952	443	41	1397	2.50	2980	1507
1953	531	19	1448	1.38	2236	1821
1954	589	68	551	0.56	1740	1589
1955	442	128	970	1.33	1968	1473
1956	404	73	907	1.63	1913	1583
1957	532	44	1215	2.29	3410	1629
1958	590	37	555	0.82	1890	1053
1959	316	57	710	2.09	1759	1339
1960	–	–	–	–	–	–

year	March		August sample		September count	December count
	pairs	single males	total counted	young to adult ratio		
1961	352	43	490	1.16	1369	–
1962	380	71	292	0.29	1182	–
1963	132	55	99	0.4	635	–
1964	89	30	242	1.3	1018	–
1965	92	15	96	0.7	282	–
1966	33	7	52	1.9	171	–
1967	60	12	79	0.6	172	–
1968	67	5	116	1.6	313	–
1969	58	15	144	2.1	322	–

TABLE 1.2. Grey partridge annual losses of first nests, 1949–59.

year	nests found	% lost	causes of nest loss				
			eggs predated	females predated	farming	disease and some other causes	unknown
1949	123	51	5	19	30	3	6
1950	211	55	14	28	60	3	10
1951	159	45	3	23	22	3	20
1952	159	41	–	19	29	6	11
1953	222	37	9	12	36	39	17
1954	233	53	18	39	23	10	34
1955	138	51	15	23	15	1	16
1956	207	55	20	44	23	–	27
1957	252	44	6	28	56	2	20
1958	238	50	8	32	35	3	42
1959	108	56	5	16	33	1	5
Total	2,050	44	103	283	362	41	208

TABLE 1.3. Grey partridge: estimates of chicks hatched and mortality before mid-August, 1948–59.

year	estimated number of chicks hatched	% chick mortality by mid-August
1948	2,227	23
1949	2,572	17
1950	3,848	58
1951	3,307	61
1952	4,650	52
1953	6,448	77
1954	5,456	88
1955	3,922	77
1956	3,713	65
1957	5,707	57
1958	5,332	82
1959	2,243	41
Totals	49,425	

TABLE 1.4. Grey partridge: pen-reared young partridges released, 1946–69.

year	Perdix	year	Perdix	year	Perdix
1946	0	1954	63	1962	300
1947	0	1955	236	1963	305
1948	0	1956	62	1964	650
1949	118	1957	146	1965	0
1950	132	1958	111	1966	0
1951	41	1959	152	1967	0
1952	40	1960	0	1968	0
1953	0	1961	0	1969	0

TABLE 1.5. Grey partridges shot 1946–69.

| Year | ADULTS | | | YOUNG | | | | Total | % of Sept. count |
| | | | | wild | | not examined | | | |
	males	females	sex?	males (pen reared)	females (pen reared)	for sex	at all		
1946	–	–	–	–	–	–	–	–	–
1947	3	1	–	6	3	–	–	13	1
1948	64	38	17	82	105	43	23	372	19
1949	132	121	–	333 (3)	335 (3)	3	27	951	31
1950	171	117	–	221 (4)	195 (3)	–	2	706	27
1951	150	98	–	148 (1)	143 (1)	–	5	544	24
1952	227	171	–	303 (1)	292 (3)	–	2	995	33
1953	97	65	1	91	58	1	–	313	14
1954	73	47	–	22	23	–	–	165	9
1955	76	50	–	80 (5)	59 (6)	–	2	267	14
1956	94	49	–	84 (6)	83 (1)	–	–	310	16
1957	246	165	–	372 (18)	358 (12)	2	–	1,143	34
1958	186	107	–	130 (8)	147 (16)	–	2	572	30
1959	106	51	–	98 (3)	95 (7)	1	–	351	20
1960	–	–	–	–	–	–	–	346	?
1961	–	–	–	–	–	–	–	414	30
1962	–	–	–	–	–	–	–	153	13
1963–69	No Shooting								

APPENDIX 2: SOME MEASUREMENTS OF FIELD SIZE WHERE GREY PARTRIDGES WERE STUDIED

Field size (ha)	Year	Place	Authority
9	1907	Great Witchingham	Potts, 1980
9.7	1938	Wisconsin	McCabe & Hawkins, 1946
10	1940	Washington	Yocom, 1943
6.5	1945	England	Westmacott & Worthington, 1981
2	1946	Britain	Pollard et al., 1967
3.9	1947	Hungary	Faragó, 1997
4	1947	CLF, North Yorkshire	Potts, 1986
1	1949	Elbe Lowlands, Czech.	Figala et al., 2001
100	1952	South Russia	Poyarkov, 1955
6.44	1955	Damerham	This study
1.5	1959	Germany	Frank, 1970
4	1960	Denmark	Møller, 1983
7	1969	South Gatenais, France	Gindre & Allion, 1971
14	1970	West Barsham	Potts, 1980
11.0	1972	England	Westmacott & Worthington, 1981
16.0	1972	North Farm, SSA	Potts & Vickerman, 1974
16	1972	Beauce	Aubineau et al., 1974
17	1972	Saskatchewan	Hunt, 1974
30	1975	Montana	Weigand, 1977
3	1975	Witry–les-Reims	Pépin, 1981
20	1978	North Dakota	Schulz, 1980
3.4	1978	Wetterau, Germany	Döring & Helfrich, 1986
30	1978	Wisconsin	Church, 1980
24	1980	Iowa	McCrow, 1982

9	1980	Denmark	Møller, 1983
15.0	1981	Norfolk	Green, 1984
9.5	1982	Seine et Marne	Birkan, 1977b, 1985
1	1985	Southeast Poland	Dudzinski, 1988
6	1985	CLF, North Yorkshire	Potts, 1986
20	1986	Damerham	This study
20	1986	Norfolk Estate	Potts, 1980
12	1987	Salisbury Plain	Tapper et al., 1996
1.5	1989	Thessalonika	Thomaides & Papageorgiou, 1992
45	1989	Lajta, Hungary	Faragó, 1997
13.7	1996	Elbe Lowlands, Czech.	Figala et al., 2001
2.4	1996	Tuscany, Italy	Rosin et al., 2009
148	2005	Sal'skie Steppe, Russia	this study
10	2011	Norfolk Estate	this study

See also Joannon et al. (2008)

APPENDIX 3: GREY PARTRIDGE: STUDIES CALCULATING NEST LOSSES FROM COUNTS AT END OF BREEDING SEASON

Site	Years incl.	Keeper?	% Nest losses	Authority
Gatchina, Russia	1886–1909	1	29	Dits, 1917
Great Withingham	1903–15	1	31	Middleton, 1936a
Esterhazy, Hungary	1922–33	1	19	de Karkovany, 1935
Manydown	1934–38	1	22	Potts, 1986
West Barsham	1935–52	1	31	Potts, 1986
Damerham	1947–61	1	31	Blank & Ash, 1962
Micheldever	1952–55	1	29	Jenkins, 1956

West Barsham	1953–78	1	32	Potts, 1986
North Farm	1957–67	1	35	Potts, 1986
Manydown	1957–85	1	35	Potts, 1986
NGC UK	1961–77	1	29	Potts, 1986
Damerham	1962–85	2	37	Potts, 1986
Sussex	1968–85	1	37	Potts, 1986
Sussex	1968–85	2	66	Potts, 1986
Applesham	1970–85	2	51	Potts, 1986
Germany	1977–80	2	28	Schulz & Döring, 1982
Boconnoc	1977–83	1	21	Potts, 1986
Germany	1979–83	2	28	Döring & Helfrich, 1986
Salisbury Plain	1984–91	1	19	Tapper et al., 1999
		2	47	
Applesham	1986–10	2	66	This study
Sussex	1986–10	2	63	This study
Lajta, Hungary	1989–95	2	60	Faragó, 1997
Walbeck, Germany	1991–93	1	53	Pethig, 1993
Loddington	1991–2000	1	36	This study
Tuscany, Italy	1998–2004	2	66	Rosin et al., 2009
Hicter Farms, France	2000–05	1	35	This study
Sussex	2004–10	1	15	This study
Sussex	2004–10	2	50	This study

Losses on areas with fulltime control of ground predators and Corvidae = 1; other = 2.
Data from reared and released birds have been excluded so far as possible.

APPENDIX 4: THE VARIETY AND ABUNDANCE OF RAPTORS SEEN DURING GREY PARTRIDGE STUDIES IN ENGLAND, US, FRANCE, HUNGARY, RUSSIA; DAURIAN PARTRIDGE IN CHINA; AND RED-LEGGED PARTRIDGES IN SPAIN AND PORTUGAL

	all year observation				stubble counts only					
	Damerham 1951–4 (Ash, 1960)	Montana 1969–71 (Weigand, 1977)	Sussex 2005–11*	Portugal 2010–11*	Sussex 1970–2011*	Russia 2004*	Hungary 1996*	China 1996*	Spain 1996–2005*	France 2001–5*
black vulture	o	o	o	4	o	o	o	o	12	o
griffon vulture	o	o	o	6	o	o	o	o	o	o
black kite	o	o	o	12	1	o	o	o	168	o
red kite	o	o	21	2	3	o	o	o	o	o
black-shouldered kite	o	o	o	3	o	o	o	o	o	o
Montagu's harrier	1	o	1	2	6	13	6	o	121	1
pallid harrier	o	o	2	o	1	31	o	o	o	o
unidentified harrier	o	o	o	o	4	21	o	o	o	2
hen harrier	24	42	30	2	7	4	o	4	o	2
marsh harrier	o	o	10	o	22	15	37	o	18	18
goshawk	1	o	2	4	1	o	1	o	1	4
sparrowhawk	100	o	73	o	184	4	o	3	1	3
Levant sparrowhawk	o	o	o	o	o	1	o	o	o	o
Japanese sparrowhawk	o	o	o	o	o	o	o	1	o	o
sharp-shinned hawk	o	1	o	o	o	o	o	o	o	o
honey buzzard	o	o	o	o	1	1	o	o	1	o
buzzard	223	o	278	4	399	o	47	2	53	7
steppe buzzard	o	o	o	o	o	19	o	o	o	o
upland buzzard	o	o	o	o	o	o	o	2	o	o
long-legged buzzard	o	o	o	o	o	6	o	o	o	o

	Damerham 1951–4 (Ash, 1960)	Montana 1969–71 (Weigand, 1977)	Sussex 2005–11*	Portugal 2010–11*	Sussex 1970–2011*	Russia 2004*	Hungary 1996*	China 1996*	Spain 1996–2005*	France 2001–5*
Swainson's hawk	0	7	0	0	0	0	0	0	0	0
short-toed eagle	0	0	0	8	0	0	1	0	12	0
imperial eagle	0	0	0	9	0	0	6	0	10	0
lesser spotted eagle	0	0	0	0	0	9	0	0	0	0
Bonelli's eagle	0	0	0	1	0	0	0	0	2	0
golden eagle	0	13	0	0	0	0	0	0	4	0
booted eagle	0	0	0	2	0	0	0	0	25	1
red-footed falcon	0	0	0	0	0	1	10	0	0	0
amur falcon	0	0	9	0	0	0	0	1	0	0
merlin	22	1	0	0	16	0	0	0	0	0
kestrel	377	0	163	8	795	4	21	0	27	14
lesser kestrel	0	0	0	0	0	0	0	0	17	0
American kestrel	0	9	0	0	0	0	0	0	0	0
hobby	12	0	5	0	31	0	3	0	2	1
peregrine	11	0	13	0	17	2	0	1	2	0
saker falcon	0	0	0	0	0	0	2	0	0	0
prairie falcon	0	4	0	0	0	0	0	0	0	0
eagle owl	0	0	0	14	0	0	0	0	3	0
short-eared owl	–	47	12	0	5	1	0	0	0	0
long-eared owl	–	0	1	0	0	0	0	0	0	0
tawny owl	–	0	0	1	2	0	0	0	0	0
little owl	–	0	5	0	43	0	0	0	9	0
burrowing owl	0	1	0	0	0	0	0	0	0	0
scop's owl	0	0	0	1	0	0	0	0	0	0
barn owl	–	0	34	0	20	0	0	0	0	0
totals	**771**	**132**	**661**	**93**	**1,558**	**132**	**134**	**14**	**488**	**53**

NOTE: Counts where author involved indicated by *. For the preparation of Fig 209, 'Spain 1996–2005' was divided into three estates. Data for Hungary (2) are not given here, being taken from Faragó & Buday (1998) which gave 1,294 sightings of 9 species.

List of Species

MAMMALS

American badger	*Taxidea taxus*
American mink.	*Mustela vison*
badger	*Meles meles*
bank vole	*Myodes glareolus*
bison	*Bison bison*
brown bear	*Ursus arctos*
brown hare	*Lepus europaeus*
brown rat	*Rattus norvegicus*
browsing rhinoceros . . .	*Indricotherium (extinct)*
cave bear	*Ursus spelaeus*
cheetah	*Acinonyx jubatus*
common raccoon	*Procyon lotor*
common shrew.	*Sorex araneus*
common vole	*Microtus arvalis*
cougar.	*Puma concolor*
coyote	*Canis latrans*
dingo	*Canis dingo*
Egyptian mongoose. . . .	*Herpestes ichneumon*
Eurasian beaver.	*Castor fiber*
European mink.	*Mustela lutreola*
field vole	*Microtus agrestis*
fox	*Vulpes vulpes*
garden dormouse.	*Eliomys quercinus*
genet	*Genetta genetta*
golden jackal.	*Canis aureus*
grey fox	*Urocyon cinereoargenteus*
ground squirrels	*Sciuridae*
hamadryas baboon	*Papio hamadryas*
harvest mouse	*Micromys minutus*
common hedgehog	*Erinaceus europaeus*
southern white-breasted hedgehog	*Erinaceus concolor*
house mouse.	*Mus musculus*
Hundsheim rhinoceros . .	*Stephanorhinus*
Iberian lynx	*Felis pardinus*
Irish elk.	*Megaloceros giganteus*
leopard	*Panthera pardus*
lion	*Panthera leo*
long-tailed weasel.	*Mustela frenata*
lynx.	*Felis lynx*
marbled polecat	*Mustela peregusna*
marmots (ground squirrels)	*Marmota*
mole	*Talpa europaea*
musk ox.	*Ovibos moschatus*
North American beaver . .	*Castor canadensis*
olive baboon	*Papio anubis*
opossum	*Didelphis sp.*
Pallas's cat	*Otocolobus manul*
pikas	*Ochotonidae*
pine marten	*Martes martes*
polar bear	*Ursus maritimus*
polecat	*Mustela putorius*
pygmy shrew.	*Sorex minutus*
rabbit	*Oryctolagus cuniculus*
raccoon dog	*Nyctereutes procyonoides*
spotted hyena	*Hyaena hyaena*
steppe polecat	*Mustela eversmanii*
stoat	*Mustela erminea*
stone marten.	*Martes foina*
striped skunk	*Mephitis mephitis*
water shrew	*Neomys fodiens*
water vole	*Arvicola amphibius*
weasel	*Mustela nivalis*
wild dog.	*Lycaon pictus*
wildcat	*Felis sylvestris*
wisent.	*Bison bonasus*
wolf.	*Canis lupus*
wolverine	*Gulo gulo*
wood mouse	*Apodemus sylvaticus*
yellow-necked wood mouse	*Apodemus flavicollis*

BIRDS

altai snowcock	*Tetraogallus altaicus*
Arabian partridge.	*Alectoris melanocephala*

arctic tern	*Sterna paradisaea*
bald eagle	*Haliaeetus leucocephalus*
barbary partridge	*Alectoris barbara*
barn owl	*Tyto alba*
black grouse	*Tetrao tetrix*
black kite	*Milvus migrans*
blackbird	*Turdus merula*
blackcap	*Sylvia atricapilla*
black-shouldered kite . . .	*Elanus caeruleus*
blood pheasant	*Ithaginis cruentus*
blue tit	*Cyanistes caeruleus*
bobwhite quail	*Colinus virginianus*
bonelli's eagle	*Hieraaetus fasciatus*
booted eagle	*Hieraaetus pennatus*
bullfinch	*Pyrrhula pyrrhula*
buzzard	*Buteo buteo*
california quail	*Callipepla californica*
capercaillie	*Tetrao urogallus*
carrion crow	*Corvus corone*
chaffinch	*Fringilla coelebs*
chiffchaff	*Phylloscopus collybita*
chukar partridge	*Alectoris chukar*
cirl bunting	*Emberiza cirlus*
collared dove	*Streptopelia decaocto*
coopers hawk	*Accipiter cooperi*
corn bunting	*Emberiza calandra*
corncrake	*Crex crex*
cuckoo	*Cuculus canorus*
curlew	*Numenius arquata*
Daurian partridge . . .	*Perdix dauurica*
dunnock	*Prunella modularis*
eagle owl	*Bubo bubo*
eastern imperial eagle . . .	*Aquila heliaca*
ferruginous hawk	*Buteo regalis*
fieldfare	*Turdus pilaris*
golden eagle	*Aquila chrysaetos*
goldfinch	*Carduelis carduelis*
goshawk	*Accipiter gentilis*
grasshopper warbler . . .	*Locustella naevia*
great auk	*Pinguinis impennis*
great bustard	*Otis tarda*
great skua	*Stercorarius skua*
great tit	*Parus major*
greater prairie-chicken . .	*Tympanuchus cupido*
green finch	*Carduelis chloris*
grey heron	*Ardea cinerea*
grey partridge	*Perdix perdix*
guinea fowl	*Numida meleagris*
gyr falcon	*Falco rusticolus*
hazel grouse	*Tetrastes bonasia*
hen harrier	*Circus cyaneus*
hooded crow	*Corvus cornix*
horned owl	*Bubo virginianus*
house sparrow	*Passer domesticus*
Iberian imperial eagle . . .	*Aquila adalberti*
jackdaw	*Corvus monedula*
jay	*Garrulus glandarius*
kestrel	*Falco tinnunculus*
kittiwake	*Rissa tridactlyla*
lapwing	*Vanellus vanellus*
large-billed crow	*Corvus macrorhynchos*
linnet	*Carduelis cannabina*
little bustard	*Tetrax tetrax*
little owl	*Athene noctua*
long-eared owl	*Asio otus*
long-tailed tit	*Aegithalos caudatus*
magpie	*Pica pica*
mallard	*Anas platyrhynchos*
marsh harrier	*Circus aeruginosus*
marsh tit	*Poecile palustris*
martial eagle	*Polemaetus bellicosus*
meadow pipit	*Anthus pratensis*
merlin	*Falco columbarius*
mistle thrush	*Turdus viscivorus*
montagu's harrier	*Circus pygargus*
nightingale	*Luscinia megarhynchos*
nightjar	*Caprimulgus europeus*
nuthatch	*Sitta europea*
Pallas's sandgrouse	*Syrraptes paradoxus*
pallid harrier	*Circus macrourus*
peregrine falcon	*Falco peregrinus*
pheasant	*Phasianus colchicus*
philby's partridge	*Alectoris philbyi*
pied wagtail	*Motacilla alba*
prairie falcon	*Falco mexicanus*
Przevalski's partridge . . .	*Alectoris magna*
ptarmigan	*Lagopus muta*
pygmy owl	*Glaucidium passerinum*
quail	*Coturnix coturnix*
raven	*Corvus corax*
red grouse	*Lagopus lagopus scoticus*
red kite	*Milvus milvus*
red-backed shrike	*Lanius collurio*
red-legged partridge . . .	*Alectoris rufa*
red-shouldered hawk . . .	*Buteo lineatus*
red-tailed hawk	*Buteo jamaicensis*
redwing	*Turdus iliacus*
reed bunting	*Emberiza schoeniclus*
ringed plover	*Charadrius hiaticula*
robin	*Erithacus rubecula*
rock partridge	*Alectoris graeca*
rough-legged buzzard . . .	*Buteo lagopus*
sage grouse	*Centrocercus urophasianus*
scops owl	*Otus scops*
shag	*Phalacrocorax aristotelis*
sharp-shinned hawk . . .	*Accipiter striatus*
sharp-tailed grouse	*Tympanuchus phasianellus*
short-eared owl	*Asio flammeus*
short-toed eagle	*Circaetus gallicus*
skylark	*Alauda arvensis*
snowy owl	*Bubo scandiacus*
stock dove	*Columba oenas*

song thrush . . . . Turdus philomelos
sparrowhawk. . . . . . . Accipiter nisus
starling . . . . Sturnus vulgaris
stone curlew . . . . Burhinus oedicnemus
stonechat . . . . Saxicola torquatus
Swainson's hawk . . . . . Buteo swainsoni
swallow . . . . Hirundo rustica
Szechenyi's monal-
    partridge. . . . . Tetraophasis szechenyii
tawny owl . . . . Strix aluco
Tibetan partridge. . . . . Perdix hodgsoniae
tree sparrow . . . . Passer montanus
treecreeper. . . . . Certhia familiaris
turtle dove . . . . Streptopelia turtur
wheatear. . . . . Oenanthe oenanthe
whinchat . . . . Saxicola rubetra
white-eared pheasant . . . Crossoptilon crossoptilon
whitethroat . . . . Sylvia communis
wild turkey. . . . . Meleagris gallopavo
willow grouse . . . . . . Lagopus lagopus lagopus
willow tit . . . . Poecile montana
woodlark . . . . Lullula arborea
woodpigeon . . . . Columba palumbus
wren . . . . Troglodytes troglodytes
wryneck . . . . Jynx torquilla
yellow wagtail . . . . . . Motacilla flava
yellowhammer . . . . . . Emberiza citrinella

PLANTS

annual meadow-grass . . . Poa annua
bent grass . . . . Agrostis espec A.
    stolonifera
black bindweed. . . . . . Fallopia
    convolvulus
black medick. . . . . . . Medicago lupulina
bulbous buttercup . . . . Ranunculus bulbosus
bulbous meadow-grass . . Poa bulbosa
camelthorn . . . . Alhagi maurorum
canary grass . . . . Phalaris canariensis
cheatgrass . . . . Bromus tectorum
chickweed . . . . Stellaria media
Christ's thorn . . . . . . Paliurus spina-christi
cleavers . . . . Galium aparine
cockspur grass . . . . . Echinochloa crus-galli
common broom . . . . . Cytisus scoparius
common field speedwell. . Veronica persica
common orache . . . . . Atriplex patula
common poppy . . . . . Papaver rhoeas
common wild oat . . . . . Avena fatua
coral-berry. . . . . Symphoricarpos
    orbiculatus
corn buttercup . . . . . Ranunculus arvensis
corn chamomile . . . . . Anthemis arvensis
corn cleavers . . . . Galium tricornutum
corn gromwell . . . . . . Lithospermum arvense
corn mint . . . . Mentha arvensis
corn spurrey . . . . Spergula arvensis
cornflower . . . . Centaurea cyanus

crab grass . . . . Digitaria sanguinalis
creeping thistle. . . . . . Cirsium arvense
crested wheat-grass . . . . Agropyron pectiniforme
dandelions. . . . . Taraxacum spp.
dwarf spurge . . . . Euphorbia exigua
einkorn . . . . Triticum monococcum
emmer . . . . Triticum dicoccum
false oat-grass . . . . . . Arrhenatherum elatius
    bulbosum
fat hen . . . . Chenopodium album
feather-grass . . . . Stipa e.g lessingiana
fescue . . . . Festuca
fiddelneck . . . . Amsinkia
field pansy . . . . Viola arvensis
field pennycress . . . . . Thlaspe arvense
fine-leaved fumitory . . . Fumaria parviflora
forget me not . . . . . . Myosotis arvensis
fumitory . . . . Fumaria officinalis
globe thistle . . . . Echinops viscosus
golden-yellow tulip . . . . Tulipa sylvestris
greater knapweed . . . . . Centaurea scabiosa
greater plantain . . . . . Plantago major
green pigeon-grass . . . . Setaria viridis
gum rock rose . . . . . . Cistus ladanifer
hawkweeds. . . . . Hieracium spp.
heath rush . . . . Juncus squarrosus
hemp . . . . Cannabis sativa
hemp nettle . . . . Galeopsis tetrahit
hogweed. . . . . Heracleum sphondylium
jersey buttercup . . . . . Ranunculus paludosus
knotgrass . . . . Polygonum aviculare
land quillwort . . . . . . Isoetes histrix
larkspur . . . . Consolida ajacis
larkspur, forking . . . . . Consolida regalis
lesser burdock . . . . . . Arctium minus
many seeded goosefoot . . Chenopodium
    polyspermum
marsh arrowgrass. . . . . Triglochin palustris
meadowsweet . . . . . . Filipendula ulmari/
    vulgaris
moss campion . . . . . . Silene acaulis
mountain aven . . . . . . Dryas octopetala
mugwort . . . . Artemisia vulgaris
narrow-fruited cornsalad . Valerianella dentata
night-flowering catchfly . . Silene noctiflora
oilseed rape . . . . Brassica napus
pale pigeon-grass . . . . . Setaria glauca
perennial sow thistle . . . Sonchus arvensis
persicaria . . . . Persicaria lapathifolia
pheasant's eye . . . . . . Adonis annua
pickly poppy . . . . Papaver argemone
pigweed . . . . Amaranthus retroflexus
prairie star. . . . . Lithophragma glabra
Provence broom . . . . . Cytisus purgans
prickly ash . . . . Xanthoxylem
    americanum
ragweed . . . . Ambrosia artemisiifolia
raspberry . . . . Rubus occidentalis
red hemp-nettle . . . . . Galeopsis angustifolia

redshank . . . . Persicaria maculosa
rose. . . . . Rosaceae
rye . . . . Secale cereale
ryegrass . . . . Lolium spp.
sandwort . . . . Arenaria serpyllifolia
scentless mayweed . . . . Tripleurospermum
    inodorum
shepherd's needle. . . . . Scandix pecten-veneris
shepherd's purse . . . . Capsella bursa-pastoris
siberian peashrub. . . . Caragana arborescens
soft rush. . . . . Juncus effusus
sorghum . . . . Sorghum bicolor
spear-leaved orache . . . Atriplex prostrata
spreading hedge parsley . Torilis arvensis
spreading pigweed . . . . Amaranthus blitoides
stinking chamomile. . . . Anthemis cotula
sumac. . . . . Rhus spp.
tartary lily . . . . Ixiolirion tartaricum
thistles . . . . espec. Cirsium spp.
thorny burnet . . . . . Sarcopterium spinosum
three-lobed beggarsticks. . Bidens tripartita
tobacco . . . . Nicotiniana tabacum
tuberous cranesbill . . . Geranium tuberosum
tuberous hawkbit . . . . Leontodon tuberosus
vetches . . . . Vicia spp.
wheatgrass. . . . . . . Agropyron spp.
white millet . . . . . . Panicum miliaceum
wild barley. . . . . . . Hordeum vulgare
winter wild oat . . . . . Avena ludoviciana

REPTILES

grass snake . . . . . . Natrix natrix
Montpellier snake . . . . Malpolon
    monspessulanus
ocellated lizard . . . . . . Timon lepidus

INVERTEBRATES

armoured bugs . . . . . . Pentatomidae
birch sawfly . . . . . . Cimbex femoratus
bird cherry aphid . . . . Rhopalosiphon padi
black bean-aphid . . . . Aphis fabae
black-flies . . . . Simuliidae
blossom beetle . . . . . Meligethes aeneus
carabid . . . . Anchomenus dorsale
carabid . . . . Demetrias atricapillus
centipedes . . . . Chilopoda
click beetles . . . . . . Elateridae
comb-clawed beetle . . . . Pseudocistela muhldorfi
conical snail . . . . . . Cochlicella acuta
crane-fly. . . . . Tipulidae
dor beetle . . . . Geotrupes stercorarius
earwig. . . . . Forficula auricularia
field grasshopper . . . . . Chorthippus brunneus
finch louse-fly . . . . . Onithomyia fringillina
firebug . . . . Pyrrhocoris apterus
flea beetles. . . . . . . Chrysomelidae
frit flies . . . . Oscinella spp

froghoppers . . . . . . Cercopoidea
garden snail . . . . . . Helix aspera
grove snail . . . . Cepaea nemoralis
harvester ant . . . . . . Messor barbarus
harvestmen . . . . . . Opiliones
heather beetle . . . . . Lochmaea suturalis
humming bird hawk moth. Macroglossum
    stellatarum
Kentish snail. . . . . . Monacha cantiana
knotgrass beetle . . . . Gastrophysa polygoni
leafhopper . . . . Cicadellidae
leather jacket. . . . . . Tipulidae larvae
orange blossom-midge . . Sitodiplosis mosellana
long-horned beetle . . . Longicorn
lucerne flea . . . . . . Sminthurus viridis
lucerne weevil . . . . . Hypera postica
maize leaf-weevil . . . . Tanymecus dilaticollis
meadow grasshopper . . . Chorthippus parallelus
mites . . . . Acari
lemon blossom-midge . . Contarinia tritici
painted lady . . . . . . Vanessa cardui
pear sawfly. . . . . . . Caliroa cerasi
plant bugs . . . . Heteroptera
plant hoppers . . . . . Delphacidae
Russian ground beetle . . Zabrus tenebrioides
sawfly . . . . Hymenoptera: Symphyta
seven-spot ladybird . . . Coccinella
    septempunctata
short-horned grasshopper . Calliptamus italicus
snails . . . . Gastropoda
soldier beetles . . . . . Cantharidae
speckled bush cricket . . . Leptophyes
    punctatissima
spiders . . . . Araneae
spittle bug . . . . Cercopidae
St Mark's fly . . . . . . Bibio marci
steppe cockroach . . . . Ectobius duskei
strawberry seed-beetle. . . Harpalus rufipes
sunn pest . . . . Eurygaster integriceps
thistle longhorn . . . . . Agapanthes
    villosoviridescens
tiger crane fly . . . . . Nephrotoma flavescens
tortoise beetle . . . . . Cassida spp.
turnip sawfly . . . . . . Athalia rosae
wireworm . . . . Elateridae (Coleoptera)
    larvae
woodlice. . . . . Oniscidea (Crustacea)
yellow meadow ant . . . . Lasius flavus

FISH

three-spined stickleback. . Gasterosteus aculeatus

DISEASES

barley leaf-blotch . . . . . Rhynchosporium secalis
mildew . . . . Erysiphe graminis

References

Abdou, A. H. (1958) The life-cycle of *Davainea proglottina* and relations between the proglottids discharged daily and the number of tapeworms in the Domestic Fowl. *Canadian Journal Comp Med Vet Sci.*, 10, 338–343.

Adamran, M. S. & Klem, D. (1999) *Handbook of the birds of Armenia*. American University of Armenia, Yerevan.

Adams, J. M. & Faure, H. (1997) Palaeovegetation map of the world since the last glaciation. *Journal of Archaeological Science*, 24, 623–647.

Aebischer, N. J. & Potts, G. R. (1990) Sample size and area: implications based on long-term monitoring of partridges. *Pesticide Effects on Terrestrial Wildlife* (eds L. Somerville & C. H. Walker), pp. 257–270. Taylor & Francis Ltd, London.

Aebischer, N. J. & Potts, G. R. (1990) Long-term changes in numbers of cereal invertebrates assessed by monitoring. *Proceedings 1990 British Crop Protection Conference – Pests and Diseases.* pp. 163–172. British Crop Protection Council, Farnham.

Aebischer, N. J. (1990) Assessing pesticide effects on non-target invertebrates using long-term monitoring and time series modelling. *Journal of Functional Ecology*, 4, 369–373.

Aebischer, N. J. (1991) Twenty years of monitoring cereal fields. *The Ecology of Temperate Cereal Fields* (eds L. G. Firbank, N. Carter, J. F. Darbyshire & G. R. Potts), pp. 305–331. Blackwell Scientific, London.

Aebischer, N. J. (1992) Time-series models of invertebrate populations and pesticide effects. *Journal of Agricultural Science*, 118, 399.

Aebischer, N. J. & Potts, G. R. (1994) 5 species of partridge and the quail. *Birds in Europe: Their Conservation Status* (eds G. M. Tucker & M. F. Heath), pp. 210–223. Bird Life, Cambridge.

Aebischer, N. J. & Potts, G. R. (1998) Spatial changes in grey partridge distribution in relation to 25 years of changing agriculture in Sussex, U.K. *Gibier Faune Sauvage*, 15, 293–308.

Aebischer, N. J., Potts, G. R. & Rehfish, M. (1999) Using ringing data to study the effect of hunting on bird populations. *Ringing and Migration*, 19, 67–81.

Aebischer, N.J. (1999). Multi-way comparisons and generalized linear models of nest success: extensions of the Mayfield method. *Bird Study*, 46S: 22–31.

Aebischer, N. J. & Reitz, F. (2000) Estimating brood production and chick survival rates of Grey Partridges: an evaluation. *Hungarian Small Game Bulletin*, 5, 191–209.

Aebischer, N. J., Ewald, J. A. & Potts, G. R. (2001) Preliminary results from using GIS to examine spatial variation in grey partridge demography over 30 years in

Sussex, UK. *Proceedings of the International Union of Game Biology*, 24, 23–33.

Aebischer, N.J. (2002) European Turtle Dove (*Streptopelia turtur*) in *The Migration Atlas: Movements of the birds of Britain & Ireland*. Eds Wernham, C., Toms, M., Marchant, J., Clark, J. Siriwardena, G. & Baillie, S. p 420–422.

Aebischer, N. J. & Ewald, J. A. (2004) Managing the UK grey partridge *Perdix perdix* recovery: population change, reproduction, habitat and shooting. *Ibis*, 146S2, 181–191.

Aebischer, N. J. & Ewald, J. A. (2010) Grey Partridge *Perdix perdix* in the UK: recovery status, set-aside and shooting. *Ibis*, 152, 530–542.

Afonin, A. N., Greene, S. L., Dzyubenko, N. I. & Frolov, A. N. (2008) Interactive Agricultural Ecological Atlas of Russia and Neighbouring Countries. Economic Plants and their Diseases, Pests and Weeds. www.agroatlas.ru.

Agüero, M., Fernández-Pinero, J., Buitrago, D., Sánchez, A., Elizalde, M., San Miguel, E., Villalba, R. & Llorente, F. (2011) Bagaza Virus in Partridges and Pheasants,Spain, 2010. *Emerging Infectious Diseases* 17, 1498–1500. www.cdc.gov/eid.

Aksin, N., Oncel, T. (2011) The presence of chewing lice (Insecta: Phthiraptera) Species on Wild Grey Partridge (*Perdix perdix canescens*). *Journal of Animal and Veterinary Advances* 10, 1660–1662.

Alcorn, J. R. & Richardson, F. (1951) The chukar partridge in Nevada. *Journal of Wildlife Management*, 15, 265–275.

Alington, C. E. A. (1904) *Partridge Driving*. Murray, London.

Alkon, P. U. (1983) Nesting and brood production in an Israeli population of Chukars, *Alectoris chukar* (Aves: Phasianidae). *Israel Journal of Zoology*, 32, 185–193.

Alkon, P. U., Degen, A. A., Pinshow, B. & Shaw, P. J. (1985) Phenology, diet and water turnover rates of Negev desert Chukars. *Journal of Arid Environments*, 9, 51–61.

Allee, N. C., Emerson, A. E., Park, O. & Schmidt, K. P. (1949) Principles of Animal Ecology. W. B. Saunders, Philadelphia.

Altum, B. (1894) Uber förmen des Rebhuhns, *Starna cinerea*. *Journal für Ornithologie*, 42, 254–269.

Alvarez-Lao, D. & Garcia, N. (2011) Geographical distribution of Pleistocene cold-adapted large mammal faunas in the Iberian Peninsula. *Quaternary International*, 233, 159–170.

Amar, A., Thirgood, S., Pearce-Higgins, J. & Redpath, S. (2008) The impact of raptors on the abundance of upland passerines and waders. *Oikos*, 117, 1143–1152.

Andersen, J. (1955) The food of the Danish badger. *Danish Review of Game Biology*, 3, 1–52.

Andersen, J. (1993) Beetle remains as indicators of the climate in the Quaternary. *Journal of Biogeography*, 20, 557–562.

Anderson, R. C. (2000) *Nematode Parasites of Vertebrates*. Oxford University Press, Oxford.

Annenkov, B. P. & Litun, V. I. (1989) Distribution and numbers of gamebirds in the Alakol Depression and neighbouring mountains (Russian). *Ecology and Natural Resources of Game and Fishing Birds* pp. 90–97. All Russian Fur Research Institute, Kirov RF.

Archer, M., Hand, S. J. & Godthelp, H. (2000) *Australia's Lost World: Riversleigh World Heritage Site*. Reed New Holland, Sydney.

Archibald, C. F. (1892) Wild birds useful and injurious. *Journal of the Royal Agricultural Society*, 3, 658–684.

Armstrong, M. H., Braun, E. L. & Kimball, R. C. (2001) Phylogenetic utility of avian ovomucoid intron G: a comparison of nuclear and mitochondrial phylogenetics in Galliformes. *Auk*, 118, 799–804.

Ash, J. S. (1952) Siphonaptera bred from birds' nest. *Entomologists Monthly Magazine*, 88, 217–222.

Ash, J. S. (1960) Birds of Prey numbers on a Hampshire game preserve during 1952–1959. *British Birds*, 57, 285–300.

Ash, J. S. (1965) Toxic chemicals and wildlife in Britain. *Transactions of the VI Congress of the International Union of Game Biologists* (ed. T. H. Blank), pp. 379–388. The Nature Conservancy, London.

Ash, J. S. (1965) Partridges in Austria. *The Game Conservancy Annual Review*, 4S1, 73–74.

Ash, J. S. (1966) Some mutations of the partridge and red-legged partridge. *British Birds*, 59, 15–22.

Astor, V. B., Rowntree, S. & Bateson, F. W. (1946) *Mixed Farming and Muddled Thinking: an analysis of current farming policy*. Macdonald, London.

Atlas Equipa (2008) *Atlas das aves nidificantes em Portugal (1999–2005)* [in Portuguese]. Instituto da Conservção Natureza e da Biodiversidade, Lisbon.

Aubineau, J., Olivier, J. & Birkan, M. (1974) Effet d'aménagements de l'habitat sur la densité des couples et la réussite de la reproduction chez la perdrix grise (*Perdix perdix* L.) sur le territoire de chasse de Vauberon (Aisne). *Bulletin de l'Office National de la Chasse, Spécial*, 2, 121–152.

Aubineau, J. (1981) Quelques resultats sur la reproduction de la perdrix grise dans des territoires de Beauce, du Soissonnais et de la Marne de 1973–1977. *Bulletin Mensuel de l'Office National de la Chasse*, 44, 7–9.

Aufradet, D. (1996) *La Perdrix grise: comportments, gestion, chasse*. Editions du Gerfaut, Paris.

Aufradet, D. & Birkan, M. (2001) Comportement et devenir de perdrix grises (*Perdix perdix*) celibataires en Seine-et-Marne, France. *Game and Wildlife Science*, 18, 403–410.

Augustine, P. C. & Lund, E. E. (1974) The fate of eggs and larvae of *Ascaridia galli* in earthworms. *Avian Diseases*, 18, 394–398.

Avancini, R. M. & Ueta, M. T. (1990) Manure breeding insects (Diptera and Coleoptera) responsible for cestoidosis in caged layer hens. *Journal of Applied Entomology*, 110, 307–312.

Avcioglu, H., Burgu, A. & Balukbas, C. S. (2008) *Ascaridia numidae* (Leiper, 1908; Travassos, 1913) in Rock Partridge (*Alectoris chukar*) in Turkey. *Parasitological Research*, 102, 527–530.

Baba, Y., Fujimaki, Y., Yoshii, R. & Hiroko, K. (2001) Genetic variabillty in the mitochondrial control region of the Japanese rock ptarmigan *Lagopus mutus japonicus*. *Japanese Journal of Ornithology*, 50, 53–64.

Bach, R. N. (1943) Strongylosis in Hungarian Partridge. *North Dakota Outdoors*, 6, 13–14.

Badulin, A.V. (1983) Parasites and predators of the wheat leaf sawfly. In *Noveishĭe dostizheniya sel'skokhozy-aĭstvennoi entomologii (po materialam Ush s"ezda VEO, Vil'nyus, 9–13 Oktybrya 1979)*, 13–16, Vilnius.

Baines, D., Redpath, S., Richardson, M. & Thirgood, S. (2008) The direct and indirect effects of predation by Hen Harriers Circus cyaneus on trends in breeding birds on a Scottish grouse moor. *Ibis*, 150(S1), 27–36.

Ballmann, P. (1969) Les oiseaux miocènes de La-Grive-Saint-Alban (Isère). *Geobios*, 2, 157–204.

Bannerman, D. A. & Lodge, G. (1955) *The Birds of the British Islands, Vol. 4*. Oliver & Boyd, Edinburgh.

Bao, X. K., Gu H.J. & Naifa, L. (2008) A Review of the phylogenetic research on gamebirds (Aves, Galliformes). *Acta Zootaxonomica Sinica*, 33, 720–732.

Bao, X. K., Naifa, L., Qu, J. Y., Wang, X. L., An, B., Wen, L. Y. & Song, S. (2010) The phylogenetic position and speciation dynamics of the genus *Perdix* (Phasianidae, Galliformes). *Molecular Phylogenetics and Evolution*, 56, 840–847.

Baranov, F. I. (1918) On the question of the biological basis of fisheries. *Nauchnyi issledovatelskii iktiologicheskii Institute, Izvestiia*, 1, 18–218.

Barbanera, F., Guerrini, M., Khan, A. A., Panayides, P., Hadjigerou, P., Sokos, C., Gombataar, S., Samadi, S., Khan, B. Y., Tofanelli, S., Paoli, G. & Dini, F. (2009) Human-mediated introgression of exotic chukar (*Alectoris chukar*, Galliformes) genes from East Asia into Mediterranean partridges. *Biological Invasions*, 11, 333–348.

Barbanera, F., Pergams, O. R. W., Guerrini, M., Forcina, G., Panayides, P. & Dini, F. (2010) Genetic consequences of intensive management in game birds. *Biological Conservation*, 143, 1259–1268.

Barfknecht, R. (1987) The releasing of red-legged partridges and its influence on a grey partridge population. Proceedings *IUGB*, 18, (Vol.) 2, 241–244.

Barilani, M., Bernard-Laurent, A., Mucci, N., Tabarroni, C., Kark, S., Garrido, J. A. P. & Randi, E. (2007) Hybridisation with introduced chukars (*Alectoris chukar*) threatens the gene pool inegrity of native rock and red-legged partridge populations. *Biological Conservation*, 137, 57–69.

Barker, A. & Maczka, C. M. (1996) The relationships between host selection and subsequent larval performance in three free-living graminivorous sawflies. *Ecological Entomology*, 21, 317–327.

Barker, A. (1998) The identification of the larvae of eight graminivorous species of the sawfly genus *Dolerus* Panzer 1801 (Hymenoptera: Tenthredinidae) regularly found in grass and cereal fields in southern England. *Journal of Natural History*, 32, 1181–1215.

Barker, A. (1999) The Ecology of Sawflies on intensively managed farmland. Report on Grant F612A awarded by the Leverhulme Trust. Fordingbridge, The Game Conservancy.

Barker, A. & Reynolds, C. M. (2005) Do host-plant interactions and susceptibility to soil cultivation determine the abundance of graminivorous sawflies on British farmland? *Journal of Agricultural and Urban Entomology*, 21, 257–269.

Barker, A. (2006) Further descriptions of *Dolerus* larvae (Hymenoptera: Tenthredinidae) with notes on larval identification and feeding habits. *Recent Sawfly Research: Synthesis and Prospects* (eds S. M. Blank, S. Schmidt & A. Taeger), pp. 83–96. Goecke & Evers, Keltern.

Barnard, P. C. (2011) *The Royal Entomological Society Book of British Insects*, Wiley-Blackwell.

Bayes J.C., Dawson, M. J. & Potts, G. R. (1964) The food and feeding behaviour of the great skua (*Catharacta skua*) in the Faroes. *Bird Study*, 11, 272–279.

Bayliss, D. I., Bray, R. A. & Harris, E. A. (2005) Host parasite database of the Natural History Museum, London. www.nhm.ac.uk/researchprojects/host-parasitedatabase.

Báldi, A. & Faragó, S. (2007) Long-term changes of farmland game populations in a post-socialist country (Hungary). *Agriculture, Ecosystems and Environment*, 118, 307–311.

Beani, L. & Dessì-Fulgheri, F. (1984) Leadership and social inter-actions in a group of grey partridges. *Monitore Zoologico Italiano*, 18, 159–160.

Beani, L., Cervo, R. & Dessì-Fulgheri, F. (1992) Influence of mate choice on reproductive success of captive grey partridges (*Perdix perdix*). *Gibier Faune Sauvage*, 9, 729–742.

Beani, L. & Dessì-Fulgheri, F. (1995) Mate choice in the grey partridge, *Perdix perdix*: role of physical and behavioural male traits. *Animal Behaviour*, 49, 347–356.

Beani, L., Panzica, G., Briganti, F., Persichella, P. & Dessì-Fulgheri, F. (1995) Testosterone-Induced Changes of Call Structure, Midbrain and Syrinx Anatomy in Partridges. *Physiology & Behaviour*, 58, 1149–1157.

Beani, L. & Dessì-Fulgheri, F. (1998) Anti-predator behaviour of captive Grey partridges (*Perdix perdix*). *Ethology Ecology & Evolution*, 10, 185–196.

Beer, J. R. & Tidyman, W. (1942) The substitution of hard seeds for grit. *Journal of Wildlife Management*, 6, 70–82.

Beer, J. V. (1976) Trends in the occurrence of gamebird disease. *The Game Conservancy Annual Review*, 8, 62–69.

Beer, J. V. & Jenkinson, G. (1982) Game bird diseases in the past decade. *The Game Conservancy Annual Review*, 13, 112–115.

Beer, J. V. (1985) Prospects for the health of gamebirds. *The Game Conservancy Annual Review*, 16, 81–84.

Behrendt, S. & Hanf, M. (1979) *Grass Weeds in World Agriculture.* BASF, Gütersloh.

Beljanski, B. (1960) Zimska ischrana i prezimljavanje jarebica. [Winter food and wintering]. *Vojvodjanski Lovac,* 6, 171–173.

Bellrose, F. C. (1959) Lead poisoning as a mortality factor in waterfowl populations. *Illinois Natural History Survey Special Publication,* 27, 233–288.

Bendell, J. F. & Lisk, R. D. (1957) *Dispharynx nasuta* in Hungarian partridge in Ohio. *Journal of Wildlife Management,* 21, 238.

Benjamin, A. & McCallum, B. (2009) *A World without Bees.* Guardian Books, London.

Benson, R. B. (1950) An introduction to the natural history of British sawflies (Hymenoptera: Symphyta). *Transactions of the Society for British Entomology,* 10, 45–142.

Benton, T. G., Bryant, D. M., Cole, L. & Crick.H.Q.P. (2002) Linking agricultural practice to insect and bird populations: a historical study over three decades. *Journal of Applied Ecology,* 39, 673–687.

Berger, J., Swenson, J. E. & Persson, I. L. (2001) Recolonizing carnivores and naïve prey: conservation lessons from Pleistocene extinctions. *Science,* 291, 1036–1039.

Bergerud, A. T. (1988) Increasing the numbers of grouse. *Adaptive Strategies and Population Ecology of Northern Grouse* (eds A. T. Bergerud & M. W. Gratson), pp. 686–731. University of Minnesota, Minneapolis.

Bergerud, A. T. (1992) Rareness as an antipredator strategy to reduce predation risk for Moose and Caribou. *Wildlife Populations* (eds D. R. McCullough & R. H. Barrett), pp. 1008–1021. Elsevier, New York.

Bernard-Laurent, A. & Boev, Z. (1997) Rock Partridge, in E. J. M. Hagemeijer & Blair (Eds) *The EBCC Atlas of European Breeding Birds: Their Distribution and Abundance.* T & A D Poyser.

Bernard-Laurent, A. (1986) Regime alimentaire automnal de la perdrix bartavelle, *Alectoris graeca saxatilis,* dans les Alpes-Maritimes. *Revue d'Ecologie – La Terre et la Vie,* 41, 39–57.

Bernard-Laurent, A. (1989) Importance de la predation sur une population de perdix rochassieres (*Alectoris graeca saxatilis* x *Alectoris rufa rufa*) des Alpes Meridionales. *Gibier Faune Sauvage,* 6, 361–382.

Bernard-Laurent, A. (1990) Biologie de reproduction d'une population de perdrix rochassiere *Alectoris graeca saxatilis* x *Alectoris rufa* rufa dans les Alpes meridionales. *Revue d'Ecologie la Terre et la Vie,* 45, 321–344.

Bernard-Laurent, A. & de Franceschi, P. F. (1994) Statut, evolution et facteurs limitant les populations de perdrix bartavelle (*Alectoris graeca*): synthese bibliographique. *Gibier Faune Sauvage,* 11S, 265–307.

Bernard-Laurent, A., Bosser, P. V., Carisio, L., Chioso C., Grignolio, S. & Viterbi, R. (2012) Status of rock partridge (*Alectoris graeca saxatilis*) populations along the western Alps: output of an Alcotra programme. Conference on Mediterranean populations of the Genus *Alectoris,* Alessandria, Italy, 14–15 November 2011. *Avocetta* in press.

Bertoletti, I., Bianchi, A. & Magnino, S. (2005) First report of *Chlamydophila psittaci* and *C. abortus* in wild rock Partridges (*Alectoris graeca saxatilis*) in the Central Alps. *Proceedings of IUGB,* 27, 285.

Besnard, A., Novoa, C. & Gimenez, O. (2010) Hunting impact on the population dynamics of Pyrenean grey partridge *Perdix perdix hispanicus. Wildlife Biology,* 16, 135–143.

Bey-Biyenko, G. Ya. (1939) Regional classification of crops by pest groups (based on the ecology of a wheat field). *Zap.Leningr.sel'skokhoz.inst.nov.izd.,* 3, 123–134.

Bey-Biyenko, G. Ya. (1961) Some features of changes in invertebrate fauna when virgin steppe is cultivated. *Review of Entomology URSS,* 40, 427–434.

Bezubik, B. (1959) Helminthofauna of partridge (*Perdix perdix* L.) in the Lublin Palatinate. *Acta Parasitologica Polonica,* 7, 179–188.

Bezzel, E. & Obst, J. &. W. K. H. (1976) Zur Ernährung und Nahrungswahl des Uhus (*Bubo bubo*). *Journal für Ornithologie*, 117S, 210–238.

Bialas, T., Hell, P. & Slamecka, T. (1996) Investigation of gizzard stones among partridges and pheasants. *Zeitschrift für Jagdwissenschaft*, 42, 36–40.

Bidstrup, P. L. & Payne, D. J. H. (1951) Poisoning by Dinitro-*Ortho*-Cresol: Report of eight fatal cases in Great Britain. *British Medical Journal*, July 7, 16–27.

Bijleveld, M. G. (1974) *Birds of Prey in Europe*. Macmillan, London.

Binazzi, R., Zaccaroni, M., Nespoli, A., Massola, A. & Dessì-Fulgheri, F. (2011) Anti-predator behaviour of the Red-legged Partridge *Alectoris rufa* to simulated terrestrial and aerial predators. *Ethology Behaviour*, 78, 106–112.

Bingham, R. J., Larsen, R. T., Bissonette, J. A. & Flinders, J. T. (2009) Causes and consequences of ingested lead pellets in Chukars. (eds R. T. Watson, M. Fuller, M. Pokras & W. G. Hunt), pp. 190–193. The Peregrine Fund, Boise, Idaho.

Bircham, P. (2007) *A History of Ornithology*. New Naturalist, Collins, London

Birkan, M. (1970) Le régime alimentaire de la Perdrix grise d'après les contenus des jabots et des estomacs. *Annales de Zoologie – Ecologie Animale*, 2, 121–153.

Birkan, M. (1971) Populations de perdrix grise (*Perdix perdix*) et agriculture sur un territoire de chasse près de Provins (Seine-et-Marne). *Bulletin Spécial du Conseil Supérieur de la Chasse*, 15, 1–8.

Birkan, M. (1977a) Reconnaissance du sexe et de l'âge chez la perdrix grise (*Perdix perdix*) et la perdrix rouge (*Alectoris rufa*). *Écologie du Petit Gibier et Aménagement des Chasses* (eds P. Pesson & M. Birkan), pp. 23–54. Gauthier Villars, Paris.

Birkan, M. (1977b) Populations de perdrix grise et agriculture: évolution des tableaux de chasse et distribution des couples au printemps sur un territoire de chasse près de Provins [Seine et Marne], pp.137–159. *Écologie du Petit Gibier et Aménagement des Chasses* Gauthier Villars, Paris.

Birkan, M. (1977c) Analyse des tableaux de chasse de perdrix (*Perdix perdix* et *Alectoris rufa*): courbes d'éclosion, structure et dynamique des population, plan de chasse. *Écologie du Petit Gibier et Aménagement des Chasses* (eds P. Pesson & M. Birkan), pp. 55–77. Gauthier Villars, Paris.

Birkan, M. (1979) *Perdrix Grises et Rouges de Chasse et d'Elevage*. La Maison Rustique, Paris.

Birkan, M. (1980) Dynamique de population de perdrix grises (*Perdix perdix*): Analyse des facteurs-clé. *L'Oiseau et la Revue Française d'Ornithologie*, 50, 263–270.

Birkan, M. (1983) Influence de l'homme sur la répartition géographique de quelques espèces de gallinacés-gibier en France. *Comptes Rendus de la Société de Biogéographie*, 59, 382.

Birkan, M. & Angibault, J.-M. (1983) Problèmes posés par le radiotracking chez la Perdrix grise. *Bulletin Intérieur de la Société Française pour l'Etude du Comportement Animal*, 1, 59–62.

Birkan, M. & Pépin, D. (1984) Tableaux de chasse et de piégeage d'un même territoire entre 1950 et 1971: fluctuations numériques des espèces et facteurs de l'environnement. *Gibier Faune Sauvage*, 2, 97–111.

Birkan, M., Olivier, J. & Aubineau, J. (1985) Dynamique de population chez la Perdrix grise (*Perdix perdix*) et plan de chasse sur un territoire aménagé (Vaubéron, Aisne). *International Union of Game Biology*, 17, 63–69.

Birkan, M. (1985) Dynamique de population et relation avec l'occupation du milieu par la Perdrix grise (*Perdix perdix*). *Proceedings of Congress of IUGB*, 17, 927–934.

Birkan, M. (1986) Sachez regarder vivre vos perdrix: Où vont-elles bien se nicher? *La Revue National de la Chasse*, 465,34–39.

Birkan, M. & Serre, D. (1986) Le problème du choix alimentaire chez le possin de perdrix grise. Proceedings of the Common Partridge (*Perdix perdix* L.) International Symposium 1985. (ed. Pielowski, Z.). Warsaw, Polish Hunting Association.

Birkan, M. & Jacob, M. (1988) *La Perdrix Grise.* Hatier, Paris.

Birkan, M. & Serre, D. (1988) Disparition, domaine vital et utilization du milieu de Janvier a Mai chez la perdrix grise (Perdix perdix L.) dans la Beauce du Loiret (Fr.) *Gibier Faune Sauvage,* 5, 389–409.

Birkan, M., Serre, D., Pelard, E. & Skibniewski, S. (1990) Effects of irrigation on adult mortality and reproduction of Gray partridge in a wheat farming system. *Perdix,* 5, 257–271.

Birkan, M., Potts, G. R., Aebischer, N. J. & Dowell, S. D. (1992) Proceedings of Perdix VI: The first International Symposium on Partridges,Quails and Francolins. *Gibier Faune Sauvage,* 9, 1–918.

Birkan, M., Avignon, T., Reitz, F. & Vignon, V. (1994) Influence d'une autoroute sur le succes reproducteur de la perdix grise (*Perdix perdix*) en plaine de grande culture. *Gibier Faune Sauvage,* 11, 207–218.

Bishop, R. A., Nomsen, R. C. & Andrews, R. D. (1977) A look at Iowa's Hungarian partridge. *Perdix,* 1, 10–31.

Blanc, F., Ledème, P. & Blanc, Ch. P. (1986) Variation géographique de la diversité génétique chez la perdrix grise (*Perdix perdix*). *Gibier Faune Sauvage,* 3, 5–41.

Blanco-Aguiar, J.A., Delibes-Mateos, M.,Arroyo, B., Ferreras, P., Casas, F., Real, R.,Vargas, J.M., Villafuerte, R. & Viñuela, J. (2012) Is the interaction between rabbit haemorrhagic disease and hyperpredation by raptors a major cause of the red-legged partridge decline in Spain? *European Journal of Wildlife Research* 58, 433–439.

Blank, T. H. & Ash, J. S. (1954) A population of partridges *Perdix p. perdix* and *Alectoris r. rufa* in a Hampshire Estate. *Acta XI Congres Int. Orn., Bâle.* 424–427.

Blank, T. H. & Ash, J. S. (1956) The concept of territory in the partridge *Perdix p. perdix.* *Ibis,* 98, 379–389.

Blank, T. H. & Ash, J. S. (1957) Factors controlling brood-size in the Partridge (*Perdix perdix*) on an estate in south England. *Danish Review of Game Biology,* 3, 39–41.

Blank, T. H. & Ash, J. S. (1960) Some aspects of clutch size in the partridge (*Perdix perdix*). *Proceedings of the International Union of Game Biology,* 12, 118–126.

Blank, T. H. & Ash, J. S. (1962) Fluctuations in a partridge population. *The Exploitation of Natural Animal Populations* (eds E. D. Le Cren & M. W. Holdgate), pp. 118–130. Blackwell, Oxford.

Blank, T. H., Southwood, T. R. E. & Cross, D. J. (1967) The ecology of the partridge. I. Outline of population processes with particular reference to chick mortality and nest density. *Journal of Animal Ecology,* 36, 549–556.

Blasco, R. & Peris, J.F. (2009) Middle Pleistocene Bird Consumption at Level XI of Bolomor Cave (Valencia, Spain). *Journal of Archaeological Science,* 36, 2213–2223.

Blaxland, J. (1951) Newcastle disease in shags and cormorants and its significance as a factor in the spread of this disease among domestic poultry. *The Veterinary Record,* 47, 731–733.

Blois, J. L., McGuire, J. L. & Hadley, E. A. (2010) Small mammal diversity loss in response to late-Pleistocene climatic change. *Nature,* 465, 771–774.

Blois, J. L. & Hadley, E. A. (2011) Climate impacts on ecosystem structure: lessons from the Palaeolithic. Dept of life Sciences, Stanford University-online.

Bloom, P.H. & Hawks, S.J. (1982) Food habits of nesting Golden Eagles in north-east California and north-west Nevada. *Raptor Research* 16: 110–115.

Blome, R. (1686) *The Gentleman's Recreation: Horsemanship, Hawking, Hunting, Fowling, Fishing, and Agriculture.* S. Roycroft, London.

Blumler, M. (1992) Independent inventionism and recent genetic evidence on plant domestication. *Economic Botany,* 46, 98–111.

Blüchel, K. G. (2005) *Game and Hunting.* Könemann, Germany.

Boback, A. W. (1973) *Das Rebhuhn* (Perdix perdix L.). *Das Buch Der Hege, Vol. 2* (ed. H. Stubbe), pp. 25–38.

Bodey, T. W., McDonald, R. A. & Bearhop, S. (2011) Mesopredators constrain a top-predator: competetive release of ravens after culling crows. *Biol.Lett.*, 5, 617–620.

Boev, Z. N. (1997) *Chauvireria balcanica gen. n.,sp.n.* (Phasianidae-Galliformes from the Middle Villafranchian of Western Bulgaria. *Geologica Balcanica*, 27, 69–76.

Boev, Z. N. (2001) Birds over the mammoths' head in Bulgaria. The World of Elephants International Congress, Rome, pp 180–186.

Boev, Z. N. (2002) Tetraonidae Vigors, 1825 (Galliformes-Aves) in the Neogene-Quaternary record of Bulgaria and the origin and evolution of the family. *Acta zoologica cracoviensis*, 45S, 263–282.

Bondarenko, L. F., Barush, V. I. & Sonin, M. D. (1979) Nematodes of wild phasianids of Tadzhikistan. *Trudy Gel'mintologicheskoi Laboratorii*, 29, 22–28.

Borchect, P. L. & Duncan, L. (1974) Dust bathing and feather lipids in Bobwhite (*Colinus virginianus*). *Condor*, 76, 471–472.

Borg, K., Wanntorp, H., Erne, K., Hanko, E. (1969) Alkyl Mercury poisoning in terrestrial Swedish wildlife. Vitrevy 6, 301–379.

Borg, C. & Toft, S. (1999) Value of the aphid *Rhopalosiphum padi* as food for Grey Partridge *Perdix perdix* chicks. *Wildlife Biology*, 5, 55–58.

Borg, C. & Toft, S. (2000) Importance of insect prey quality for grey partridge chicks *Perdix perdix*: a self-selection experiment. *Journal of Applied Ecology*, 37, 557–563.

Borg, S. (2005) The quality of aphids as food for generalist predators: implications for natural control of aphids. *Eur. J. Entomol.* 102: 371–383.

Borralho, R., Rego, F. & Onofre, N. (1992) Raptors and Game: The assessment of a net predation rate. *Gibier Faune Sauvage*, 10, 155–163.

Borralho, R., Rego, F. & Vaz Pinto, P. (1997) Demographic trends of Red-legged Partridges in Portugal after implementation of management actions. *Gibier Faune Sauvage*, 14, 585–599.

Borralho, R., Rito, A., Rêgo, F., Simôes, H., Pinto, P.V. (1998) Summer distribution of red-legged partridges (*Alectoris rufa*) in relation to water availability on Mediterranean farmland. *Ibis*, 140, 620–662.

Both, C., Piersma, T. & Roodbergen, S. P. (2005) Climate change explains much of the 20th century advance in laying date of Northern Lapwing *Vanellus vanellus* in The Netherlands. *Ardea*, 93, 79–88.

Bouchner, M. (1966) Nesting of partridges and clutch losses. *Symposium O Koroptvi.* 72–82. Vyzkumny Ustav Lesniho Hospodarstvi A Myslivosti Ceskoslovensky Myslivecky Svaz.

Bouchner, M. & Fišer, Z. (1967) A contribution to the nesting bionomy of partridges and to the nest and egg losses. *Lesnicky Casopis*, 13, 713–728.

Bourne, W. R. P. (1996) The South Downs in the 1940s. *Sussex Bird Report*, 47, 123–124.

Boxall, P. C. & Lein, M. R. (1982) Feeding ecology of the Snowy Owl *Nyctea scandiaca* wintering in Alberta. *Arctic*, 35, 282–290.

Boyce, D. A. J. (1985) Prairie Falcon prey in the Mohave desert, California. *Raptor Research*, 19, 128–134.

Brandon, P. (1998) *The South Downs*. Butler & Tanner, London.

Brankovic, M., Davidovic, M. & Popeskovic, D. (1967) Some thermogenic characteristics and the resistance of the partridge (*Perdix perdix*) against extremely low external temperature. *Proceedings of the International Union of Game Biology*, 7, 251–253.

Brashares, J. S., Prugh, L. R., Stoner, C. J. & Epps, C. W. (2010) Ecological and Conservation Implications of Mesopredator Release. *Trophic Cascades: Predators, Prey, and the Changing Dynamics of Nature* (eds J. Terborgh & J. A. Estes), Island Press, Washington.

Brenchley, W. E. & Warington, K. (1930) The weed seed populations of arable soil: Numerical estimation of viable seeds and observations on natural dormancy. *Journal of Ecology*, 18, 235–272.

Brian, M. V. (1977) *Ants* (New Naturalist Series). William Collins Sons & Co Ltd, London.

Brickle, N. W. & Harper, G. C. (1999) Diet of nestling Corn Buntings *Miliaria calandra* in southern England examined by compositional analysis of faeces. *Bird Study*, 46, 319–329.

Brickle, N. W., Harper, G. C., Aebischer, N. J. & Cockayne, S. H. (2000) Effects of agricultural intensification on the breeding success of corn buntings *Milaria calandra*. *Journal of Applied Ecology*, 37, 742–755.

Briggs, M. (2001) The Sussex Rare Plant Register. Sussex Wildlife Trust.

Bro, E., Reitz, F., Mayot, P., Havet, p., Taran, E. & Berthos, J. C. (1998) Suivi de populations de perdrix grises (*Perdix perdix*) en periode de reproduction en France. [A field survey of Grey Partridge populations during breeding in France]. *Gibier Faune Sauvage*, 15, 535–544.

Bro, E., Clobert, J. & Reitz, F. (1999) Effects of radiotransmitters on survival and reproductive success of Gray partridge. *Journal of Wildlife Management*, 63, 1044–1051.

Bro, E., Reitz, F., Mayot, P. & Migot, P. (2000) Environmental correlates of the demographic pattern of declining populations of grey partridge (*Perdix perdix*) in France. *Hungarian Small Game Bulletin*, 5, 241–256.

Bro, E., Reitz, F. & Clobert, J. (2000) Nest-site selection of Grey Partridge (*Perdix perdix*) on agricultural lands in north-central France. *Game & Wildlife Science*, 17, 1–16.

Bro, E., Sarrazin, F., Clobert, J. & Reitz, F. (2000) Demography and the decline of the grey partridge *Perdix perdix* in France. *Journal of Applied Ecology*, 37, 432–448.

Bro, E., Reitz, F., Clobert, J., Migot, P. & Massot, M. (2001) Diagnosing the environmental causes of the decline in Grey Partridge *Perdix perdix* survival in France. *Ibis*, 143, 120–132.

Bro, E., Deldalle, B., Massot, M., Reitz, F. & Selmi, S. (2003) Density dependence of reproductive success in grey partridge *Perdix perdix* populations in France: management implications. *Wildlife Biology*, 9, 93–102.

Bro, E., Mayot, P., Corda, E. & Reitz, F. (2004) Impact of habitat management on grey partridge populations; assessing wildlife cover using a multisite BACI experiment. *Journal of Applied Ecology*, 41, 846–857.

Bro, E., Reitz, F. & Landry, P. (2005) Grey partridge *Perdix perdix* population status in central northern France: spatial variability in density and 1994–2004 trend. *Game & Wildlife Science*, 11, 287–298.

Bro, E., Clobert, J., Migot, P. & Massot, M. (2006) Nesting success of Grey Partridge (*Perdix perdix*) on agricultural land in North-Central France, relation to nesting cover and predator abundance. *Game and Wildlife Science*, 17, 199–218.

Bro, E., Arroyo, B. & Migot, P. (2006) Conflict between grey partridge *Perdix perdix* hunting and hen harrier *Circus cyaneus* protection in France: a review. *Wildlife Biology*, 12, 233–247.

Brooks, D.R., Storkey, J., Clark, S.J., Firbank, L.G., Petit, S. & Woiwood, I.P. (2012) Trophic links between functional groups of arable plants and beetles are stable at a national scale. *Journal of Animal Ecology* 81, 4–13.

Brown, V. K. (1983) *Grasshoppers*, Cambridge University Press.

Browne, S. J. & Aebischer, N. J. (2003) Temporal changes in the migration phenology of turtle doves *Streptopelia turtur* in Britain, based on sightings from coastal bird observatories. *Journal of Avian Biology*, 34, 65–71.

Browne, S. J., Aebischer, N. J., Moreby, S. J. & Teague, L. (2006) The diet and disease susceptibility of grey partridges *Perdix perdix* on arable farmland in East Anglia, England. *Wildlife Biology*, 12, 3–10.

Brugger, L. (1941) A survey of the endoparasites of the digestive and respiratory tracts of the Hungarian Partridge in Whitman County, Washington. MSc Thesis, Washington State College, 26 pp.

Brun, J.-C. (1991) La nidification des perdrix: une période bien délicate. *Faune Sauvage (ONC)*, 161, 11–20.

Brust, G. E. (1990) The effect of herbicides on beetles. *Pesticide Science*, 30, 309–320.

Brüll, H. & Lindemann, W. (1954) Der derzeitige Stand subtiler unserer Kenntnis vom Leben des Rebhuhns. *Deutsch J.Zeitung*, 103, 253–338.

Brüll, H. (1960) Der derzeitige Stand subtiler Äsungsstudies des Flugwildes. *Inst.Biol. Field res.Meded*, 50, 18–28.

Brüll, H. (1964) A study of the importance of the goshawk (*Accipiter gentilis*) and sparrow hawk (*Accipiter nisus*) in their ecosystem. *Birds of Prey and Owls* International Council for Bird Preservation, Caen, France.

Buckley, K., O'Loughlin-Irwin, S., Kelly, P. & Armitage, D. V. (2009) Report: Breeding Lapwing on the Irish Grey Partridge Conservation Project Area in 2009.

Budgett, H. M. (1933) *Hunting by Scent*. Eyre & Spottiswoode, London.

Bud'nichenko, A. S. (1965) Birds and their food in forestry plantations of the steppes [Russian]. *Birds of forestry plantations* (ed. A. S. Bud'nichenko), pp. 5–285. Voronezh University Press, Voronezh.

Buenestado, F. J., Gortázar, C., Millán, J. & Höfle, U. (2004) Descriptive study of an avian pox outbreak in wild red-legged partridges (*Alectoris rufa*). *Epidemiology and Infections*, 132, 369–374.

Buenestado, F. J., Ferreras, P., Blanco-Aguiar, J. A., Tortosa, F. S. & Villafuerte, R. (2009) Survival and causes of mortality among wild Red-legged Partridges in southern Spain: implications for conservation. *Ibis*, 151, 720–730.

Bugalho, J.F.F. & Lopes, F.J. (1979) Progress Report on the Red-legged Partridge (*Alectoris rufa*) Study in Portugal. *Les Perdrix du genre Alectoris*. Proceedings of a CIC Symposium, Athens May 25, 105–106.

Buner, F., Jenny, M., Zbinden, N. & Naef-Daenzer, B. (2005) Ecologically enhanced areas-a key habitat structure for re-introduced grey partridges *Perdix perdix*. *Biological Conservation*, 124, 373–381.

Buner, F., Browne, S. J. & Aebischer, N. J. (2011) Experimental assessment of release methods for the re-establishment of a red-listed Galliformes, the grey partridge (*Perdix perdix*). *Biological Conservation*, 144, 593–601.

Bureau, L. (1911) L'age des perdrix. *Bulletin de la Société des Sciences naturelles de l'Ouest de la France ser* 3, 1, 1–124; also (1913) 3, 3, 1–149.

Busche, G. H. J., Raddatz, J. & Kostrzewa, A. (2004) Nistplatz-Konkurrenz und Prädation zwischen Uhu (*Bubo bubo*) und Habicht (*Accipter gentilis*): erste Ergebnisse aus Norddeutschland. *Vogelwarte*, 42, 169–177.

Butler, D. A., Sage, R. B., Draycott, R. A. H., Carroll, J. P. & Potts, G. R. (2005) Lead shot exposure in ring-necked pheasants on shooting estates in Great Britain. *Wildlife Society Bulletin*, 33, 583–589.

Butler, D. A. (2005) Incidence of lead shot ingestion in red-legged partridges (*Alectoris rufa*) in Great Britain. *Veterinary Record*, 157, 661–662.

Buturlin, S. A. (1906) On the birds collected in Transcaucasia (ed. A.M. Kobylin). *Ibis*, 6, 407–427.

Byrne, P. & Moles, R. (2002) *Trichostrongylus tenuis* in Irish Red Grouse at a site in. Co Limerick. *Irish Naturalists' Journal*, 27, 73–75.

Calderon, J. (1977) The role of the red-legged partridge in the diet of predators in Spain. *Doñana (Acta Vertebrata)*, 4, 61–126.

Calvete, C., Estrada, R., Lucientes, J. & Telletxea, I. (2003) Correlates of helminth community in the red-legged partridge (*Alectoris rufa* L.) in Spain. *Journal Parasitology*, 89, 445–451.

Camp, M. & Best, L. B. (1994) Nest Density and Nesting Success of Birds in Roadsides Adjacent to Rowcrop Fields. *American Midland Naturalist*, 131, 347–358.

Campbell, J. W. (1936) On the food of some British birds. *British Birds*, 30, 209–219.

Cao, M., Naifa, L., Wang, X. L. & Guan, M. (2010) Genetic diversity and genetic structure of the Daurian Partridge (*Perdix dauurica*) in China, assessed by microsatellite variation. *Chinese Birds*, 1, 51–64.

Capponi, F. (1979) Ornithologia latina. 1st Filologica Class. e Mediovale, Genova.

Caro, J., Ontiveros, D. & Pleguezuelos, J. M. (2011) The feeding ecology of Bonelli's eagle (*Aquila fasciata*) 'floaters' in southern Spain: implications for conservation. *European Journal of Wildlife Research*, 57, 729–736.

Carroll, J. P. (1988) The shoulder spot in Gray Partridge. *Wilson Bulletin.*, 100, 677–679.

Carroll, J. P. (1989) *Ecology of Gray Partridge in North Dakota.* PhD University of North Dakota, Grand Forks.

Carroll, J. P. (1990) Winter and Spring Survival of Radio-Tagged Gray Partridge in North Dakota. *Journal of Wildlife Management*, 54, 657–662.

Carroll, J. P. (1992) A model of grey partridge *Perdix perdix* population dynamics in North Dakota. *Gibier Faune Sauvage*, 9, 337–349.

Carroll, J. P., Crawford, R. D. & Schulz, J. W. (1995) Gray partridge winter home range and use of habitat in North Dakota. *Journal of Wildlife Management*, 59, 98–103.

Carter, I. (2001) *The Red Kite.* Arlequin.

Cartright, B. W. (1944) The crash decline in Sharp-tailed Grouse and Hungarian Partridge in Western Canada and the role of the predator. *Transactions of the American Wildlife Conference*, 9, 324–329.

Casas, F., Mougeot, F. & Viñuela, J. (2009) Double-nesting behaviour and sexual differences in breeding success in wild Red-legged Partridges *Alectoris rufa. Ibis*, 151, 743–751.

Casas, F. & Viñuela, J. (2010) Agricultural practices or game management: which is the key to improve red-legged partridge nesting success in agricultural landscapes? *Environmental Conservation*, 37, 177–186.

Casas, F., Mougeot, F., Sánchez-Barbudo, I., Davila, J. A. & Viñuela, J. (2011) Fitness consequences of anthropogenic hybridization in wild red-legged partridge (*Alectoris rufa*, Phasianidae) populations. *Biol Invasions*,14, 295–305.

Case, A. A. & Ackert, J. E. (1940) New Intermediate Hosts of Fowl Cestodes. *Transactions of the Kansas Academy of Science*, 43, 393–396.

Castilla, A. M., Dhondt, A. A., Diaz-Uriarte, R. & Westmoreland, D. (2007) Predation in ground nesting birds: an experimental study using natural egg-colour variation. *Avian Conservation and Ecology*, www.ace-eco.org/vol2/iss1/art2

Castroviejo, I. (1967) Zur Variation des Iberishcen Rebhuhns *Perdix perdix hispaniensis* (Reichenow, 1892). *Bonner Zoologische Beiträge*, 18, 321–332.

Cattadori, I. M., Hudson, P. J., Merler, S. & Rizzoli, A. (1999) Synchrony, scale and temporal dynamics of rock partridge (*Alectoris graeca saxatilis*) populations in the Dolomites. *Journal of Animal Ecology*, 68, 540–549.

Cergh, J. A. (1943) The European grey partridge in Persia. *Journal of Bombay Natural History Society*, 44, 297–298.

Ceugniet, M., Aubin, T., Bernard-Laurent, A. & Soyez, D. (2002) Coding and decoding systems of the rally call of two species of partridges and their hybrids [abstract]. *Bioacoustics*, 13, 97–98.

Chaigneau, A. (1974) La perdrix rouge (*Alectoris rufa* L.). *Les Habitudes du Gibier pp* 158–163. Payot, Paris.

Chakarov, N. & Krüger, O. (2010) Mesopredator Release by an Emergent Superpredator: A Natural Experiment of Predation in a Three Level Guild. *PLoS ONE*, 5 (12): e15229. doi:10.1371/journal.pone.0015229

Chalmers P.R. (1928) *The frequent gun and a little fishing.* Philip Allen & Co, London.

Chambers, R. J., Sunderland, K. D., Wyatt, I. J. & Vickerman, G. P. (1983) The effects of predator exclusion and acging on cereal aphids in winter wheat. *Journal of Applied Ecology*, 20,209–224.

Cheneval, J. (2000) The avifauna of Sansan. *Memoires du Museum National d'Histoire Naturelle*, 183, 321–388.

Cheng, T-H. (1976) *Distribution of birds in China* [in Chinese]. Institute of Zoology, Beijing.

Cheng, T-H, Li,D., Wang, Z.,Wang, Z., Zhihua, J. & Lu, T. (1983) *The avifauna of Xizang*. The Northwest Plateau, Institute of Biology, Academia Sinica, Xining, Quinghai.

Cheylan, G. (1977) La place trophique de l'Aigle de Bonnelli *Hieraetus fasciatus* dans les biocenosis mediterraneennes. *Alauda*, 45, 1–15.

Chiriac, E., Manolache, L. & Constantinescu, Z. (1972) Contributii la studiul helmintofaunei potirnichii (*Perdix perdix* L.) din Romania [Contributions to the study of helminth fauna of the partridge (*Perdix perdix* L.)]. *Studii si Cercetări de Biologie, Seria Zoologie*, 24, 101–104.

Chitty, D. (1996) Do lemmings commit suicide? Beautiful hypotheses and ugly facts. Oxford University Press, Oxford.

Chiverton, P. A. (1999) The benefits of unsprayed cereal crop margins to Grey Partridges *Perdix perdix* and Pheasants *Phasianus colchicus*. *Wildlife Biology*, 5, 83–92.

Christensen, G. C. (1970) The Chukar Partridge. *Nevada Department of Fish and Game Biological Bulletin*, 4, 1–82.

Church, K. E., Harris, H. J. & Stiehl, R. B. (1980) Habitat utilization by grey partridge (*Perdix perdix* L.) pre-nesting pairs in east-central Wisconsin. *Perdix II. Grey Partridge Workshop* (eds S. R. Peterson & L. Nelson), pp. 9–20. Forest, Wildlife and Range Experiment Station, University of Idaho.

Church, K. E. (1984) Nesting Biology of gray partridge in East-Central Wisconsin. *Perdix*, 3, 46–53.

Church, K. E. (1993) Survival and nesting biology of translocated Grey Partridge (*Perdix perdix*) in New York State, USA. *Gibier Faune Sauvage*, 10, 281–291.

Church, K. E. (1993) Summer habitat use and home range of translocated grey partridge (*Perdix perdix*) in New York State, USA. *Gibier Faune Sauvage*, 10, 281–291.

Churchwell, R., Ratti, J. T. & Edelmann, F. (2004) Comparison of Fall and Winter Food Habits for Sympatric Chukar and Grey Partridge in Hell's Canyon of Idaho and Oregon. *Northwest Science*, 78, 42–47.

Clapham, P. A. (1933) On the life-history of *Heterakis gallinae*. *Journal of Helminthology*, 11, 67–86.

Clapham, P. A. (1935) Some Helminth Parasites from Partridges and other English Birds. *Journal of Helminthology*, 13, 139–148.

Clapham, P. A. (1936) Further Observations on Occurrence and Incidence of Helminths in British Partridges. *Journal of Helminthology*, 14, 61–68.

Clapham, P. A. (1937) On some lesions associated with Helminths in birds of economic importance. *Journal of Helminthology*, 15, 49–52.

Clapham, P. A. (1938) New records of Helminths in British Birds. *Journal of Helminthology*, 16, 47–48.

Clapham, P. A. (1939a) On Flies as Intermediate Hosts of *Syngamus tracheae*. *Journal of Helminthology*, 17, 61–64.

Clapham, P. A. (1939b) Three new intermediate vectors for *Syngamus tracheae*. *Journal of Helminthology*, 17, 191–192.

Clapham, P. A. (1939c) On a sex difference in the infection rate with *Syngamus tracheae*. *Journal of Helminthology*, 17, 192–194.

Clapham, P. A. (1940) On wild birds as transmitters of helminth parasites to domestic stock. *Journal of Helminthology*, 18, 39–44.

Clapham, P. A. (1949) On *Capillaria cadovulvata*, pathogenic to *Perdix perdix*. *Journal of Helminthology*, 23, 69–71.

Clapham, P. A. (1957) Helminth parasites in some wild birds. *Bird Study*, 4, 193–196.

Clapham, P. A. (1961) Recent Observations on Helminthiasis in some British Game Birds. *Journal of Helminthology*, 35, 35–40.

Clarke, R., Combridge, P. & Middleton, N. (2003) Monitoring the diets of farmland winter seed-eaters through raptor pellet analysis. *British Birds*, 96, 360–375.

Clarke, J. H., Cook, S. K., Harris, D., Wiltshire, J. J. J., Henderson, I. G., Jones, N. E., Boatman, N. D., Potts, S. G., Westbury, D. B., Woodcock, B. A., Ramsay, A. J., Pywell, R. F., Goldsworthy, P. E., Holland, J. M., Smith, B. M.,

Tipples, J., Morris, A. J., Chapman, P. & Edwards, P. (2007) The SAFFIE Project Report. Boxworth, UK, ADAS.

Clausen, B. & Wolstrop, C. (1979) Lead poisoning in game in Denmark. *Danish Review of Game Biology*, 11, 1–22.

Clay, T. (1949) Some problems in the evolution of a group of ectoparasites. *Evolution*, 3, 279–299.

Clotte, J. (2010) *Cave Art.* Phaidon, London.

Coles, C. L. (1979) Red-legged Partridge management in Portugal. Fordingbridge, The Game Conservancy.

Collinge, W.E. (1917) The food and feeding habits of the partridge, *Journal of the Land Agents' Society* June 1917.

Collinge, W. E. (1938) Food of the partridge. *Nature*, 141, 834.

Conrad, K. F., Warren, M. S., Fox, R., Parsons, M. S. & Woiwood, I. P. (2006) Rapid declines of common, widespread British moths provide evidence of an insect biodiversity crisis. *Biological Conservation*, 132, 279–291.

Conway, G. R. & Pretty, J. N. (1991) *Unwelcome Harvest: Agriculture and Pollution.* Earthscan, London.

Coulson, J. C., Deans, I. R., Potts, G. R., Robinson, J. & Crabtree, A. N. (1972) Changes in organochlorine contamination of the marine environment of eastern Britain monitored by shag eggs. *Nature*, 236, 454–456.

Cox, R., Newborn, D., Baines, D., Thomas, C. J. & Sherratt, T. N. (2010) No Evidence for Resistance to Fenbendazole in *Trichostrongylus tenuis*, a Nematode Parasite of the Red Grouse. *The Journal of Wildlife Management*, 74, 1799–1805.

Craighead, J. J. & Craighead, F. C. (1956) Hawks, Owls and Wildlife. Stackpole, New York.

Cram, E. B. (1928) Nematodes of pathological significance found in some economically important birds in North America. *United States Department of Agriculture Technical Bulletin*, 49, 1–10.

Cram, E. B., Jones, M. F. & Allen, E. A. (1932) Internal parasites and parasitic diseases

of the Bobwhite. *The Bobwhite Quail, It's Habits, Preservation and Increase.* 229–338, Scribners.

Crook, N. E. & Sunderland, K. D., (1984) Detection of aphid remains in predatory insects and spiders by ELISA. *Annals of Applied Biology*, 105,413–422.

Crooks, K. R. & Soulé, M. E. (1999) Conservation Biology: Top dogs maintain diversity. *Nature*, 400, 510–511. Crooks, K. R. & Soulé, M. E. (1999) Mesopredator release and avifaunal extinctions in a fragmented ecosystem. *Nature*, 400, 563–566.

Crowe, T. M., Bowie, R. C. K., Bloomer, P., Mandiwana, T. G., Hedderson, T. A. J., Randi, E., Pereira, S. L. & Wakeling, J. (2006) Phylogenetics, biogeography and classification of, and character evolution in gamebirds (Aves:Galliformes); effect of character exclusion, data partitioning and missing data. *Cladistics*, 22, 495–532.

Csányi, S., Lehoczki, R. & Sonkoly, K. (2010) National Game Management Database of Hungary. *International Journal of Information Systems and Social Change*, 1, 34–43.

Cucco, M., Malacarne, G., Ottonelli, R. & Tanvez, A. (2008) Yolk testosterone levels and dietary carotenoids influence growth and immunity of grey partridge chicks. *General and Comparative Endocrinology*, 156, 418–425.

Cuckler, A. C. & Alicata, J. E. (1944) The Life History of *Subulura brumpti*, a cecal nematode of poultry in Hawaii. *Transactions of the American Microscopical Society*, 63, 345–357.

Curtis, B. C., Rajaram, S. & Gómez-Macpherson, H. E. (2002) Wheat improvement and production. Food & Agriculture Organisation, Rome.

Da Silva Reis, F. & Vizeu Pinheiro, M. F. (1973) Agumas normas a observar nas largadas de perdizes para repovamento. *Estudos e divulação Técnica Grupo A Secção Zoologia Florestal e Cinegética*, 1973, 5–67.

Dahlgren, J. (1987) *Partridge activity, growth rate and survival: Dependence on insect abundance.* PhD thesis University of Lund, Sweden.

Dahlgren, J. (1990) The significance of arthropods in the Grey Partridge diet. *Perdix*, 5, 202–213.

Dal', S. K. (1944), Pozvonochnye zhivotnye Sarai Bulakskogo khrebta (Vertebrates of the Sarai Bulaksk Range). *Zoologicheskii sbornik AN Armenia SSR*, 3, 5–46.

Dalton, P. (1996) Use of dimetridazole in gamebirds. *Veterinary Record*, 138, 399.

Danova C. B., Vidus-Rosin A., Andreoli E., Mattiello S., Meriggi A. (2012) Fall diet of the Rock Partridge (*Alectoris graeca saxatilis*) in the central sector of Italian Alps. *Avocetta* in press.

Dansgaard, J. W. C. White & S. J. Johnsen (1989) The abrupt termination of the Younger Dryas climate event. *Nature* 339, 532–534.

Davis, B. N. K. (1967) Bird feeding preferences among different crops in an area near Huntingdon. *Bird Study*, 14, 227–237.

Davison, G. W. H. (1976) Function of the tail pattern in game birds. *British Birds*, 69, 371–372.

Dayani, A. (1986) Fall food items utilized by Chukars in central Alborz protected region, Iran. *Linzer boil. Beitr.* 18, 95–99

De Leo, G. A., Focardi, S., Gatto, M. & Cattadori, I. M. (2004) The decline of the Grey Partridge in Europe: comparing demographics in traditional and modern agricultural landscapes. *Ecological Modelling*, 177, 313–335.

Degen, A. A., Pinshow, B. & Shaw, P. J. (1984) Must desert chukars (*Alectoris chukar sinaica*) drink water? Water influx and body mass changes in response to dietary water content. *Auk*, 101, 47–52.

Dekker, D. & Court, G. (2003) Gyr Falcon predation on mallards and the interaction of Bald Eagles wintering in central Alberta. *Journal of Raptor Research*, 37, 161–163.

del Hoyo, J., Elliott, A. & Sargatal, J. (1994) *Handbook of Birds of the World* Vol. 2. Lynx Ediciones, Barcelona.

Delacour, G. (1987) Statut de la perdrix grise (*Perdix perdix L.*) en Alsace, 1975–1984. Université de Bourgogne.

Delius, J. D. (1965) A population study of Skylarks *Alauda arvensis*. *Ibis*, 107, 466–492.

Dement'ev, G. P., Gladkov, N. A. & Isakov, Y. A. (1952) Birds of the Soviet Union, vol. 4 [Ru]. Sovetskaya Nauka, Moscow.

Dement'ev, G. P. & Gladkov, N. A. (1967) Ptitsy Sovetskogo Soyuza translation by A. Birron & Z.S.Cole. Programme for Scientific Translations, Moskva and Jerusalem.

Demers, D. J. & Garton, E. O. (1980) An evaluation of Gray Partridge (*Perdix perdix*) Aging Criteria. *Perdix*, 2, 21–44.

Demers, D. J. (1981) Plumage Development and Food Preferences of Captive Gray Partridge. Thesis University of Idaho.

Deng W.H., Zheng G.M., Garson P.J., Zhang, Z. W. & McGowan P.J.K. (2005) Providing artificial nest platforms for Cabot's Tragopan *Tragopan caboti* (Aves: Galliformes): a useful conservation tool? *Oryx*, 39, 158–163.

Depéret, C. (1887) Recherches sur la succession des faunes de Vertébrés Miocènes de la Vallée du Rhone. *Archives du Muséum d'Histoire Naturelle de Lyon*, 4, 45–313.

Depéret, C. (1892) Animaux Pliocènes de Rousillon. *Mém.Soc.Géol.France, Paleontologie*, 3, 117–136.

des Forges, G. & Harber, D. D. (1963) *A Guide to the Birds of Sussex*. Oliver & Boyd, Edinburgh.

Dessì-Fulgheri, F. & Mingozzi, T. (1985) *Seminario tenuto all'Università della Calabria Biologia dei Galliformi, Problemi di gestione venatoria e conservazione*. Università della Calabria, Arcavacata.

Dessì-Fulgheri, F., Beani, L. & Piazza, R. (1986) Vocalisation of the grey partridge (*Perdix perdix*): a spectrographic analysis. *Monitore Zoologico Italiano*, 20, 441–458.

Dessì-Fulgheri, F., Gentle, A. & Papeschi, A. (2001) Effects of a high-fibre diet on laying, hatching and chick weight in the Pheasant (*Phasianus colchicus*). *Game & Wildlife Science*, 18, 545–558.

Didillon, M. C. & Chapuis, J. L. (1987) Diet of the rock partridge (*Alectoris graeca saxatilis*) In the maritime alps. A methodological approach. *Revue d'Ecologie – La Terre et la Vie*, 4S, 59–65.

Didillon, M. C. (1988) Regime alimentaire de la perdix rochassiere (*Alectoris graeca saxatilis x Alectoris rufa rufa*) dans les Alpes-Maritimes. *Gibier Faune Sauvage*, 5, 149–170.

Dits, V. R. (1917) Grey partridge in Imperial Hunting Preserves (in Ru). *Orn.Vestnik*, 8, 57–58.

Dobson, A., Lafferty, K. D., Kuris, A. M., Hechinger, R. F. & Jetz, W. R. (2008) Homage to Linnaeus: How many parasites? How many hosts? *Proceedings of the National Academy of Sciences*, 105, 11482–11489.

Dobzhansky, T. (1973) Nothing in biology makes sense except in the light of evolution. *The American Biology Teacher*, 35, 125–129.

Donald, P. F. & Vickery, J. A. (2000) The importance of cereal fields to breeding and wintering skylarks *Alauda arvensis* in the UK. In Aebischer, N. J., Evans, A. D., Grice, P. V., and Vickery, J. A. *Ecology and Conservation of Lowland Farmland birds*. pp. 140–150, British Ornithologists Union.

Donald, P. F., Buckingham, D. L., Moorcroft, D. & Muirhead, L. B. (2001) Habitat use and diet of skylarks *Alauda arvensis* wintering on lowland farmland in southern Britain. *Journal of Applied Ecology*, 38, 536–547.

Donald, P. F., Evans, A. D., Muirhead, L. B., Buckingham, D. L., Kirby, W. B. & Schmidt, S. I. A. (2002) Survival rates, causes of failure and productivity of Skylark *Alauda arvensis* nests on lowland farmland. *Ibis*, 144, 652–664.

Donald, P. F. (2004) *The Skylark*. T.& A.D.Poyser, London.

Doncaster, C. P. (1992) Testing the role of intraguild predators in regulating hedgehog populations. *Proceedings Royal Society Ser B*, 249, 113–117.

Donlan, C. J., Berger, J., Bock, C. E., Bock, J. H., Burney, D. A., Estes, J. A., Foreman, D., Martin, P. S., Roemer, G. W., Smith, F. A., Soulé, M. E. & Greene, H. W. (2006) Pleistocene Rewilding: an Optimistic Agenda for Twenty-First Century Conservation. *The American Naturalist*, 168, 660–681.

Douglas-Home, H. (1938) Partridge eccentricities: the bird who's every war is watched. *The Field* 1938, 607.

Dowell, S. D. (1987) The development of antipredator responses in gamebird chicks. *The Game Conservancy Annual Review*, 18, 93–98.

Dowell, S. D. (1988) Some effects of the method of rearing on the behaviour and ecology of grey partridges. *The Game Conservancy Annual Review*, 19, 125–132.

Dowell, S. D. (1990) The Ontogeny of Anti-Predator Behaviour in Gamebird Chicks. DPhil Thesis, University of Oxford.

Dowell, S.D. (1992) Problems and pitfalls of gamebird reintroduction and restocking: an overview. *Gibier Faune Sauvage* 9: 773–780.

Doxon, E. D., Davis, C. A. & Fuhlendorf, S. D. (2011) Comparison of two methods for sampling invertebrates: vacuum and sweep-net sampling. *Journal of Field Ornithology*, 82, 60–67.

Döring, V. & Helfrich, R. (1986) Zur Ökologie einer Rebhuhnpopulation (*Perdix perdix, L. 1758*) im Unteren Naheland (Rheinland-Pfalz; Bundesrepublik Deutschland). Ferdinand Enke Verlag, Stuttgart.

Dragoev, V. (1974) On the population of the Rock Partridge (*Alectoris graeca* Meisner) in Bulgaria and methods of census. *Acta Ornithol.*, 14, 251–255.

Draycott, R.A.H. & Armenteros Santos, J-Á (2012) Intestinal nematodes of shot wild grey partridges in Norfolk, England. *Veterinary Record* (in press).

Droneig, H. (1955) Partridges' nest on a stack of barley-straw. *Aquila*, 59, 455.

Drovetski, S. V. (2003) Plio-Pleistocene Climate oscillations, Holarctic biogeography and speciation in an avian subfamily (grouse). *Journal of Biogeography*, 30, 1173–1181.

Duarte, J., Farfan, M. A. & Vargas, J. (2011) New data on mortality, home range, and dispersal of red-legged partridges (*Alectoris rufa*) released in a mountain range. *European Journal of Wildlife Research*, 57.

Dudzinski, W. (1988) Wintering grounds of the partridge. *Common Partridge International Symposium,* pp. 165–184. Polish Hunting Association, Warsaw.

Dudzinski, W. (1988) Some aspects of the effect of predators on a partridge, *Perdix perdix* L., population. *Transactions of the XVIIIth Congress of the International Union of Game Biologists* (eds B. Bobek, K. Perzanowski & W. L. Regelin), pp. 245–248. Swiatt Press, Kraków-Warszwa.

Dudzinski, W. (1990) The impact of predators on a partridge population in winter. *Transactions of the XIX Congress of the International Union of Game Biologists* (ed. S. Myrberget), pp. 125–128. Norwegian Institute for Nature Research (NINA), Trondheim.

Dudzinski, W. 1992. Grey Partridge (*Perdix perdix*) predator relationships in cropland and forest habitat of central Poland. *Gibier Faune Sauvage,* 9, 455–466.

Dukas, R. & Kamil, A. C. (2001) Limited attention: the constraint underlying search images. *Behavoural Ecology,* 12, 192–199.

Duncan, J. S., Reid, H. W., Moss, R., Phillips, J. P. D. & Watson, A. (1978) Ticks, louping-ill and red grouse on moors in Speyside, Scotland. *Journal of Wildlife Management,* 42, 500–505.

Dwenger, R. (1991) Das Rebhuhn. A. Ziemsen Verlag, Wittenberg Lutherstadt.

Dyke, G. J. & Crowe, T. M. (2008) Avian paleontology: opinions and quasi-phenetics versus characters and cladistics. *Cladistics,* 24, 77–81.

Eastham, A. (2005) Papageno down the ages: A study in fowling methods, with particular reference to the Palaeolithic of Western Europe. *Munibe (Antropologia-Arkeologia),* 57, 369–397.

Elbert, A., Haas, M., Springer, B., Thielert, W. & Nauen, R. (2008) Applied aspects of neonicotenoid use in crop protection. *Pesticide Management Science,* 64, 1099–1105.

Elmhagen, B. & Rushton, S. P. (2007) Trophic control of mesopredators in terrestrial ecosystems: top-down or bottom-up? *Ecology Letters,* 10, 197–206.

Elmhagen, B., Ludwig, G., Rushton, s. P., Helle, P. & Linden, H. (2010) Top predators, mesopredators and their prey: interference ecosystems along bioclimatic productivity gradients. *Journal of Animal Ecology,* 79, 785–794.

Elton, C. (1930) *Animal ecology and evolution.* Oxford University Press, Oxford.

Enck, J. W. (1986) *Brood-rearing ecology of Gray Partridge in New York.* Ph.D Thesis. Cornell University.

Enck, J. W. (1987) The effect of insect abundance on gray partridge chick survivorship in New York State. *Perdix,* 4, 3–16.

Enck, J. W. (1990) Roost site characteristics of gray partridge broods. *Perdix V: Gray Partridge and Ring-necked Pheasant Workshop* (eds K. E. Church, R. E. Warner & S. J. Brady), pp. 214–222. Mankato, Minnesota.

Enigk, K. & Sticinsky, E. (1959) Die Zwischenwirte der Hühnerband würmer. *Zeitschrift für Parasitenkunde,* 19, 278–308.

Eo, S. H., Binenda-Emonds, O. R. P. & Carroll, J. P. (2009) A phylogenetic supertree of the fowls (Galloanserae, Aves). *Zoologica Scripta,* 38, 465–481.

Eraud, C., Boutin, J.-M., Riviere, M., Brun, J.-C., Barbraud, C. & Lormee, H. (2009) Survival of Turtle Doves *Streptopelia turtur* in relation to western Africa environmental conditions. *Ibis,* 151, 186–190.

Erbajeva, M. A. & Alexeeva, N. V. (2000) Pliocene and Pleistocene biostratigraphic succession of Transbaikalia with emphasis on small mammals. *Quaternary International,* 68–71, 67–75.

Ergun, H. & Merdivenci, A. (1953) Studies on the nematodes of the grey partridge (*Perdix perdix canescens*) and chukar (*Alectoris chukar*) [Turkish]. *Veterinary and Bacteriological Institute Ankara,* 23, 755–762.

Erikstad, K. E. & Spidso, T. K. (1982) The influence of weather on food intake, insect prey selection and feeding behaviour in Willow Grouse chicks in northern Norway. *Ornis Scandinavica,* 13, 176–182.

Erpelding, R., Kimmel, R. O. & Lockman, D. J. (1987) Foods and feeding behaviour of young gray partridge in Minnesota. *Perdix IV: Gray*

Partridge Workshop (eds R. O. Kimmel, J. W. Schulz & G. J. Mitchell), pp. 17–30. Minn. Dep. Nat. Resour., Madelia.

Errington, P. L. & Hamerstrom, F. N. (1936) The Northern Bob-White's Winter Territory. *Agricultural Experiment Station Iowa State College*, 201, 301–443.

Errington, P. L. & Hamerstrom, F. N. (1938) Observations on the effect of a spring drought on reproduction in the Hungarian Partridge. *Condor*, 40, 71–73.

Errington, P. L. (1945) Some contributions of a fifteen-year local study of the northern bobwhite to a knowledge of population phenomena. *Ecological Monographs*, 15, 1–34.

Esch, G. W. (2004) *Parasites, People and Places. Essays on Field Parasitology.* Cambridge University Press.

Estes, J.A. and 23 others (2011) Trophic Downgrading of Planet Earth. *Science*, 333, 301–306.

Evans, A. H. (1903) *Turner on Birds: a short and succinct history of the birds noticed by Pliny and Aristotle translated with commentary by William Turner published in 1544.* University of Cambridge Press, Cambridge.

Evans, L. T. (1998) *Feeding the ten billion.* Cambridge University Press, Cambridge.

Evans, W. (1912) Food of the common partridge. *Scottish Naturalist*, 1912, 278–279.

Ewald, J. A. & Aebischer, N. J. (1999) Pesticide use, avian food resources and bird densities in Sussex. Joint Nature Conservation Committee, Report No 296, Peterborough.

Ewald, J. A. & Aebischer, N. J. (2000) Trends in Pesticide Use and efficacy during 26 years of changing agriculture in southern England. *Environment Monitoring and Assessment*, 64, 493–529.

Ewald, J. A., Aebischer, N. J., Brickle, N. W., Moreby, S. J., Potts, G. R. & Wakeham-Dawson, A. (2002) Spatial variation in densities of farmland birds in relation to pesticide use and avian food resources. *Avian Landscape Ecology IALE Conference UK*, 11, 305–312.

Ewald, J. A. & Touyéras, H. (2002) Examining the spatial relationship between pheasant (*Phasianus cochicus*) release pens and grey partridge (*Perdix perdix*) population parameters. *Zeitschrift für Jagdwissenschaft*, 48, 354–363.

Ewald, J. A., Aebischer, N. J., Richardson, S. M., Grice, P. V. & Cooke, A. I. (2010) The effect of agri-environment schemes on grey partridges at the farm level in England. *Agriculture, Ecosystems and Environment*, 138, 55–63.

Ewald, J. A. & Aebischer, N. J. (2010) Grey Partridge and agri-environment schemes: Science, implementation and assessment. *Aspects of Applied Biology*, 100, 101–109.

Ewald, J. A., Potts, G. R. & Aebischer, N. J. (2012) Restoration of a Wild Grey Partridge Shoot: a Major Development in the Sussex Study. *Animal Biodiversity and Conservation*, 35 (in press).

Fàbiàn, H. (1979) Genetical consideration over the variation of the grey partridges's breast coloration, *Aquila*, 86, 13–16.

Fabro, C., Visintin, A., Filacorda, S., Frangipane di Regalbono, A. & Artuso, I. (2011) Relation between parasites, reproductive index and habitat change in Rock Partridge (*Alectoris graeca*) populations in the central southern alps. www.alectoris.disav.unipm.it

Fagasinski, A. (1964) Helminth parasites of partridge (*Perdix perdix* L.) of chosen hunting grounds. *Acta Parasitologica Polonica*, 12, 433–439.

Faragó, S. (1997) Dynamics of the grey-partridge population covered by the Lajta Project (Western Hungary) 1989–1995. *Hungarian Small Game Bulletin*, 1, 107–132.

Faragó, S. (1997) Habitat selection of the grey partridge population covered by the Lajta Project (Western Hungary). *Hungarian Small Game Bulletin*, 1, 133–151.

Faragó, S. & Buday, P. (1998) A Lajta Project Fogoly (*Perdix perdix*) Populációjának és Környezetének vizsgálata 1989–1997. *Magyar Apróvad Közlemények [Hungarian Small Game Bulletin]*, 2, 1–250.

Faragó, S. (2000) The Lajta project – the pilot project of the Hungarian partridge conservation program. *Hungarian Small Game Bulletin*, 5, 301–312.

Faragó, S. (2007) *Magyar Vadász Enciklopédia.* Totem Kiadó, Budapest.

Faragó, S., Dittrich, G., Horváth-Hangya, K. & Winkler, D. (2012) 20 years of the Grey Partridge population in the LAJTA Project (Western Hungary). *Animal Biodiversity and Conservation,* 35 (in press).

Farr, M. M. (1961) Further observations on the survival of the protozoan parasite Histamonas meleagridis and eggs of poultry nematodes in faeces of infected birds. *Cornell Veterinary Journal,* 51, 3–13.

Farský, O. (1926) O užitecnosti koroptví a bažantu jako ochráncu polních plodin proti škudcum živocišným. *Stráž Myslivost,* 4, 223–225.

Farský, O., Cech & Glatz (1928) Game birds and certain types of liver fluke in sheep (Cz.). *Stráž Myslivost,* 6.?

Fazer, K. (1925) Jokioisten Metsästys-Ja Riistanhoitoalue [Fin]. *Metsästys ja Kalastus,* 14, 13–16.

Fábián, G. (1979) Genetical consideration over the variation of the Grey Hungarian Partridge's breast coloration. *Aquila,* 86, 13–16.

Fenech, N. (1992) *Fatal Flight: The Maltese Obsession with Killing Birds.* Quiller Press, London.

Ferrandis, P., Mateo, R., Lopez-Serrano, F. R., Martínez -Duro, M. & Martinez-Duro, E. (2008) Lead-Shot Exposure in Red-Legged Partridge (*Alectoris rufa*) on a Driven Shooting Estate. *Environment Science Technology,* 42, 6271–6277.

Ferrero, M., Blanco-Aguiar, J. A., Loughheed, S. C., Sanchez-Barbudo, I., de Nova, P. J., Villafuerte, R. & Davila, J. A. (2011) Phylogeography and genetic structure of the red-legged partridge (*Alectoris rufa*): more evidence for refugia within the Iberian glacial refugium. *Molecular Ecology,* 20.2628–42.

Figala, J., Prchalová, J. & Tester, J. R. (2001) GIS Assessment of the decline of Gray Partridge (*Perdix perdix*) Nesting Habitat in the Elbe River Lowlands, the Czech Republic 1949–1996. *Ekológia (Bratislava),* 20, 209–218.

Fisher, R. J. (1943) Winter feeding station tests of grains in Washington. *Journal of Wildlife Management,* 7, 344–345.

Fog, M. (1988) On the grey partridge in Denmark. *Proceedings of the Common Partridge (Perdix perdix L.) International Symposium* (ed. A. Arcimowicz), pp. 93–104. Polish Hunting Association, Warsaw.

Ford, J., Chitty, H. & Middleton, A. D. (1938) The food of Partridge chicks (*Perdix perdix*) in Great Britain. *Journal of Animal Ecology,* 7, 251–265.

Formenti, N., Viganò, R., Ferrari, N., Cerutti, M. C. & Lanfranchi, P. (2011) Helminths communities of Rock Partridge (*Alectoris græca*) in western Alps: effect of age and sex. www.alectoris.disav.unipm.it

Formozov, A. N. (1946) Snow cover as an integral factor of the environment and its importance in the ecology of mammals and birds. *Materials for Fauna and Flora of the U.S.S.R.* Moscow Society of Naturalists (Translation published by Boreal Institute for Northern Studies, University of Alberta, Canada).

Foronda, P., Casanova, J. C., Figueruelo, E., Abreu, N. & Feliu, C. (2005) The helminth fauna of the Barbary partridge *Alectoris barbara* in Tenerife, Canary Islands. *Journal of Helminthology,* 79, 133–138.

Fortuna, M. Á. (2002) Selección de hábitat de la Perdiz roja *Alectoris rufa* en período reproductor en relacion con las característcas del paisaje de un agrosistema de La Mancha (España). *Ardeola,* 49, 59–66.

Frampton, G. K. & Dorne, J.-L. C. M. (2007) The effects on terrestrial invertebrates of reducing pesticide inputs in arable crop edges: a meta-analysis. *Journal of Applied Ecology,* 44, 362–373.

Frank, H. (1970) Die Auswirkung von Raubwild- und Raubzeugminderung auf die Strecken von Hase, Fasan und Rebhuhn in einem Revier mit intensivster landwirtschaftlicher Nutzung. *Transactions of the IX Congress of the International Union of Game Biologists* (eds A. G. Bannikov, A. A. Kistchinski & V. S. Pokrovsky), pp. 472–479. IUGB, Moscow.

Frank, H. (1971) *Das Rebhuhn.* Deutscher jagdschutz-Verband E.V., Merkblatt Nr.8, Bonn.

Freedman, R. (2011) Famine Foods-Poaceae. www.hort.purdue/edu/ff families/Poaceae

Freehling M, & Moore J. (1993) Host specificity of *Trichostrongylus tenuis* from red grouse and northern bobwhites in experimental infections of northern bobwhites. *J. Parasitol.*, 79, 538–541.

Friend, M., McLean, R. G. & Dein, F. J. (2001) Disease emergence in birds: Challenges for the 21st century. *Auk*, 118, 290–303.

Fussell, G. E. (1972) The Classical Tradition in Western European Farming. David & Charles, Newton Abbott.

Gagarin, V. G. (1954) Materials on the helminth fauna of commercial birds of the order Galliformes in Kırghız SSR. Trudy Inst. Zool. Parazit., Kirgiz. Akod. Nauk. USSR. 2:83–111.

Garcia-Castellanos, D., Estrada, F., Jiménez-Munt, C., Gorini, M., Fernàndez, J., Vergés, J. & Devicente, R. De. (2009) Catastrophic flood of the Mediterranean after the Messinian salinity crisis. *Nature*, 462, 778–781.

Gates, J. M. (1973) Gray partridge ecology in southeast-central Wisconsin. *Wisconsin Division of Forestry, Wildlife & Recreation Technical Bulletin*, 70, 1–9.

Gaudiosa Lacasa, V.R., Garcia-Abad, C.G., Prieto Martin, R., Bartolomé Rodriguez, D.J.,Pérez Garrido, J.A., Alonso de La Varga, M.E. (2010) Small game water troughs in a Spanish agrarian pseudo steppe: visits and water site choice by wild fauna. *European Journal Wildlife Research* 56, 591–599.

Georgiev, Ž. (1955) Studies of the food and nutrition of the Grey Partridge (*Perdix perdix* L.) in Bulgaria [Bulgarian]. *Bulletin de l'Institut Zoologique de l'Academie des Sciences de Bulgarie*, 4–5, 374–416.

Georgiev, Ž. (1958) The reproduction of the Thracian Rock Partridge (*Alectoris graeca cypriotes* Hartert) in the State of Harmanli [Bulgarian]. *Isv. Zool.Inst. and Muzei, Sofia*,9, 367–381.

Georgiev, Ž. (1961) The food of the adult Thracian Rock Partridge (*Alectoris graeca cypriotes* Hartert) [Bulgarian]. *Proc.Zool.Inst. Bulg.Acad.Sci.*, 10, 267–292.

Georgiev, Ž. (1963) The food of the young of Thracian Rock Partridge (*Alectoris graeca cypriotes* Hartert) [Bulgarian]. *Izv. Zool. Inst and Museum*, 14, 141–151.

Georgiev, Ž. (1964) Some additional data on the reproduction of the Thracian Rock partridge (*Alectoris graeca cypriotes* Hartert). *Izv. Zool. Inst and Museum*, 15, 17–22.

Gerstell, R. (1942) The place of winter feeding in practical wildlife management. *Pennsylvania Game Commission, Harrisburg, Research Bulletin*, 3, 1–121.

Gibson, D. I., Bray, R. A., Harris, E. A. & Compilers (2005). Online Host-Parasite Database Natural History Museum, London.

Gibson, G. (2005) *The bedside book of Birds: an avian miscellany*. Bloomsbury, London.

Gindre, R. & Allion, Y. (1971) Le Petit Gibier de Plaine dans un secteur du Gatenais-est. Contribution á l'estimation des potentialités de son habitat. *International Union of Game Biologists*, 10, 53–67.

Gindre, R. & Allion, Y. (1971) Le Petit Gibier de Plaine dans un secteur du Gâtenais-est. *Bulletin Spécial du Conseil Supérieur de la Chasse Gallinacés Gibier*, 15, 9–22.

Glänzer, U. (1984) Das Rebhuhn als Indikator für den Artenverlust in der modernen Agrarlandschaft. *Symposium: Das Freilebende Tier als Indikator für den Funktionszustand der Umwelt* Wien.

Glänzer, U., Havelka, P. & Thieme, K. (1993) Rebhuhn-Forschung in Baden-Württemberg mit Schwerpunkt im Strohgäu bei Ludwigsburg. *Veröffentlichungen zu Naturschutz und Landschaftspflege in Baden-Württemberg*, 70, 1–108.

Glue, D.E. (1977): Feeding Ecology of the Short-eared Owl in Britain and Ireland, *Bird Study*, 24, 70–78

Glutz von Blotzheim, U. N., Bauer, K. M. & Bezzel, E. (1973) Handbuch der Vögel Mitteleuropas (Volume 5). Akademishce Verlagsgesellschaft, Frankfurt am Main.

Gogoi, A. R. & Chaudhuri, R. P. (1982) Contribution to the biology of fowl cestodes *Raillietina tetragona, Raillietina*

echinobothrida and *Raillietina cesticillus. Indian Journal of Animal Sciences,* 52, 246–253.

Goldová, M., Paluš, V., Letková, V., Kocišová, A., Curlik, J. & Mojžišová, J. (2006) Parasitoses of pheasants (*Phasianus colchicus*) in confined systems. *Veterinary Archives* 76S, 83–89.

Goldschmidt, H. & Toft, S. (1997) Variable degrees of granivory and phytophagy in insectivorous carabid beetles. *Pedobiologia,* 41, 521–525.

Goldstein, M. I., Lacher, T. E., Woodbridge, B., Bechard, M. J., Canavelli, S. B., Zaccagnini, M. E., Cobb, G. P., Scollon, E. J., Tribolet, R. & Hopper, M. J. (1999) Monocrotophos-Induced Mass Mortality of Swainson's Hawks in Argentina, *Ecotoxicology,* 8, 201–214.

Gollop, J. B. (1965) Snowy owls and Gray Partridge near Saskatoon in the winter of 1963–64. *Blue Jay,* 23, 28–31.

Goodwin, D. (1953) Observations on voice and behaviour of the Red-legged partridge, *Alectoris rufa. Ibis,* 95, 581–614.

Gosselink, T. E., Van Deelen, T. R., Warner, R. E. & Mankin, P. C. (2007) Survival and Cause-Specific Mortality of Red Foxes in Agricultural and Urban Areas of Illinois. *The Journal of Wildlife Management,* 71, 1862–1872.

Göhlich, U. B. & Mourer-Chauviré, C. (2010) Revision of the Phasianids (Aves: Galliformes) from the Lower Miocene of Saint-Gérand-le-Puy (Allier, France). *Palaeontology,* 48, 1331–1350.

Göth, A. (2001) Innate predator recognition in the Australian Bush-Turkey (*Alectura lathami*) hatchlings. *Behaviour,* 138, 117–136.

Grachev, Y. N. (1983) The Chukar (*Alectoris chukar*) Biology, Exploitation and Conservation [Kazakh.]. Kazakh SSR, Alma-Ata.

Green, R. E. (1980) Do red-legged partridge broods need insects? *The Game Conservancy Annual Review,* 11, 73–76.

Green, R. E. (1983) Report to NERC on the Red-legged Partridge project. GWCT.

Green, R. E. (1984a) The feeding ecology and survival of partridge chicks (*Alectoris rufa* and *Perdix perdix*) on arable farmland in East Anglia, U.K. *Journal of Animal Ecology,* 21, 817–830.

Green, R. E. (1984b) Double nesting of the Red-legged Partridge *Alectoris rufa. Ibis,* 126, 332–346.

Green, R. E., Rands, M. R. W. & Moreby, S. J. (1987) Species differences in diet and the development of seed digestion in partridge chicks *Perdix perdix* and *Alectoris rufa. Ibis,* 129, 511–514.

Green, R. E., G. Rocamora & N. Schäffer (1997) Populations, ecology and threats to the Corncrake *Crex crex* in Europe. *Vogelwelt* 118: 117–134.

Green, R. E (1998) Long-term decline in the thickness of eggshells of thrushes, *Turdus* spp., in Britain. *Proc. R. Soc. Lond. B,* 265, 679–684. doi:10.1098/rspb.1998.0347

Green, W. A. (1999) *Agriculture & Colonization: Tell Brak [Syria] in the Uruk Period.* M. Phil. Thesis University of Cambridge.

Green, W. E. & Hendrickson, G. O. (1938) The European Partridge in North-Central Iowa. *Iowa Bird Life,* 8, 18–22.

Greig-Smith, P., Frampton, G. K. & Hardy, T. (1992) *Pesticides, Cereal Farming and the Environment [Boxworth].* H.M.S.O., London.

Grimmett, R., Inskipp, C. & Inskipp, T. (1998) *Birds of the Indian Subcontinent.* Christopher Helm, London.

Grondahl, C. R. (1959) Incidence of lead shot in pheasants and Hungarian partridge. *North Dakota Game & Fish. Pitman-Robertson Reports W-35-R-5 and W-35-R-6.*

Grubešic, E. M., Šegri, V. & Konjević, D. (2006) Analysis of counts of grey partridge (*Perdix perdix* L.) in natural breeding grounds in central Croatia. *Vet.arhiv,* 76S, 161–166.

Grzegorz, G. O., Czarnecka, J. & Panek, M. (2011) Autumn-winter diet of Grey Partridges *Perdix perdix* in winter crops, stubble fields and fallows. *Bird Study,* 58, 473–486.

Guthery, F.S. (2002) *The technology of Bobwhite Management: The theory behind the practice.* Iowa State Press, Ames.

Gutiérrez, R. J., Zink, R. M. & Yang, S. Y. (1983) Genic variation, systematic, and biogeographic relationships of some galliform birds. *Auk* 100: 33–47.

Gutiérrez, R. J., Barrowclough, G. F. & Grothy, J. G. (2000) A classification of grouse (Aves: Tetraonidae) based on mitochondrial DNA sequences. *Wildlife Biology*, 6, 205–210?

Gvozdev, E. V. (1956) Parasites of the Chukar in Kazakhstan [Ru]. *Trudy Inst.Zool.Akad. Nauk Kaz.S.S.R.*, 5, 61–76.

Gvozdev, E. V. (1957) The parasite fauna of the bearded partridge (*Perdix dauurica* Pall.) [Ru]. *Trudy Inst.Zool.Akad.Nauk Kaz.S.S.R.*, 7, 166–169.

Gvozdev, E. V. (1958) *Parasitic Worms of Galliform Birds in Kazakhstan* [Ru]. Publishing House of the Academy of Sciences, Kazakh S.S.R. (in Russian), Alma-Alta.

Habermehl, K. H. & Hofmann, R. (1963) Geschlechts-und Alterskennzeichen am Kopf des Rebhuhnes. *Sonderdruck aus Z.Jagdwissensch.*, 9, 29–35.

Hagemeijer, E. J. M. & Blair, M. J. (1997) *The EBCC Atlas of European Breeding Birds: Their Distribution and Abundance.* T. & A. D. Poyser, London.

Hakkarainen, H, Mykrä, S., Kurki, S., Tornberg, R. & Jungell, S. (2004) Competetive interactions amongst raptors in boreal forests. *Oecologia*, 141, 420–424.

Hakkarainen, H. & Korpimäki, E. (1996) Competetive and predatory interactions among raptors. Ecology, 77, 1134–1142.

Hakhumian, K. S. & Khanbekian, R. A. (1982) The helminth fauna of Chukar, Grey Partridge, Caucasian Blackcock and Snowcock in Armenia [transl.]. *Armenia Academy of Science*, 18, 9–45.

Hall, P.C. (1980) *Sussex Plant Atlas: An Atlas of the Distribution of wild plants in Sussex.* Booth Museum of Natural History, Brighton.

Hamilton, C. M. (1931) *Capillaria annulata* in Hungarian partridges. *American Vet.Med. Assoc.*, 78, 865–866.

Hammer, M., Koie, M. & Spärck, R. (1955) Undersogelser over Ernaeringen Hos Agerhons, Fasaner Og Urfugle I Denmark [Studies on the food of partridges, pheasants and black grouse in Denmark]. *Danske Vildtundersogelser*, 4, 1–24.

Hammer, M., Koie, M. & Spärck, R. (1958) Investigations on the food of partridges, pheasants and black grouse in Denmark. *Danish Review of Game Biology*, 3, 183–208.

Harper, H. T., Harry, B. H. & Bailey, W. D. (1958) The Chukar Partridge in California. *California Fish and Game*, 44, 5–50.

Harrison, J. R. (1952) On the history of the partridge in the German Friesian Islands, with the description of a new race from the island of Borkum. *Bulletin of the British Ornithologists Club*, 72, 18–21.

Harrison, J. R. (1952) The distinction of the Peat-Partridge (*Perdix p sphagnetorum*) in N. W. Germany. *Bull Br Ornithol Club*, 72.

Harrison, J. R. (1968) On the 'Montana' variety of the common partridge. *Bulletin of the British Ornithologists Club*, 88, 45–53.

Harrison, C. J. O. & Stewart, J. R. (1999) Avifauna. In *Boxgrove: A Middle Pleistocene hominid site at Eartham Quarry, Boxgrove, West Sussex.* Eds Roberts, M.B. & Parfitt, S.A. pp. 187–96.

Hart, J. D., Milsom, T. P., Fisher, G., Wilkins, V., Moreby, S. J., Murray A.W.A. & Robertson, P. A. (2006) The relationship between yellowhammer breeding performance, arthropod abundance and insecticide applications on arable farmland. *Journal of Applied Ecology*, 43, 81–91.

Haugen, A. O. (1941) Roosting and Rising Habits of the Hungarian Partridge. *Wilson Bulletin*, 53, 235–236.

Hawker, P. & Parker, E. (1922 edition of 1844) *Instructions to young Sportsmen in all that relates to guns and shooting.* Herbert Jenkins Ltd., London.

Hawkins, A. S. (1937) Hungarian Partridge nesting studies at Faville Grove. *Transactions of the North American Wildlife Conference*, 2, 481–484.

Hawkins, A. S. (1937) Winter feeding at Faville Grove, 1935–1937. *Journal of Wildlife Management*, 1, 62–69.

Hawkins, A. S. (1940) A wildlife history of Faville Grove, Wisconsin. *Transactions Wisconsin Academy of Sciences, Arts and Letters*, 32, 29–65.

Hector, A. & Hooper, R. E. (2002) Darwin and the first ecological experiment. *Science*, 295, 639–640.

Heinroth, O. & Heinroth, M. (1928) *Die Vögel Mitteleuropas* Vol.3. Berlin.

Helenius, J., Tuomela, S. & Nummi, P. (1995) Viljely-ympäristön muutosten vaikutus peltopyyn ravintoon [Fin]. *Suomen Riista*, 41, 42–45.

Helfrich, R. (1984) Das Rebhuhn. Merkblätter zum Artenschutz, Nr. 53, Landesanstalt für Ökologie; Nordrhein-Westfalen.

Helfrich, R. (1986) *Analyse der biotischen und abiotischen Faktoren des Oekosystems einer teilmarkierten Rebhuhnpopulation im Unteren Naheland*. PhD University of Giessen, Germany.

Hell, P. (1965) K niekotorým otázkam chovu jarabic y západoslovenskom krajii. *Zool Listy*, 14, 37–46.

Hell, P., Herz, J. & Ginter, F. (1971) Auswertung de Produktion der Rebhühner in der Slowakei im Jahre 1969. *Polovnicky Zbornik (Folia Venatoria)*, 1, 137–156.

Helldin, J. O., Liberg, O. & Glöersen, G. (2006) Lynx (*Lynx lynx*) killing red foxes (*Vulpes vulpes*) in boreal Sweden – frequency and population effects. *Journal of Zoology*, 270, 657–663.

Helm-Bychowski, K. M. & Wilson, A. C. (1986) Rates of nuclear DNA evolution in pheasant-like birds: Evidence from restriction maps. *Proceedings National Academy Science USA*, 83, 688–692.

Heltai, M., Szemethy, L., Lanszky, J. & Csányi, S. (2011) Returning and new mammal predators in Hungary: the status and distribution of golden jackal (*Canis aureus*), racoon dog (*Nyctereutes procyonides*) and racoon (*Procyon lotor*). *Beiträge zur Jagd- und Wildforschung*, 26, 95–102.

Henke, S. E. & Bryant, F. C. (1999) Effect of Coyote removal on the faunal community of western Texas. *Journal of Wildlife Management*, 63, 1066.

Hennache, A. & Ottavani, M. (2005) Monographie des Faisans [two volumes]. World Pheasant Association, France, Clères, France.

Hennache, A. & Ottavani, M. (2011) *Cailles, Perdrix et francolins de l'Ancien Monde*. World Pheasant Association, Clères, France

Hermes, J. C., Woodard, A. E., Vohra, P. & Snyder, R. L. (1984) The effect of light intensity, temperature, and diet on growth in the Red-legged Partridge. *Poultry Science*, 63, 871–874.

Hermoso de Mendoza, M., Poveda, J. B., Arenas, A., Carranza, J., Perea, J. A., Mir, A., Lecn, L. & Molera, M. (1986) Crop candidiasis in *Alectoris rufa. Med.Vet.*, 3, 113–116.

HerreL, A., Huyghe, K., Vanhooydonck, B., Backeljau, T., Breugelmans, K., Grbac, I., Van Damme, R. & Irschik, D. J. (2008) Rapid large-scale evolutionary divergence in morphology and performance associated with exploitation of a different dietary resource. *Proceedings of the National Academy of Sciences*, 105, 4792–4795.

Hetherington, D. (2006) The Lynx in Britain's past, present and future. *Ecos*, 27, 66–74.

Heydemann, B. (1983) Die Beeurtilung von Zielkonflikten zwischen Landwirtschaft. *Schriftenreihe für ländliche Sozialfragen*, 88, 51–78.

Hickling, R., Roy, D. B., Hill, J. K., Fox, R. & Thomas, C. D. (2006) The distributions of a wide range of taxonomic groups are expanding polewards. *Global Change Biology*, 12, 450–455.

Hill, D. A. (1985) The feeding ecology and survival of pheasant chicks on arable farmland. *Journal of Applied Ecology*, 22, 645–654.

Hill, D. A. & Robertson, P. A. (1988) *The Pheasant: Ecology, Management and Conservation*. BSP Professional, Oxford.

Hillman, G., Hedges, R., Moore, A. & College, S. E. P. (2001) New Evidence of Late-glacial cereal cultivation at Abu Hureyra on the Euphrates. *The Holocene*, 11, 383–393.

Ho, S. Y. W., Saarma, U., Barnett, R., Haile, J. & Shapiro, B. (2010) The effect of Inappropriate Calibration: Three Case Studies in Molecular Ecology. *Plos ONE*, 3: doi:10.1371/journal.pone.0001615

Hodge, I. & Reader, M. (2009) The introduction of Entry-Level Stewardship in England: extension or dilution in agri-environment policy? *Land Use Policy*, 27, 270–282.

Holland, J. M. & Thomas, S. R. (2000) Do polyphagous predators help control orange wheat blossom midge, *Sitodiplosis mosellana* Géhin (Dipt.,Cecidomyiidae) in winter wheat? *Journal of Applied Entomology*, 124, 325–329.

Holland, J. M. (2002) Carabid beetles: their ecology, survival and use in agroecosystems. *The Agroecology of Carabid beetles* (ed. J.M.Holland), pp. 1–40. Intercept, Andover.

Holland, J. M. & Reynolds, C. M. (2003) The impact of soil cultivation on arthropod emergence (Coleoptera and Araneae) on arable land. *Pedobiologia*, 47, 181–191.

Holland, J. M., Hutchison, M. A. S., Smith, B. & Aebischer, N. J. (2006) A review of invertebrate and seed-bearing plants as food for farmland birds in Europe. *Annals of Applied Biology*, 148, 49–71.

Holland, J. M. & Oakley, J. (2007) Importance of arthropod pests and their natural enemies in relation to recent farming practice changes in the UK. Report 64. Home Grown Cereals Authority.

Hölldobler, B. & Wilson, E.O (1990) *The Ants*, Harvard Univ. Press.

Holloway, S. (1996) *The Historical Atlas of Breeding Birds in Britain and Ireland*. T & A D Poyser, London.

Holstad, Ø., Karbøl, G. & Skorping, A. (1994) *Trichostrongylus tenuis* from willow grouse (*Lagopus lagopus*) and ptarmigan (*Lagopus mutus*) in northern Norway. *Bulletin of the Scandinavian Society for Parasitology*, 4, 9–13.

Honek, A. & Jarošík, V. (2000) The role of crop density, seed and aphid presence in diversification of field communities of Carabidae (Coleoptera). *European Journal Entomology*, 97, 517–525.

Honek, A. & Martinkova, Z. (2005) Long-term changes in abundance of *Coccinella septempunctata* (Coleoptera: Coccinellidae) in the Czech Republic. *European Journal of Entomology*, 102, 443–448.

Horsfall, M. W. & Jones, M. F. (1937) The life history of *Chaenotaenia infundibulum*, a cestode parasite in chickens. *Journal of Parasitology*, 23, 435–450.

Horsfall, M.W. (1938) A new unarmed cysticercoid, *Cysticercus setiferus*. *Parasitology*, 30, 61–64.

Hou Lianhai (1987) The Aragonian vertebrate fauna of Xiacaowan, Jiangsu-6 [Chinese]. Aves. *Vertebratica Palasiatica*, 25, 57–68.

Hötker, H. (2010) Correction factors for hatching success rates of meadow birds not derived by the Mayfield method. *Wader Study Group Bulletin*, 117, 59–61.

Huang, Z., Naifa, L., Zhang, L., Xiaio, Y. & Long, J. (2008) Mitochondrial DNA diversification and phylogeny among subspecies of chukar partridge (*Alectoris chukar*). *Genes and Genomics*, 30, 181–190.

Huband, P. (1969) The Farmland Habitat Survey 1968. *Report Game Research Association*, 8 (S1), 18–20.

Hudec, K. (1966) Some notes on the research of partridges in Czechoslovakia. *Symposium O koroptvi*. 40–45. Vyzkumny Ustav Lesniho Hospodarstvi A Myslivosti Ceskoslovensky Myslivecky Svaz.

Hudson, P. J. (1992) *Grouse in Space and Time*. The Game Conservancy, Fordingbridge.

Hudson, W. H. (1900) *Nature in Downland*. Longmans Green & Co., London.

Hume, L., Martinez, J. & Best, K. (1983) The biology of Canadian weeds. 60. *Polygonum convolvulus* L. *Canadian Journal of Plant Science*, 63, 959–971.

Hunt, H. M. (1974) Habitat relations and reproductive ecology of Hungarian partridge in a hedgerow complex in Saskatchewan. Saskatchewan Department of Tourism Renewable Resources & Wildlife. 3, 1–51.

Hunting, J. C. (1925) Partridges from Czechoslovakia (Hungarian partridges) and Notes on the French System of Partridge Rearing. Gaybird Ltd, Prestwood, Great Missenden, Buckinghamshire, England.

Huntley, B., Green, R. E., Collingham, Y. C. & Willis, S. G. (2007) *Climatic Atlas of European Breeding Birds.* University of Durham, Royal Society for the Protection of Birds & Lynx Edicions, Barcelona.

Hupp, J. W., Smith, L. M. & Ratti, J. T. (1980) Gray Partridge nesting biology in eastern South Dakota. *Perdix*, 2, 55–69.

Huss, H. (1983) Zur Ernährung des Rebhuhns (*Perdix perdix* L.) in einem nordburgenländischen Ackerbaugebiet. *Egretta*, 26, 1–14.

Iezekiel, S., Bakaloudis, D. E. & Vlachos, C. G. (1997) The diet of Bonelli's Eagle *Hieraaetus fasciatus* in Cyprus. Report: Forestry Department of Cyprus, Nicosia.

Ilkka, A., Putaala, A. & Hissa, R. K. (1995) Antipredator behaviour of wild, hand-reared and parent-reared grey partridge chicks. *Suomen Riista*, 41, 53–65.

Illner, H. (1992) Effect of roads with heavy traffic on grey partridge (*Perdix perdix*) density. *Gibier Faune Sauvage*, 9, 467–480.

Inglada, D. V. (2007) *Parásitos de la Perdiz Roja.* PhD Thesis University Castilla-La Mancha.

Inman, D. L. (1973) Cellulose digestion in Ruffed Grouse, Chukar and Bobwhite Quail. *Journal of Wildlife Management*, 37, 114–121.

Itämies, J., Putaala, A., Pirenen, M. & Hissa, R. (1996) The food composition of Grey Partridge chicks *Perdix perdix* in central Finland. *Ornis Fennica*, 73, 27–34.

James, P. E. (1996) *Birds of Sussex.* Sussex Ornithological Society.

Janda, J. (1956) Potrava Dospelych Koroptvi (*Perdix perdix* L.) v CSR. *Vestnik Ceskoslovenske Zoologicke Spolecnosti.Acta Societatis Zoologicae Bohemoslovenicae*, 20, 147–161.

Janda, J. (1957) Užitecnost a polnohospodárský význam dospélé koroptve polni (*Perdix perdix* L.). *Vĕdecké Práce (Bratislava)*, 1, 123–143.

Janda, J. (1958) Body weight, weights and measurements of some organs of adult gray partridge (*Perdix perdix* L.). *Zoologické Listy*, 7, 57–64, 5.

Janda, J. (1959a) Zur Ernährung der jungen Rebhühner (*Perdix perdix* L.) [On the food habits of juvenile gray partridge (*Perdix perdix* L.)]. *Zoologické Listy*, 8, 377–383.

Janda, J. (1959b) Potrava mladých koroptví, *Perdix perdix* (L.). *Zoologické Listy*, 22, 377–385.

Janda, J. (1966) Natural foods of grey partridge (*Perdix perdix* L.) in nature. *Symposium O Koroptvi.* 93–100. Vyzkumny Ustav Lesniho Hospodarstvi A Myslivosti Ceskoslovensky Myslivecky Svaz.

Javorszky, J. (1979) Feeding habits and behavioural activities of the partridge (*Perdix perdix* L.). *Vadbiologiai Kutatas*, 23, 12–14.

Jánossy, D. (1976) Plio-pleistocene bird remains from the Carpathian Basin II. Galliformes 2: Phasianidae. *Aquila*, 83, 29–42.

Jánossy, D. (1991) Late Miocene Bird Remains from Polgárdi (W-Hungary). *Aquila*, 98, 13–34.

Jánossy, D. (1994) Subfossil bird Faunas from Greece and Turkey. *Aquila*, 101, 45–52.

Jäckel, A. J. (1891) *Systematische Übersicht der Vögel Bayerns.* München and Leipzig.

Jenkins, D. (1955) Causes of death in partridges. *Bird Study*, 2, 142–143.

Jenkins, D. (1956) *Factors governing population density in the partridge.* DPhil Thesis, Oxford University.

Jenkins, D. (1957a) The breeding of the red-legged partridge. *Bird Study*, 4, 97–100.

Jenkins, D. (1957b) Chick survival in a partridge population. *Animal Health*, 7, 6–10.

Jenkins, D. (1961a) Social behaviour in the partridge (*Perdix perdix*). *Ibis*, 103a, 155–188.

Jenkins, D. (1961b) Population control in protected partridges (*Perdix perdix*). *Journal of Animal Ecology*, 30, 235–258.

Jenkins, D. (2003) *Of Partridges & Peacocks- and of things about which I knew nothing.* TLA Publications, Aboyne.

Jennings, A. R. (1954) Diseases in wild birds. *Journal of Comparative Pathology and Therapeutics,* 64, 356–359.

Jenny, M., Weibel, U.; Lugrin, B., Josephy, B.; Regamey, J.-L. & Zbinden, N. (2002) Grey Partridge final report 1991–2000. 1–77. Bern, Swiss Agency for the Environment. Forests and Landscape (OFEFP) Publication 335.

Jensen, B. (1970) The effect of a fox control programme on the bag of some other game species. *International Congress of Game Biologists,* 9, 480–485.

Jiménez, R., Hódar, J. A. & Camacho, I. (1991) La alimentación de la Perdiz común, *Alectoris rufa* en otoño-invierno en el sur de España. *Gibier Faune Sauvage,* 8, 43–54.

Joannon, A., Bro, E., Thenail, C. & Baudry, J. (2008) Crop patterns and habitat preferences of the grey partridge farmland bird. *Agronomy for Sustainable Development,* 28, 379–387.

Johnsgard, P. A. (1973) *Grouse and quails of North America.* University of Nebraska, Lincoln.

Johnsgard, P. A. (1988) *The Quails Partridges, and Francolins of the World.* Oxford University Press, Oxford.

Johnsgard, P. A. (2002) *Grassland Grouse and their Conservation.* Smithsonian Institution, Washington DC.

Johnson, C. G., Dobson, R. M., Southwood, T. R. E. & Taylor, R. L. (1955) Preliminary observations on the effects of the weed killer DNOC on insect populations. *Rothamsted Experimental Station Report for 1954,* 129–130.

Johnson, C. N. (2006) *Australia's Mammal Extinctions: A 50,000 year history.* Cambridge University Press, Cambridge.

Johnson, K. P., Weckstein, J. D., Meyer, M. J. & Clayton, D. H. (2011) There and back again: switching between host orders by avian body lice (Ischnocera: Goniodidae). *Biological Journal of the Linnaean Society,* 102, 614–615.

Johnson, N. J., Isaac, J. L. & Fisher, D. O. (2007) Rarity of a top predator triggers continent wide collapse of mammal prey: dingoes and marsupials in Australia. *Proceedings Royal Society Ser B,* 274, 341–346.

Jones, M. F. & Horsfall, M. W. (1935) Ants as intermediate hosts. *Journal of Parasitology,* 21, 442–443.

Jones, M. F. (1966) Sinusitis in game birds. *The Game Research Association Annual Report,* 5 (Ser1), 86–87.

Jones, M. F. (1966) Attempts to find a preventive for moniliasis. *The Game Research Association Annual Report,* 5 (Ser 1), 55–57.

Joyeux, C. & Baer, J. G. (1936) *Faune de France: Cestodes.* Lechevalier et Fils.

Junco Ruis, E. & Reque Kilchenmann, J. A. (1998) Pyrenean Grey Partridge (*Perdix perdix hispaniensis*) demography and habitat use in the Cantabrian Mountains. *Gibier Faune Sauvage,* 15, 331–338.

Junco Ruis, E., (2002) La perdiz pardilla (*Perdix perdix hispaniensis*) y la Perdiz roja (*Alectoris rufa*) en la montaña de Palencia. Bases bioecológicas para su gestión. Ph.D Thesis Univ. Valladolid, Spain.

Kaiser, W. (1994) Rebhuhnforschungsprojekt Feuchtwangen: Von Hecken und Huehnern. *Wild und Hund,* 2, 22–24.

Kaiser, W. (1998) Grey partridge (*Perdix perdix*) survival in relation to habitat quality. *Gibier Faune Sauvage,* 15, 157–162.

Kaiser, W. and I. Storch. (1996) Rebhuhn und Lebensraum. Raumnutzung, Habitatwahl und Dynamik einer Rebhuhnpopulation in Mittelfranken. *Report, Munich Wildlife Society.* Ettal, Germany. 107 pp. (Ger).

Kaleta, E. F. & Taday, E. M. A. (2003) Avian host range of *Chlamydophila spp.* based on isolation, antigen detection and serology. *Avian pathology,* 32, 435–462.

Kam, M., Degen, A. A. & Nagy, K. A. (1987) Seasonal Energy, Water and Food Consumption of Negev Chukars. *Ecology,* 68, 1029–1037.

Kantrud, H. & Higgins, K. (1992) Nest and nest site characteristics of some ground-nesting, non-passerine birds of northern grasslands. *Prairie Naturalist,* 24, 67–84.

Karlovic, M. (1982) Diseases of rock partridges, *Alectoris graeca. Veterinarski Glasnik*, 36, 247–252.

Karpov, F. F. & Belyalov, O. V. (2005) Hybridisation between *Perdix perdix arenicola* and *Perdix dauurica. Kazakh ornithological bulletin*, 2004, 175–177.

Kasimov, G. B. (1956) *Helminth Fauna of Domestic Fowls and Gamebirds of the Order Galliformes [Ru]*. Trud Helminthologickeskoi Laboratorii: Izdatelstvo Akademii Nauk S.S.S.R.

Kasparyan, D. K. (1973) Ichneumon flies (Ichneumonidae) sub-family Tryphonini [Ru]. *Fauna of the U.S.S.R.: Hymenoptera*, 3, 1–320.

Kasprzykowski, Z. & Goławski, A. (2009) Does the use of playback affect the estimates of numbers of grey partridge *Perdix perdix? Wildlife Biology*, 15, 123–128.

Katzner, T. E., Bragin, S., Knick, S. T. & Smith, A. (2005) Relationship between demographics and dietary specificity of Imperial Eagles in Kazakhstan. *Ibis*, 147, 576–586.

Kauffman, M. J., Brodie, J. F. & Jules, E. S. (2010) Are wolves saving Yellowstone's aspen? A landscape-level test of a behaviourally mediated trophic cascade. *Ecology*, 91, 2742–2755.

Kay, C. E. (1998) Are ecosystems structured from the top-down or bottom-up; a new look at an old debate. *Wildlife Society Bulletin*, 26, 484–498.

Kay, C. E. (2009) Two Views of the Serengeti: One True, One Myth. *Conservation and Society*, 7, 145–148.

Kayser, Y. (1999) Forte prédation sur des oiseaux de proies par un couple de Faucons pèlerins *Falco peregrinus* dans le Parc National du Mercantour, France. *Nos Oiseaux*, 46, 205–206.

Károlyi, L. (1953) *Život zasvätený poľovníctvu*. Haupt-József Károlyi CIC reprint and edition 2003, Budapest.

Kellogg, F. E. & Prestwood, A. (1968) Gastrointestinal helminths from wild and pen-raised Bobwhites. *Journal of Wildlife Management*, 43, 468–475.

Kellogg, F. E. & Calpin, J. P. (1971) A checklist of parasites and diseases reported from the bobwhite quail. *Avian Diseases*, 15, 704–715.

Kelly, A., Leighton, K. & Newton, J. (2010) Using stable isotopes to investigate the provenance of a Eurasian Eagle Owl (*Bubo bubo*) found in Norfolk, England. *British Birds*, 103, 213–222.

Kelm, H. (1979) Populationsuntersuchungen am heidehuhn (*Perdix perdix sphagnetorum*) und bemerkungen zur taxonomie west- und mitteleuropaeischer rebhuhner. *Bonner Zoologische Beiträge*, 30, 117–157.

Kelso, L. (1932) A note on the food of the Hungarian partridge. *Auk*, 49, 204–207.

Kenward, R. E. (2006) *The Goshawk*. T & A D Poyser, London.

Kerr, K. C. R., Birks, S. M., Kalyakin, M. V., Red'kin, Y. A., Koblik, E. A. & Hebert, P. D. N. (2010) Filling the gap-COI barcode resolution in eastern Palearctic birds. *Frontiers in Zoology*, 6, 29–42.

Keymer, I. F. (1961) Infectious sinusitis on pheasants and partridges. *Veterinary Record*, 73, 1034–1038.

Keymer, I. F. & Austwick, P. K. C. (1961) Moniliasis in partridges (*Perdix perdix*). *J.Int.Soc.Human Anim.Mycol.*, 1, 22–29.

Keymer, I. F., Rose, J. H., Beesley, W. N. & Davies, S. F. M. (1962) A Survey and Review of Parasitic Diseases of Wild and Game Birds in Britain. *Veterinary Record*, 74, 887–894.

Keymer, I. F. & Stebbings, R. S. J. (1987) Lead poisoning in a partridge (*Perdix perdix*) after ingestion of gunshot. *Veterinary Record*, 120, 276–277.

Khaleghizadeh, A. & Sehhatisabet, M.E. (2006) Contribution to the knowledge of the diet of Iranian Birds. *Ecology: 'Golden Eagle'* [transl.] 15, 145–150.

Khanmammedov, A. I. (1955) On the Biology of the Chukar in Azerbaijan [Latin-Azeri]. *Proceedings Institute of Zoology of Azerbaijan Academy of Sciences*, 18, 117–187.

Khanmammedov, A. I. (1962) Ecology [Laying, moult and food of adult] *Perdix perdix canescens/furvescens* in NE Azerbaijan [Latin Azeri Ru summary]. *Izv.Akad.Nauk.Azerb. SSR Ser.Biology and Medicine*, 1, 39–51.

Khanmammedov, A. I. (1969) The biology of the Transcaucasian Common Partridge in Azerbaijan. *Ornithology of the USSR Vol 2.* Ashkabad.

Kiessling, W. (1923) *Das Rebhuhn und seine Jagd.* Neudamm.

Kimball, R. T., Braun, E. L., Zwartjes, P. W., Crowe, T. M. & Ligon, J. D. (1999) A molecular phylogeny of the pheasants and partridges suggests that these lineages are not monophyletic. *Molecular Phylogenetics and Evolution,* 11, 38–54.

Kirwan, G., Boyla, K., Castell, P., Demerci, B., Welch, H. & Marlow, T. (2008) *The Birds of Turkey.* Christopher Helm, London.

Knauer, F.; Kuechenhoff, H.; Pilz, S. (2010) A statistical analysis of the relationship between red fox *Vulpes vulpes* and its prey species (grey partridge *Perdix perdix,* brown hare *Lepus europaeus* and rabbit *Oryctolagus cuniculus*) in Western Germany from 1958 to 1998. *Wildlife Biology:* 16, 56–65.

Knott, N. P., Ball, C. C. & Yocom, C. F. (1943) Nesting of the Hungarian partridge and ring-necked pheasant in Whitman County, Washington. *Journal of Wildlife Management,* 7, 283–291.

Knox, A. E. (1849) *Ornithological Rambles in Sussex.* Van Voorst, London.

Kobriger, G. D. (1980) Foods, food availability, nutrition and body weights of grey partridge in North Dakota. *Perdix,* 2, 70–86.

Kobriger, G. D. (1983) Food habits of the Hungarian partridge. *North Dakota Outdoors,* 45, 15–19.

Koh, L. P. & Wilcove, D. S. (2008) Is oil palm agriculture really destroying tropical biodiversity? *Conservation Letters,* 1, 60–64.

Kokeš, O. & Knobloch, E. (1947) *Koroptev, Její Život, Chov a Lov* [The Partridge, its Life History, Propagation and Hunting [transl. Israel programme]. Nakladatelstvi Studentske Knightiskarny v Praze, Prague.

Koning, F. J. (2003) Sparrowhawk numbers reduced by Goshawk. Report to World Working Group on Birds of Prey and Owls.

Kornegay, J. R., Kocher, T. D., Williams, L. A. & Wilson, A. C. (1993) Pathways of lyzozyme evolution inferred from sequences of cytochrome *b* in birds. *Journal of Molecular Evolution,* 37, 367–379.

Korpimäki, E. & Nordström, M. (2004) Native predators, alien predators and the return of native top predators: beneficial and detrimental effects on small game. *Suomen Riista,* 50, 33–45.

Koskimies, J. (1962) Ontogeny of thermoregulation and energy metabolism in some gallinaceous birds. *Ricerche di Zoologia Appl.Alla Caccia,* 4, 149–160.

Kostron, K. & Hromas, J. (1970) The pterylography of the mature partridge *Perdix perdix* L. *Folia Morphologica,* 18, 172–180.

Kovács, G. (1997) A fogoly (*Perdix perdix*) a Hortobágyon [The grey partridge on the Hortobágy (eastern Hungary)]. *Hungarian Small Game Bulletin,* 1, 177–184.

Kozakiewicz, B., Maszewska, I. & Wisniewski, B. (1983) Internal parasites of *Perdix perdix* in Wilkopolska (Polish). *Medycyna Weterynaryjna,* 39, 25–27.

Kozhokov, M. K. (2007) Formation of Parasite Fauna of Birds of the North Caucasus. *Russian Agricultural Sciences,* 33, 404–407.

Kreager, N., Wainman, B. C., Jayasinghe, R. K. & Tsuji, L. J. S. (2008) Lead pellet ingestion and liver-lead concentrations in upland game birds from southern Ontario, Canada. *Archives of Environmental Contamination and Toxicology,* 54, 331–336.

Krebs, C. J., Boutin, S. & Boonstra, R. (2001) *Ecosystem dynamics of the Boreal Forest: the Kluane Project.* Oxford University Press, Oxford

Kretzoi, M. (1957) Birds remains from the Hipparion-fauna of Csàkvàr. *Aquila,* 63–64, 239–248.

Kretzoi, M. (1962) Fauna und Faunenhorizont von Csarnóta. *Magyar Állami Földtani Intézet évi jelentése, az 1959:* 344–395.

Krüger, O. (2002) Interactions between common buzzard *Buteo buteo* and Goshawk *Accipiter gentilis. Oikos,* 96, 441–452.

Krüger, O. (2002) Analysis of Nest Occupancy and Nest Reproduction in Two Sympatric Raptors: Common Buzzard *Buteo buteo* and Goshawk *Accipiter gentilis. Ecography,* 25, 523–532.

Kubantsev, B. S. & Vasil'ev, I. E. (1983) Composition, distribution and numbers of birds in crop fields in northern regions along the lower Volga River. *Ékologiya*, 5, 62–65.

Kuijper, D. P. J., Oosterveld, E. & Wymenga, E. (2009) Decline and potential recovery of the European grey partridge (*Perdix perdix*) population-a review. *European Journal of Wildlife Research*, 55, 455–463.

Kurashvili, B. E. (1956) Zoogeographical characteristics of the helminth fauna of partridges in Georgia [Georgian]. *Soobshcheniya Academii Gruzinskol SSR*, 17, 935–940.

Kurashvili, B. E. (1957) *Helminths of Georgian game and domestic birds as regards fauna and ecology* [Russ.]. *Akademia Moscow*.

Kurochkin, E. N. (1985) Birds of Central Asia in the Pliocene. *Sovmestnaya Sovetsko-Mongol'skaya Paleontologicheskaya Ekspeditsiya Trudy*, 26, 1–119.

Kurtpinar, H. K., Ergun, H. & Merdivenci, A. (1954) The Nematodes and Cestodes in the Grey Partridge, (*Perdix perdix*) and Chukar (*Alectoris chukar*) [Turkish]. *The Turkish Veterinarian Society Monthly Magazine*, 24, 1375–1384.

Kuz'mina, M. (1992) The Tetraonidae and Phasianidae of the USSR [1977 translated 1992]. Smithsonian Institution Library translation by P.M.Rao and D.Siegel-Causey, Washington and Delhi.

Kyselý, R. (2010) Review of the oldest evidence of domestic fowl *Gallus gallus f. domestica* from the Czech Republic in its European context. *Acta Zoologica Cracoviensia – Series A: Vertebrata*, 53, 9–34.

Lack, D. (1947) The significance of clutch size in the Partridge (*Perdix perdix*). *Journal of Animal Ecology*, 16, 19–25.

Lack, D. (1954) *The Natural Regulation of Animal Numbers*. Clarendon, Oxford.

Lafferty, K. D., Dobson, A. P. & Kuris, A. M. (2006) Parasites dominate food web links. *PNAS*, 103, 11211–11216.

Lahti, D. C. (2009) Why we have been unable to generalize about bird nest predation. *Animal Conservation*, 12, 279–281.

Lampio, T. (1946) Game Diseases in Finland 1924–43. *Suomen Riista*, 1, 93–141.

Lampio, T. (1951) On the significance of predators in the control and dispersal of the diseases of game. *Papers on Game Research*, 6, 3–20.

Larsen, R. T., Flinders, J. T., Mitchell, D. L., Perkins, E. R. & Whiting, D. G. (2007) Chukar Watering Patterns and Water Site Selection. *Rangeland Ecology & Management*, 60, 559–565.

Larsen, R. T., Flinders, J., Mitchell, D. L. & Perkins, E. R. (2007) Grit size preferences and ingestion of lead pellets by chukars in Utah. *Western North American Naturalist*, 67, 152–155.

Larsen, R. T., Bissonette, J. A., Flinders, J. T., Hooten, M. B. & Wilson, T. L. (2009) Summer spatial patterning of chukars in relation to free water in western Utah. *Landscape Ecology*, 25, 135–145.

Laudenslager, M. L. & Hammel, H. T. (1977) Environmental temperature selection by the Chukar partridge, *Alectoris chukar*. *Physiology & Behaviour*, 19, 543–548.

Launay, M. (1975) Disponibilité en insectes dans les cultures et dans les aménagements. Ses rapports avec le régime alimentaire du poussin de Perdrix grise. *Bulletin de l'Office National de la Chasse.*, 4 [N.Ser.], 170–192.

Le Page, M. (2011) Why evolution is going nowhere fast. *New Scientist*, issue 2806, 5 April.

Lebedev, J. A. (1976) The seasonal dynamics in the number of Chukar [transl. from Ru]. *Izvestiya Academy of Sciences of the Tajik SSR*, 63, 2–4.

Lebeurier, E. (1958) Du régime de la perdrix grise (*Perdix perdix armoricana* Hartert) dans le Finistère. *L'Oiseau et la Revue Française d'Ornithologie*, 28, 213–227, 300–308.

Leopold, A. (1933) Game Management. University of Wisconsin, Madison.

Leopold, A. (1939) The Hungarian partridge pioneers. What's new in Farm Science: Directors Annual Report. *Wisconsin Agr. Exp. Stat.* 446, 21–23.

Leopold, A. S. (1977) *The California Quail.* University of California Press, Berkeley.

Lescourret, F., Birkan, M. & Novoa, C. (1987) Morphological characteristics of the Pyrenean Grey Partridge, *Perdix perdix hispaniensis*, compared to the Beauce Partridge and *Perdix perdix perdix*. *Gibier Faune Sauvage*, 4, 49–66.

Letty, J., Reitz, F. & Mettaye, G. (1998) Validation de plans de chasse à la Perdrix Grise (*Perdix perdix*): apport d'une modélisation de la dynamique des populations. *Gibier Faune Sauvage*, 15, 575–602.

Letty, J., Marchandeau, S. & Aubineau, J. (2007) Problems encountered by individuals in animal translocations: Lessons from field studies. *Ecoscience*, 14, 420–431.

Lever, C. (2009) *The naturalized animals of Britain and Ireland.* New Holland, London

Levy, S. (2011) *Once and Future Giants.* Oxford University Press, New York.

Lindbloom, A. J., Reese, K. P. & Zager, P. (2003) Nesting and brood-rearing characteristics of Chukars in west central Idaho. *Western North American Naturalist*, 63, 429–439.

Lindow, B. E. K. & Dyke, G. J. (2007) A small Galliforme bird from the lower Eocene Fur formation, north-western Denmark. *Bulletin of the Geological Society of Denmark*, 55, 59–63.

Lindström E. & Morner, T. (1985) The spread of sarcoptic mange among Swedish red Foxes. *Revu Ecology (Terre Vie)*, 40, 211–216.

Lisitsyna, O. I. (1994) The spiny-headed worms of the genus *Mediorhynchus* (Acanthocephala) – bird parasites of the Ukrainian fauna. *Vestnik Zoologii*, 3, 12–18.

Little, R., Crowe, T. & Barlow, S. (2000) *Gamebirds of Southern Africa.* Struik, Cape Town.

Litun, V. I. (1980) Influence of agricultural activity on numbers of *Perdix perdix* in the Kirov region (Ru). *Proceedings of a Scientific Conference 14–16 May 1980, The Influence of Man's Agriculture Activity on Populations and Habitat of Game Animals* (ed. V. G. Safonov), All-Union Science Research Institute for Game Conservancy and Fur Farming, Kirov.

Litun, V. I. (1982a) Partridge (*Perdix dauurica*). *Migrations of Birds of Eastern Europe and Northern Asia* (Ru). 180–196. Academy of Sciences of the U.S.S.R., Nauka, Moscow.

Litun, V. I. (1982b) Movements of Galliformes: *Perdix perdix* and *Perdix dauurica*. *Migrations of birds of Eastern Europe and Northern Asia* (Ru) (ed. Co-ordinating Council), pp. 179–184. Academy of Sciences of the USSR A. N. Severtzov Institute, Moscow.

Litun, V. I. (1983) Daurian partridge ecology in southern Transbaikal (Ru). *Bulletin of Moscow Society of Naturalists, Biological Series*, 88, 25–31.

Litun, V. I. & Annenkov, B. P. (1989) Chukar in the Dzungarskiy Alatau [Ru.]. *Ecology and resources of game and other economically important birds [Russ.]* (ed. B. M. Zhitov), pp. 109–122. All-Union Science Research Institute, Kirov.

Litun, V. I. (1991) Dynamics and productivity of Daurian partridge in the southern Transbaikal. *Transactions of the Congress of the International Union of Game Biologists*, 18, 605–607.

Litun, V. I. (1992) Immature sex ratio and autumn population density of Bearded Partridges (*Perdix dauurica*). *Gibier Faune Sauvage*, 9, 371–376.

Litun, V. I. & Flint, V. E. (1993) *The Daurian Partridge* [transl.Shergalin]. Moscow.

Litzbarski, H. & Watzke H. (2007) Studies of arthropod populations essential in the diet of Great Bustard chicks at breeding sites in the Saratov region. *Bustard Studies*, 6, 37–51.

Liu, C. Z., Wang, G. & Yan, L. (2007) Effects of imidacloprid on arthropod community structure and its dynamics in alfalfa fields [in Chinese]. *Chinese Journal of Applied Ecology*, 10, 2379–2383.

Liukkonen-Anttila, T., Putaala, A. & Hissa, R. K. (1996) Elainravinnon merkitys peltopyyn poikasten kehitykselle. [The importance of animal food to development of grey partridge chicks.]. *Suomen Riista*, 42, 15–24.

Liukkonen-Anttila, T., Putaala, A. & Hissa, R. K. (2000) Effect of change in diet on the nutritional status of hand-reared grey partridge (*Perdix perdix*). *Hungarian Small Game Bulletin*, 5, 171–178.

Liukkonen-Anttila, T., Uimaniemi, M. O. & Lumme, J. (2002) Mitochondrial DNA variation and the phylogeography of the grey partridge (*Perdix perdix*) in Europe: from Pleistocene history to present day populations. *Journal of Evolutionary Biology*, 15, 971–982.

Liwei H., Bo D., Bo Z., Xiuyue Z., Bisong Y. & Jing L. (2009) The complete mitochondrial genome of the Sichuan Hill Partridge (*Arborophila rufipectus*) and a phylogenetic analysis with related species. *Gene*, 435, 23–28.

Llandrés, C. & Otero, C. (1985) Predadores de la perdiz roja (*Alectoris rufa*) en la Encomenda de Guedea (Almedina-Ciudad Real) 1982–1984. Informe inèdito Fundación José Blanc.

Logminas, V. & Petraitis, A. (1970) Population Dynamics and Population Structure of the Partridge (*Perdix perdix*) in Lithuania [Ru Eng summ]. *International Union of Game Biology*, 9, 435–439.

Long, W. H. (1969) *A Survey of the Agricultural History of Yorkshire*. Royal Agricultural Society of England, London.

Lorenzen, E. D. & 25 others. (2011) Species-specific responses of late Quaternary megafauna to climate and humans. *Nature*, 479, 359–364.

Loshkarev, G. A. (1975) Population dynamics of partridge (*Perdix perdix*) in the foothills of the northern Caucasus. *Écologia*, 3, 100–101.

Lourenço, R. (2006) The food habits of Eurasian Eagle Owl in South Portugal. *Journal of Raptor Research*, 40, 297–300.

Lourenço, R., Santos, S. M., Rabaço, J. E. & Penteriani, V. (2011) Super-predation patterns in four large European Raptors. *Population Ecology*, 53, 175–185.

Louzis, C. (1978) La Maladie de Newcastle ou pseudo-peste aviaire. *Pesticides et gibier, maladies du gibier* (ed. P. Pesson), pp. 229–240. Gauthier-Villars Bordas, Paris.

Louzis, C., Ledoujet, C., Thiébaud, M., Laroche, M., Capafons, M., Paniaga, E. & Barre, N. (1988) Pathologie du Petit Gibier en Milieu Naturel: Bilan des travaux du laboratoire central de recherches vétérinaires de 1972 à 1984. *Recueil de Médecine Vétérinaires*, 919–928.

Love, R. A., Webbon, C., Glue, D. E. & Harris, S. (2000) Changes in the food of British Barn Owls between 1974 and 1997. *Mammal Reviews*, 30, 107–129.

Lovegrove, R. (2007) *Silent Fields: The long decline of a nation's wildlife*. Oxford University Press, Oxford.

Lu, X., Gong, G. & Ren, C. (2003) Reproductive Ecology of Tibetan Partridge *Perdix hodgsoniae* in Lhasa Mountains, Tibet. *Journal of the Yamashina Institute for Ornithology*, 34, 270–278.

Lucas, A. (1957) Quelques Maladies de la Perdrix et du Faisan. *Journées D'Études Avicoles*, 1957, 1–19.

Lucas, A. (1963) *La perdrix, son élevage, ses maladies*. Crepin-Leblond et cie, Paris.

Lucas, P., Loucus, L., Laroche, M. & Monin, L. (1967) Histomoniasis in the partridge. *Recueil de Médecine Vétérinaire*, 132, 527–531.

Lucchini, V. & Randi, E. (1999) Molecular evolution of the mtDNA control-region in birds. *Proceedings of the International Ornithological Congress*, 22, 732–739. BirdLife South Africa, Johannesburg.

Lucchini, V., Hoglund, J., Klaus, S., Swensom, J. & Randi, E. (2001) Historical biogeography and a mitochondrial DNA phylogeny of grouse and ptarmigan. *Molecular Phylogenetics and Evolution*, 20, 149–162.

Lucio, A. J., Purroy, F. J. & De Buruaga, M. S. (1992) *La Perdiz Pardilla (Perdix perdix hispaniensis) en España*. Instituto Nacional para la Conservacion de la Naturaleza, Madrid.

Lucio, A. J., Purroy, F. J., Sáenz de Buruaga, M. & Llamas, O. (1996) Consecuencias del abandono agroganadero en areas de montaña para la conservacion y aprovechamiento cinegetico de las perdices roja y pardilla en España. *Revista Florestal*, 9, 305–318.

Lund, E. E., Wehr, E. E. & Ellis, D. J. (1966) Earthworm transmission of *Heterakis gallinarum* to Turkeys and Chickens. *Journal Parasitology*, 52, 899–902.

Lund, E. E. & Chute, A. M. (1972) Reciprocal responses of eight species of Galliforme birds and three parasites: *Heterakis gallinarum, Histomonas meleagridis* and *Parahistomonas wenrichi. The Journal of Parasitology*, 58, 940–945.

Lund, E. E. & Chute, A. M. (1974) The Reproductive potential of *Heterakis gallinarum* in various species of Galliforme Birds: Implications for Survival of *H. gallinarum* and *Histomonas meleagridis* to recent times. *International Journal Parasitology*, 4, 455–461.

Lynn-Allen, E. & Robertson, A. W. P. (1956) *Partridge Year.* Geoffrey Bles, London.

Lynov, Yu. S. (1978) Spatial distribution of *Alectoris kakelik kakelik* (Falk.) during the nesting period and time of rearing their young.[Ru]. *Uzbekskii Biologicheskii Zhurnal [Brief Scientific Reports]*, 1978, 77.

Macdonald, H. (2006) *Falcon.* Reaktion Books, London.

Macdonald, J. W. & Potts, G. R. (1970) New species of sub-cutaneous mite in shags and cormorants. *British Birds*, 63, 80–81.

Mackie, R. J. & Buechner, H. K. (1963) The reproductive cycle of the Chukar. *Journal of Wildlife Management.*, 27, 246–260.

Madsen, H. (1941) The occurrence of helminths and coccidia in partridges and pheasants in Denmark. *Journal of Parasitology*, 27, 29–34.

Madsen, H. (1945) The species of *Capillaria* (Nematodes, Trichinelloidea) parasitic in the digestive tract of Danish gallinaceous and anatine game birds, with a revised list of species of Capillaria in birds. *Danish Review of Game Biology*, 1, 1–112.

Madsen, H. (1950) Studies on Species of *Heterakis* (Nematodes) in Birds. *Danish Review of Game Biology*, 1, 3–43.

Madsen, H. (1952) A study on the nematodes of Danish gallinaceous gamebirds. *Danish Review of Game Biology*, 2, 1–126.

Madsen, H. & Wingstrand, K. G. (1959) Some behavioural reactions and structures enabling birds to endure winter frost in arctic regions. *Vidensk, Medd.fra Dansk Naturh.Foren.*, 120, 15–23.

Madsen, H. (1962) On the interaction between *Heterakis gallinarum, Ascaridia galli*, Blackhead and the Chicken. *Journal Helminthology*, 36, 107–142.

Madsen, S. A., Madsen, A. B. & Elmeros, M. (2002) Seasonal food of badgers (*Meles meles*) in Denmark. *Mammalia*, 66, 341–352.

Manios, N., Papazahariadou, M., Frydas, S., Papageorgiou, N., Tsachalidis, E. & Georgopoulou, J. (2002) Tetrathyridium [larval *Mesocestoides*] as a mortality factor of rock partridge (*Alectoris graeca*) in Central Greece. *Zeitschrift für Jagdwissenschaft*, 48, 378–382.

Manios, N., Papageorgiou, N. K. I., Alexiou, B. I., Chatzinikos, E. & Skarafigka, M. (2007) The effect of predation on the nests of rock partridge (*Alectoris graeca*) in Greece. *Proceedings IUGB Hannover (Abstracts)*, 28, 237.

Manolache, L. (2012) Râspindirea potirnichilor (*Perdix perdix* L.) in România s,i extindera lor in zona forestiera. *Communicari de Zoologie*, 14, 209–218.

Mañosa, S. (1994) Goshawk diet in a Mediterranean area of north-eastern Spain. *Journal of Raptor Research*, 28, 84–92.

Marchant, J. H., Hudson, R., Carter, S.P. & Whittington, P. (1990) *Population trends in British breeding birds.* Tring (BTO)

Marcström, V., Kenward, R. E. & Engren, E. (1988) The impact of predation on boreal Tetraonids during vole cycles: an experimental study 1976–1984. *Journal of Animal Ecology*, 57, 859.

Marjoniemi, K., Hohtola, E., Putaala, A. & Hissa, R. (1995) Development of temperature regulation in the Grey Partridge (*Perdix perdix*). *Wildlife Biology*, 1, 39–46.

Martinez-Nistal, M. C., Diez Banos, P., Cordero del Campillo, M. & Nunez Guttierez, M. C. (1986) The grey partridge, *Perdix perdix hispaniensis* Reichenow, 1892 (Aves: Galliformes), a new host for *Goniocotes obscurus* Giebel, 1874 (Mallophaga: Goniodidae). *Anales de la Facultad de Veterinaria de Leon*, 32, 85–94.

Mastrorilli, M. & Barattieri, M. (2001) Unusual predations by a tawny owl *Strix aluco* pair in northern Italy. *Biota* 2, 171–173.

Maxwell, A. (1911) *Partridges and Partridge Manors.* A. & C. Black, London.

Mayfield, H. F. (1961) Nesting success calculated from exposure. *Wilson Bull.* 73, 255–261.

Mayr, G. (2005) The Paleogene fossil record of birds in Europe. *Biological Reviews*, 80, 1–28.

Mayr, G. (2006) New specimens of the early Eocene stem group Galliforme Paraortygoides (Gallinuliodidae) with comments on the evolution of a crop in the stem lineage of Galliformes. *Journal of Ornithology*, 147, 31–37.

Mayr, G., Poschmann, M. & Wuttke, M. (2006) A nearly complete skeleton of the fossil Galliforme bird *Palaeortyx* from the late Oligocene of Germany. *Acta Ornithol.*, 41, 129–135.

Mayr, G. (2008) The fossil record of Galliforme birds: comments on Crowe *et al.* (2006). *Cladistics*, 24, 74–76.

McCabe, R. A. & Hawkins, A. S. (1946) The Hungarian partridge in Wisconsin. *American Midland Naturalist*, 36, 1–75.

McCrow, V. P. (1982) *Gray Partridge habitat use and nesting biology in North-Central Iowa.* PhD Iowa State University, Ames.

McDiarmid, A. (1965) Modern trends in animal health and husbandry; infectious diseases of free-living wildlife. *British Veterinary Journal*, 121, 245–257.

McKelvie, C. L. & Robjent, R. (1993) *The Partridge: studies in Words and Pictures.* Fine Sporting Interests, Holt, Norfolk.

McGowan, P. & Madge, S. (2002) *Pheasants, Partridges and Grouse.* Christopher Helm, London.

Mearns, B. & Mearns, R. (1988) *Biographies for Birdwatchers.* Academic Press, London.

Mel'nichenko, A. N. (1949) Shelter belts of the Steppe (Volga) region and their influence on the reproduction of animals which are useful and harmful to agriculture [Russian]. MOIP, Moscow.

Melinchuk, R. W. (1981) Food habits of Gray Partridge during Fall and Winter in Saskatchewan. *Saskatchewan Wildlife Technical Report* 81–9, 1–23. 1981.

Melinchuk, R. W. (1983) Body Condition of Gray Partridge (*Perdix perdix*) During Fall and Winter in Saskatchewan. Lakehead University, Thunder Bay, Ontario.

Melinchuk, R. W. (1987) Field trip to Eyebrow Lake study area. *Perdix IV: Gray Partridge Workshop* (eds R. O. Kimmel, J. W. Schulz & G. J. Mitchell), pp. 119–122. Minnesota Department of Natural Resources, Madelia.

Melis, C., Cagnacci, F. & Bargagli, L. (2002) Food habits of the badger in a rural Mediterranean area. *Zeitschrift für Jagdwissenschaft*, 48S, 236–246.

Melling, T., Dudley, S. & Doherty, P. (2008) The Eagle Owl in Britain. *British Birds*, 101, 478–490.

Mendel, G. W. (1979) *The Hungarian Partridge in the Palouse Region of Northern Idaho.* Thesis University of Idaho, Moscow.

Mendel, G.W & Peterson, S.R. (1983) Management implications of Gray Partridge habitat use on the Palouse Prairie, *Idaho Wildlife Society Bulletin* 11, 348–356.

Mendelewska, J. (1982) Parazytofauna Kuropatw (*Perdix perdix* L.) Odlawianych we wschodniej i centralnej Polsce. *Wiadomosci Parazytologiczne*, 27, 67–69.

Menzdorf, A. (1976) Ontogeny of some Rock partridge calls. *Zool. Anzeiger Jena*, 196, 236.

Meriggi, A. & Prigioni, C. (1985) Some aspects of the reproductive biology of the Grey Partridge *Perdix perdix* in Apennines of northern Italy. *Avocetta*, 9, 73–80.

Meriggi, A. & Prigioni, C. (1985) Productivity of a population of partridge (*Perdix perdix*) in northern Apennines (Italy), and habitat partitioning with the red-legged partridge (*Alectoris rufa*). *Transactions of the XVII Congress of the International Union of Game Biologists* (ed. S. A. de Crombrugghe), 351–358. Brussels.

Meriggi, A., Montagna, D. & Zacchetti, D. (1991) Habitat use by partridges (*Perdix perdix* and *Alectoris rufa*) in an area of northern Apennines, Italy. *Bulletin Zoology*, 58, 85–90.

Meriggi, A., Saino, N., Montagna, D. & Zacchetti, D. (1992) Influence of habitat on density and breeding success of grey and red-legged partridges. *Bollettino di Zoologia* 59: 289–295.

Meriggi, A., Brangi, A. & Cuccus, P. (2002) High mortality rate in a re-introduced grey partridge population in central Italy. *Italian Journal of Zoology*, 69, 19–24.

Meriggi, A. & della Stella, R. M. (2004) Dynamics of a reintroduced population of Red-legged Partridges *Alectoris rufa* in central Italy. *Wildlife Biology*, 10, 1–9.

Mégnin, P. (1881) L'Épizootie actuelle des Faisanderies et sur le parasite qui la cause le *Syngamus trachéalis* (Siebold). *Mémoires de a Société de Biologie*, 1880, 45–71.

Mezquida, E. T., S. J. Slater, & C. W. Benkman. (2006) Sage-grouse and indirect interactions: potential implications of coyote control on sage-grouse populations. *Condor* 108:747–759.

Middleton, A. D. (1934) Periodic fluctuations in British game populations. *Journal of Animal Ecology*, 3, 231–249.

Middleton, A. D. (1934) The population of partridges (*Perdix perdix*) in 1933 and 1934 in Great Britain. *Journal of Animal Ecology*, 4, 137–145.

Middleton, A. D. (1935) The food of a Badger (*Meles meles*). *Journal of Animal Ecology*, 4, 291.

Middleton, A. D. (1936a) The population of partridges (*Perdix perdix*) in Great Britain during 1935. *Journal of Animal Ecology*, 5, 252–261.

Middleton, A. D. (1936b) Factors controlling the population of the partridge (*Perdix perdix*) in Great Britain. *Proceedings of the Zoological Society of London*, 106, 795–815.

Middleton, A. D. & Chitty, H. (1937) The foods of adult Partridges, *Perdix perdix* and *Alectoris rufa*, in Great Britain. *Journal of Animal Ecology*, 6, 322–336.

Middleton, A. D. (1937) The population of partridges (*Perdix perdix*) in Great Britain during 1936. *Journal of Animal Ecology*, 6, 318–321.

Middleton, A. D. (1958) Management and conservation of game birds in Britain. *Transaction of the III Congress of the International Union of Game Biologists* (ed. H. M. Thamdrup). Danish Review of Game Biology, 3, 28–29.

Middleton, A. D. & Huband, P. (1966) Increase in red-legged partridges. *The Game Research Association Annual Report*, 5 (Ser 1), 14–25.

Middleton, A. D. (1967) Predatory mammals and the conservation of game in Great Britain. *Annual Review of the Game Conservancy Trust*, 6 [Ser 1], 14–21.

Mikkola, H. (1976) Owls killed by owls and other raptors. *British Birds*, 69, 144–154.

Mikkola, H. (1983) *Owls of Europe*. T. & A. D. Poyser, Calton.

Milanov, Z. B. (1996) Effect of mowing fodder plants on small game populations in central Bulgaria. *Proceedings of the International Union of Game Biologists*, 12, 394–397.

Millán, J., Gortazar, C. & Villafuerte, R. (2003) Does supplementary feeding affect organ and gut size of wild red-legged partridges *Alectoris rufa*? *Wildlife Biology*, 9, 229–233.

Millán, J., Gortázar, C., Martín-Mateo, M. P. & Villafuerte, R. (2004) Comparative survey of the ectoparasite fauna of wild and farm-reared red-legged partridges (*Alectoris rufa*), with an ecological study in wild populations. *Parasitological Research*, 93, 79–85.

Millán, J., Gortázar, C. & Villafuerte, R. (2004) A comparison of the helminth faunas of wild and farm-reared red-legged partridges. *Journal of Wildlife Management*, 68, 701–707.

Millán, J., Gortazar, C. & Villafuerte, R. (2004) Ecology of nematode parasitism in red-legged partridges (*Alectoris rufa*) in Spain. *Helminthologia*, 41, 33–37.

Millán, J. (2009) Diseases of the Red-legged Partridge (*Alectoris rufa* L.): A Review. *Wildlife Biology*, 5, 70–88.

Miller, R. H. & Pike, K. S. (2002) Insects in wheat-based systems. *Bread Wheat: Improvement and Production* (eds B. C. Curtis, S. Rajaram & H. Gómez-Macpherson), pp. 367–393. online Food and Agriculture Organization, Rome.

Millon, A., Bourrioux, J.-L., Riols, C. & Bretagnolle, V. (2002) Comparative breeding biology of hen harrier and Montagu's harrier: an 8-year study in north-eastern France. *Ibis*, 144, 94–105.

Milne-Edwards, M.A. (1869) *Recherches anatomiques et paléontologiques pour servir á l'histoire des oiseaux fossiles de la France*, vol. 2. E.Martinet, Paris

Milonoff, M. (1994) An overlooked connection between goshawk and tetraonids; corvids! *Suomen Riista*, 40, 91–7.

Mitchell, B. (1963) Ecology of two carabid beetles, *Bembidion lampros* (Herbst) and *Trechus quadristriatus* (Shrank). I. Life cycles and feeding behaviour. *Journal of Animal Ecology*, 32, 289–299.

Mlíkovský (1995) Revision of Plio-Pleistocene quails of the Western Palaearctic. *Geolines (Praha)*, 2, 9–10.

Mlíkovský (2002) *Cenozoic birds of the world*. Ninox Press, Praha.

Moilanen, P. (1968) On the nest site selection of the Partridge (*Perdix perdix*) in southern Finland. *Souomen Riista* 20, 105–111.

Mohammad, K. M., Jasim, M. K. & Al-Moussawi, A. (2001) Haematozoa of the Phasianidae in Iraq. *Bulletin Iraq Natural History Museum*, 9, 57–61.

Mohammed, O. B., Hussein, H. S. & Elowni, E. E. (1988) The ant, *Pachycondyla sennaarensis* (Mayr) as an intermediate host for the poultry cestode, *Raillietina tetragona* (Molin). *Veterinary Research Communications*, 12, 325–327.

Moleón, M., Almaraz, P. & Sánchez-Zapata, J. A. (2008) An emerging infectious disease triggering large-scale hyperpredation. *PLoS ONE*, 3 (6): e2307. doi: 10.1371/journal.pone.0002307

Moleón, M., Sanchez-Zapata, J. A., Gil-Sanchez, J. M., Barea-Azcon, J. M., Ballesteros-Duperon, E. & Virgos, E. (2011) Laying the Foundations for a Human-Predator Conflict Solution: Assessing the Impact of Bonelli's Eagle on Rabbits and Partridges. *PLoS ONE*, 6 (7): e22851. doi: 10.1371/journal.pone.0022851

Møller, A. P. (1983) Changes in Danish Farmland Habitats and Their Populations of Breeding Birds. *Holarctic Ecology*, 6, 95–100.

Montagna, D. & Meriggi, A. (1991) Population dynamics of Grey Partridge (*Perdix perdix*) in northern Italy. *Boll Zool*, 58, 151–155.

Montagu, G. (1811) Gapeworms. *Transactions Wernerian Nat.Hist.Society*, 1, 194.

Moravec, F. (1981) Proposal of a new systematic arrangement of nematodes of the family Capillariidae. *Folia Parasitologica (Ceske Budejovice)*, 29, 119–132.

Moravec, F., Prokopic, J. & Shlikas, A. V. (1987) the biology of nematodes of the family Capillaridae (Neveu-Lemaire 1936). *Folia Parasitologica*, 34, 39–56.

Moreby, S. J. (1988) An aid to the identification of arthropod fragments in the faeces of gamebird chicks (Galliformes). *Ibis*, 130, 520–526.

Moreby, S. J. (1988) A preliminary survey of important chick food insects – the plant bugs (*Heteroptera*). *The Game Conservancy Annual Review*, 19, 92–95.

Moreby, S. J. (1994) *The influence of agricultural practices on Heteroptera in arable field margins*. MPhil Thesis University Southampton.

Moreby, S. J. (1996) The effects of organic and conventional farming methods on plant bug densities (Hemiptera: Heteroptera) within winter wheat fields. *Annals of Applied Biology*, 128, 415–421.

Moreby, S. J. & Sotherton, N. W. (1997) A comparison of some important chick-food insect groups found in organic and conventionally-grown winter wheat fields in southern England. *Entomological Research in Organic Agriculture*, 15, 51–60.

Moreby, S. J., Novoa, C. & Dumas, S. (1999) Diet of Pyrenean Grey Partridge (*Perdix perdix hispaniensis*) Broods in the Eastern French Pyrenees. *Gibier Faune Sauvage*, 16 355–364.

Moreby, S. J., Southway, S., Barker, A. & Holland, J. M. (2001) A comparison of the effects of new and established insecticides on non-target invertebrates of winter wheat fields. *Environmental Toxicology and Chemistry*, 20, 2243–2254.

Moreby, S. J., Aebischer, N. J. & Southway, S. (2006) Food preferences of grey partridge chicks, *Perdix perdix*, in relation to size, colour, and movement of insect prey. *Animal Behaviour*, 71, 871–878.

Morgan, D. O. & Clapham, P. A. (1934) Some observations on Gape-worm in poultry and game Birds. *Journal of Agricultural Science*, 12, 63–70.

Morgan, D. O. & Wilson, J. E. (1939) The Occurrence of *Heterakis gallinae* in Poultry and its Relation to Disease, Breed, and to other Helminths. *Journal of Helminthology*, 17, 177–182.

Morris, A. J. & Gilroy, J. J. (2008) Close to the edge: predation risks for two declining farmland passerines. *Ibis*, 150 S1, 168–177.

Mougeot, F., Pérez-Rodríguez, L., Sumozas, N. & Terraube, J. (2009) Parasites, condition, immune responsiveness and carotenoid-based ornamentation in male red-legged partridge *Alectoris rufa*. *Journal Avian Biology*, 40, 67–74.

Mourão, J. L., Outor-Monteiro, D. & Pinheiro, V. M. (2010) Age affects the laying performance and egg hatchability of red-legged partridges (*Alectoris rufa*) in captivity. *Poultry Science*, 89, 2494–2498.

Mourer-Chauviré, C. (1975) *Les oiseaux du Pléistocène moyen et supérieur de France.* Doc. Thesis Lab. Géol. Fac. Sci. Lyon.

Mourer-Chauviré, C. (1993) The Pleistocene Avifaunas of Europe. *Archaeofauna*, 2, 53–66.

Mourer-Chauviré, C. (2010) The Galliformes (Aves) from the Phosphorites du Quercy (France): systematics and biostratigraphy. *Natural History Museum of Los Angeles County Science Series*, 36, 67–95.

Mourer-Chauviré, C. & Geraads, D. (2010) The Upper Pliocene Avifauna of Ahl al Oughlam, Morocco: Systematics and Biogeography. *Records of the Australian Museum*, 62, 157–184.

Muir, D. A. (1954) Ants *Myrmica rubra* L. and *M. scabrinodis* Nylander as Intermediate Hosts of a Cestode. *Nature*, 173, 688–689.

Nadakal, A. M., Mohandras, A., John, K. O. & Muraleedharen, K. (1973) Contribution to the Biology of the Fowl Cestode *Raillietina echinobothrida* with a Note on Its Pathogenicity. *Transactions of the American Microscopical Society*, 92, 273–276.

Nadal, J. & Rodriguez Teijeiro, J. D. (1990) Red-legged partridge density: comparisons among agrosystems and between years. *Proceedings Congress of the International Union of Game Biologists.* 19, 117–124. Trondheim, Norwegian Institute for Nature Research.

Nadal, J., Nadal, J. & Rodriguez Teijeiro, J. D. (1996) Red-legged Partridge (*Alectoris rufa*) age and sex ratios in declining populations in Huesca (Spain) applied to management. *Revue d'Ecologie – La Terre et la Vie*, 51, 243–257.

Naifa, L. & Yang, Y. (1992) Ecological studies of *Alectoris graeca magna*. *Dongwuxue Yanjiu*, 3, 69–76.

Naifa, L. (1992) Ecology of Przewalski's Rock Partridge (*Alectoris magna*). *Gibier Faune Sauvage*, 9, 605–615.

Naumann, J. F. (1805 et seq) *Naturgeschichte der Vögel Europas.* Bd. 6. Gera-Untermhaus.

Nefedov, N. I. (1943) The agricultural importance of the partridge (*Perdix perdix* L.) on the lower Volga (Ru. En. summ.). *Zool.Zh.*, 22, 41–43.

New, L. F., Buckland, S. T., Redpath, S. M. & Matthiopoulos, J. (2011) Hen harrier management: insights from demographic models fitted to population data. *Journal of Applied Ecology*, 48, 1187–1194.

Newman, J. A. (2005) Climate change and the fate of cereal aphids in southern Britain. *Global Change Biology*, 11, 940–944.

Newton, A. (1861) On the possibility of taking an ornithological census. *Ibis* 3, 190–196.

Newton, I. (1986) *The Sparrowhawk.* Poyser, Calton.

Niethammer, G. (1942) *Handbuch der Deutschen Vogelkunde.* Leipzig.

Nikiforov, M. E. (1992) Size and mobility of grey partridge *Perdix perdix* winter coveys in Belorussia. *Perdix VI. First International Symposium on Partridges, Quails and Francolins* (eds M. Birkan, G. R. Potts, N. J. Aebischer & S. D. Dowell), *Gibier Faune Sauvage*, 9–447-453.

Nolte, W. (1934) *Zur Biologie des Rebhuhns. Das Rebhuhn als Jagdwild 1932 und 1933.* J. Neumann, Neudamm.

Notini, G. (1948) Biological Studies on the Badger (*Meles meles*) [Swedish]. *Svenska Jägareförbundets Medd*, 13, 1–256.

Nováková, E. (1966) Influence of anthropogenic changes on partridge numbers in the region of Trebon, Beroun [in Czech.). *Symposium O Koroptvi.* 45–67. Prague.

Novikov, B. G. (1939) Sex hormones and sexual characters in *Perdix perdix. Socialistes*, 3, 440–444.

Novoa, C. & Gonzalez, R. G. (1988) Comparaison des Biotopes Sélectinnés por le Lagopède Alpin (*Lagopus mutus*) et la Perdrix Grise de Pyrénnés sur le massif due Carlit. *Gibier Faune Sauvage*, 5, 187–202.

Novoa, C. & Dumas, S. (1994) Spring dispersal of the Pyrenean grey partridge (*Perdix perdix hispaniensis*) in two study areas in the eastern Pyrenees. *Gibier Faune Sauvage*, 11, 133–144.

Novoa, C., Garcia Gonzalez, R. & Aldezabal, A. (1999) Le régime alimentaire automnal de la Perdrix grise (*Perdix perdix hispaniensis*) dans les Pyrénées-orientales. *Revue d'Ecologie – La Terre et la Vie*, 54, 149–166.

Novoa, C., Aebischer, N. J. & Landry, P. (2002) Upland habitat use by Pyrenean grey partridges *Perdix perdix hispaniensis* during the breeding season. *Wildlife Biology*, 8, 99–107.

Novoa, C., Dumas, S. & Resseguier, J. (2006) Home-range size of Pyrenean grey partridges *Perdix perdix hispaniensis* during the breeding season. *Wildlife Biology*, 12, 11–18.

Nyenhuis, H. (2005) Einflüsse der Witterung auf das Rebhuhn (*Perdix perdix* L.). *Beiträge zur Jagd-und Wildforschung*, 30, 147–156.

O'Gorman, E. C. (2001) *Home range and habitat use of the endangered grey partridge (Perdix perdix) in the Irish Midlands.* PhD Trinity College Dublin.

O'Rourke, F. J. (1952) The medical and veterinary importance of the Formicidae. *Insectes Sociaux*, 3, 107–118.

Oakleaf, R. J. & Robertson, J. H. (1971) Fall food items utilized by chukars in Kashmir, India. *Journal of Wildlife Management*, 35, 395–397.

Odoric of Pordenone (1330) *Cathay and the way hither.* www.archive.org/details/cathaywaythithero2yule.

Ogilvie-Grant, W. R. (1895). Mountain Partridge, in A *Handbook to the Game Birds*, pp147-148. Allen's Naturalists Library Vol 1, London

Ogilvie-Grant, W. R. (1911) On two remarkable seasonal changes of plumage in the common partridge (*Perdix perdix*). *Bull Br Ornithol Club*, 29, 39–41.

Ogilvie-Grant, W. R. (1912) Breeding and eclipse plumages of the common partridge. *British Birds*, 5, 234–236.

Oko, Z. (1963a) Studies in analysis of food of young Partridges, *Perdix perdix* (L.) [Pol]. *Przeglad Zoologiczny*, 7, 337–342.

Oko, Z. (1963b) Studies on the food of the adult Partridges in the Poznan province in a year cycle. *Poznanskie Towarz Przyj.*, 14, 39–96.

Oko, Z. (1971) Sklad jakosciowy i ilosciowy gastrolitów kuropatwy *Perdix perdix* (L.). *Przeglad Zoologiczny*, 15, 305–307.

Olech, B. (1970) Productivity of partridge population and factors determining it. *Proceedings International Congress of Game Biologists*, 9, 440–442.

Olech, B. (1971) Realised production, mortality and sex structure of a partridge (*Perdix perdix* L.) population and its utilisation for game purposes in Poland. *Ekologia Polska*, 19, 617–650.

Olech, B. (1987) Do weather conditions or density-dependent factors control numbers of partridges? *Proceedings International Union of Game Biologists*, 18, 617–619.

Olech, B. (1988a) Changes in numbers of partridges in Poland in 1964–1984. *Proceedings of the Common Partridge (Perdix perdix L.) International Symposium* (ed. A. Arcimowicz), pp. 111–122. Polish Hunting Association, Warsaw.

Olech, B. (1988b) Clutch size and breeding success of the partridge in Poland in 1974–1984. *Proceedings of the Common Partridge (Perdix perdix L.) International Symposium* (ed. A. Arcimowicz), pp. 157–164. Polish Hunting Association, Warsaw.

Orlowski, G. & Czarnecka, J. (2009) Granivory of Birds and Seed Dispersal: Viable seeds of *Amaranthus retroflexus* L. recovered from the droppings of the Grey Partridge *Perdix perdix* L. *Polish Journal of Ecology*, 57, 177–182.

Orlowski, G., Czarnecka, J. & Panek, M. (2011) Autumn-winter diet of Grey Partridges *Perdix perdix* in winter crops, stubble fields and fallows. *Bird Study*, 58, 473–486.

Orts-Anspach, M & Dalimer, P. (1954) *Perdix Montana* Brisson: aberration, polymorphism, or mutation? *Gerfaut* 44, 12–39; 304–306.

Osmolovskaya, V. I. (1961) Nasekomoyadnye ptitsy Nizhnego Povolzh'yabi ikh znachenie v organichenii chislennosti vreditelei lesa (Insectivorous birds of the Lower Volga region and their importance in controlling forest pests). In *Polezashchitnoe Lesorazvedenie na Kashtanovykh Pochvakh (Afforestation on chernozem soils),Vol 1.Moscow.*

Osmolovskaya, V. I. (1966) The population density and distribution of the partridge (*Perdix perdix* L.) in the European part of the U.S.S.R. *Zoolologicheskij Zhurnal Moskva*, 45, 90–98.

Otero, C. (1999) *Patrimonio Natural Y Propiedad Rural En España* [Spanish]. Exlibres Ediciones, S.L., Madrid.

Otnes, G. & Otnes, M. (1984) Feeding behaviour of gray partridge. *Loon*, 56, 73.

Padgett, K. A. & Boyce, W. M. (2005) Ants as first intermediate hosts of *Mesocestoides* on San Miguel Island, USA. *Journal of Helminthology*, 79, 67–73.

Pages-Mante, A., Pages-Bosch, M., Majo-Masferrer, N., Gomez-Couso, H. & Ares-Mazas, E. (2007) An outbreak of disease associated with Cryptosporidium on a red-legged partridge (*Alectoris rufa*) game farm. *Avian pathology*, 36, 275.

Palomares, F., Ferreras, P. & Delibes, M. (1995) Positive effects on game species of top predators by controlling smaller predator populations- an example with lynx, mongooses and rabbits. *Conservation Biology*, 9, 295–305.

Paludan, K. (1954) Agerhønens ynglesæson 1953. *Meddelelse fra Vildtbiologisk Station Kalø, Rønde*, 14, 4–19.

Paludan, K. (1963) Partridge markings in Denmark. *Danish Review of Game Biology*, 4, 25–60.

Panasyuk, D. I., Vasil'iev, A. P. & Ganyushkin, V. Ya. (1972) Biocenosis of helminths and microflora, its significance in Veterinary science and animal husbandry [Ru]. *Referativnyi Zhurnal Zhivotnovodstvo Veternariya*, 8. 58.639.

Panek, M. (1991) Changes in the population dynamics of partridges *Perdix perdix* in the region of Czempiń, western Poland during the period 1968–1988. *Zeitschrift für Jagdwissenschaft*, 37, 116–124.

Panek, M. (1992) The effect of environmental factors on the survival of grey partridge (*Perdix perdix*) chicks in Poland during 1987–89. *Journal of Applied Ecology*, 29, 745–750.

Panek, M. (1992) Mechanisms determining population levels and density regulation in Polish Grey Partridges (*Perdix perdix*). *Perdix*, 6, 325–335.

Panek, M. (1997) Density-dependent brood production in the grey partridge *Perdix perdix* in relation to habitat quality. *Bird Study*, 44, 235–238.

Panek, M. (1997) The effect of agricultural landscape structure on food resources and survival of grey partridge *Perdix perdix* chicks in Poland. *Journal of Applied Ecology*, 34, 787–792.

Panek, M. (1998) Use of call counts for estimating spring density of the grey partridge (*Perdix perdix*). *Acta Ornithologica*, 33, 143–148.

Panek, M. & Kamieniarz, R. (2000) Effect of landscape structure on nest site selection and nesting success of Grey partridge *Perdix perdix* in western Poland. *Polish Journal of Ecology*, 48, 239–247.

Panek, M. & Kamieniarz, R. (2000) Habitat use by the Partridge Perdix perdix during the breeding season in the diversified agricultural landscape of western Poland. *Acta Ornithologica*, 35, 183–189,

Panek, M. (2000) Predation on grey partridges during breeding season near Czempiń (Western Poland) in the 1990s. *Wloclawskie Towarzystwo Naukowe, Wloclawek*, 162.

Panek, M. (2002) Space use, nesting sites and breeding success of grey partridge (*Perdix perdix*) in two agricultural management systems in western Poland. *Game and Wildlife Science*, 19, 313–326.

Panek, M. (2005) Demography of Grey Partridges *Perdix perdix* in Poland in the years 1991–2004: reasons of population decline. *European Journal of Wildlife Research*, 51, 14–18.

Panek, M. (2006) Monitoring Grey Partridge (*Perdix perdix*) Populations in Poland: Methods and Results. *Wildl.Biol.Pract*, 2, 78.

Parish, D.M.B & Sotherton, N.W. (2007) The fate of released captive-reared grey partridges *Perdix perdix*: implications for reintroduction programmes. – *Wildl. Biol.* 13: 140–149.

Park, K. J., Robertson, P. A., Campbell, S. T., Foster, R., Russell, Z. M., Newborn, D. & Hudson, P. J. (2001) The role of invertebrates in the diet, growth and survival of red grouse (*Lagopus lagopus scoticus*) chicks. *Journal of Zoological Society of London*, 254, 137–145.

Parker, E. (1927) *Partridges: Yesterday and Today.* The Field Press, London.

Parmelee, A. (1959) *All the Birds of the Bible.* Lutterworth, London.

Passmore, C. W. (1992) Farming in an environmentally sensitive area. *Journal of the Royal Agricultural Society England*, 153, 45–53.

Pauly, D. & Maclean, J. (2003) *In a Perfect Ocean.* Island Press, Washington DC.

Pavia, M., Göhlich, U. B., Mourer-Chauviré, C. (2012) Description of the type-series of *Palaeocryptonyx donnezani* Depéret, 1892 (Aves: Phasianidae) with the selection of a lectotype. *Comptes Rendus Palevol.* doi:10.1016/j.crpv.2011.12.002

Pavlova, E. A. (1987) On a geographical variability of the grey partridge *Perdix perdix* L. within the area of the USSR [Ru]. *Proceedings of the Zoological Institute, Leningrad*, 163, 53–70.

Pavlović I., Jakić-Dimić D., Kulišić Z., Florestean I., (2003) Most frequent nematode parasites of artificially raised pheasants (*Phasianus colchicus* L) and measures for their control. *Acta veterinaria*, 53, 393–398.

Payne-Gallwey, R. (1892) *Letters to Young Shooters.* Longmans, Green & Co., London.

Páv, J. (1961) Parasitic worms of the European Partridge (*Perdix perdix* L.) and their influence on Partridge State of Health [transl]. *Lesnictví*, 34, 521–550.

Páv, J., Zajícek, D. & Kotrlý, A. (1966) Helminths of partridges in Czechoslovakia. *Symposium on Partridge* (ed. P. Husek), pp. 100–107. Vyzkumny Ustav Lesniho Hospodarstvi a Myslivosti a Ceskoslovensky Myslivecky Svaz v Ustavu Vedeckotechnichych Informaci MZLH, Praha.

Pegel, M. (1987) Das Rebhuhn (*Perdix perdix* L.) im Beziehungsgefüge seiner Um- und Mitweltfaktoren. *Systematische Untersuchungen über die Existenz- und Gefahrdungskriterien einheimischer Wildtiere, Tiel 2*, 18, 1–200.

Peiro, V. & Blanc, Ch. P. (2011) Predicting the spring abundance distribution of red-legged partridge populations in agricultural regions using environmental models and an application for game management. *Folia Zoologica*, 60, 203–213.

Pekic, B. (1968) The results of many years research on the partridge. *Glas.zav.zast, prirode Titograd*, 1, 85–93 (in Serbian with English summary).

Pena, E. A., Curdi, L. J., Hernandez, C. J. A., Acedo, C. S. & Femenias, G. M. (1984) *Alectoris rufa*, a new host of *Ixodes ventalloi* and *Ixodes (Pholeoixodes) hexagonus* in Spain. *Revista Iberica de Parasitologia*, 44, 215–216.

Penev, D. (1983) Study on the nutrition of the partridge *Perdix perdix* in Bulgaria. *Gorskostopanska* 20, 71–75.

Pennycott, T. (1996) Gamebird Diseases. *Annual Review The Game Conservancy Trust*, 28, 63–65.

Pennycott, T. (1996) Gamebird diseases: the need for more research. *Annual Review The Game Conservancy Trust*, No. 28, 63–68.

Pennycott, T. (1997) Some protozoal diseases of game birds – an unfolding story. *State Veterinary Journal*, 7, 6–9.

Pereira, S. L. & Baker, A. J. (2010) A molecular timescale for Galliforme birds accounting for uncertainty in time estimates and hetereogeneity of rates of DNA substitutions across lineages and sites. *Molecular Phylogenetics and Evolution*, 38, 499–509.

Permin, A., Bisgaard, M., Frandsen, F., Pearman, J., Kold, J. & Nansen, P. (1999) Prevalence of gastrointestinal helminths in different poultry production systems. *British Poultry Science*, 40, 439–443.

Peters, J. (1934) *Check-list of birds of the world.* University of Harvard Press, Cambridge USA.

Peterson, M. J. (2007) Diseases and Parasites of Texas Quails. *Texas Quails* (ed. L. A. Brennan), pp. 89–116.

Pethig, H. (1994) *Exogene Einflußfaktoren von Rebhuhnpopulationen (Perdix perdix L.) in zwei Untersuchungsgebieten der niederrheinebene.* PhD Universität des Saarlandeserstellt.

Petrov, P., Dragoev, P. & Georgiev, Ž. (1969) On the sub-species of the Rock partridge in eastern Rhodope Mountains, Bulgaria. *Gorkospanska Nauka*, 6, 91–106.

Petty, S. J., Anderson, D. I. K., Davison, M., Little, B., Sherratt, T. N., Thomas, C. J. & Lambin, X. (2003) The decline of the Common Kestrel *Falco tinnunculus* in a forested area of northern England: the role of the Northern Goshawk, *Accipiter gentilis*. *Ibis*, 145, 472.

Peus, F. (1929) *Perdix perdix sphagnetorum* (Altum), eine aussterbende Rebhuhnrasse. *Ornithologische Monatsberichte*, 37, 129–135.

Pépin, D. (1985) Morphological characteristics and sex classification of red-legged partridge. *Journal of Wildlife Management*, 49, 228–237.

Pépin, D. & Fouquet, M. (1992) Factors affecting the incidence of dawn calling in Red-legged and Grey Partridges. *Behaviour Processes*, 26, 167–176.

Pépin, D., Birkan, M. & Angibault, J.-M. (2008) Factors affecting changes in grey partridge population dynamics in a French arable farmland over an eleven-year period. *European Journal of Wildlife Research*, 54, 179–187.

Péterfay, J. (1935) Az időjárás vadszapporodási kihatásai. *Erdészeti Lapok*, 74, 540–548.

Péterfay, J. (1938) Időjárás és vadszaporodás 1938-ban. *Erdészeti Lapok*, 77, 1080–1094.

Phillips, D.H.P. (2011) An investigation into the success of the Grey Partridge (*Perdix perdix*) Restoration Project on the Northumberland Estates. M Phil., Thesis University Cambridge.

Pielowski, Z. (1982) Über die Bedeutung des Fuchses (*Vulpes vulpes* L. 1758) in der Jagdwirtschaft der Volksrepublik Polen. *Beiträge zur Jagd-und Wildforschung*, 12, 71–77.

Pis, T. (2001) Development of thermoregulation in hand-reared Grey Partridges (*Perdix perdix*). *Game & Wildlife Science*, 18, 509–520.

Pis, T. (2003) Energy metabolism and thermoregulation in hand-reared Chukars (*Alectoris chukar*). *Comparative Biochemistry and Physiology – Part A: Molecular & Integrative Physiology*, 136, 757–770.

Pitts, M. & Roberts, M. (1998) *Fairweather Eden: Life in Britain half a million years ago as revealed by the excavations at Boxgrove.* Random House/Arrow Books, London.

Pollard, E., Hooper, M. D. & Moore, N. W. (1967) *Hedges.* Collins, New Naturalist Series, London.

Pollard, J. (1977) *Birds: Folklore: Greece*. Westview Press, Boulder, Colo.

Ponce, F. (1989) *Etude du régime alimentaire du poussin de perdrix rouge Alectoris rufa en relation avec la gestion des milieux*. Mémoire DEA, Ecole Pratique des Hautes Etudes University Montpellier.

Portal, M. & Collinge, W. E. (1932) Partridge Disease and its causes. Country Life Ltd., London.

Porter, R. D. (1955) The Hungarian Partridge in Utah. *Journal of Wildlife Management*, 19, 93–109.

Porter, R. D. & White, C. M. (1973) The Peregrine Falcon in Utah, emphasizing ecology and competition with the Prairie Falcon. *Brigham Young Univ.Sci.Bull.* 18, 1–74.

Potapova, O.R. and Baryshnikov, G.F. (1993) Birds from the Acheulean occupation in Treugolnaya cave in the Northern Caucasus [Ru]. *Works of Zoological institute RAN* 249, 48–65.

Potapov, R. L. (2003) New data on winter life of the Grey Partridge *Perdix perdix* in Leningrad Province. *Russian Journal of Ornithology*, 225, 630–636.

Potts, G. R. (1970a) Recent changes in the farmland fauna with special reference to the decline of the grey partridge (*Perdix perdix*). *Bird Study*, 17, 145–166.

Potts, G. R. (1970b) The effects of the use of herbicides in cereals on the feeding ecology of partridges. *Proceedings of the British Weed Control Conference*, 10, 299–302.

Potts, G. R. (1970c) Studies on the changing role of weeds of the genus *Polygonum* in the diet of the partridge (*Perdix perdix*). *Journal of Applied Ecology*, 7, 567–576.

Potts, G. R. (1971) Facteurs régissant le taux de survie des jeunes chez la Perdix grise (*Perdix perdix*). *Bulletin Spécial du Conseil Supérieur de la Chasse*, 15, 23–34.

Potts, G. R. (1971) Agriculture and the survival of partridges. *Outlook on Agriculture*, 6, 267–271.

Potts, G. R. (1972) Factors governing the chick survival rate of the grey partridge (*Perdix perdix*). *Proceedings of the International Congress of Game Biologists*, 10, 85–94.

Potts, G. R. (1973) Pesticides and the fertility of the grey partridge (*Perdix perdix*). *Journal of Reproduction and Fertility*, 19S, 391–402.

Potts, G. R. & Vickerman, G. P. (1974) Studies on the cereal ecosystem. *Advances in Ecological Research*, 8, 107–197.

Potts, G. R. (1974) The grey partridge; problems of quantifying the ecological effects of pesticides. *Proceedings of the International Congress of Game Biologists Stockholm*, 11, 405–413.

Potts, G. R. & Vickerman, G. P. (1975) Arable ecosystems and the use of agrochemicals. *The Ecology of Resource Degradation and Renewal*. 17–29. Oxford.

Potts, G. R. (1977a) Some effects of increasing the monoculture of cereals. *Origins of Pest, Parasite, Disease and Weed Problems: The 18th Symposium of the British Ecological Society* (eds J. M. Cherret & G. R. Sagar), pp. 183–202. Blackwell Scientific Publications, Oxford.

Potts, G. R. (1977b) Population dynamics of the Grey Partridge: overall effects of herbicides and insecticides on chick survival rates. *Transactions of the XIII Congress of the International Union of Game Biologists* (ed. T. J. Peterle), pp. 203–211. Wildlife Society & Wildlife Management Institute, Washington D.C.

Potts, G. R. (1977c) Current studies on wild partridge management in England. *Ecologie du petit gibier, et amenagement des chasses* (eds P. Pesson & M. Birkan), pp. 119–135. Gauthier-villars, Paris.

Potts, G. R. (1978) Mathematical models as an aid to studies of gamebird populations. *Proceedings of the "Woodland Grouse" Symposium, Inverness, Scotland, 4–8 December*, 115–119. World Pheasant Association.

Potts, G. R. (1979) Can the methods of wild partridge management in Britain also help endangered pheasants in Asia? *Pheasants in Asia* (ed. C. D. W. Savage), pp. 92–95. WPA, Reading.

Potts, G. R. (1980) The effects of modern agriculture, nest predation and game management on the population ecology of partridges, (*Perdix perdix* and *Alectoris rufa*). *Advances in Ecological Research*, 11, 1–82.

Potts, G. R. (1980) Sheep, sheep ticks, grouse and hill farming. *The Game Conservancy Annual Review*, 11, 24–30.

Potts, G. R. (1980a) Population regulation mechanisms in partridges and the use of computer simulation models. *Proceedings of Perdix II Gray Partridge Workshop* (eds S. R. Peterson & L. J. Nelson), pp. 137–146. The forest, Wildlife and Range Experiment Station, University of Idaho, Moscow, Idaho.

Potts, G. R. (1980b) Simple computer models as aids to studies on the regulation of Alectoris population densities. *Les Perdrix du Genre Alectoris* (eds C. L. Coles, M. Reydellet, G. van Tuyll, L. van Maltzahn & J. Bugalho), pp. 62–70. Conseil International de la Chasse et de la Conservation du Gibier.

Potts, G. R. (1982) Population regulation mechanisms in partridge and the use of computer simulation models. *Transactions of the XIV International Congress of Game Biologists, Dublin, Ireland, October 1–5, 1979* (eds F. O'Gorman & J. Rochford), pp. 39–45. Irish Wildlife Publications, Dublin.

Potts, G. R. (1984) Grey partridge population dynamics: comparisons between Britain and North America. *Perdix III: Grey Partridge and Ring-Necked Pheasant Workshop* (eds R. T. Dumke, R. B. Stiehl & R. B. Kahl), pp. 7–12. Wisconsin Department of Natural Resources, Campbellsport.

Potts, G. R., Tapper, S. C. & Hudson, P. J. (1984) Population fluctuations in Red Grouse: analysis of bag records and a simulation model. *Journal of Animal Ecology*, 53, 21–36.

Potts, G. R. (1984) Monitoring changes in the cereal ecosystem. *Proceedings of the NERC ITE Symposium No. 13 'Agriculture and the Environment'* (ed. D. Jenkins), pp. 128–134. Monks Wood Experimental Station, Monks Wood.

Potts, G. R. (1985) The partridge situation in Italy: a view from Britain. *Seminario tenuto all'Universita della Calabria' 'Biologia dei Galliformi, Problemi di gestione venatoria e conservazione'* (eds F. Dessì-Fulgheri & T. Mingozzi), pp. 9–13. Dipartimento di Ecologia dell'Universita della Calabria, Arcavacata.

Potts, G. R. (1985) Herbicides and the decline of the partridge: an international perspective. Proceedings of the 1985 British Crop Protection Conference. Pp. 983–990., Wallingford, BCPC.

Potts, G. R. (1986) *The Partridge: Pesticides, Predation and Conservation.* Collins, London.

Potts, G. R. (1986) The red-legged and the grey partridge. *The Atlas of Wintering Birds in Britain and Ireland* (ed. P. Lack), pp. 162–165. Poyser, Calton.

Potts, G. R. (1987) Are the results of research on the partridge in Britain relevant to the conservation of this species in North America? *Saskatchewan Department of Natural Resources Wildlife Report*, 17, 31–37.

Potts, G. R. (1988) Causes of the decline of the partridge in Europe and North America and recommendations for future management. *Proceedings of the Common Partridge (Perdix perdix L.) International Symposium* (ed. A. Arcimowicz), pp. 129–134. Polish Hunting Association, Warszawa.

Potts, G. R. (1988) Farming and the grey partridge. *Journal of the Royal Agricultural Society of England*, 148, 92–100.

Potts, G. R. & Sotherton, N. W. (1988) Investigation of farming systems on integrated crop protection in cereals. *Integrated Crop Protection in Cereals* (eds R. Cavalloro & K. D. Sunderland), pp. 305–315. Balkema, Rotterdam.

Potts, G. R. & Aebischer, N. J. (1989) Control of population size in birds: the grey partridge as a case study. *Toward a More Exact Ecology. The 30th Symposium of the British Ecological Society, London 1988* (eds P. J. Grubb & J. B. Whittaker), pp. 141–161. Blackwell Scientific Publications.

Potts, G. R. (1990) The causes of the decline in population of the partridge (*Perdix perdix*) and effect of the insecticide dimethoate on chick mortality. *The Future of Wild Galliformes in the Netherlands* (eds J. T. Lumeij & Y. R. Hoogeveen), pp. 62–71. Gegevens Koninklijke Bibliotheek, The Hague.

Potts, G. R. (1990) Agricultural programs: the European perspective. *Perdix V: Gray Partridge and Ring-necked Pheasant Workshop* (eds K. E. Church, R. E. Warner & S. J. Brady), pp. 347–358. Kansas Department of Wildlife and Parks, Emporia, Kansas.

Potts, G. R. & Aebischer, N. J. (1991) Modelling the population dynamics of the Grey Partridge: conservation and management. *Bird Population Studies: Relevance to Conservation and Management* (eds C. M. Perrins, J. D. Lebreton & G. J. M. Hirons), pp. 373–390. Oxford University Press, Oxford.

Potts, G. R. (1991) The environmental and ecological importance of cereal fields. *The Ecology of Temperate Cereal Fields* (eds l. G. Firbank, N. Carter, J. F. Darbyshire & G. R. Potts), pp. 3–21. Blackwell Scientific Publications, Oxford.

Potts, G. R., Lecocq, Y., Swift, J. & Havet, p. (1991) Wise Use as a Conservation Strategy. *Gibier Faune Sauvage*, 8, 1–422.

Potts, G. R. (1992) Conservation through wise-use hunting? *Wildlife 2001:Populations* (eds D. R. McCullough & R. H. Barrett), pp. 718–726. Elsevier, New York.

Potts, G. R. (1993) Agriculture fit for the countryside. *Environmental aspects of the Reform of the Common Agriculture Policy.* 86–104. House of Lords, London.

Potts, G. R. (1993) The Grey Partridge and the Red-legged Partridge. *The New Atlas of Breeding birds in Britain and Ireland* (ed. D. W. Gibbons), pp. 134–137.

Potts, G. R. & Robertson, P. A. (1994) Gamebird research in North America and Europe: The way forward, a critique and a plea. *Transactions of the 59th North American Wildlife & Natural Resources Conference.* 415–420. Wildlife Management Institute, Washington D.C.

Potts, G. R. (1994) Set-Aside-Benefits to the Farmland Environment? *Journal of the Royal Agricultural Society*, 155, 45–47.

Potts, G. R. & Aebischer, N. J. (1995) Population dynamics of the grey partridge *Perdix perdix* 1793–1993: monitoring, modelling and management. *Ibis*, 137, S29–S37.

Potts, G. R. (1997) Cereal farming, pesticides and grey partridges. *Farming and Birds in Europe* (eds D. J. Pain & M. W. Pienkowski), pp. 150–177. Academic Press, London.

Potts, G. R. (1998) Global dispersion of nesting hen harriers *Circus cyaneus. Ibis*, 140, 76–88.

Potts, G. R. & Faragó, S. (2000) Partridges in Hungary. *Hungarian Small Game Bulletin*, 5, 267–290.

Potts, G. R. (2000) Using the scientific method to improve game bird management and research: Time. *Quail*, 5, 2–6.

Potts, G. R. (2001) Grey Partridge. *The Migration Atlas: Movements of the birds of Britain and Ireland* (eds C. V. Wernham, M. P. Toms, J. H. Marchant, J. A. Clark, G. M. Siriwardena & S. R. Baillie), pp. 259–260. Poyser.

Potts, G. R. (2002) Arable farming: The options for game and wildlife. *Journal of the Royal Agricultural Society*, 163, 72–82.

Potts, G. R. (2003) Balancing Biodiversity and Agriculture, 35–44. BCPC: Crop Science and Technology.

Potts, G. R. (2003) The myth of the overwintered stubble. *Bird Study*, 50, 91–93.

Potts, G. R. (2004) Myth of the overwintered stubble: reply. *Bird Study*, 51, 97–98.

Potts, G. R. (2004) Incidence of ingested lead gunshot in wild grey partridges in the UK. *Journal of European Wildlife Research*, 51, 1–6.

Potts, G. R. (2007) Biodiversity Management: We need more practitioners and better theorists. *Frontiers in Wildlife Science: Linking Ecological Theory with Management Applications* CRC Press USA.

Potts, G. R. (2009) Long-term changes in the prevalences of caecal nematodes and Histomoniasis in gamebirds in the UK and the interaction with poultry. *Veterinary Record*, 164, 715–718.

Potts, G. R., Ewald, J. A. & Aebischer, N. J. (2010) Long-term changes in the flora of the cereal ecosystem on the Sussex Downs, England, focusing on the years 1968–2005. *Journal of Applied Ecology*, 47, 215–226.

Poulsen, J. G., Sotherton, N. W. & Aebischer, N. J. (1998) Comparative nesting and feeding ecology of Skylarks *Alauda arvensis* on arable land in southern England with special reference to set-aside. *Journal of Applied Ecology*, 35, 131–147.

Poyarkov, D. V. (1955) Ecology of the Grey Partridge in the steppe zone of the European part of USSR [Russian]. *Uchen zap.Mosk gorod.Pedological Institute*, 38, 157–1213.

Prater, A. J. (1986) The decline to extinction of the Stone Curlew in Sussex. *Sussex Bird Report*, 38, 65–66.

Price, R. D., Hellenthal, R. A., Palma, R. L., Johnson, K. P. & Clayton, D. H. (2003) The Chewing Lice: World Checklist and Biological Overview. *Illinois Natural History Survey Special Publication*, 24, 1–501.

Prokoviev, S. M. (1975) the Daurian Partridge in the steppe and forest zone of Khakassia. *Protection and wise management of forests* [all Ru]. Krasnoyarsk, 147–159.

Prothero, R. E. (1917) *English farming: Past and Present.* Green & Co, London.

Prugh, L. R., Stoner, C. J., Epps, C. E., Bean, W. T., Ripple, W. J., Laliberte, A. S. & Brashares, J. S. (2010) The rise of the Mesopredator. *BioScience*, 59, 779–791.

Puga, M. Y., Herranz, J., de la Puente, J. & Suárez, F. (2002) La Perdiz Roja. Identidad de los depredadores e intensidad de la depredación. 135–147. Conveno Junta de Comunidodes de Castilla-La Mancha/ C.S.I.C. *La Perdiz Roja. I curso.* V-Fedenca.

Pullen, A. J., Jepson, P. C. & Sotherton, N. W. (1992) Terrestrial non-target invertebrates and the autumn application of synthetic pyrethroids: experimental methods and the trade-off between replication and plot size. *Archives of Environmental Contamination and Toxicology*, 23, 246–258.

Pulliainen, E. (1965) Studies on the weight, food and feeding behaviour of the partridge (*Perdix perdix*). *Annales Academeiae Scientarium Fennicae Series A IV Biologica*, 93, 1.

Pulliainen, E. (1966) Food habits of the partridge (*Perdix perdix*) in autumn and winter. *Suomen Riista*, 18, 117–132.

Pulliainen, E. (1966) Behaviour of the partridge (*Perdix perdix*) in winter. *Suomen Riista*, 18, 20–29.

Pulliainen, E. (1966) Peltopyyn talviekologiasta. [On the winter ecology of the partridge (*Perdix perdix*) in Finland]. *Suomen Riista*, 19, 46–62.

Pulliainen, E. (1968) Breeding success of a partridge (*Perdix perdix* L.) population in Ostrobothnia, West Finland, in 1967. *Annales Zoologici Fennici*, 5, 183–187.

Pulliainen, E. (1968) On the spring food of the partridge in Ostrobothnia, western Finland. *Suomen Riista*, 20, 94–101.

Pulliainen, E. (1971) Clutch size of the partridge (*Perdix perdix* L.). *Ornis Scandinavica.* 2, 69–73.

Pulliainen, E. (1983) Changes in the composition of the autumn food of the partridge (*Perdix perdix*) In southern Ostrobothnia, western Finland, over twenty years. *Suomen Riista*, 30, 15–21.

Pulliainen, E. (1996) Reversal in the use of animal matter by the grey partridge *Perdix perdix*: A comment. *Ornis Fennica*, 73, 186–187.

Pulliainen, E. (2007) *Peltopyy.* Ochre Chronicles Oy, Helsinki.

Putaala, A. & Hissa, R. K. (1993) Mortality and reproduction of wild and hand-reared grey partridge in Finland. *Suomen Riista*, 39, 41–52.

Putaala, A. (1997) *Survival and Breeding Success of Wild and Released Grey Partridges (Perdix perdix) an Ecophysiologcal Approach.* University of Oulu, Finland.

Putaala, A. & Hissa, R. K. (1998) Breeding dispersal and demography of wild and hand-reared grey partridges *Perdix perdix* in Finland. *Wildlife Biology*, 4, 137–145.

Rackham, O. (2006) *Woodlands*. HarperCollins, New Naturalist Series, London.

Raitis, T. (1970) Intestinal Parasites in Finnish Gallinaceous Game Birds. *International Union of Game Biology*, 9, 647–651.

Randi, E., Csaikl, U. & Csaikl, F. (1989) DNA analysis of Galliformes species: New aspects for phylogenetic relationships. *Biochemical Systematics and Ecology*, 17, 77–81.

Randi, E., Alkon, P. U. & Meriggi, A. (1992) A new model of *Alectoris* evolution based on biochemical analysis. *Gibier Faune Sauvage*, 9, 661–666.

Randi, E., Meriggi, A., Lorenzini, R., Fusco, G. & Alkon, P. U. (1992) Biochemical analysis of relationships of Mediterranean *Alectoris* partridges. *The Auk*, 109, 358–367.

Randi, E. A. (1996) Mitochondrial Cytochrome B Phylogeny of the *Alectoris* Partridges. *Molecular phylogenetics and Evolution*, 6, 214–227.

Randi, E. & Lucchinin, V. (1998) Organization and Evolution of the Mitochondrial DNA Control Region in the Avian Genus *Alectoris*. *J. Mol. Evol.* 47,449–462.

Randi, E., Bernard-Laurent, A., Havet, P., Taran, E. & Berthos, J. C. (1998) Introgression des allozymes et de l'adn mitochondrial de la perdrix rouge (*Alectoris rufa*) dans les populations alpines de perdrix bartavelle (*Alectoris graeca*): consequences genetiques de l'hybridation naturelle. *Gibier Faune Sauvage*, 15, 435–444.

Randi, E., Tabarroni, C., Rimondi, S., Lucchini, V. & Sfougaris, A. (2003) Phylogeography of the rock partridge (*Alectoris graeca*). *Molecular Ecology*, 12, 2201–2214.

Randi, E., Li Vigni, V. P., Marangoni, C., Morandini, C., Parodi, R., Gàbici, F., Sabelli, B., Bonfitto, A., Malacarne, G., Negri, A., Baccetti, N. & de Faveri, A. (2003) Identificazione genetica della Starna italica. Report: Ozzano Emilia, Instituto Nazionale per la Fauna Selvatica "Alessandro Ghigi".

Rands, M. R. W. (1985) Pesticide use in cereals and the survival of Grey Partridge chicks: a field experiment. *Journal of Applied Ecology*, 22, 49–54.

Rands, M. R. W. (1986a) The survival of gamebird (Galliformes) chicks in relation to pesticide use in cereals. *Ibis*, 128, 57–64.

Rands, M. R. W. (1986b) The effect of hedgerow characteristics on partridge breeding densities. *Journal of Applied Ecology*, 23, 479–487.

Rands, M. R. W. & Sotherton, N. W. (1986) Pesticide use on cereal crops and changes in the abundance of butterflies on arable farmland in England. *Biological Conservation*, 36, 71–82.

Rands, M. R. W. (1987) Hedgerow management for the conservation of partridges (*Perdix perdix* and *Alectoris rufa*). *Biological Conservation*, 40, 127–139.

Rands, M. R. W. (1988) The effect of nest site selection on nest predation in Grey Partridge *Perdix perdix* and Red-legged Partridge *Alectoris rufa*. *Ornis Scandinavica*, 19, 35–40.

Ranoux, F. (1998) Models to predict grey (*Perdix perdix*) and red-legged (*Alectoris rufa*) management spring densities in the Massif Central. *Gibier Faune Sauvage*, 15, 339–354.

Ransom, B. H. (1921) The turkey is an important factor in the spread of gapeworms. 1921. Washington, DC, United States Dept. of Agriculture: 939.

Rasmussen, P. N., Steenfeldt, S. & Jensen, T. S. (1992) Insects as food for Danish partridge *Perdix perdix* chicks. *Flora og Fauna*, 98, 87–92.

Ratcliffe, D. (1997) *The Raven*. Poyser, London.

Ratti, J. T. & Giudice, J. H. (2001) Assessment of Chukar and Gray Partridge populations and habitats in Hells Canyon. Final Report to the Idaho Power Company, Boise.

Redpath, S. M. & Thirgood, S. J. (1997) *Birds of Prey and Red Grouse*. London, Stationery Office.

Reece, R. L., Ireland, L. & Barr, D. A. (1985) Infectious sinusitis associated with *Mycoplasma gallisepticum* in game-birds. *Australian Veterinary Journal*, 63, 167, 1985.

Reichholf, J. (1973) The influence of land clearance on stocks of Partridge (*Perdix perdix*). *Anzeiger der Ornithologischen Gesselschaft in Bayern*, 12, 100–105.

Reid, W. M. & Carmon, J. L. (1958) Effects of numbers of *Ascaridia galli* in depressing weight gains in chicks. *Journal of Parasitology*, 44, 183–186.

Reitz, F., Buscarlet, L.-A. & Pinet, J.-M. (1984) Détermination du métabolisme énergétique des poussins de Perdrix grise (*Perdix perdix*) par la méthode à l'eau doublement marquée. *Gibier Faune Sauvage*, 1, 97–107.

Reitz, F. (1987) Elements of the demography of the grey partridge populations in the north of France. *Abstracts of the XVIII Congress of the International Union of Game Biologists* (eds B. Bobek, K. Perzanowski & W. L. Regelin), pp. 164. IUGB, Kraków-Warsaw.

Reitz, F. (1988) A model for estimating breeding success in the Grey Partridge *Perdix perdix* L. from weather conditions. *Gibier Faune Sauvage*, 5, 203–212.

Reitz, F., Scherrer, B. & Garrigues, R. (1988) La distribution de la taille des couvées de perdrix grise (*Perdix perdix* L.) et son utilisation pour l'estimation de parametres de réussité de la reproduction. *Gibier Faune Sauvage*, 5, 411–426.

Reitz, F., Bro, E., Mayot, P. & Migot, P. (1999) Influence de l'habitat et de la prédation sur la démographie des perdrix grises. *Bulletin Mensuel de l'Office National de la Chasse*, 240, 10–21.

Reitz, F. & Mayot, P. (1999) Effect of habitat characteristics on the predation risk of grey partridges. *International Union of Game Biology*, 24, 248–258.

Reitz, F. (2000) The status of partridges in north-central France. *Hungarian Small Game Bulletin*, 5, 151–164.

Reitz, F. & Mayot, P. (2000) Characteristics of grey partridge movements from the end of summer to the next spring: a comparative study. *Hungarian Small Game Bulletin*, 5, 257–266.

Reitz, F. (2001) Perdrix grise: quel est l'impact de l'agrainage sur les populations? *Faune Sauvage (ONCFS)*, 254, 4–9.

Reitz, F. (2004) Grey Partridge feeders: What impact do they have on partridge populations? ONCFS.

Renzoni, A. (1974) The decline of the Grey Partridge in Italy. *Biological Conservation*, 6, 213–215.

Retallack, G. J. (1997) Neogene expansion of the North American prairie. *Palaios*, 12, 380–390.

Reynolds, J. C., Dowell, S. D., Brockless, M. H. & Boatman, N. D. (1992) Tracking partridge predation. *Annual Review of the Game Conservancy Trust*, 23, 60–62.

Reynolds, J. C. & Tapper, S. C. (1995) Predation by foxes *Vulpes vulpes* on brown hares *Lepus europaeus* in central southern England, and its potential impact on annual population growth. *Wildlife Biology*, 1, 145–158.

Reynolds, J. C., Stoate, C., Brockless, M. H., Aebischer, N. J. & Tapper, S. C. (2010) The consequences of predator control for brown hares (*Lepus europaeus*) on UK farmland. *European Journal of Wildlife Research*, 56, 549.

Ricci, J.-C., Mathon, J. F., Garcia, A., Berger, F. & Esteve, J. P. (1990a) Effect of habitat structure and nest site selection on nest predation in Red-legged Partridges (*Alectoris rufa* L.) in French Mediterranean farmlands. *Gibier Faune Sauvage*, 7, 231–253.

Ricci, J.-C. (1990b) Nest site selection in red-legged partridges in French Mediterranean farmlands. *Transactions of the XIX Congress of the International Union of Game Biologists* (ed. S. Myrberget), pp. 357–358. Norwegian Institute for Nature Research (NINA), Trondheim.

Rickenbach, O., Grüebler, M. U., Schaub, M., Kollar, A., Naef-Daenzer, B. & Schifferli, L. (2011) Exclusion of ground predators improves Northern Lapwing *Vanellus vanellus* chick survival. *Ibis*, 153, 531–542.

Rippa, D., Masselli, V., Soppelsa, O. & Fulgione, D. (2011) The impact of agro-pastoral abandonment on the Rock

Partridge *Alectoris graeca* in the Appenines. *Ibis*, 153, 721–734.

Ritchie, E. G. & Johnson, C. N. (2009) Predator interactions, mesopredator release and biodiversity conservation. *Ecology Letters*, 12, 982–998.

Rizzoli, A., Rosso, F., Ferrari, N., Manfredi, M. T., Rosa, R., Farre, L. & Hudson, P. J. (2003) Infection of *Ascaridia compar* (Schrank 1790) in Rock Partridge (*Alectoris graeca saxatilis*): effects on egg hatching and some haematochemical parameters. *Ibex Journal of Mountain Studies*, 7S, 291–294.

Roberts, M. B. & Parfitt, S. A. (1999) *Boxgrove: A Middle Pleistocene hominid site at Eartham Quarry, Boxgrove, West Sussex*. English Heritage.

Robinson, M. (1999) Neolithic bread at Yarnton excavation. Report by Oxford University Museum.

Robinson, A. C. (2007) *Trapping, survival and probable cause of mortality of the Chukar Partridge*. MSc Brigham Young University.

Robinson, R. A. & Sutherland, W. J. (2002) Post-war changes in arable farming and biodiversity in Great Britain. *Journal of Applied Ecology*, 39, 157–172.

Robinson, R. A., Lawson, B., Toms, M. P., Peck, K. M., Kirkwood, J. K. & *et al.* (2010) Emerging Infectious Disease Leads to Rapid Population Declines of Common British Birds. *PLoS ONE*, 5: doi:10.1371/journal.pone.0012215

Rodriguez-Caabeiro, F., Jimenez-Gonzalez, A. & Criado-Fornelio, A. (1983) A new species of *Menacanthus* from the partridge (*Alectoris rufa*). *Nouv.Rev.Entomology*, 13, 337–344.

Rollins, D., Taylor, B. D., Sparks, T. D., Wadell, T. E. & Richards, G. (2006) Species Visitation at Quail Feeders and Guzzlers in Southern New Mexico. Athens Georgia USA, University Athens. *Gamebird*, 2006, A Joint Conference – Quail VI and Perdix XII: Managing Gamebirds in the 21st Century. pp 210–219.

Rolshausen, G., Segelbacher, G., Hobson, K. A. & Schaefer, H. M. (2009) Contemporary Evolution of Reproductive Isolation and Phenotypic Divergence in Sympatry along a Migratory Divide. *Current Biology*, 19, 2097–2101.

Romić, S. (1975) O plodnosti trcke (*Perdix perdix* L.) od 1933.do 1966. *Conspectus Agriculturae Scientificus*, 35, 167–184.

Romić, S. (1975) O promjenama vrijednosti tijela trcke (*Perdix perdix* L.) kroz protekle 33 godine. *Conspectus Agriculturae Scientificus*, 35, 145–165.

Rosa, R., Bolzoni, L., Rosso, F., Pugliese, A., Hudson, P. J. & Rizzoli, A. (2011) Effect of *Ascaridia compar* infection on rock partridge population dynamics: empirical and theoretical investigations. *Oikos*, 120, 1557–1567.

Rosenzweig, V. Ye. (1997) Revised classification of the *Calocoris* complex and related genera (Heteroptera: Miridae). *Zoosyst. Rossica*, 6, 139–169.

Rosin, A. V., Meriggi, A., Pella, F. & Zaccaroni, M. (2010) Demographic parameters of reintroduced Grey Partridges in central Italy and the effect of weather. *European Journal of Wildlife Research*, 56, 369–375.

Rotella, J. & Ratti, J. T. (1988) Seasonal variation in Gray Partridge vocal behaviour. *The Condor*, 90, 304–310.

Rotella, J., Ratti, J. T., Reese, K. P., Taper, M. L. & Dennis, B. (1996) Long-term population analysis of gray partridge in eastern Washington. *Journal of Wildlife Management*, 60, 817–825.

Roth.T.C.II. & Lima, S. L. (2007) The predatory behaviour of wintering *Accipiter* hawks: temporal patterns in activity of predators and prey. *Oecologia*, 152, 169–178.

Rothschild, M. & Clay, T. (1952) *Fleas, Flukes & Cuckoos*. Collins New Naturalist Series, London.

Rörig, G. (1900) Magenuntersuchungen Land-Forstwirtschaftlich Wichtiger Vögel: Rebhuhn. *Arbeiten an der Biologischen Abteilung für Land-u.Forstwirtschaft am Kaiserlichen Gesundheitsamt*, 1, 50–56.

Rudd, R. L. (1964) *Pesticides and the Living Landscape*. University Wisconsin, Madison.

Rueda, M. J., Baragaño, J. R. & Notario, A. C. L. (1993) Estudio de la alimentacion natural de los pollos de Perdizes rojas (*Alectoris rufa*). *Ecologia*, 7, 429–445.

Ryder, W. D. (1967) The Dispersal of Certain Species of Mallophaga Which Infest the Domestic Fowl, *Gallus domesticus*. *Journal of Applied Ecology*, 4, 309–323.

Sage, R. B., Woodburn, M. I. A., Davis, C. & Aebischer, N. J. (2002) The effect of an experimental infection of the nematode *Heterakis gallinarum* on hand-reared grey partridges. *Parasitology*, 124, 529–535.

Šálek, M. & Marhoul, P. (1999) Seasonal dynamics and causes of loss in the Grey Partridge (*Perdix perdix* L.): results of counts and telemetry observations. *Sylvia*, 35S. 55–67.

Šálek, M., Marhoul, P. & Pintír, J. (2002) Pairing rate, sex ratio and age structure of a Grey Partridge (*Perdix perdix*) population in Prague, February 2000–2002. *Sylvia*, 38, 29–40.

Šálek, M., Marhoul, P. & Pintír, J. (2002) Spring to autumn home range and habitat use of a high density population of the grey partridge (*Perdix perdix*) in Praha. *Folia Zoologica*, 51, 299–306.

Šálek, M., Marhoul, P., Pintír, J., Kopecký, T. & Slabý, L. (2004) Importance of unmanaged wasteland patches for the grey partridge *Perdix perdix* in suburban habitats. *Acta Oecologica*, 25, 23–33.

Šálek, M. & Marhoul, P. (2008) Spatial movements of grey partridge *Perdix perdix*: male-biased spring dispersal and effect of habitat quality. *Journal of Ornithology*, 149, 329–335.

Salisbury, E. J. (1961) *Weeds and Aliens*. Collins New Naturalist Series, London.

Sánchez-Marco, A. (2006) *Miophasianus* and Palaeoperdix (Galliformes, Aves) from three Miocene localities of Spain. *Estudios Geológicos*, 62, 249–256.

Sánchez-Marco, A. (2009) New Iberian Galliformes and Reappraisal of some Pliocene and Pleistocene Eurasian Taxa. *Journal of Vertebrate Paleontology*, 29, 1148–1161.

Sandars, H. G. (1939) *An Outline of British Crop Husbandry*. Cambridge University Press, Cambridge.

Sandfort, W. W. (1963) Chukar trapping and transplanting (including release of game-farm birds). Colorado Division of Wildlife.

Sankey, J. H. P. (1988) Provisional Atlas of Harvest-spiders of the British Isles. Biological Records Centre, Monkswood.

Sargeant, A. B. & Allen, S. H. (1989) Observed interactions between Coyotes and Red Foxes. *Journal of Mammalogy*, 70, 631–633.

Sass, B. & Gorgacz, E. J. (1978) Cerebral nematodiasis in a chukar partridge. *Journal of the American Veterinary Medical Association*, 173, 1248–1249.

Savage, D. E., Young, J. A. & Evans, R. A. (1969) Utilisation of Medusahead and Downy Brome caryopses by Chukar partridges. *Journal of Wildlife Management*, 33, 975–978.

Savory, A. (1999) *Holistic Management*. Island Press, Washington DC.

Sawai, H., Kim, H. L., Kuno, K., Suzuki, S., Gotoh, H. T. M., Takahada, N., Satta, Y. & Akishinonomiya, F. (2010) The Origin and Genetic Variation of Domestic Chickens with Special Reference to Junglefowls *Gallus g. gallus* and *G. varius*. *PLoS ONE*, 5 (5): e 10639.doi. 10.1371/journal pone 0010639

Schei, E., Holmstad, P. R. & Skorping, A. (2005) Seasonal infection patterns of parasites in willow Grouse do not support the presence of parasite-induced winter losses. *Ornis Fennica*, 82, 137–146.

Scheinin, S., Yom-Tov, Y., Motro, U. & Effen, E. (2006) Behavioural responses of red foxes to an increase in the presence of golden jackals: a field experiment. *Animal Behaviour*, 71, 577–584.

Schladweiler, P. (1975) *Effects of coyote predation on game populations in Montana*. Montana Dept. Fish & Game. Pitman Robertson Report W120R6.

Schmidt, G. D. (1986) *Handbook of tapeworm identification*. CRC Press, Boca Raton, Florida.

Schorger, A. W. (1966). *The wild turkey. Its history and domestication*. Norman, Oklahoma: University of Oklahoma Press.

Schricke, E. (1978) Pathologie et maîtrise de l'état sanitaire dans les élevages de gibier: Région Centre. *Pesticides et gibier, maladies du gibier* (ed. P. Pesson), pp. 205–227. Gauthier-Villars, Bordas, Paris.

Schulz, J. W. (1976) Great Horned Owl predation on Gray Partridge. *Prairie Naturalist*, 8, 21–22.

Schulz, J. W. (1977) Population dynamics of Hungarian Partridge in north-central North Dakota: 1946–1977. *Perdix*, 1, 133–145.

Sekera, I. J. (1959) Causes of variation and diminution of the partridge populations in Tcheckoslovakia. *Lesnictví*, 5, 493–500.

Sekera, I. J. (1966) Problém koroptvi v Ceskoslovensku. *Symposium O Koroptví.* 5–14. Prague.

Seoane, L. V. (1891) *Perdices de Europa (Perdix cinerea charrela)*. La Coruña.

Sergio, F., Marchesi, F. & Pedrini, P. (2003) Spatial refugia and the co-existance of a diurnal raptor with its intra-guild owl predator. *Journal of Animal Ecology*, 72, 232.

Sergio, F. & Hiraldo, F. (2008) Intraguild predation in raptor assemblages: a review. *Ibis*, 150S, 132–145.

Serjeantson, D. (2009) *Birds*. Cambridge Manuals in Archaeology.

Serre, D. & Birkan, M. (1985) Incidence de traitements insecticides sur les ressources alimentaires de poussins de perdrix grise. *Gibier Faune Sauvage*, 4, 21–61.

Serre, D., Birkan, M., Pelard, E. & Skibniewski, S. (1989) Mortalité, Nidification et Réussite de la Reproduction des Perdrix grises (*Perdix perdix belesiae*) dans le contexte agricole de la Beauce. *Gibier Faune Sauvage*, 6, 97–124.

Sfougaris, A., Giannakopoulos, A. & Goumas, H. (2003) Food habits of the Rock Partridge (*Alectoris graeca graeca*) in Central Greece. Proceedings of the X International Perdix Symposium Braga, Portugal.

Shamuratov G.Sh. & Deordiev I.T. (1990) Lucerne weevil and decrease of its population. 15–17 pp. (In Russian). *Sbornik nauchn. trudov [Ru]* (ed. G. Sh. Shamuratov), pp. 15–17. Nukus.: Izd. Karakalpakstan.

Shipley, A. E. (1909) Internal Parasites of Birds allied to the Grouse. *Proceedings Zoological Society*, 1, 363–368.

Shipley, A. E. (1911) The Ectoparasites of the Red Grouse (*Lagopus scoticus*). *The Grouse in Health and in Disease Vol 1.* 347–371.

Shortall, C. R., Moore, A., Smith, E., Hall, M. J., Woiwood, I. P. & Harrington, R. (2009) Long-term changes in the abundance of flying insects. *Insect Conservation and Diversity*, 2, 251–260.

Shrestha, T.K. (2001) *Birds of Nepal, Vol 2: Field Ecology, Natural History & Conservation*, Bimala Shrestha, Kathmandu.

Shrubb, M. (2003) *Birds, Scythes and Combines*. Cambridge University Press, Cambridge.

Shrubb, M. (2007) *The Lapwing*. T & A D Poyser, London.

Sibley, C. G. & Alquist, J. E. (1990) Phylogeny and Classification of Birds. Yale University Press, New Haven.

Siivonen, L. (1953) On the destruction of nests of Gallinaceous birds in Finland 1946–52. *Suomen Riista*, 8, 46–48.

Simmons K. E. L. (1957) A review of the anting behaviour of passerine birds. *British Birds* 50, 401–421.

Simmons, R. E. (2000) Harriers of the world: their behaviour and ecology. Oxford University Press, Oxford.

Sinclair, A. R. E., Mduma, S. & Brashares, J. S. (2003) Patterns of predation in a diverse predator-prey system. *Nature*, 425, 288–290.

Sironi, G., Rampon, T. & Burzoni, G. (1991) Cryptosporidiosis in game birds. *The Veterinary Record*, 337–338.

Skoracki, M. & Sikora, B. (2011) Quill mites (Acari: Syringophilidae) associated with galliform birds (Aves: Galliformes). *Zootaxa*, 2966, 13–30.

Skrjabin, K. I. & Udinzey, A. N. (1930) Two new trematodes from the bile-duct of birds from Armenia: Chukar. *Journal of Parasitology*, 16, 213–219.

Skultéty, J. (1965) The protection of nesting partridges in the cutting of agricultural cultures. *Communicationes Instituti Forestalis Cechosloveniae*, 3, 49–60.

Skultéty, J. (1971) Use of a tin foil scare to protect nesting Partridges in Slovakia[Cz]. *Acta Instituti Forestalis Zvolenensis*, 487–498.

Sladek, I. J. (1966) Contribution to the problem of harmful influence of buzzard (*Buteo buteo*) on partridge. *Symposium O Koroptví*. 88–93. Výzkumný Ústav Lesního Hospodárstvi A. Myslivosti Ceskoslovensky Myslivecký Svaz, Prague.

Smith, B. D. (1998) *The Emergence of Agriculture.* Scientific American Library, New York.

Smith, L. M., Hupp, J. W. & Ratti, J. T. (1982) Habitat use and home range of Gray Partridge in eastern South Dakota. *Journal of Wildlife Management*, 46, 580–586.

Smith, T., Rose, K. D. & Gingerich, P. D. (2006) Rapid Asia-Europe-North America geographic dispersal of earliest Eocene primate Teilhardina during the Paleocene-Eocene Thermal Maximum. *Proceedings National Academy Science USA*, 103, 11223–11227.

Sobrino, R., Acevedo, P., Escudero, M. A., Marco, J. & Gortázar, C. (2009) Carnivore population trends in Spanish agrosystems after the reduction in food availability due to rabbit decline by rabbit haemorrhagic disease and improved waste management. *European Journal of Wildlife Research*, 55, 161–165.

Sokolov, G. A., Balagura, N. N. & Maksimushkin, V. G. (1979) The feeding ecology of the Hazel Grouse and Daurian Partridge near the Enisey River, Western Sayan. *Ornitologiya*, 14, 221–224.

Sole, J. (2000) Depredaciones de zorro Vulpes vulpes sobre buho real Bubo bubo en un area del litoral Iberico. *Ardeola*, 47, 97–99.

Soler, R. F., Oropesa, J. A. L., García, C. J. P. & Pérez, L. M. (2004) Lead exposure by gunshot ingestion in Red-legged Partridge *Alectoris rufa*. *Veterinary and Human Toxicology*, 46, 133–134.

Sonin, M. D. & Barus, V. (1996) *The Nematodes of Wild Galliformes of the Palearctic.* Proceedings Academy of Science, Moscow.

Soon Hyung Eo, Olaf R.P.Bininda-Edmonds & John P.Carroll (2009) A Phylogenetic supertree of the fowls (Galloanserae, Aves). *Zoologica Scripta*, 38, 465–481.

Sotherton, N. W. (1982) Predation on a Chrysomelid beetle (*Gastrophysa polygoni*) in cereals by polyphagous predators. *Annals of Applied Biology*, 101, 196–199.

Sotherton, N. W. (1984) The distribution and abundance of predatory arthropods overwintering on farmland. *Annals of Applied Biology*, 105, 423–429.

Sotherton, N. W., Wratten, S. D. & Vickerman, G. P. (1984) The role of egg predation in the population dynamics of *Gastrophysa polygoni* (Coleoptera) in cereal fields. *Oikos*, 43, 301–308.

Sotherton, N. W. (1985) The distribution and abundance of predatory Coleoptera overwintering in field boundaries. *Annals of Applied Biology*, 106, 17–21.

Sotherton, N. W., Moreby, S. J. & Langley, M. G. (1987) The effects of the foliar fungicide pyrazophos on beneficial arthropods in barley fields. *Annals of Applied Biology*, 111, 75–87.

Sotherton, N. W. (1991) Conservation Headlands: A practical combination of intensive cereal farming and conservation. *The Ecology of Temperate Cereal Fields* (eds l. G. Firbank, N. Carter, J. F. Darbyshire & G. R. Potts), pp. 373–397.

Soulsby, E. J. L. (1977) *Helminths, Arthropods and Protozoa of Domesticated Animals.* Bailliere, Tindall and Cassell, London.

Southwood, T. R. E. & Leston, D. (1959) *Land and Water Bugs of the British Isles.* Warne.

Southwood, T. R. E. (1967) The ecology of the partridge II. The role of pre-hatching influences. *Journal of Animal Ecology*, 36, 557–562.

Southwood, T. R. E. & Cross, D. J. (1969) The ecology of the partridge III. Breeding success and the abundance of insects in natural habitats. *Journal of Animal Ecology*, 38, 497–509.

Southwood, T. R. E. (1972) Farm management in Britain and its effect on animal populations. *Proceedings of the Tall Timbers Conference on Ecological Animal Control by Habitat Management* 3, 29–51.

Southwood, T. R. E. & Hendersen, P. A. (2000) *Ecological Methods* (3rd edn). Blackwell, Oxford.

Southwood, T. R. E. & Cross, D. J. (2002) Food requirements of grey partridge *Perdix perdix* chicks. *Wildlife Biology*, 8, 175–183.

Southwood, T. R. E., Henderson, P. A. & Woiwood, I. P. (2003) Stability and change over 67 years-the community of Heteroptera as caught in a light trap at Rothamsted, UK. *European Journal of Entomology*, 100, 557–561.

Sovada, M. A., Sargeant, A. & Greir, J. W. (1995) Differential effects of Coyotes and Red Foxes on Duck nest success. *Journal of Wildlife Management*, 59, 1–9.

Spano, S. & Csermely, D. (1985) Male brooding in the red-legged partridge *Alectoris rufa*. *Boll.Zool.*, 52, 367–369.

Spano, S. (2010) *La Pernice Rossa*. Edizioni II Piviere S.r.l.

Spindler, L. A. (1967) Experimental Transmission of *Histomonas meleagridis* and *Heterakis gallinarum* by the Sowbug, *Porcellio scaber*, and its implications for further research. *Proceedings Helminthological Society*, 34, 26–29.

Spittler, H. (1973) Zur Populationsdynamik des Fuchses (*Vulpes vulpes* L.) in Nordrhein-Westfalen. *Proceedings International Congress of Biologists*. 11, 167–174. Stockholm, National Swedish Environment Protection Board.

Sprake, L. (1934) *Perdix the Partridge*. H.F. & G. Witherby, London.

Springer, M. A. & Kirkley, J. S. (1978) Inter and intraspecific interactions between Red-tailed Hawks and Great Horned Owls in central Ohio. *Ohio Journal of Science*, 78, 323–327.

Staller, E. L., Palmer, W.E., Carroll, J.P. Ryan P. Thornton, R.P. & Sisson, D.C. (2005) Identifying Predators at Northern Bobwhite Nests. The Journal of Wildlife Management, 69, 124–132

Stantschinsky, W. W. (1929) Zur geographischen Varialbilität des Rebhuhns. *Orn.Monatsberichte*, 37, 135–139.

Starling-Westerberg, A. E. (2001) The habitat use and diet of Black Grouse *Tetrao tetrix* in the Pennine hills of northern England. *Bird Study*, 48, 76–89.

Steenfeldt, S., Rasmussen, P. N. & Jensen, T. S. (1991) Food selection in a population of Partridge *Perdix perdix* in Danish arable farmland. *Dansk Ornithologisk Forenings Tidsskrift*, 85, 67–76.

Stewart, J. R. (2005) The use of modern geographical ranges in the identification of archaeological bird remains. *Documenta Archaeobiologiae*, 3, 43–54.

Stewart, J. R. (2003) *The bird remains from Boxgrove Project D (the hominid area)*. University College London, Department of Anthropology and AHRB Centre for the Evolutionary Analysis of Cultural Behaviour.

Stewart, J. R. (2007) The fossil and archaeological record of the Eagle Owl in Britain. *British Birds*, 100, 481–486.

Stiner, M. C. (1999) Paleolithic population growth pulses evidenced by small animal exploitation. *Science*, 283, 190–194.

Stiner, M. C., Munro, N. D. & Surovell, T. A. (2000) The Tortoise and the Hare, Small-Game Use, the Broad-spectrum Revolution and Palaeolithic Demography. *Current Anthropology*, 41, 39–73.

Stresemann, E. (1924) Da Berg Rebhuhn, Orn Monatsberichte., 32, 132–135.

Stoate, C., Moreby, S. J. & Szczur, J. (1998) Breeding ecology of farmland yellowhammers (*Emberiza citrinella*). *Bird Study*, 45, 109–121.

Stoate, C. & Leake, A. (2002) *Where the Birds Sing*. The Game & Wildlife Conservation Trust.

Stoddard, H. L. (1932) *The Bobwhite Quail, It's Habits, Preservation and Increase*. Charles Scribner's & Sons, New York.

Stoimenov, K. & Trifonov, T. (1964) Studies on the Helminthofauna of the Grey Partridge (*Perdix perdix perdix* L.) in the eastern parts of Bulgaria transl Bulgarian. *Bulletin of the Central Helminthological Laboratory*, 9, 125–128.

Stoyanov, S. & Ninov, N. (1995) Dependences between insect food and partridge stocks in the bird's natural habitats. *Transactions of the International Union of Game Biologists*, 22, 77–82.

Strandgaard, H. & Asferg, T. (1980) Fluctuations and Trends in the Game Bag Records in the years 1941–1976 and the geographical distribution of the bag in 1976. *Danish Review of Game Biology*, 11, 1–112.

Stuart-Wortley, A. J. (1894) *The Partridge*. Fur and Feather Series. Longman's Green, London.

Subramanian, S., Denver, D. R., Millar, C. D., Heupink, T., Aschrafi, A., Emslie, S. D., Baroni, C. & Lambert, D. M. (2009) High mitogenomic evolutionary rates and time dependency. *Trends in Genetics*, 25, 482–486.

Suhonen, J., Halonen, M., Mappes, T. & Korpimäki, E. (2007) Interspecific competition limits larders of pygmy owls. Journal of Avian Biology 38: 630–634.

Sunde, P. (2005) Predators control post-fledging mortality in Tawny Owl *Strix aluco*. *Oikos*, 110, 461–472.

Sunderland, K. D. (1975) The diet of some predatory arthropods in cereal crops. *Journal of Applied Ecology*, 12, 507–515.

Sunderland, K.D. (1987) Spiders and cereal aphid in Europe. *Bulletin* SROP/WPRS, 1987/X/1, 82–102.

Sunderland, K. D., Chambers, R. J. & Carter, O. C. R. (1988) Potential interactions between varietal resistance and natural enemies in the control of cereal aphids. *Integrated Crop Protection in Cereals* (eds R. Cavalloro & K. D. Sunderland), pp. 41–56. Balkema, Rotterdam.

Sunderland, K. D. (2002) Invertebrate pest control by carabids. *The Agroecology of Carabid Beetles* (ed. J. M. Holland), pp. 165–214. Intercept, Andover.

Sychra, O. (2005) Chewing lice (Phthiraptera: Amblycera, Ischnocera) from chukars (*Alectoris chukar*) from a pheasant farm in Jinacovice (Czech Republic). *Veterinary Medicine Czechoslovakia.*, 50, 213–218.

Szederjei, A.; Szederjei, M.; Studinka, L.; Sternberg, J. (1959): *Hasen, Rebhühner, Fasanen.* Dt. Bauernverlag, Berlin.

Szemethy, L. & Heltai, M. (2001) Ragadozógazdálkodási stratégia-a jövö lehetöségei. *Hungarian Small Game Bulletin*, 6, 59–78.

Szentkirályi, F. (2002) Fifty-year long insect survey in Hungary: T Jermy's Contribution to light-trapping. *Acta Zoologica Scientarium Hungaricae*, 48(S1), 85–105.

Tapper, S. C. (1976) The diet of weasels (*Mustela nivalis*) and stoats (*Mustela erminea*) during early summer in relation to predation on gamebirds. *Journal of Zoology*, 179, 219–224.

Tapper, S. C. (1976) Weasel and stoat predation on partridge chicks. *The Game Conservancy Annual Review*, 7, 34–37.

Tapper, S. C. (1979) The effect of fluctuating vole numbers (*Microtus agrestis*) on a population of weasels (*Mustela nivalis*) on farmland. *Journal of Animal Ecology*, 48, 603–617.

Tapper, S. C., Green, R. E. & Rands, M. R. W. (1982) Effects of mammalian predators on partridge populations. *Mammal Review*, 12, 159–167.

Tapper, S. C. (1992) *Game Heritage.* Game Conservancy Ltd, Fordingbridge.

Tapper, S. C., Brockless, M. H. & Potts, G. R. (1993) Effet de la limitation des predateurs sur les populations de perdrix grise (*Perdix perdix*) et de lievre d'Europe (*Lepus europaeus*). *Actes du colloque predation et gestion des predators*, 20, 37–44.

Tapper, S. C., Potts, G. R. & Brockless, M. H. (1996) The effect of an experimental reduction in predation pressure on the breeding success and population density of grey partridges Perdix perdix. *Journal of Applied Ecology*, 33, 965–978.

Tapper, S. C. (1999) A Question of Balance: Game animals and their role in the British Countryside. The Game Conservancy Trust, Fordingbridge.

Tavares, P., de Carmo Magalhães, M. & Fontoura, P. M. (1996) Estudo da alimentação de perdiz vermelha (*Alectoris rufa*) numa zona agrícola do concelho de Santarém. *Revista Florestal*, 9, 255–265.

Taylor, R. L., Maxwell, B. D. & Boik, R. J. (2006) Indirect effects of herbicides on bird food resources and beneficial arthropods. *Agriculture, Ecosystems and Environment*, 116, 157–164.

Terborgh, J. & Estes, J. A. (2010) *Trophic Cascades: Predators, Prey, and the changing dynamics of nature.* Island Press, Washington DC.

Thaisz, L. & Csiki, E. (1912) Results of analyses made of the contents of 285 partridge crops from different parts of Hungary from partridges shot, mostly in August [transl.]. *Aquila,* 19, 166–201.

Thieme, H. (1997) Lower Palaeolithic hunting spears from Germany. *Nature,* 385, 807–810.

Thirgood, S. J., Redpath, S. M., Rothery, P. & Aebischer, N. J. (2000) Raptor predation and population limitation in red grouse. *Journal of Animal Ecology,* 69, 504–516.

Thomaides, C., Vavalekas, C., Papaevangelou, E. & Papageorgiou, N. (1992a) Nest-site characteristics and nest success of the Rock Partridge (*Alectoris graeca*). *Abstract of Perdix VI, First International Symposium on Partridges, Quails and Francolins* (eds M. Birkan, G. R. Potts, N. J. Aebischer & S. D. Dowell), pp. 886. Office National de la Chasse, Paris.

Thomaides, C. & Papageorgiou, N. (1992b) Nesting Biology and Habitat Use of the Gray Partridge (*Perdix perdix*) in Northern Greece. *Gibier Faune Sauvage,* 9, 443–446.

Thomas, D. H., Pinshow, B. & Degen, A. A. (1984) Renal and lower intestinal contributions to the water economy of desert-dwelling phasianid birds: comparison of free-living and captive Chukars and Sand Partridges. *Physiological Zoology,* 57, 128–136.

Thompson, K., Bakker, J.P. & Bekker, R.M. (1997) *The soil seed banks of North West Europe.* Cambridge University Press.

Thonon, Ph. (1974) *Les populations entomologiques des territoires agricoles entant que potentialités alimentaires pour les poussins de perdrix grise (Perdix perdix Linné, 1758) dans un secteur du Gatenais du Sud-Est.* PhD Thesis University Orléans.

Tibbits, D. F. & Babero, B. C. (1969) Report of *Ascaridia galli* (Schrank, 1788) from the chukar partridge (*Alectoris graeca*), in Nevada. *Journal of Parasitology,* 55, 1252.

Tillmann, J. E. (2009a) Fear of the dark: night-time roosting and anti-predation behaviour in the grey partridge (*Perdix perdix* L.). *Behaviour,* 146, 999–1023.

Tillmann, J. E. (2009b) An ethological perspective on defecation as integral part of antipredatory behaviour in the grey partridge (*Perdix perdix* L.) at night. *Journal of Ethology,* 27, 117–124.

Tillmann, J.E., Beyerbach, M. & Strauss, E. (2012) Do hunters tell the truth? Evaluation of hunters' spring pair density estimations of the grey partridge (*Perdix perdix* L.). *Wildlife Biology,* 18, in press.

Tischler, W. (1965) *Agrarökologie,* Jena.

Tittensor, R. (1991) *West Dean: A History of Conservation on a Sussex Estate.* Felpham Press, Bognor Regis.

Toft, S. (2005) The quality of aphids as food for generalist predators: implications for natural control of aphids. *European Journal of Entomology,* 102, 371–383.

Tolgay, N., Hwang, J. C. & Weher, E. E. (1960) Helminth parasites from the Chukar Partridge, *Alectoris graeca,* of Turkey with notes on their life histories, pathogenicity and control. *A.Ü.Vet.Fak.Derg.,* 6, 184–206.

Tompkins, D. M., Dickson, G. & Hudson, P. J. (1999) Parasite-mediated competition between pheasant and grey partridge: a preliminary investigation. *Oecologia Berlín,* 119, 378–382.

Tompkins, D. M., Draycott, R. A. H. & Hudson, P. J. (2000a) Field evidence for apparent competition mediated via the shared parasites of two gamebird species. *Ecology Letters,* 3, 10–14.

Tompkins, D. M., Greenman, J. V., Robertson, P. A. & Hudson, P. J. (2000b) The role of shared parasites in the exclusion of wildlife hosts: *Heterakis gallinarum* in the ring-necked pheasant and the grey partridge. *Journal of Animal Ecology,* 69, 829–840.

Topping, C. J. (2011) Evaluation of wildlife management through organic farming. *Ecological Engineering,* 37, 2009–2017.

Toso, S. & Cattadori, I. M. (1993) La starna (*Perdix perdix* L.) in Italia: analisi dell'origine e della presenza storica di una specie in uenzata dalle attività antropiche. *Selvaggina*, 21, 175–186.

Traugott, M., Bell, J. R., Broad, G. R., Powell, W., Van Veen, J. F., Volhardt, I. M. G. & Symondson, W. O. C. (2008) Endoparasitism in cereal aphids: molecular analysis of a whole parasitoid community. *Molecular Ecology*, 17, 3928–3938.

Trautman, C. G., Fredrickson, L. F. & Carter, A. V. (1974) Relationship of red fox and other predators to populations of ring-necked pheasants and other prey, South Dakota. *Transactions of the 39th North American Wildlife Conference*. 241–252.

Traylor, S. S., Church, K. E. & Draheim, D. L. (2001) Range expansion of grey partridge (*Perdix perdix*) in the Central Great Plains, USA. *Game & Wildlife Science*, 18, 243–252.

Trout, R. C. (1976) *An ecological study of populations of wild Harvest mice (Micromys minutus soricinus Hermann)*. Ph.D. University of London.

Trout, R. C. (1978) A review of studies on populations of wild Harvest mice (*Micromys minutus* (Pallas). *Mammal Review*, 8, 143–158.

Tryjanowski, P. (2001) Proximity of raven (*Corvus corax*) nests modifies breeding bird community on intensively used farmland. *Annales Zoologici Fennici*, 38, 131–138.

Tryjanowski, P., Goldyn, B. & Surmacki, A. (2002) Influence of the red fox (Vulpes vulpes, Linnaeus 1758) on the distribution and number of breeding birds in an intensively used farmland. *Ecological Research*, 17, 395–399.

Turner, T. W. (1954) *Memoirs of a Gamekeeper*. Geoffrey Bles, London.

Tyrberg, T. (1995) Palaeobiogeography of the genus *Lagopus* in the West Palaearctic. *Courier Forschungsinstitut Senckenberg*, 181, 275–291.

Tyrberg, T. (1996) Pleistocene Birds of the Palearctic: A catalogue. *Nuttall Ornithological Club Publications*, 27.

Tyšer, L., Hamouz, P., Nováková, K., Neèasova, M. & Holec, J. (2009) Changes in weed communities in selected areas with a 30 years interval. *Scientia Agriculturae Bohemica*, 40, 18–25.

Ul'yanin, N. S. (1949) K ekologii tereva, beloi i seroi kuropatok Severngo Kazakhstana. *Trudy Nauzumskogo gosudarstvennogo zapovednika, Moskva*, 2, 5–57.

Upgren, H. T. (1968) Hungarian partridge. *North Dakota Outdoors*, 30, -11.

Upgren, H. T. (1969) *Ecology of the Hungarian Partridge in North Dakota*. North Dakota Game & Fish Department.

Uttendörfer, O. (1939) *Die Ernährung der deutschen Raubvögel und Eulen und ihre Bedeutung in der heimischen Natur*. Neumann, Neudamm.

Uttendörfer, O. (1952) Neue Ergebnisse über die Ernährung der Greifvögel und Euien. E. Ulmer, Stuttgart.

Valkama, J., Korpimäki, E., Arroyo, B., Beja, P., Bretagnolle, V., Bro, E., Kenward, R. E., Mañosa, S., Redpath, S. M., Thirgood, S. J. & Viñuela, J. (2005) Birds of prey as limiting factors of gamebird populations in Europe: a review. *Biological Reviews*, 80, 171–203.

Vallance, M., Arnauduc, J.-P., Migot, P. & Iwach, B. (2008) *Atlas de la Biodiversité de la Faune Sauvage*. Hachette Pratique, Paris.

van den Bosch, R. (1978) *The Pesticide Conspiracy*. Doubleday & Company, New York.

Van Troostwijk, D.W.J. (1968) Das Rebhuhn (*Perdix perdix*) in den Niederlanden. *Zeitscrift für Jagdwissenschaft*, 14, 1–12.

Varela, M. C. (1974) *Some ecological and epidemiological aspects of helminth fauna of the red-legged partridge (Alectoris rufa (L.) in the forest perimeter of Contenda [transl. Port]*. School of Veterinary Medicine, Technical University, Lisbon.

Vargas, J.M; Duarte, J.; Farfán, M.A.; Villafuerte, R.; Fa, J.E. (2012) Are reclamo hunting seasons for the Spanish red-legged partridge off the mark? *Journal of Wildlife Management*. published online: 12 Jan 2012 DOI: 10.1002/jwmg.329

Vasil'ev, I. E. (1992) Helminths in Thracian Rock Partridge (*Alectoris chukar*) in Bulgaria. *Helminthologia*, 29, 117–120.

Vasil'ev, I. E. (1995) On interactions between different species of genus *Ascaridia* when parasitizing in *Alectoris chukar kleini*: I. After simultaneous invasion. *Comptes Rendus de l'Académie Bulgare des Sciences*, 48, 117–119.

Vavalekas, K., Thomaides, C., Papaevangelou, E. & Papageorgiou, N. (1993) Nesting biology of the rock partridge *Alectoris graeca graeca* in northern Greece. *Acta Ornithologica*, 28, 97–101.

Vera, F. W. M. (2000) *Grazing Ecology and Forest History.* CABI, Wallingford.

Vertse, A., Zsák, Z. & Kaszab, Z. (1955) Die Ernährung des Rebhuhns und seine landwirtschaftliche Bedeutung in Ungarn [Food and agricultural importance of the partridge (*Perdix p. perdix* L.) In Hungary]. *Aquila*, 59–62, 13–68.

Vesey-Fitzgerald, B. (1946) *British Game.* Collins New Naturalist, London.

Vetiska, K. (1979) *Die Botanische und Zoologische Zusammensetzung des Kropfinhaltes bei Fasan Phasianus colchicus und Rebhuhn Perdix perdix [German].* Med Doc Universität in Wien.

Viart, M. (1978) Nourrisage Hivernal d'une Population de Perdrix à poste fixe, 1977–1983. R.F.F.,30, 367–379.

Vickerman, G. P. & Sunderland, K. D. (1975) Arthropods in cereal crops: nocturnal activity, vertical distribution and aphid predation. *Journal of Applied Ecology*, 12, 755–766.

Vickerman, G. P. (1976) The food of grey partridge chicks. *The Game Conservancy Annual Review*, 7, 33–34.

Vickerman, G. P. & Potts, G. R. (1977) The 1975 cereal aphid outbreak. *Journal of Applied Ecology*, 14, 167–177.

Vickerman, G. P. & Sunderland, K. D. (1977) Some effect of dimethoate on arthropods in winter wheat. *Journal of Applied Ecology*, 14, 767–777.

Vickerman, G. P. (1978) The arthropod fauna of under-sown grass and cereal fields. *Scientific Proceedings of the Royal Dublin Society*, 6, 156–165.

Vickerman, G. P. & O'Bryan, M. (1979) Partridges and insects. *The Game Conservancy Annual Review*, 9, 35–43.

Vickery, P. D., Hunter, M. C. & Wells, J. V. (1992) Evidence of Incidental nest predation and its effects on nests of threatened birds. *Oikos*, 63, 281–288.

Viklund, K. (1998) Cereals, weeds and crop processing in iron age Sweden. *Archaeology & Environment University of Umeå, Sweden*, 14, 1–192.

Villanúa, D., Pérez-Rodríguez, L., Casas, F., Alzaga, V., Acevedo, P., Viñuela, J. & Gortázar, C. (2008) Sanitary risks of red-legged partridge release: introduction of parasites. *European Journal of Wildlife Research*, 54, 199–204.

Vizeu Pinheiro, M. F. (1977) Estudio sobre la alimentacion de la Perdiz roja (*Alectoris rufa*, L.). *Boletin de la Estacion Central de Ecologia*, 6, 105–117.

Volin, L. (1970) *A Century of Russian Agriculture.* University of Harvard, Cambridge Ma.

von Burg, S., Van Veen, J. F., lvarez-Alfageme, F. & Romeis, J. (2011) Aphid parasitoid community structure on genetically modified wheat. *Biol.Lett.*, 7, 387–391.

Von Thüngen, C. E. F. (1876) *Das Rebhuhn, Dessen Naturgeschichte, Jagd Und Hege: Ein Monographischer Beitrag Zur Jagd Und Naturkunde (1876).* Kessinger Legacy Reprints.

Von Troostwijk, D. W. J. (1968) Das Rebhuhn (*Perdix perdix*) in den Niederlanden. *Zeitschrift für Jagdwissenschaft*, 14, 1–12.

Voríšek, P., Jiguet, F., van Strein, A., Škopilová, J., Klvaňová, A. D. & Gregory, R. D. (2010) Trends in abundance and biomass of widespread European farmland birds: how much have we lost? *BOU Proceedings – Lowland Farmland Birds III.* www.bou.org.uk/bouproc-net/lfb3/vorisek-etal.pdf.

Vražic, O. (1957) Parasites of the Common Partridge (*Perdix perdix* L.) in Croatia. *Veterinary Archives*, 27, 25–32.

Wakeham-Dawson, A., Szoszkiewicz, K., Stern, K. & Aebischer, N.J. (1998). Breeding Skylarks *Alauda arvensis* on Environmentally Sensitive Area arable reversion grass in southern England: survey-based and experimental determination of density. *J. Appl.Ecol.* 35: 635–648.

Walker, B. L. & Naugle, D. E. (2011) West Nile Virus ecology in sagebrush habitats and impacts on greater sage-grouse populations. *Greater sage-grouse: Ecology and conservation of a landscape species and its habitats.* (eds S. T. Knick & J. W. Connelly).

Walker, H. D. (1897) The gape worm of fowls (*Syngamus trachealis*); the earthworm (*Lumbricus terrestris*), its intermediate host. Also, On the prevention of the disease in fowls called the gapes, which is caused by this parasite. Private, Franklinville New York.

Walsingham, L. (1888) The Gape Worm of Fowls (*Syngamus trachealis*). *Nature*, 1888, 324–325.

Walsingham, L. & Payne-Gallwey, R. (1895) *Shooting: Field and Covert.* Longmans, Green & Co., London.

Walter, H. (2002) Natural history and ecology of the Chukar (*Alectoris chukar*) in the northern Great Basin. *Great Basin Birds* 5 2002, 28–37.

Walter, H. & Reese, K. P. (2003) Fall diet of Chukars (*Alectoris chukar*) in Eastern Oregon and discovery of ingested lead pellets. *Western North American Naturalist*, 63, 402–405.

Warburton, D. H. (1928) Louse fly *Ornithomyia avicularia* as the carrier of Mallophaga with some records of phoresy in insects. *Parasitology*, 20, 175–178.

Warren, S. D. & Clark, R. A. (1986) The effect of daily winter temperature extremes on food intake by Chukars. *Condor*, 88, 527–528.

Wasscher, J. (1941) De Graanonkruidassociaties in Groningen en Noord-Drente. *Nederlandsch Kruidkundig Archief*, 51, 435–441.

Watson, A. & Shaw, J. L. (1991) Parasites and Scottish Ptarmigan numbers. *Oecologia*, 88, 359–361.

Watson, A. & Moss, R. (2008) *Grouse* (New Naturalist Series). HarperCollins, London.

Watson, G. E. (1962) Three sibling species of *Alectoris* partridges. *Ibis*, 104, 353–367.

Watson, M. (2004) *The effects of raptor predation on Grey Partridges Perdix perdix.* DPhil Thesis, University of Oxford.

Watson, M., Aebischer, N. J., Potts, G. R. & Ewald, J. A. (2007) The relative effects of raptor predation and shooting on over-winter mortality of grey partridges in the UK. *Journal of Applied Ecology*, 44, 972–982.

Watson, R. T., Fuller, M., Pokras, M., Hunt, G. & (Eds) (2009) Ingestion of Lead from Spent Ammunition: Implications for Wildlife and humans. The Peregrine Fund, Boise, Idaho.

Weaver, H. R. & Haskell, W. L. (1967) Some fall foods of Nevada chukar partridge. *Journal of Wildlife Management*, 31, 582–584.

Wehr, E. E. (1940) Nematodes of Domestic Fowls transmissable to wild game birds. *Veterinary Medicine*, 35, 1–7.

Weigand, J. P. (1977) *The Biology and Ecology of Hungarian (European Gray) Partridge (Perdix perdix) in North-Central Montana.* Montana State University.

Weigand, J.P. (1980) Ecology of the Hungarian Partridge in North-Central Montana. *Wildlife Monographs*, 74, 1–106.

Weigel, R. D. (1963) Oligocene birds from Saskatchewan. *Quarterly Journal of the Florida Academy of Sciences*, 26, 257–262.

Weiss, E., Mordechai, E., Simchoni, O., Nadel, D. & Tschauner, H. (2008) Plant-food preparation area on an Upper Paleolithic brush hut floor at Ohalo II, Israel. *Journal of Archaeological Science*, 35, 2400–2414.

Wen Long-ying, Zhang Li-xun & Naifa, L. (2005) Phylogenetic Relationship of *Perdix dauurica* inferred from Mitochondrial Cytochrome b Gene. *Zoological Research*, 26, 69–75.

Westerskov, K. E. (1948) Management practices for the European partridge in Ohio and Denmark and remarks on general decline factors. *Tenth Midwest Wildlife Conference* 4. Ann Arbor, Michigan, 4 pp. (Mimeogr. presentation).

Westerskov, K. E. (1949) The recent decline of the Hungarian partridge. *Ohio Conservation Bulletin*, 13, 20–21.

Westerskov, K. E. (1949b) *A comparative study of the ecology and management of the English Partridge Perdix perdix in Ohio and Denmark.* MSc University of Ohio.

Westerskov, K. E. (1951) Om Aldersfordeling og Goldhed i Agerhønsebestanden. *Særtryk af Dansk Jagttidende*, 5, 26–28.

Westerskov, K. E. (1952) Wildlife Research and Management in Scandinavia. *New Zealand Science Review*, 10, 136–144.

Westerskov, K. E. (1957) The value of renesting in birds. *New Zealand Outdoors*, 22, 7–26.

Westerskov, K. E. (1966) Winter food and feeding habits of the partridge (*Perdix perdix*) in the Canadian Prairie. *Canadian Journal of Zoology*, 44, 303–322.

Westerskov, K. E. (1977) Covey-orientated partridge management in France. *Biological Conservation*, 11, 185–191.

Westerskov, K. E. (1990) Partridges and pheasants: competitors or sharers? *Perdix*, 5, 183–201.

Westmacott, R. N. & Worthington, R. (1974) *New agricultural landscapes: report of a study*. Cheltenham, Countryside Commission.

Whitlock, 1. (1987) *Roots in the Soil (Biography of Sir Joseph Nickerson)*. Plas, Hertford.

Whitmore, R. W. & Preuss, K. P. (1982) Responses of Pheasant chicks to adult Coccinellidae. *Journal of Kansas Entomological Society*, 55, 474–476.

Wiesenthal, Dr. (1799) The Gapeworm. *Medical & Physical Journal*, 2, 204.

Wiles, J.A. & Jepson, P.C. (1992) *In situ* bioassay techniques to evaluate the toxicity of pesticides to beneficial invertebrates in cereals. *Aspects of Applied Biology*, 31: 61–68.

Willcox, G. (1999). Agrarian change and the beginnings of cultivation in the Near East: Evidence from wild progenitors, experimental cultivation and archaeobotanical data. In: Hather, J., & Gosden, C. (Eds) *The Prehistory of food*. Routledge, London, pp 479–500.

Williams, I. C. (1961) A list of parasitic worms, including twenty-five new records from British Birds. *Annals and Magazine of Natural History*, 4 (Ser. 13), 467–480.

Wilson, G. R. (1977) Another look at grouse disease. *Country Landowner*, 28, 30–31.

Wilson, J. D., Evans, J., Browne, S. J. & King, J. R. (1997) Territory distribution and breeding success of Skylarks *Alauda arvensis* on organic and intensive farmland in southern England. *Journal of Applied Ecology*, 34, 1462–1478.

Wing, L. E. (1953) Cycles in European Partridge Abundance. *Journal of Cycles Research*, 2, 56.

Witherby, H. F., Jourdain, F. C. R. & Ticehurst, N. F. (1944) The Common Partridge – (*Perdix perdix perdix*). *Handbook of British Birds*. 240–246. H.F. & G. Witherby Ltd, London.

Woiwood, I. P. (1991) The Ecological Importance of Long-Term Synoptic Monitoring. *The Ecology of Temperate Cereal Fields* (eds L. G. Firbank, N. Carter, J. F. Darbyshire & G. R. Potts), pp. 275–304. Blackwell, Oxford.

Wolley-Dod, A. H. (1937) Flora of Sussex. Chatsford House Press, Bristol.

Wood, N. A. (1969) The control of Candidiasis (Moniliasis) in Partridges with Formic Acid. *Veterinary Record*, 443.

Wood, N. A. (1970) Survey of gamebird diseases 1969. *The Game Conservancy Annual Review*, 1, 67–70.

Woodford, E. K. (1964) Weed control in arable crops. *Proceedings of the 7th British Weed Control Conference*. 944–962.

Wood-Gush, D.G.M., Duncan, I.J.H. & Savory, C. J. (1978) Observations on the social behaviour of domestic fowls in the wild. *Biology & Behaviour*, 3, 193–205.

Wookey, B. (1987) *Rushall: the story of an organic farm*. Blackwell, Oxford.

Wratten, S. D., Mead-Briggs, M., Vickerman, G. P. & Jepson, P. C., (1988) Effects of the fungicide pyrazophos on predatory insects in winter barley. *BCPC Monograph Environmental Effects of Pesticides*, 40, 327–334.

Wratten, S. D. & Powell, W. (1991) Cereal Aphids and their Natural Enemies. *The Ecology of Temperate Cereal Fields* (eds l. G. Firbank, N. Carter, J. F. Darbyshire & G. R. Potts), pp. 233–257. Blackwell, Oxford.

Wratten, S. D. (2004) *Enhancing the Eco-Efficiency of Agriculture.* (ed. Fisher, J.) British Crop Protection Council. BCPC Forum: Elvetham Hall, Alton.

Wright, V. L., Graham, D. L., Farris, A. L. & Fiedler, W. R. (1980) Effects of *Heterakis* and *Histomonas* on the survival of Juvenile Grey Partridge. *Perdix,* 2, 156–164.

Wübbenhorst, D. & Leuschner, C. (2006) Vegetation structure at the breeding sites of the Partridge (*Perdix perdix* L.) in central Europe and its possible importance for population density. *Polish Journal of Ecology,* 54, 57–67.

Xiangtao, L. (1996) *The Gamebirds of China: Their distribution and Status.* International Academic Publishers, Beijing.

Yahya, H. S. A. (2000) Galliformes in Saudi Arabia with notes on the Chukar, Arabian and Sand Partridge. *International Galliformes Symposium* 2, 45–48.

Yalden, D. W. (1999) *The History of British Mammals.* T. & A.D. Poyser, London.

Yalden, D. W. & Albarella, U. (2009) *The History of British Birds.* Oxford University Press.

Yan, M., Zhang, X., Xu, Y., Yue, B. & Ran, J. (2011) Isolation and Characterization of Twelve Polymorphic Microsatellite Loci in the Buff-throated partridge (*Tetraophasis szechenyii*). *Russian Journal of Genetics,* 47.

Yapp, W. B. (1983) Game-birds in medieval England. *Ibis,* 125, 218–221.

Yeatter, R. E. (1934) The Hungarian partridge in the Great Lakes region. *University of Michigan School of Forestry and Conservation Bulletin,* 5, 1–92.

Yeatter, R. E. (1939) Food habits of Hungarian partridge. *Wildlife Review,* 22, 46–47.

Yeshurun R., Bar-Oz G., Weinstein-Evron M. (2009). The role of foxes in the Natufian economy: A view from Mount Carmel, Israel. *Before Farming* 2009/1 article 3.

Yocom, C. F. (1943) The Hungarian Partridge *Perdix perdix* Linn. in The Palouse Region, Washington. *Ecological Monographs,* 13, 167–202.

Young, A. (1804) *A General Review of the Agriculture of Norfolk.* London, Board of Agriculture.

Zelenkov, N. V. (2009) Phylogenetic Analysis of Some Neogene Phasianid Genera. *Palaeontological Journal,* 43, 438–443.

Zelenkov, N. V. & Kurochkin, E. N. (2009) Neogene Phasianids (Aves: Phasianidae) of Central Asia: 2. Genera *Perdix, Plioperdix* and *Bantamyx. Palaeontological Journal,* 43, 318–325.

Zhang, K., Yang, N., Xu, Y., Ran, J., Lloyd, H. & Yue, B. (2011) Nesting Behaviour of Szechenyi's Monal-Partridge in Treeline Habitats, Pamuling Mountains, China. *Wilson Journal of Ornithology,* 123, 93–96.

Zhang, Z. W. & Wu, Y.-C. (1992) The Daurian partridge (*Perdix dauurica*) in north-central China. *Perdix VI, First International Symposium on Partridges, Quails and Francolins* (eds M. Birkan, G. R. Potts, N. J. Aebischer & S. D. Dowell), pp. 591–595. Office National de la Chasse, Paris.

Zhang, Z. W., Liang, W. & Sheng, G. (1994) Studies on the nest site selection of Daurian partridge. *Zoological Research,* 15, 37–43.

Zhang, Z. W. & Liang, W. (1997) Study on the breeding ecology of the Daurian Partridge (*Perdix dauurica*) in Shanxi [Ch.]. *Chinese Journal of Zoology,* 2, 23–25.

Zhao, Z-J., Wu, J. & Zhang, S. (1992) A traditional method for hunting the Daurian Partridge (*Perdix dauurica suschkini*) in China. *Gibier Faune Sauvage,* 9, 831–835.

Zhao, Z.-J., Zhang, S. & Feng, K. F. (1992) The biology of the Daurian partridge (*Perdix dauurica suschkini*) in northeastern China. *Perdix VI, First International Symposium on Partridges, Quails and Francolins* (eds M. Birkan, G. R. Potts, N. J. Aebischer & S. D. Dowell), pp. 597–604. Office National de la Chasse, Paris.

Index

2, 4-D 206

A

Acuaria gruveli 264
Aebischer, Nicholas x, 216,
    358
Aegilops 72, 76
Africa 6, 35, 53, 60, 61, 62, 63,
    72, 86, 105, 108, 146, 147,
    282, 358, 375
Agrostis 197
Albany Quail Project 381
Allen, Fred 16
Allodapa suctoria 240, 257, 264
Alps 26, 70, 78, 86, 160, 178,
    250, 286, 320
Amara spp. 218, 236, 269, 363
Amberley Mount 110, 161,
    346, 368
American badger 149
annual meadow-grass 75, 335
ants 70, 75, 78, 84, 85, 128,
    157, 158, 159, 160, 161,
    164–6, 169, 170, 172–3, 176,
    177, 178, 180–3, 185, 186,
    188, 191, 195, 197, 224, 225,
    233, 239, 240, 255, 256, 259,
    261–2, 264, 265, 266, 267,
    270, 271
Apennines 78, 86, 117
aphids 17, 156, 157, 163, 164,
    167, 168, 170, 171, 173, 174,
    176, 177, 178, 182, 184–6,
    187, 189, 190, 195, 198, 200,
    209, 211–17, 218, 219, 220,
    224, 225, 230, 233, 234, 236,
    238, 337, 349, 367
Applesham 14, 16, 197, 198,
    226, 228, 229, 363, 365
Arabian partridge 52, 53

Arctic Circle 63
Arctic tern 312
Aristotle 3, 106, 117, 126
Artemisia spp. 71, 74, 90,
    233
Arundel 305
Arun valley 362
Ascaridia compar 256, 257,
    264
Ascaridia galli 257
Ash, John 12, 385–8, 392–3
aspergillosis 242, 244, 255
aurochs 71
Australia 72, 73, 149, 205,
    206
Austria 53, 81, 82, 113, 144
Azerbaijan 266

B

badger 21, 138, 139, 140, 141,
    142, 149, 292, 339, 394
Bagaza virus 263
bag records 14, 146, 316
Baines, David 160
bank vole 373, 374, 394
Bao, Xinkang 42, 45
Barbary partridge 11, 26, 52,
    53, 54, 63, 117, 126, 415
barley 70, 76, 81, 82, 83, 87,
    98, 159, 185, 197, 201, 202,
    210, 211, 214, 215, 217, 219,
    220, 228, 230, 279, 335, 336,
    337, 346
barley leaf blotch 220
barley yellow dwarf virus
    215, 219
barn owl 373, 374
bastard cabbage 334
Bavaria 78, 112
bearberry 69

beaver 150
Beer, John 241, 253, 257, 261
beetle banks 17, 24, 25, 83,
    132, 281, 328, 329–31, 337,
    339, 344, 356, 370, 378
Belgium 50, 69, 229
Bembidion spp. 136, 167, 168,
    184, 218, 219, 269
Benomyl 220
Bibionidae 154
bilberry 69
biodiversity ix, 1, 34, 91, 102,
    105, 136, 197, 235, 303, 323,
    326, 327, 347, 363, 372, 376,
    378, 380, 381, 384
Biodiversity Species Action
    Plan 369, 372
bird-cherry oat aphid 188
bird flu 263
BirdLife 12, 21
Birkan, Marcel 154, 167
bison 71, 73, 147, 394
black bindweed 74, 77, 79,
    80, 81, 82, 87, 88, 92–3, 96,
    101, 158, 162, 169, 325
blackcap 370
black grouse 44, 49, 69, 74,
    160, 225, 250
blackhead 239, 243, 244,
    246–7, 249, 250, 271
blackthorn 71, 290, 337,
    370, 372
black wood-partridge 60
Blank, Terence 12
block cropping 336
blood pheasant 59, 98
Boatman, Nigel 21, 24
bobwhite quail 25, 117, 137,
    139, 150, 217, 238, 247, 249,
    265, 290, 296

bogs 1, 69, 71, 75, 78, 153, 159, 282
Borlaug, Norman 102
Bourne, Bill 16
box 58, 69, 98, 210, 337
Boxgrove 36, 38, 40, 41, 314
Boxworth Experimental Husbandry Farm 17
braconids 230
brambles 71, 116, 214, 283, 290, 374
Bray, Roger 385–8
Brazil 102, 105, 234
Brisson, M. J. 2
British Trust for Ornithology 201, 358
broadleaved weeds 22, 79, 80, 81, 82, 89, 90, 191, 195, 210, 333, 335, 341, 347, 350
Brockless, Malcolm xi, 23, 24, 25
bromes 76
Brood production rate (BPR) 19, 20, 21, 30, 118, 128, 129, 353
broom 69, 71, 117, 159, 300
brown bear ix, 49, 146, 394
Browne, Stephen 183
brown hare 372
Bt genetically modified crops 234, 236
Buckley, Kieran 75, 279, 320, 378
buckthorn 71, 117, 291
buffalo 73
bulbous meadow grass 75, 83, 85
bulbs 9, 85, 86
Bulgaria 8, 41, 50, 81, 85, 117, 124, 154, 159, 170, 176, 178, 264, 266
bullfinch 356
bunch grass 74
Buner, Francis 340
burdock 90, 349, 356, 370
Burpham 90, 342
bustard 238

butterflies 16, 21, 199, 350, 370
buzzard 21, 275, 283, 284, 285, 286, 287, 303, 306, 310, 311, 351, 382, 392, 395

C
caeca 188, 249, 252, 254, 260, 296
California 26, 102, 124, 149, 240, 296
California quail 102
Calliptamus italicus 268
Canada 2, 79, 239
Cantabrian 69, 70, 117
capercaillie 49
Capillaria spp. 242, 243, 253, 255, 264, 280
Carbon 14 36, 47, 50
Cassida spp. 173, 174, 222
caterpillars 78, 152, 157, 158, 160, 162, 164, 167, 173, 175, 176, 177, 178, 182, 185, 189, 190, 195, 231, 233, 234, 238, 162, 364, 367, 370, 371
cattle 66, 70, 71, 72, 74, 86, 196, 197, 224, 360
Caucasus mountains 48
centipedes 156, 163, 173, 206, 207, 239
central Europe 35, 72, 115
cereal aphid 18, 185, 188, 200, 201, 211, 213, 214, 233
cereal crops 31, 78, 89, 90, 92, 94, 95, 111, 112, 115, 123, 153, 155, 160, 161, 162, 165, 168, 181, 182, 183, 188, 190, 191, 192, 194, 198, 200, 201, 206, 207, 210, 212, 213–20, 222–4, 226, 229, 232, 304, 341, 344, 366, 384
cereal leaf miners 223
Cereals and Gamebirds Project 21
chalcid wasps 230
chamomile 347
Channel Islands 52
Chauvet cave 147

Cheilospirura gruveli 256
chick food 7, 159, 165, 166, 167, 171, 174, 177, 178, 183, 190, 191–2, 201, 206, 215, 218, 221, 228, 233, 236, 267, 350, 370
chick survival rate 13, 18, 19, 20, 21, 24, 31, 32, 115, 134, 152, 153, 169, 245, 334, 376
chickweed 80, 82, 84, 87, 88, 95, 96, 97, 162, 175, 222, 336, 348
chicory 101, 331, 332, 337
China 27, 42, 44, 52, 55, 58, 60, 66, 71, 77, 85, 102, 235, 236, 250, 271, 291, 314, 315, 392, 393
chlorpyrifos 215
Christ's thorn 71, 117, 290
Chrysomelidae 70, 105, 221
chukar partridge ix, 1, 3, 6, 8, 9, 10, 21, 26, 27, 30, 33, 35, 44, 52, 53, 54, 55–7, 62, 63, 76, 81, 84, 85, 86, 88, 101, 116, 117, 118, 124, 125, 126, 142, 153, 158, 159, 162, 170, 171, 176, 177, 178, 179, 188, 191, 194, 205, 211, 222, 248, 249, 250, 252, 258, 259, 260, 261, 263, 266, 272, 285, 286, 290, 314, 315, 322, 323, 324, 340
Church, Kevin 155
CIC (International Council for Game and Wildlife Conservation) 135, 143, 324
clades 45, 46, 48, 50, 55
Clapham, Phyllis 12, 239, 241, 245, 246, 267, 268
cleavers 333, 334, 346
click beetles 363
Closterotomus norwegicus 183, 184, 210
Clostridia 255
Clothianidin 217
clover 78, 82, 84, 97, 161, 197, 209, 211, 229, 332, 333, 334, 335

coccidiosis 242, 243, 244, 253, 255
cocksfoot 229, 330, 337
cockspur grass 75, 76, 79, 81
Coles, Charles 34
Collinge, Walter 267
Common Agricultural Policy 103, 327
conservation headland 22, 25, 31, 77, 89, 91, 152, 153, 164, 180, 191, 192–4, 201, 206, 209, 210, 211, 216, 221, 222, 232, 233, 234, 282, 288, 328, 329, 330, 332, 333, 334, 335, 337, 341, 342, 343, 344, 345, 346, 348, 349, 350, 351, 353, 354, 355, 357, 358, 369, 370, 371, 378, 380, 383, 384
Contenda 82
Convention on Biological Diversity 27, 104, 326
Cook, Tom 102
Cooper's hawk 139, 285, 290, 293, 310
cormorant 262
corn bunting 363, 364, 384
corn buttercup 342
cornflower 22, 79, 81, 88, 169, 334
corn gromwell 345
corn spurrey 76, 88, 169, 344, 348
corvids 139, 311
couch 22, 197, 348
coveys 4, 9, 57, 75, 99, 100, 101, 117, 277, 278, 279, 283, 289, 291, 292, 294, 295, 296, 297, 301, 320, 322, 333
coyote 148, 149, 150
crabgrass 76, 79, 85
Craighead brothers 311, 371
Cram, Eloise 265
crane flies 78, 154, 160, 164, 167, 189, 190, 195, 217, 223, 233, 363, 367, 368, 370
crane fly larvae 154
crested wheat grass 74, 75
Crimea 52, 67

Croatia 20, 38, 260, 264
crop irrigation 65
Cross, David 192
Crowe, Tim 58
crows 123, 140, 142, 144, 243, 274, 310, 339
Cryptosporidium spp. 254
Cyrnea eurycerca 264
Cyrnea parroti 257
cysticercoids 240, 259, 269, 270
Czech Republic 52, 61, 79, 80, 82, 112, 115, 120, 121, 134, 140, 144, 161, 166, 181, 214, 222, 251, 252, 257, 261, 264, 265, 266, 314, 316, 321
Czempiń Research Station 169

D
Dahlgren, Jens 153, 188
Damerham 12, 13, 14, 15, 19, 21, 25, 28, 29, 31, 32, 45, 120, 130, 133, 135, 138, 139, 140, 141, 143, 162, 175, 177, 178, 184, 201, 226, 245, 262, 278, 292, 298, 301, 317, 343, 354, 389, 390, 391
Darwin, Charles 229, 341
Daurian partridge xi, 1, 2, 4, 5, 8, 40, 41, 43, 44, 45, 46, 50, 60, 61, 63, 66, 76, 77, 78, 80, 86, 110, 118, 120, 140, 141, 157, 245, 264, 291
Davainea andrei 264
DDT 17, 203
Dead Sea 35, 52
DEFRA 93, 378
Denmark 45, 82, 120, 134, 136, 145, 168, 181, 251, 257, 263, 264, 389, 390
Devensian 48, 49, 52, 146
Dicrocoelium petrovi 256, 267
dieldrin 203, 204, 205, 244, 278, 279, 376
dimethoate 215
diprotodontoids 73
Dispharynx spiralis 265

DNA 2, 34, 35, 36, 37, 42, 43, 45, 46, 47, 50, 53, 58, 59, 60, 61, 62, 69, 213, 234, 240, 251
Dolerus spp 171, 225, 226, 227, 228, 230
Dolichopoda 224
domestic fowl 13, 66, 99, 109, 153–4, 189, 190, 202, 237, 239, 243, 245–7, 248, 249–50, 252, 253, 257, 261, 265, 269
Donald, Paul 368
dormouse 123, 373
double brooding 107, 125, 126, 127, 128
Dover, John 22
downland 111
driven shooting 48, 128, 199, 202, 229, 274, 282, 315, 317, 318, 320, 321, 322, 324, 325, 375, 376, 380, 381
Duke of Norfolk, Edward xi, 327
D-vac x, 190, 199, 201, 206, 208, 209, 218, 222
dwarf spurge 345

E
eagle owl 27, 146, 286, 290, 292, 304, 305, 306, 307, 308, 309, 310, 311, 393
earthworms 239, 246, 249, 264, 265, 267, 271
earwig 163, 177, 209
East Anglia 19, 144, 165, 176, 193, 239, 252, 267, 304, 340
Eastern Europe 38, 48, 60, 76, 115, 144, 150, 268, 314
Eastop, Victor 212
elephant 27, 71, 72, 73, 326
emmer wheat 76
English Civil War 197
Environmentally Sensitive Areas (ESA) 328, 329, 378
Eragrostis 76, 85
Erbajeva, Margarita 39
erysipelas 255

European Agriculture Fund for Rural Development (EAFRD) 105
European Community 34
European Union (EU) 11, 103, 104, 105, 107, 234, 254, 378, 379, 380
Ewald, Julie xi, 201, 215

F
fat hen 76, 79, 81, 82, 83, 87, 88, 192
feather grass 9, 31, 43, 74, 152, 156, 157, 158, 184
feather-grass steppe 110, 184
feather lice 183, 260, 261, 262
feather mites 262
feral cat 139, 140, 142, 144
feral dog 142, 144
fescues 75
fescue-tansy 77
field boundaries 219
field grasshopper 209, 268
field pansy 87, 93
field penny-cress 77
field size 12, 24, 25, 32, 33, 112, 113, 115, 116, 119, 281, 300, 329, 330
field vole 374
fine-leaved fumitory 344
Finland 2, 20, 28, 29, 46, 50, 69, 87, 91, 100, 120, 121, 122, 140, 146, 149, 170, 185, 189, 257, 264, 267, 277, 298, 300, 303
fleas 262, 268
flukes 240, 256, 259, 266, 267, 271
Fordingbridge xi, 12, 14, 53, 165, 183, 245, 401, 410, 420, 448
fossil bones 314
fossil record 34, 36, 38, 39, 48, 50, 54, 61, 69, 159, 304
fox 2, 20, 21, 27, 108, 114, 118, 123, 135, 137, 138, 139, 140, 141, 142, 143, 144, 145, 146,

fox cont.
147, 148, 149, 150, 203, 225, 244, 248, 277, 278, 283, 289, 292, 295, 309, 311, 338, 339, 363, 372, 381, 394
foxtail millets 65
France xi, 3, 6, 8, 20, 25, 38, 40, 41, 48, 49, 50, 53, 54, 60, 61, 64, 69, 81, 97, 98, 99, 102, 111, 112, 113, 114, 116, 117, 121, 123, 124, 125, 130, 131, 139, 140, 141, 144, 145, 147, 167, 168, 176, 189, 190, 200, 202, 216, 217, 243, 250, 253, 263, 270, 272, 279, 280, 281, 282, 285, 291, 296, 297, 298, 299, 304, 309, 311, 314, 322, 326, 355, 357, 358, 369, 389, 391, 392, 393
francolins 53, 62, 86
frit fly 223
fungicides 198, 220, 221, 234, 335

G
Galliformes 25, 188, 239, 260, 293
Game and Wildlife Conservation Trust (GWCT) x, xi, 8, 11, 12, 21, 23, 24, 32, 34, 57, 63, 64, 119, 127, 160, 165, 182, 183, 193, 200, 203, 212, 215, 216, 220, 221, 226, 228, 239, 240, 241, 242, 246, 247, 251, 252, 253, 255, 273, 277, 279, 292, 298, 339
gamekeepers ix, xi, 11, 13, 14, 17, 21, 98, 103, 118, 119, 125, 128, 133, 139, 142, 143, 144, 146, 161, 166, 277, 279, 298, 309, 326, 327, 338, 376, 381
gannet 262
gapes 245, 267, 268, 279
gapeworm 165, 242, 243–6, 251, 252, 255, 264, 267, 268, 271, 338

Garza-Williamson index 50
Genetically-modified crops (GM) 105, 234, 235, 236
Georgia 264, 381
Germany 53, 60, 61, 62, 70, 79, 123, 135, 138, 142, 144, 146, 160, 168, 263, 272, 274, 283, 284, 306, 307, 308, 314, 321, 325, 380, 389, 391
Gibraltar 11, 53, 54, 63
gizzard contents 83, 152, 162, 163, 167, 169, 179
gizzard worm 264, 265
Glasshouse Crops Research Association 17, 199
globe thistle 117
glyphosate 336
glyphosate-tolerance 105, 235
golden jackal 149, 150
golden-yellow tulip 75
goldfinch 349, 356, 370
Goniocotes microthorax 261
goshawk 81, 113, 133, 140, 272, 278, 279, 283, 286, 292, 303, 305, 306, 307, 308, 309, 310, 311
Grala, Jean 99
grasshoppers 70, 75, 78, 83, 84, 156, 157, 158, 159, 160, 161, 163, 171, 172, 173, 176, 177, 178, 181, 185, 188, 195, 197, 209, 233, 257, 264, 265, 268, 271, 351, 364, 367
grass mirid 165, 183
Great Bustard Group 156
greater knapweed 75
great horned owl 285, 290, 305, 310, 311
Great Plains, The 103, 156
great skua 312, 377
Great Witchingham 12, 28, 31, 32, 110, 337
Greece 3, 8, 50, 55, 111, 116, 125, 142, 178
greenfinch 237, 254, 360, 372
green pigeon-grass 75, 77, 79, 85

Green, Rhys 20, 126, 127, 165, 170, 176, 219
grey partridge x, xi, 1, 2, 3, 4, 5, 6, 9, 11, 12, 13, 14, 17–21, 24, 25, 26, 27, 28, 31, 32, 33, 35, 38, 39, 43, 44–52, 55, 61, 62, 63, 64, 66–9, 70, 74–6, 77, 78–9, 80, 81, 82, 83, 84, 85, 88, 91, 93, 94, 96, 98, 100, 101, 103, 106, 107, 108, 109–14, 115, 116, 117, 118, 119, 123, 125, 128, 130, 131, 132, 133, 134, 135, 136, 137, 138, 139, 140, 141, 143, 144, 145–7, 150, 151, 153, 154, 155, 156–60, 161, 162, 166, 167, 168, 169, 170, 175, 176, 178, 179, 180, 181, 183, 184–6, 188, 189, 190, 191, 193, 194, 195, 198, 201, 203–5, 210, 211, 221, 222, 225, 226, 231, 235, 239, 243, 245, 246, 247, 248, 249, 250, 251, 252, 253, 254, 255, 257, 258, 259, 260, 261, 262, 263–4, 265, 266, 267, 268, 269, 270, 271, 272, 273, 274, 275, 276, 277, 278, 279, 281, 283, 284, 285, 286, 287–9, 290, 291, 292, 294, 295, 296, 297, 301, 302, 303, 305, 308, 309, 312, 314, 315, 316, 317, 318, 319, 320, 322, 323, 325, 326, 327, 328, 330, 331, 338, 339, 340, 351, 353, 354, 355, 359, 362, 368, 372, 375–6, 380, 384
grey-winged francolin 86
ground beetles 155, 158, 163, 164, 167, 169, 170, 185, 190, 195, 208, 213, 218, 219, 232, 233, 236, 259, 265, 267, 268, 269, 271, 350, 364, 367
Grouse Inquiry team 323
guinea fowl 99, 249, 250
Gullick, Tom 102

H
Haemoproteus spp. 258
haplotypes 47
harvester ants 270
harvestmen 155, 156, 160, 163, 173, 176, 177, 188, 190, 207, 232, 351
harvest mouse 373, 374
hatching dates 201, 202
Hawaii 6, 55, 238, 410
hawthorn 71, 108, 231, 290, 337, 369
heather beetle 156
heathland 69, 153, 159, 225, 365
hedgehog 138, 139, 140, 141, 142, 144
hedgerows xi, 32, 98, 106, 110, 111, 112, 114, 115, 116, 117, 133, 135, 292, 333, 337, 339, 370
Hell's Canyon 84, 85, 86
hemp nettle 77, 78, 80, 81, 82, 87, 88, 91, 92, 101
hen harrier 21, 108, 140, 252, 272, 275, 281, 282, 285, 286, 287, 291, 303, 304, 305, 309, 392
herbicides 11, 17, 21, 22, 28, 31, 65, 76, 78, 79, 88, 89, 90, 91, 92, 93, 95, 97, 117, 165, 169, 189, 191, 192, 193, 194, 195, 198, 202, 203, 206, 210, 220, 229, 233, 234, 235, 236, 318, 333, 334, 336, 341, 347, 348, 350, 367, 376, 380
Heterakis spp. 239, 242, 246, 247, 248, 249, 250, 251, 252, 255, 256, 257, 264
Hicter, Jacques xi, 3, 99, 100, 106, 130, 131, 168, 205, 295, 296, 379, 391
Highclere 17, 189, 192
Higher Level Stewardship Scheme (HLS) 22, 25, 33
hill partridge 61
hippopotamus 72, 73

Histomonas 255
histomonosis 243, 244, 246, 250
HLS+ 329, 342, 347, 351, 352, 353, 354, 355, 356, 359, 363, 364, 365, 367, 368, 370, 372, 374, 379, 380
Hodgson, Brian 2
hogweed 90, 211, 233, 349
Holocene 41, 50, 52, 68, 420
hominids 72
hopper feeding 24, 65, 97, 98, 99, 211, 295, 296, 326
house sparrow 254
hover-fly larvae 167
Hungary 20, 26, 28, 52, 60, 71, 79, 80, 81, 82, 105, 112, 123, 141, 143, 144, 145, 149, 150, 181, 205, 225, 266, 269, 304, 357, 379, 389, 390, 391
Hunt, Chris 16, 21
hybrids (Alectoris) 26, 27, 52, 56, 57, 191, 314

I
Ichneumon wasps 227, 229
ICI Game Research Department 12
Imperial College Field Station 187
insecticides 17, 22, 37, 159, 195, 198, 199, 203, 212, 214, 215, 216, 217, 218, 219, 221, 223, 231, 234, 236, 261, 276, 278, 332, 335, 363, 370, 376, 377
Institute for Research into Ecological Resources (IREC 241
Iran 2, 85, 105, 158, 159, 411
Iraq 76, 258
Ireland 1, 50, 75, 78, 103, 146, 251, 279, 282, 294, 298, 300, 303, 320, 378
Irish elk 71, 394
Irish Grey Partridge Conservation Trust 320

irrigation 65, 108, 137, 216, 336, 381
Isle of May x
Israel 2, 53, 76, 79, 81, 101, 117, 124, 314, 322
Istituto Superiore per la Protezione e la Ricerca Ambientale (ISPRA) 53
Italy 6, 8, 20, 25, 44, 45, 48, 49, 54, 56, 61, 67, 70, 116, 130, 257, 314, 320, 390, 391

J
jackdaw 139
Jenkins, David 130, 289, 297
jewel beetle 70
Joint Cereal Ecosystem Study 17, 212, 213
juniper 10, 69, 110, 159, 161, 290, 300

K
Kaiser, Wolfgang 112
kale 15, 101, 197, 206, 291, 331, 332, 337, 338, 368
Kaup, J. J. 3
Kazakhstan 2, 10, 20, 21, 44, 45, 53, 55, 60, 67, 69, 74, 85, 86, 101, 109, 115, 117, 120, 124, 142, 178, 245, 257, 258, 264, 282
kermes oak 71
Kielder forest 311
Knight, Peter xi, 330
Knights, Chris 18, 81, 97, 150, 152, 167, 176, 266, 364, 373, 375
knotgrass 17, 79, 80, 82, 84, 85, 87, 93, 158, 162, 169, 221, 325, 348, 356, 358
knotgrass beetle 17, 158, 162, 169, 221, 397
Komarek, Ed 73
Koning, F. J. 308
Kublai Khan 98

L
ladybirds 164, 198, 200, 211, 215

La Fage caves 314
Lake Baikal 39, 44
Lake Balkash 52
La Mancha xi, 6, 7, 102, 123, 125, 127, 171, 172, 175, 241, 253, 310
land quillwort 83
land snails 266, 267
Langholm 305, 309, 382
lapwing 361, 362, 384
larkspur 115
Las Ensanchas xi, 7, 83, 100, 123, 127, 128, 131, 132, 172, 304, 310
Lasius flavus 270
lead shot ingestion 244, 267, 323, 324, 325
leaf beetles 155, 160, 165, 170, 171, 178, 190, 222, 232, 233
leaf hoppers 155, 156, 160, 163, 165, 171, 174, 184, 189, 190, 211, 216, 265, 351
lemmings 67, 284
Lepidoptera 157, 158, 164, 173, 176, 177, 190, 195, 208, 216, 231, 232, 233, 364
lesser celandine 85
leukosis 242, 255
linear cover 115, 119, 123
lion 73, 146, 147
Lipeurus caponis 260
Liukkonen, Tuija 46
Loddington 21, 23, 24, 25, 108, 295, 365, 372, 391
louse flies 262
lucerne 97, 111, 134, 154, 157, 161, 163, 164, 166, 174, 177, 178, 184, 185, 186, 187, 195, 201, 208, 209, 222, 233, 236, 268
lucerne flea 154, 157, 163, 164, 166, 177, 184, 185, 186, 187, 195, 208, 209, 233, 267, 268
lucerne weevil 161, 166, 222
Luliang Mountains 66
Lygus rugulipennis 199

lynx ix, 27, 74, 146, 147, 148, 149, 150, 309, 312, 382, 394
Lyruterina nigropunctata 264

M
Madagascar 72
magpie 140, 144, 339
maize 82, 83, 87, 102, 105, 234, 235, 236, 291, 379
Maldonado Vidal, Patricia xi, 6, 7, 100, 126, 132, 174, 285, 304, 308, 310, 312, 316
Manydown 21, 22, 23, 153, 155, 193, 277, 390, 391

Marco Polo 97
marsh harrier 275, 281, 282, 286, 287, 291, 295, 304, 305
MCPA (herbicide) 206
meadow fescue 80
meadow grasshopper 209
meadow pipit 368
meadowsweet 77, 110
Mediorhynchus micracanthus 260
mega-herbivores 27, 65, 70, 71, 73, 74, 376
Meharg, Andrew 323
melilot 332
Mellor, Charlie xi, 326
Mesolithic 68
Micheldever 17, 120, 130, 226, 297, 298, 301, 390
Middleton, Doug 12, 25, 138, 141
midges 215, 221, 223, 258
mildew 219, 220, 234, 346
millet 75, 76, 79, 82, 98, 101
millipedes 206, 207, 239, 265, 271
Minnesota study 154, 185
Miocene 60, 61
mitochondrial genomes 37
mitochondrial mutations 46–7
modern farming systems 95
Moldova 49, 60
Mongolia 1, 39, 44, 60, 78, 97, 263

moniliasis 242, 244, 255
Monsanto 235
Montagu's harrier 303, 304
Montana 121, 185, 285, 299
montane grassland 300
Moreby, Steve x, 165, 201, 227
Morocco 54, 61
mountain aven 67
mountain hares 67
Mourer-Chauviré, Cécile 40
mowing 13, 106, 107, 108, 111, 118, 134, 135, 136, 161, 166, 203
mtDNA 37, 42, 46, 47, 49, 53
mustelids 123, 139, 140
mycoplasma 244
myxomatosis 262, 372

N
Napoleonic Wars 103
narrow-fruited cornsalad 346
National Gamekeeper's Organisation 165
Natural England 22, 304
Natural Environment Research Council 240
Naumann, J. A. 3
Naurzumskii National Nature Reserve 45, 74, 109
Nebraska xi, 60, 63
Negev desert 79
nematodes 239, 240, 243, 246, 250, 253, 257, 260, 261, 271
neonicotenoids 216, 217
nest dispersion 133
nesting cover 12, 25, 32, 71, 109, 110, 111, 112, 114, 115, 116, 117, 119, 125, 130, 132, 133, 137, 298, 329, 332, 339, 352, 371
nest predation 9, 11, 19, 21, 29, 32, 34, 106, 107, 118, 119, 123, 125, 129, 130, 132, 133, 139, 141, 142, 145, 146, 151, 352, 364, 366, 368

nest predators 30, 32, 138, 140, 142, 377
Netherlands 69, 70, 90, 144, 321, 347, 348
Newcastle disease 262
Newton, Sir Alfred 70, 341
New Zealand 6, 8, 55, 72
night-flowering catchfly 344, 345
Norfolk Estate v, x, 15, 22, 33, 50, 57, 77, 90, 101, 112, 123, 129, 182, 192, 193, 196, 217, 219, 226, 231, 245, 259, 277, 278, 279, 282, 294, 297, 300, 303, 315, 324, 326, 327, 328, 329, 330, 331, 333, 334, 335, 337, 338, 340, 341, 342, 343, 344, 345, 346, 347, 348, 349, 350, 351, 352, 353, 354, 355, 356, 357, 358, 359, 361, 362, 363, 364, 365, 367, 368, 370, 371, 372, 373, 374, 378, 379, 380, 382, 383, 384, 390
North America 1, 8, 29, 35, 67, 72, 103, 115, 134, 138, 140, 143, 146, 147, 156, 171, 225, 250, 251, 268, 285, 302, 305, 321, 326, 340, 380
Northern Prairie Wildlife Research station 148
North Farm 14, 15, 16, 21, 190, 245, 317, 318, 322, 340, 354, 372, 389, 391
North Rhine–Westphalia 123, 144, 292
North Stoke 329, 340, 353, 357, 359, 363, 365, 367
North Yorkshire ix, 226, 389

O
oats 22, 81, 82, 83, 87
Odoric of Pordenone 53
Office National de la Chasse 25, 167
oilseed rape 95, 97, 197, 235, 236, 291, 366
Oligocene 61
Oliver-Bellasis, Hugh 21
orache 80

orange wheat-blossom midge 221
Oxford study 161
Oxyspirura schulzi 264

P
Pakistan 6, 8, 35, 55, 205, 206, 377
Palaeoalectoris songlinensis 60
Palaeocryptonyx 58, 59, 60, 61, 62
Paleontological Institute, Moscow 40, 58
pale pigeon-grass 79
Pallas's cat 140
Palouse Prairie 108, 130, 285, 293
Panek, Marek 129, 145, 169
Paraornithofilaria lienalis 261
parasitoid wasps 164, 173, 174, 177, 181, 213, 224, 230, 234, 238
Partridge Puzzle, The xi, 171, 185
Passmore, Christopher xi, 197, 198
pea aphid 217
pea-shrub 71
peat bog 71, 75
pen-reared partridges 25, 45, 252, 315, 317, 318, 320, 321, 325, 355, 376, 377, 381
Perdix jurcsáki 40
Perdix margaritae 39, 40, 42, 44, 60, 61
Perdix palaeoperdix 40, 41, 60
perennial sow thistle 334
Persicaria 80
pesticides ix, x, 17, 22, 32, 38, 70, 103, 115, 157, 195, 198, 203, 204, 205, 206, 214, 215, 216, 219, 232, 367, 368, 370, 377
phasianid 61
pheasant 16, 59, 60, 97, 98, 99, 108, 114, 143, 153, 225, 240, 245, 246, 248, 249, 250, 251, 252, 253, 257, 262, 263, 296, 309, 333, 338, 339, 355

pheasant's eye 342, 343
Philby's partridge 52
phylogeny 53, 420, 424, 427
Picardie xi, 3, 99, 100, 130, 131, 168
pigeon grasses 75, 82
pigeons 254, 277, 296
pigweed 77, 79, 80, 81, 82, 83, 88, 157, 169, 236
pirimicarb 215
Pitt, William 347
plant bugs 155, 156, 157, 158, 159, 160, 162, 163, 165, 167, 169, 171, 172, 173, 176, 177, 178, 183, 184, 190, 191, 192, 199, 210, 211, 215, 231, 232, 233, 236, 349, 351, 367
plant hoppers 157, 163, 211, 216, 231
Pleistocene 38, 39, 44, 48, 52, 60, 61, 66, 67, 68, 146
Pliocene 43, 59, 60, 61, 66
Plioperdix africana 61
Plioperdix ponticus 60
ploughing 195, 197, 227, 229, 336
Poland 20, 29, 46, 49, 60, 79, 80, 82, 88, 112, 113, 116, 118, 121, 129, 130, 144, 145, 169, 181, 197, 210, 225, 252, 257, 264, 266, 272, 283, 321, 390
polecat 21, 139, 140, 142, 144, 292, 310
pollen record 71
Pollybell organic farm 135, 136
Polygonums 69, 70, 75, 76, 81, 82, 84, 88, 93, 115, 336, 358
Portugal xi, 6, 7, 54, 72, 73, 82, 101, 116, 117, 124, 126, 127, 142, 172, 173, 174, 175, 178, 179, 180, 182, 240, 257, 261, 284, 295, 307, 322, 382
prairie chicken 133, 248
prairie grouse 60, 146

predator control 22, 23, 24, 25, 29, 30, 33, 118, 123, 125, 128, 129, 130, 138, 142, 144, 145, 191, 288, 290, 309, 312, 318, 319, 320, 322, 326, 329, 352, 366, 368, 372, 377, 380, 381, 382, 383
predators ix, 4, 11, 13, 17, 18, 23, 27, 30, 31, 32, 33, 36, 72, 73, 74, 100, 107, 114, 115, 117, 119, 122, 123, 128, 130, 132, 138, 139, 140, 141, 142, 143, 144, 146, 147, 148, 149, 150, 151, 152, 159, 161, 182, 186, 189, 199, 203, 209, 211, 212, 213, 219, 236, 275, 283, 285, 286, 287, 288, 289, 290, 293, 294, 295, 297, 309, 310, 311, 312, 314, 326, 338, 339, 363, 364, 366, 371, 376, 377, 381, 382, 384, 391
prickly poppy 343
Prosthorhynchus transversus 260
Prunus spp. 77
Przevalski's partridge 27, 52, 128
ptarmigan 67, 69, 159
Pulliainen, Erkki 87, 91, 100, 170, 267, 277
Putaala, Ahti 122, 170
Pyrenees 49, 59, 67, 69, 70, 78, 159, 298, 300
pyrethroids 215, 216
pyrethrum 195

Q
Qaidam Basin 44
quail 26, 42, 44, 53, 58, 59, 61, 68, 69, 98, 102, 108, 117, 137, 139, 149, 150, 217, 236, 238, 247, 249, 263, 265, 290, 296, 314, 323, 356, 381
Qinghai plateau 86

R
rabbit 109, 133, 134, 149, 150, 151, 213, 224, 295, 312, 372

radio-tracking 19, 20, 34, 109, 111, 112, 118, 126, 134, 137, 138, 139, 140, 141, 153, 159, 160, 165, 169, 170, 176, 181, 182, 183, 189, 217, 219, 277, 279, 280, 293, 299, 300, 319
ragweed 115
Raillietina cesticillus 259, 269, 271
Raillietina tetragona 239, 256, 270
rain, effect on breeding 74, 106, 114, 189, 190, 191, 212, 326, 332
raised bogs 1, 75
Randi, Ettore xi, 53, 58
Rands, Mike 21, 116
raptors 5, 21, 27, 81, 97, 117, 140, 143, 203, 272, 273, 274, 275, 276, 277, 278, 279, 280, 281, 283, 284, 285, 286, 287, 288, 289, 290, 291, 293, 295, 297, 302, 303, 305, 306, 307, 309, 310, 311, 312, 331, 338, 370, 371, 372, 374, 382
rat 98, 138, 139, 142, 337, 339, 374
Reclamo, The 322
red grouse 3, 46, 50, 51, 66, 68, 69, 114, 159, 240, 250, 251, 257, 262, 267, 309
red hemp-nettle 345
red kite 21, 276, 351, 356
red-legged partridge x, xi, 3, 6, 7, 8, 9, 12, 13, 20, 24, 25, 26, 27, 50, 52–55, 56, 57, 63, 70, 82, 83, 84, 100, 101, 102, 107, 108, 116–17, 118, 123, 125–8, 130, 131, 132, 133, 134, 142, 146, 150, 151, 153, 162, 171–8, 179, 180, 181, 182, 184, 190, 191, 193, 202, 210, 211, 238, 240, 241, 242, 243, 244, 245, 246, 247, 250, 252, 253, 254, 255, 256, 257, 258, 260, 262, 263, 266, 267, 270, 271, 272, 273, 280, 283, 284, 285, 289, 296, 297, 310,

red-legged partridge *cont.*
317, 318, 320, 322–3, 324,
338, 339, 340, 341, 355
red-listed species 151, 345,
346, 347, 348, 352, 357, 358, 371
reindeer 67
Reitz, François 189
residual grass 110, 114, 115
rhinoceros 36, 71, 72, 73,
147, 394
ringed plover 361
Rio de Janeiro 27, 104
Riversleigh Station 73
rock partridge 1, 3, 6, 8, 26,
52, 53, 54, 56, 70, 86, 117,
118, 126, 128, 142, 160, 178,
250, 252, 257, 260, 286, 308,
320, 375
Romania 40, 44, 60, 264
roots, as food 9, 83, 84, 85,
86, 223
Rotavirus 257
Rothamsted Experimental
Husbandry Station 17,
199
Rothamsted Insect Survey
199
Rotterdam Convention
206
roundworm 240, 256, 257,
260, 264
Royston 24, 291, 320
Russia xi, 2, 28, 29, 39, 69,
78, 81, 104, 113, 120, 175,
264, 389, 390
Russian ground beetle 158
rusty-gate call 302
rye 76, 82, 87, 112

S
sagebrush 84
sagebrush steppe 9
sage grouse 263
sainfoin 97, 161, 197
Salisbury Plain 21, 22, 23,
24, 25, 29, 30, 107, 111, 119,
123, 128, 129, 130, 135, 141,
151, 156, 339, 390, 391
Salisbury, Sir Edward 65, 69

Sánchez Marco, Antonio
39, 54
sand partridge 60
Sardinia 11, 54, 63
Saskatchewan 4, 115, 121,
292, 321, 389
savannah 71, 72, 73, 376
Savory, Allan 72
sawfly 78, 158, 159, 160, 162,
164, 165, 171, 173, 177, 182,
184, 185, 188, 190, 195, 197,
201, 215, 216, 217, 224, 225,
226, 227, 228, 229, 230, 231,
232, 233, 335, 351, 364, 365,
367, 371
sawfly caterpillars 78, 160,
173, 177, 182, 195, 364, 371
Scandinavia 29, 257
Schleswig-Holstein 307, 308
Scotland 54, 142, 187, 226,
239, 240, 251, 262, 267, 303,
304, 305, 368
Serre, Daniel 167
set-aside 24, 25, 103, 104,
165, 197, 338, 362, 365, 370,
379
seven-spot ladybirds 200,
211
shag 204, 262, 377, 395, 410
Shanxi 77, 121
sharp-tailed grouse 67
shepherd's needle 345
shoot-boring flies 223
shoot management 317
shrew 373, 374
Siberian pea shrub 115
Sichuan 5, 43, 59, 98, 99, 107
Sicily 53
Silesia 49
Sitobion fragariae 185
skylark 135, 335, 336, 356, 365,
366, 367, 384
slugs 239, 245, 265, 267, 271
Sminthurus viridis 267, 268
snails 85, 156, 162, 163, 173,
177, 206, 207, 239, 245, 256,
259, 265, 266, 267, 271,
368, 369
snakes 139, 285, 288

song thrush 368
sorghum 82, 87
Sotherton, Nick 17, 21, 221
Soulé, Michael 381
South Africa 6, 105, 146,
427
Southwood, Dick 187, 189,
192, 203
soybean 105
Spain 6, 7, 8, 12, 25, 48, 49,
54, 58, 60, 61, 63, 70, 83,
101, 102, 115, 117, 123, 124,
125, 126, 127, 132, 133, 134,
142, 150, 171, 173, 181, 197,
216, 240, 252, 253, 256, 258,
261, 262, 263, 270, 272, 283,
285, 296, 297, 307, 310, 312,
314, 316, 322, 376, 382
sparrowhawk 21, 143, 272,
273, 274, 275, 276, 277, 278,
279, 280, 283, 287, 288,
290, 293, 295, 303, 306, 307,
308, 392, 396
speckled bush cricket 209
spiders 152, 155, 156, 160,
163, 165, 167, 169, 170, 173,
176, 177, 188, 199, 207, 211,
213, 232, 364, 367
spreading hedge-parsley
345
springtails 157, 173, 174, 176,
177, 208, 209
steppe 1, 4, 9, 31, 39, 42, 43,
49, 61, 66, 67, 69, 74, 76,
77, 78, 84, 101, 107, 110,
115, 117, 133, 140, 153, 156,
157, 158, 184, 186, 268,
365, 394
St Helena 6
St Mark's fly 154, 156
stoat 133, 134, 138, 139, 140,
144, 165, 167, 292, 339, 367
stone curlew 360
stone marten 98, 123, 137,
139, 140, 142, 143, 144, 280,
292, 310
St Petersburg Zoological
Museum 46
strawberry-seed beetle 218

strip-lynchet field system 196

strongylosis 32, 114, 238, 240, 242, 243, 244, 250, 255, 267, 271

stubble burning 69, 73, 93, 95, 210, 220, 221, 230, 348

stubble counts 13, 14, 15, 20, 93, 99, 102, 109, 118, 119, 136, 190, 202, 276, 280, 303, 356, 360, 392

sunn pest 158, 178

Sussex Botanical Recording Society 90

Sussex Downs 12, 15, 16, 56, 57, 195, 196, 304, 344, 361, 365

Sussex Study area v, x, xi, 10, 13, 14, 15, 16, 17, 18, 21, 22, 28, 29, 30, 31, 33, 35, 36, 39, 45, 50, 57, 58, 64, 71, 76, 77, 83, 88, 89, 90, 91, 92, 93, 95, 96, 103, 110, 112, 119, 121, 127, 129, 133, 155, 156, 162, 164, 165, 177, 178, 184, 185, 186, 190, 193, 195, 196, 197, 198, 199, 200, 201, 203, 206, 207, 208, 209, 210, 211, 213, 214, 215, 216, 217, 218, 220, 222, 223, 224, 225, 226, 227, 228, 229, 230, 231, 232, 233, 234, 243, 244, 245, 246, 259, 266, 272, 273, 276, 277, 278, 284, 287, 294, 295, 300, 303, 304, 305, 306, 317, 318, 322, 323, 324, 327, 329, 338, 340, 341, 342, 343, 344, 345, 347, 348, 350, 351, 353, 354, 356, 360, 362, 363, 364, 365, 367, 368, 370, 371, 372, 373, 374, 376, 378, 384

Sustainable Arable Farming For an Improved Environment (SAFFIE) 335, 367

Swainson's hawks 205

Sweden 38, 141, 145, 147, 148, 149, 153, 188, 193, 203

sweep net 156, 165, 170, 172, 198, 219

Syria 76

Szechenyi's monal-partridge 107, 108

T

Tachyporus spp. 212, 219, 220

Tanzania 73

tapeworm 238, 239, 240, 242, 244, 255, 256, 259, 264, 265, 268, 269, 270, 271

Tarangire Reserve 73

Taylor, Rebecca 185

Tew, Tom 22

thermo-regulation 189

three-lobed beggarsticks 82

thrips 156, 157, 163, 173, 174, 177, 181, 199, 215, 216

Tibet 427

Tibetan partridge xi, 2, 4, 5, 43, 44, 59, 61, 98, 115, 118, 396

Tibetan plateau 4, 35, 43, 45, 61, 62, 63, 78, 115

ticks 260, 262

Tiger crane fly 223

Tinbergen, Luke 182

Topping, Chris 136

tortoise beetle 158, 164, 174, 175, 176, 182, 222, 350

Trans-Baikal 39, 76, 110, 140, 157

transgenic crops 234, 235, 236

translocation 320, 340, 354

Trechus quadristriatus 167, 168, 218, 233, 236, 269

tree creeper 356

Trichomonas 237, 242, 253, 254, 255

Tryphon spp. 227, 229

tuberculosis 242, 244, 252, 255

tuberous hawkbit 83

tubers 9, 78, 85, 86

Tunisia 53

Turkey 2, 44, 49, 53, 63, 76, 245, 260

turnip sawfly 231

U

Ul'yanin 20, 45, 74, 75, 94, 101, 109, 110, 120

UNESCO 43

University of Stirling 201, 246

Upper Teesdale 159, 160, 225, 229

Ural mountains 46

US Department of Agriculture 156

Uvs Nuur 46

Uzbekistan 55, 101

V

Vale de Perditos 7, 127, 142, 172, 173, 175, 306, 322

Vanishing Hedgerows xi

Vauberon Farm 98

vervain 83

vetch 75, 83, 85, 97, 197

viruses 257, 262

vitamin A 91, 296

vitamin B12 188

W

Wakeham-Dawson, Andrew 365

Walbeck estate 119

walked-up shooting 315, 316, 321

Wallace, Alfred Russel 152

Wasscher, Jacob 90, 347, 348

water snails 266

water vole 374

Watson, Mark 21, 100, 273, 277, 278, 279, 289, 290, 297, 300

weasel 139, 142, 144, 162, 165, 339, 373

weevils 155, 157, 159, 164, 165, 169, 170, 176, 178, 180, 181, 184, 190, 197, 205, 222, 232, 233, 236, 351, 367
western corn rootworm 105
Western Europe 50, 55, 72, 76, 115, 136, 197, 248, 264, 271, 286
West Nile virus 263
West Sussex 15, 418, 443
wet weather, effect on breeding 114, 203, 331, 334
wheat 70, 72, 74, 75, 76, 80, 81, 82, 83, 85, 87, 91, 99, 100, 101, 103, 105, 115, 137, 156, 159, 167, 168, 197, 203, 206, 211, 212, 213, 214, 218, 220, 221, 223, 228, 230, 234, 235, 236, 296, 333, 335, 338, 364, 369, 377

wheat bulb fly 223
wheatgrass 31, 110
white-eared pheasant 98
whitethroat 370
Whitney, Beau 326
willow grouse 46, 49, 67, 68, 74, 159, 252, 257
Wilson, Phil 22
Windsor Great Park 55
wolf ix, 27, 72, 73, 74, 133, 146, 147, 148, 149, 150, 309, 382, 394
woodlice 157, 163, 169, 173, 177, 206, 239, 260, 265, 271
woolly mammoth 37, 49, 50, 67, 72
World Pheasant Association 6
World War I 15, 74, 103, 141, 144, 198, 313

World War II vii, ix, 15, 74, 103, 141, 144, 198, 227, 267

X
Xinjiang 44

Y
yellowhammer 216, 356, 369, 371, 372
yellow meadow ant 183, 184, 224, 225
Yocom, Chuck 108
Younger Dryas 67, 70

The New Naturalist Library

1. *Butterflies* — E. B. Ford
2. *British Game* — B. Vesey-Fitzgerald
3. *London's Natural History* — R. S. R. Fitter
4. *Britain's Structure and Scenery* — L. Dudley Stamp
5. *Wild Flowers* — J. Gilmour & M. Walters
6. *The Highlands & Islands* — F. Fraser Darling & J. M. Boyd
7. *Mushrooms & Toadstools* — J. Ramsbottom
8. *Insect Natural History* — A. D. Imms
9. *A Country Parish* — A. W. Boyd
10. *British Plant Life* — W. B. Turrill
11. *Mountains & Moorlands* — W. H. Pearsall
12. *The Sea Shore* — C. M. Yonge
13. *Snowdonia* — F. J. North, B. Campbell & R.Scott
14. *The Art of Botanical Illustration* — W. Blunt
15. *Life in Lakes & Rivers* — T. T. Macan & E. B. Worthington
16. *Wild Flowers of Chalk & Limestone* — J. E. Lousley
17. *Birds & Men* — E. M. Nicholson
18. *A Natural History of Man in Britain* — H. J. Fleure & M. Davies
19. *Wild Orchids of Britain* — V. S. Summerhayes
20. *The British Amphibians & Reptiles* — M. Smith
21. *British Mammals* — L. Harrison Matthews
22. *Climate and the British Scene* — G. Manley
23. *An Angler's Entomology* — J. R. Harris
24. *Flowers of the Coast* — I. Hepburn
25. *The Sea Coast* — J. A. Steers
26. *The Weald* — S. W. Wooldridge & F. Goldring
27. *Dartmoor* — L. A. Harvey & D. St. Leger Gordon
28. *Sea Birds* — J. Fisher & R. M. Lockley
29. *The World of the Honeybee* — C. G. Butler
30. *Moths* — E. B. Ford
31. *Man and the Land* — L. Dudley Stamp
32. *Trees, Woods and Man* — H. L. Edlin
33. *Mountain Flowers* — J. Raven & M. Walters

34. *The Open Sea: I. The World of Plankton* — A. Hardy
35. *The World of the Soil* — E. J. Russell
36. *Insect Migration* — C. B. Williams
37. *The Open Sea: II. Fish & Fisheries* — A. Hardy
38. *The World of Spiders* — W. S. Bristowe
39. *The Folklore of Birds* — E. A. Armstrong
40. *Bumblebees* — J. B. Free & C. G. Butler
41. *Dragonflies* — P. S. Corbet, C. Longfield & N. W. Moore
42. *Fossils* — H. H. Swinnerton
43. *Weeds & Aliens* — E. Salisbury
44. *The Peak District* — K. C. Edwards
45. *The Common Lands of England & Wales* — L. Dudley Stamp & W. G. Hoskins
46. *The Broads* — E. A. Ellis
47. *The Snowdonia National Park* — W. M. Condry
48. *Grass and Grasslands* — I. Moore
49. *Nature Conservation in Britain* — L. Dudley Stamp
50. *Pesticides and Pollution* — K. Mellanby
51. *Man & Birds* — R. K. Murton
52. *Woodland Birds* — E. Simms
53. *The Lake District* — W. H. Pearsall & W. Pennington
54. *The Pollination of Flowers* — M. Proctor & P. Yeo
55. *Finches* — I. Newton
56. *Pedigree: Words from Nature* — S. Potter & L. Sargent
57. *British Seals* — H. R. Hewer
58. *Hedges* — E. Pollard, M. D. Hooper & N. W. Moore
59. *Ants* — M. V. Brian
60. *British Birds of Prey* — L. Brown
61. *Inheritance and Natural History* — R. J. Berry
62. *British Tits* — C. Perrins
63. *British Thrushes* — E. Simms
64. *The Natural History of Shetland* — R. J. Berry & J. L. Johnston

65. *Waders* — W. G. Hale
66. *The Natural History of Wales* — W. M. Condry
67. *Farming and Wildlife* — K. Mellanby
68. *Mammals in the British Isles* — L. Harrison Matthews
69. *Reptiles and Amphibians in Britain* — D. Frazer
70. *The Natural History of Orkney* — R. J. Berry
71. *British Warblers* — E. Simms
72. *Heathlands* — N. R. Webb
73. *The New Forest* — C. R. Tubbs
74. *Ferns* — C. N. Page
75. *Freshwater Fish* — P. S. Maitland & R. N. Campbell
76. *The Hebrides* — J. M. Boyd & I. L. Boyd
77. *The Soil* — B. Davis, N. Walker, D. Ball & A. Fitter
78. *British Larks, Pipits & Wagtails* — E. Simms
79. *Caves & Cave Life* — P. Chapman
80. *Wild & Garden Plants* — M. Walters
81. *Ladybirds* — M. E. N. Majerus
82. *The New Naturalists* — P. Marren
83. *The Natural History of Pollination* — M. Proctor, P. Yeo & A. Lack
84. *Ireland: A Natural History* — D. Cabot
85. *Plant Disease* — D. Ingram & N. Robertson
86. *Lichens* — Oliver Gilbert
87. *Amphibians and Reptiles* — T. Beebee & R. Griffiths
88. *Loch Lomondside* — J. Mitchell
89. *The Broads* — B. Moss
90. *Moths* — M. Majerus
91. *Nature Conservation* — P. Marren
92. *Lakeland* — D. Ratcliffe
93. *British Bats* — John Altringham
94. *Seashore* — Peter Hayward
95. *Northumberland* — Angus Lunn
96. *Fungi* — Brian Spooner & Peter Roberts
97. *Mosses & Liverworts* — Nick Hodgetts & Ron Porley
98. *Bumblebees* — Ted Benton

99. *Gower* — Jonathan Mullard
100. *Woodlands* — Oliver Rackham
101. *Galloway and the Borders* — Derek Ratcliffe
102. *Garden Natural History* — Stefan Buczacki
103. *The Isles of Scilly* — Rosemary Parslow
104. *A History of Ornithology* — Peter Bircham
105. *Wye Valley* — George Peterken
106. *Dragonflies* — Philip Corbet & Stephen Brooks
107. *Grouse* — Adam Watson & Robert Moss
108. *Southern England* — Peter Friend
109. *Islands* — R. J. Berry
110. *Wildfowl* — David Cabot
111. *Dartmoor* — Ian Mercer
112. *Books and Naturalists* — David E. Allen
113. *Bird Migration* — Ian Newton
114. *Badger* — Timothy J. Roper
115. *Climate and Weather* — John Kington
116. *Plant Pests* — David V. Alford
117. *Plant Galls* — Margaret Redfern
118. *Marches* — Andrew Allott
119. *Scotland* — Peter Friend
120. *Grasshoppers & Crickets* — Ted Benton

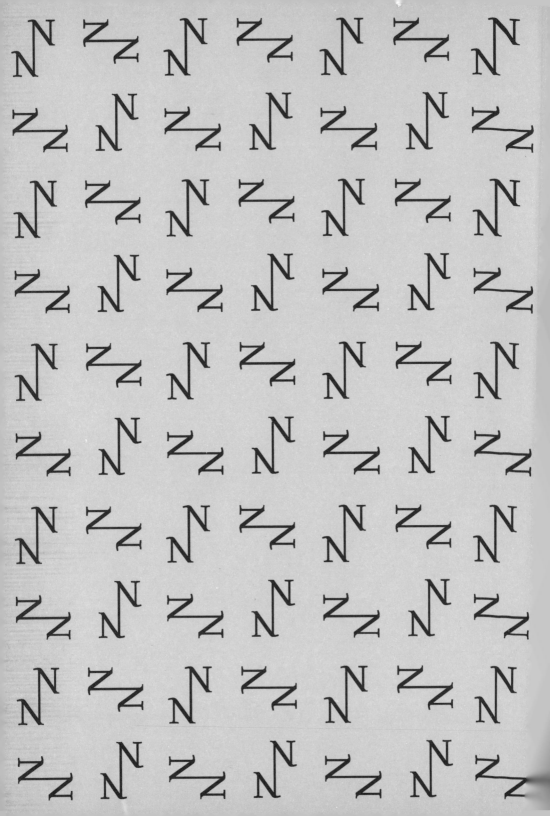